TUTORIAL
TEST GENERATION FOR VLSI CHIPS
Vishwani D. Agrawal and Sharad C. Seth

Computer Society Order Number 786
Library of Congress Number 88–61362
IEEE Catalog Number EH0278–2
ISBN 0–8186–8786–X

 THE COMPUTER SOCIETY

IEEE   THE INSTITUTE OF ELECTRICAL AND ELECTRONICS ENGINEERS, INC.

IEEE
COMPUTER
SOCIETY
PRESS

Published by Computer Society Press
1730 Massachusetts Avenue, N.W.
Washington, D.C. 20036-1903

Cover designed by Jack I. Ballestero

Sponsored by Test Techology Technical Committee

Computer Society Order Number 786
Library of Congress Number 88-61362
IEEE Catalog Order Number EH0278-2
ISBN 0-8186-8786-X (Casebound)
ISBN 0-8186-4786-8 (Microfiche)
SAN 264-620X

Order from: Computer Society   IEEE Service Center   Computer Society
Terminal Annex   445 Hoes Lane   Avenue de la Tanche, 2
Post Office Box 4699   P.O. Box 1331   B-1160 Brussels
Los Angeles, CA 90080   Piscataway, NJ 08855-1331   BELGIUM

 THE INSTITUTE OF ELECTRICAL AND ELECTRONICS ENGINEERS, INC.

To our parents

and

to out friend Anil Tole

Preface

This tutorial is intended for practicing engineers and students interested in learning about VLSI testing. No significant prior experience in testing is assumed. We emphasize concepts and current practice over comprehensiveness. We have included proven good ideas, both old and new; since this is meant to be a tutorial, inclusion of the latest research ideas can not be the guiding principle in writing and selecting material. At a conceptual level, however, a new researcher will find this tutorial a good starting point.

In our view, test generation is part of the design process while testing (test application) is part of the production process. This book is aimed at the designer. The overview presented in the first chapter places test generation in the context of other related tasks. Of the remaining material, we consider Chapters II-IV, on fault modeling, test generation, and test evaluation, to be essential to the purpose of this tutorial. The next two chapters on testability analysis and design for testability are also important. The information in Chapter VII on automatic test equipment is less crucial but is still desirable for the sake of completing the testing perspective of a test designer. The last chapter is a comprehensive bibliography of the material published in the 1980s. In addition, it contains references to most texts and many well-known papers in testing since the 1960s.

Each chapter starts with a tutorial introduction. In writing this material, we have emphasized simplicity over completeness. The purpose is to introduce the main ideas and the basic vocabulary necessary to understand the reprinted papers. In selecting the reprints, we have attempted to span two dimensions: breadth and time. The papers are taken from 18 different journals. The issues from which they are taken range from 1967 through 1987. The average publication date of the papers is 1980.

The actual task of test generation depends on the design environment. For example, if a scan method is used, test generation can be highly automated. Otherwise, tests may have to be generated manually with heavy reliance on fault simulation tools. In this tutorial, to serve a wider readership, we do not subscribe to a particular style of design. We have included papers on test generation for combinational circuits, sequential circuits, programmable logic arrays, memories and microprocessors. There is, however, a stronger emphasis on combinational test generation. There are two reasons for this. First, combinational test generation algorithms are easier to understand and, therefore, provide a good insight into the process of test generation. Such an insight is useful to any designer. Second, these algorithms make automatic test generation possible at least for scan type of designs. Attempts at automating test generation for general sequential circuits have not been very successful.

While the prevailing environment for most designers of very large-scale integration circuits may not emphasize strict adherence to scan or any other design for testability technique, the need for automation and quality is well recognized. From the viewpoint of test generation, these requirements translate into some form of design for testability. That is why we have included introductory material on testability analysis and design for testability. We recommend supplementing it with recent texts and tutorials on these topics.

Acknowledgment − The authors are thankful for the support of their management and the cooperation from their colleagues at the AT&T Bell Laboratories and at the University of Nebraska. Their wives, Prathima Agrawal and Rebecca Seth, and children, Vikas and Chitra Agrawal, and Anita and Anil Seth, were constant sources of encouragement. Finally, the editorial and managing staff of the Computer Society Press, and in particular, Margaret Brown, must be commended for their excellent work.

Table of Contents

Chapter I: Introduction

Very large-scale integration (VLSI) is the fabrication of thousands of components and interconnections at once by a common set of manufacturing steps. Its advantages are reduced system cost, better performance, and greater reliability. These advantages would be lost unless VLSI devices can be tested economically.

Manufacturing of a product consists of fabrication and testing. *Design* and *test development* precede manufacture. While design is a synthesis of manufacturable details, test development specifies the test data and the details of testing procedures. Design links the abstract specifications to the physical device through a synthesis or assembly of known parts and generates data necessary to drive the equipment that physically produces the assembly. Verification, consisting of analysis and simulation, checks correctness of design. The correctness of fabricated device is determined through testing. Thus, in order to produce a correctly working device, both design and test data are necessary.

1: VLSI Testing

The role of testing in the VLSI device realization process is illustrated in Figure 1.1 (test functions are shown in boldface). Test planning begins with specifications. A device is specified in terms of functional (input/output behavior, frequency, timing, etc.), environmental (power, temperature, humidity, noise, etc.), and reliability (incoming quality, failure rate, etc.) specifications. Types of tests and test equipment are chosen to match device specifications.

Test activities are interwoven with design. Architectural design consists of partitioning of a VLSI chip into realizable functional blocks. The next step, namely logic design, includes several test activities. Either the logic should be synthesized in a testable form or the synthesized logic should be

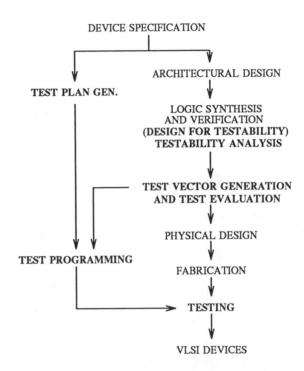

Figure 1.1: Test functions in VLSI realization.

analyzed (and improved) for testability.

After logic synthesis, test vectors are generated and combined with the test plan to develop a program for the automatic test equipment (ATE) used. The actual testing takes place after the physical design (layout, timing verification, and mask generation) and fabrication (wafer processing).

1.1: Types of Testing

Testing enters into the life cycle of a VLSI device in several places. First, in the factory, device wafers and packages are subjected to *manufacturing test*. Second, users of VLSI devices conduct *acceptance test*. Third, the devices undergo testing during the *systems test* performed on the systems (printed circuit boards, etc.) where the VLSI chips are used. Finally, the devices must undergo *mainte-nance tests* in the field. While the various types of testing have common aspects, the discussion below is primarily in terms of manufacturing and acceptance tests.

1.2: Method of Testing

Testing consists of mounting chips (either wafers or packaged chips) on ATE, applying stimuli to the input pins, and comparing responses at the output pins with the expected responses.

1.3: Requirements of Testing

Manufacturing tests are supposed to determine that each component (transistor, etc.) and each interconnection is fabricated correctly on the chip. These tests should thoroughly check every node in the circuit. The effect of every fault should be propagated to the circuit output. A normal requirement for these tests is that they detect a very high fraction (95 to 100 percent) of the *modeled faults* in the circuit. The detected fraction of faults is called the *fault coverage* of the tests.

The objective of acceptance testing is to ascertain the quality level of chips that have undergone the manufacturing test. Tests and coverage requirements are similar to those of manufacturing tests.

High fault coverage tests are also used for *in-circuit testing* of chips. This form of testing is conducted at the printed circuit board level during the manufacture or repair of boards.

1.4: Test Development Process

Tests for a VLSI circuit are developed in two phases. In the first phase, known as *design verification,* tests are generated to verify logical correctness and timing behavior of the circuit through simulation. These tests are carefully designed to exercise various functions of the circuit. Since logic circuits are mostly sequential, for any reasonably large circuit it would be impossible to use all possible input sequences. As a practical compromise, a subset of inputs, considered to be critical by the designer, is used for verification.

The second phase of test generation consists of generation of *manufacturing tests*. Verification tests

check for the right logic elements connected in the right way. They do not necessarily check for specific types of defects produced during fabrication. For example, it is quite possible that one or more transistors are missing or shorted within a gate. Ideally, manufacturing tests must cover all faults that can possibly occur during fabrication.

It is this second phase of test generation that is the main topic of this tutorial. We attempt to answer a series of questions to varying degrees of thoroughness: (1) What to test? (2) How to generate tests? (3) How to assess completeness of tests? (4) How to analyze a circuit for potential test problems? (5) How to design a circuit for guaranteed test generation? (6) How to apply tests to chips? Separate chapters are devoted to each question. The following sections provide a brief introduction.

2: Fault Modeling

Failures occur in VLSI chips throughout their life cycle. Failures are caused by design errors, material defects, process defects, extremes in operational environment, deterioration due to length of operation, aging, etc. Phenomena causing failures can be physical or chemical in nature. However, to analyze the faulty behavior and develop techniques to detect and locate failures, abstract fault models are used. Fault models allow cost effective development of test stimuli that will identify failed chips and, if necessary, diagnose the failure. Fault models also limit the number of necessary tests as opposed to applying all possible inputs.

Practical fault models depend upon the chip description, the technology, and, in some cases, the particular phase in the life cycle of the chip where analysis is conducted. Typically, one describes a VLSI chip at the following levels: specification, behavior, function, logic, circuit, and layout. The complexity of description grows in detail as we move from specification toward layout. Potential faults are errors in specification, errors in the translation from one level to another, errors in the manufacturing process, or material failures. Fault models must mimic the effect of these errors yet they should be easily analyzable. Compromises are often necessary to balance the complexity of a fault model necessary for accuracy against the tractability of analysis.

The most commonly modeled faults are line stuck type faults. In this model, each line of the circuit can have two possible faults: stuck-at-1 or stuck-at-0. For simplicity, only single faults are considered. Main advantages of stuck faults are that (1) they are modeled at the logic level and are independent of technology, (2) they can be analyzed by known methods, and (3) they have proven to be an effective measure of test quality. Recent work, however, has shown that there are certain technology-specific fault models requiring special analysis procedures. CMOS transistor stuck-open and stuck-short faults are examples of such faults. Technology-dependent faults such as these and others are subject of active research. For circuits implementing programmable logic arrays (PLA), microprocessors, and memories, specific functional fault models are commonly used.

Fault modeling is discussed in Chapter II.

3: Test Generation

A test for a fault is an input (a vector or a sequence of vectors) that will produce different outputs in the presence and absence of the fault, thus making the fault effect observable. In a combinational circuit, a specific stuck-fault can be tested by a single input vector. Testing a fault in a sequential circuit, in general, requires a sequence of vectors. Test generation for sequential circuits is much more complex than that for combinational circuits. In fact, none of the known sequential circuit test generators provides satisfactory performance.

The normal methodology used by designers for developing tests for sequential circuits is to use knowledge about functional behavior. Tests are designed to exercise all functions with selected data sequences.

Test generation can be automatic. A prerequisite for automatic test generation is an algorithm that can be programmed. Such algorithms mostly work on the principle of *path sensitization*. That is, they attempt to find an input vector (or sequence of vectors) that will sensitize a path from the fault site to a primary output. Efficient programs for combinational circuits are available based on well-defined algorithms such as *D-algorithm, PODEM,* and *FAN*. For sequential circuits, however, automatic test generators are not as effective. This provides the motivation for design for testability methods like the *scan design,* which is discussed in Chapter

VI. Sequential circuits, which are implemented by using scan design, can be tested like combinational circuits.

Test generation algorithms are discussed in Chapter III.

4: Test Evaluation

Even though there is no universally accepted criterion of coverage by verification tests, manufacturing tests are often required to cover 90 to 100 percent of all single stuck faults. The real measure of the effectiveness of manufacturing tests is the *reject ratio,* defined as the ratio of faulty chips among the chips passed by the tests. A reject ratio of 0.001 means that the average number of faulty chips after testing is one in a thousand. Indeed, the fault coverage should be high to meet this requirement. The actual coverage needed for a given reject ratio can be determined by analyzing wafer test data.

The coverage of a set of test vectors is measured through fault simulation. Several fault simulation algorithms have been developed for efficient programmability. Well known algorithms are termed *parallel, deductive,* and *concurrent.*

Because of the high complexity of fault simulation, coverage is often determined by simulating a random sample of faults. Recent efforts at reducing the complexity of fault simulation have produced several approximate methods. A form of statistical analysis, known as *STAFAN,* uses signal activity generated during good circuit simulation to determine controllability and observability of nodes.

Further, a circuit with scan design can be treated as combinational for test purposes, the simulator does not have to model the exact timing behavior. This allows the use of very efficient techniques. In the *parallel pattern single fault propagation (PPSFP)* method 256 vectors are simulated simultaneously. This method allows computation of fault detection probabilities. Another method, known as *critical path tracing,* assesses fault coverage in combinational circuits entirely by processing the data obtained from true-value simulation.

Fault evaluation is discussed in Chapter IV.

5: Testability Analysis

Testability is considered an inherent property of a circuit determined entirely by its structure. Such a definition would allow estimation of circuit testability before test generation. Of course, in order to be useful, testability analysis should be simpler than test generation. Most testability analyses employ the concepts of *controllability* and *observability* which can be related to the detection of stuck faults. Controllability of a line in the circuit is a measure of the effort required to control that line from primary inputs. Similarly, observability is a measure of the effort of observing the state of the line at a primary output. SCOAP (Sandia Controllability/Observability Analysis Program) is a popular program that computes such measures.

Actual applications of testability analysis are most effective in the early phases of design for (1) identifying hard to test portions of circuit, (2) estimating test development effort, and (3) estimating the size of a test vector set.

Because of the approximate nature of the analysis, most testability analyses results have poor accuracy. Still, they are beneficial if used in a statistical sense or for comparative evaluation. Recent efforts have redefined controllability and observability as probabilities of setting and observing circuit nodes.

Testability analysis is discussed in Chapter V.

6: Design for Testability

Design for testability commonly refers to those design techniques that produce designs for which tests can be generated by known methods. Such design techniques result in (1) reduced test generation cost, (2) reduced testing cost, (3) high quality product, and (4) effective use of computer-aided design tools.

The two most commonly employed design for testability techniques are scan and built-in self-test. In the scan design method, a test mode is added to the circuit. In this mode, all flip-flops are connected to form a shift register. This allows setting and observing of all flip-flop states. Tests can be generated through consideration of combinational part of the circuit thus simplifying the test generation problem. Scan methodology has been very successfully used in the industry.

Conventional testing of digital circuits consists of applying test vectors and comparing the output with the stored expected response. Built-in self-test

(BIST) technique can be used as an alternative method where a circuit has the added capabilities to generate its own vectors and to examine its output to produce a "good/bad" result. BIST techniques are steadily gaining popularity and have been discussed in several recent publications (see, for example, *IEEE Design & Test of Computers,* Special Issue on Built-In Self-Test, Vol. 2, April 1985.)

VLSI chips are (or should be) designed for testability not only at the wafer or package level but also at the system level. Systems designed with components having scan or BIST have much better reliability, diagnosability, and repairability.

Design for testability is not the main subject of this tutorial. Yet it has a far-reaching influence on test generation. We, therefore, review this topic briefly in Chapter VI.

7: Automatic Test Application

Actual manufacturing testing takes place in the factory after VLSI wafers have been processed. This is where the tests generated by the designer are actually used. Initial testing of a new design characterizes the design. Later, production testing separates good devices from faulty ones. ATE, test programming, etc., are essential parts of the testing scene. These topics are not the main focus of this tutorial, but their knowledge allows a test designer to be more effective in developing tests.

Automatic testing is briefly discussed in Chapter VII.

8: Conclusion

In this chapter, we have given a brief overview of VLSI testing. Various activities related to or influencing test generation are introduced. Of these, fault modeling and test evaluation have the closest relationship to test generation. Testability analysis, design for testability, and automatic testing methodology influence the activities of a test designer and a basic knowledge of these concepts is desirable.

9: Selected Reading

This chapter contains one reprinted paper that reviews the state of the art in VLSI testing. This paper, titled "Cutting Chip Testing Costs" (*IEEE Spectrum,* Vol. 22, pp. 38-45, April 1985), discusses basic principles in testing, then leads into the complexity issues, and finally provides a motivation for design for testability. Chapter VIII lists sources of information: conferences, workshops, periodicals, books, and a bibliography of material on testing that has appeared in the last five years.

Reprinted from *IEEE Spectrum*, April 1985, pages 38-45. Copyright © 1985 by The Institute of Electrical and Electronics Engineers, Inc. All rights reserved.

Cutting chip-testing costs

Designing VLSI circuits for testability is the most efficient way to reduce the relative costs of assuring high chip reliability

Most engineers would agree that the quality of an integrated circuit depends partly on the ability to test it. But many chips now hold over 10 000 devices, and the cost of testing tends to increase in proportion to the square of the number of devices on the chip. The problem of containing testing costs while ensuring chip quality is one that all semiconductor manufacturers face.

If the line width of a semiconductor device shrinks from 2 micrometers to 1, the number of devices on a die of equal size could quadruple. Thus, the time—and the money—required to develop a computer program to test this chip could increase sixteenfold. Rising costs of chip testing run counter to the recent reductions in the cost of designing and producing chips.

Testing now accounts for 10 percent of the total cost of manufacturing a 1-kilobit random-access-memory chip. For a 64-K RAM chip, the figure rises to 40 percent. New techniques, however, promise help in the struggle to hold down costs, by tackling the circuit-testing problem in the design stage.

Advances on many fronts

The new methods include computer programs that assess during design how easily a circuit can be tested, scan-design techniques for testing sequential circuitry, and ways of partitioning chips into blocks of manageable size for testing. Random testing and built-in self-testing are also employed in some cases to avoid exhaustive testing for every possible fault in a circuit.

In addition, advances in circuit simulation allow engineers to estimate the fault coverage of test programs—that is, the proportion of the possible logic errors that a test will uncover [Fig. 1]. Without this estimate, engineers cannot know how rigorous to make their test programs, and they could overcompensate by making the programs more rigorous than needed—a waste of time and resources.

New approaches to testing have been used successfully with very large-scale integrated (VLSI) chips. They ensure that the cost of testing will increase linearly with circuit complexity—that is, doubling the number of devices on a chip will double, rather than quadruple, the cost of testing it. Computer-aided design has been a prime aid in developing the new methods.

Yet no testing technique is surefire for all kinds of chips; future generations of ICs will certainly require new approaches. In addition, many circuit designs currently pose special problems that no technique or combination of techniques seems to solve entirely. For now, chip manufacturers must live with methods of testing that are inadequate in some cases.

Testing is becoming more closely related to the design and production processes. In the days when the only ICs manufactured had no more than a few hundred devices, circuit-design engineers worked in isolation from test engineers, who became part of the manufacturing cycle only after the design was complete. Now test engineers work closely with design and production engineers to help keep test costs down. And in some places, a single engineer handles both testing and designing.

Measuring the testability

VLSI chips can be much easier to test than their size might indicate. Testability analyses during the design of a VLSI chip are simple ways of measuring how easy it will be to test a circuit. An overall testability measure for a circuit is derived by calculating the difficulty of testing each node in the circuit. Testability-analysis programs are computationally simpler than generating a test for a chip, and thus they can be used relatively quickly while a circuit is being designed on a computer. These rough measures of testability are used for almost all kinds of chips, from semicustom chips—made in small quantities—to custom microprocessors that are mass-produced.

Designers use testability measures to identify portions of a circuit that would be difficult to test. Such inaccessible circuits are said to have poor controllability or observability. Controllability is a rough measure of the ease with which a test engineer can control signals in a circuit from the input pins. Similarly, observability is a rough measure of the ease of determining the behavior of a circuit from the output pins. [See Fig. 2.] After identifying a general section of a chip that has poor controllability or observability, the engineer can then modify the circuit to make it more testable.

Defining terms

Controllability—a rough numerical measure of how easily the values of digital circuit nodes can be controlled from I/O pins.

Fault coverage—the percentage of potential stuck faults in an IC that are uncovered by a set of test vectors; it is usually obtained through computer simulation.

Observability—a rough numerical measure of how easily the values of digital circuit nodes can be determined from I/O pins.

Pattern generator—a circuit that generates a test pattern, usually for built-in testing; it may take any form, with random-number generators and ROMs being the most common.

Sequential circuit—a digital circuit that changes state according to an input signal (normally under clock control); it must be tested with a sequence of signals.

Stuck fault—usually a physical IC fault that results in one input or output of a logic gate improperly remaining either high or low regardless of the behavior of the circuits surrounding it.

Test program—a computer program written in the language of a particular automatic production tester for ICs.

Test vectors (test patterns)—a set of IC inputs and outputs generated for use in test programs.

Testability measure—a rough numerical indication of how easily test vectors can be generated for a particular circuit.

Sharad C. Seth   University of Nebraska
Vishwani D. Agrawal   AT&T Bell Laboratories

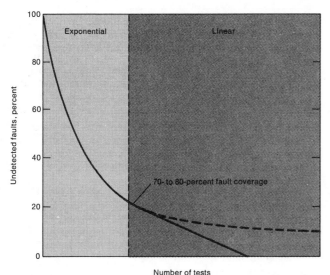

[1] The most difficult task in chip testing is generating a set of inputs and outputs, called test vectors, that will uncover close to 100 percent of all possible chip faults. At first the task goes smoothly, but when 70 to 80 percent of the faults have been detected, a change in test strategy, which entails extensive computer simulation, is required.

To get a rough measure of testability for a block of circuitry, the engineer computes the logarithm of the sum of the controllabilities and observabilities of all the nodes in a circuit. The resulting number, called a testability index, is proportional to the ultimate number of test vectors—inputs and outputs—needed to test a chip.

For example, a 50 000-gate microcontroller chip might have a testability index greater than 6, requiring 100 000 vectors to test for 90 percent of the faults; a programmable logic array with 2000 gates and an index of 5 may require only a few hundred vectors for the same fault coverage. The approximate length of a test can be predicted quite accurately in this way.

The most popular testability measurement program, the Scoap (Sandia Controllability and Analysis Program), calculates six quantities for every node (or signal) in the circuit, based on the effort needed to control and observe the node using a procedure such as the D-algorithm [see "Test design: stuck with the D-algorithm," p. 40].

The way in which a testability-measurement program operates depends on whether a circuit is largely sequential or largely combinational. A combinational circuit is basically a hierarchy of logic gates through which a signal will propagate in a single clock cycle. In such a circuit, controllability and observability are defined in terms of the number of logic gates that a test program must manipulate to either control or observe a node.

Sequential circuits generally have registers that must be clocked to allow signals to propagate. In these circuits, a series of state transitions must be made to control or observe a node. Thus, controllability and observability are defined in terms of the length of the sequence of inputs needed to control or observe a node.

Since the overall complexity of computation in Scoap increases almost linearly with the number of gates, the cost of using Scoap will increase only as quickly as chip area increases. Thus, for the next five years or so, Scoap is attractive because the cost of using it will not increase proportional to the square of chip area, which would be out of proportion to the cost of designing chips.

However, the usefulness of testability-measurement programs is limited. Analytical approaches have failed to relate the results of Scoap and other such programs to the fault coverage of particular circuit nodes; a design engineer cannot determine whether any given node in a circuit will be testable. Testability measures are poor predictors of which specific faults in a circuit will remain undetected and which will be detected in a test program. They are good, however, for indicating blocks of circuitry that may be hard to test.

Testability-analysis programs do not work well with sequential circuits because such programs are based on making some approximations when analyzing complex circuits. In combinational circuits, the complexity does not increase proportional to the size as much as in sequential circuits, for which the approximations cause great inaccuracies.

This limits the usefulness of testability-analysis programs, because most chips are a combination of both sequential and combinational circuits. Some circuits, such as microprocessors, are largely sequential, with relatively little combinational circuitry embedded in the chip.

Scan design uses artificial paths

The computation time for test generation and evaluation tends to grow at a rate approximately proportional to the square of the number of gates or the number of transistors in the circuit. Because of the greater complexity of sequential circuits, the cost of testing grows even faster than the circuit size—being proportional to the number of gates cubed. For example, a 4-bit arithmetic logic unit with about 100 gates—a typical combinational circuit—requires 30 test vectors for acceptable fault coverage. By contrast, a typical sequential circuit—a 4-bit multiplier with 350

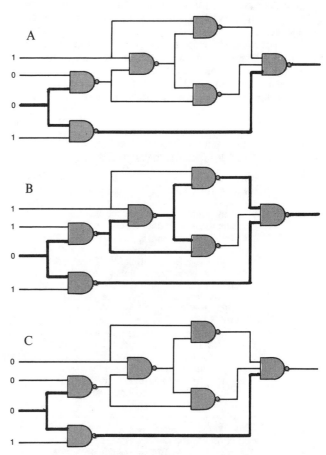

[2] Testing a node in a circuit requires control and observation from the chip's I/O pins. First, a path to the node must be sensitized by setting the surrounding values so that the value of the test node can be changed or read from the I/O pins. In A and B, the paths shown in bold lines have been sensitized by setting the values of three input pins to detect the fault at the node to the right through the remaining pin. In C, the path is not sensitized.

gates—requires 1100 test vectors for the same fault coverage. Even though the multiplier has only 3.5 times as many devices as the combinational circuit, more than 35 times as many vectors are needed to test it.

What can be done to hold down the cost of testing sequential circuits, which do not benefit much from testability measures?

For sequential circuits, chip designers are increasingly employing a technique known as scan design. Scan design gives the engineer access to sequential circuitry through artificial paths built into the circuit especially for that purpose. Through clever placement, the end effect of these artificial pathways is to convert sequential circuitry temporarily into combinational circuitry for testing purposes.

The method is analogous to test-driving automobiles. If an automobile is simple, the best way to test it is to drive it. However, if the automobile is very complex, with all sorts of electronic motor regulators and controls, test-driving alone may not be sufficient. It may be more effective to test the wiring and some of the individual components and then drive the complex automobile for only a short while. Similarly, testing complex sequential circuits requires tremendous effort—perhaps months of writing test vectors by hand.

With scan design, however, the engineer is not actually testing the circuitry by operating it as it was intended to operate in the field. Instead, the chips are designed to be put into a mode for testing each logic gate with a much simpler program than would otherwise be possible; an engineer can "check the wires" by way of the artificial pathways. Thus, with the aid of computer programs not available for sequential circuits, the engineer can usually generate test vectors in a few hours. In about one afternoon, scan design can generate the necessary vectors to test a 2000-gate digital demodulator chip at a fault coverage greater than 90 percent. Without scan, this would take a week. The benefit is even greater for more complex circuits.

Even before LSI circuits were made, engineers recognized that the problems in testing were significantly more complex for random sequential circuits than for combinational circuits of comparable size. The detection of a fault in a random sequential circuit often requires a long sequence of inputs to sensitize and observe a faulty node.

To test such circuits, engineers have tried, with little success, to model them from a purely functional rather than a structural viewpoint—in other words, they have tried to test the car simply by driving it. In this approach, sequential machines are represented by a state-transition table, which describes how the values of each node in the circuit change in response to clock cycles and certain test inputs. To model a circuit this way, checking must be done to make sure the test circuit actually behaves as the state-transition table says it should.

However, checking experiments tend to require unreasonably long computations, even for small circuits; the number of state transitions that need to be covered can be enormous. The solution is to modify the original circuit for test purposes so that the sequences of state transitions are short and easily derived. Scan design is the latest and most successful technique of this kind.

Creating 'normal' and 'scan' modes

Scan design requires that the circuit be designed with clocked flip-flops, or latches. When the chip is fabricated, it can be put into either a "normal" or a "scan" mode by way of an input/output pin especially designated for that purpose. In the normal mode, in which the circuit is largely inaccessible, the inputs are interconnected to form a sequential circuit that performs the intended function. However, in the scan mode, the latches are chained together to form shift registers. Digital test vectors are shifted into the register from a scan-in pin of the chip. With the test vectors thus implanted in the circuitry, the circuit can be switched back to the normal mode and tested. The circuit is then switched over to the scan mode, and the resulting values in the shift register are shifted out through a scan-out pin, which, like the mode pin, is added to the circuit for the sole purpose of testing.

Test design: stuck with the D-algorithm

New methods to simplify chip testing are needed partly because the basis of VLSI testing is essentially the same as that developed for the first ICs, which were extremely simple by today's standards. In essence, tests seek only two types of "classical faults" in both bipolar and MOS ICs: stuck-at-1 and stuck-at-0. A stuck fault is an input or an output of a logic gate that remains either a logical "1" or a logical "0" even if its value should change. Stuck faults are usually caused by an error in the fabrication process rather than by design errors, which have presumably been corrected by computer simulation by the time production tests are performed.

Although the model has little relation to the physical behavior of digital circuits and can only represent a subset of possible faults, experience has shown that a test program that uncovers about 95 percent of all possible stuck faults will yield a good-quality product. (Test engineers debate the percentage figure by a few points either way.)

Some engineers argue that the stuck-fault model is doomed to obsolescence because of the difficulty in automating test development for VLSI chips when the model is used. The old algorithms for generating test vectors to cover 95 percent of all stuck faults are unwieldy. For complex random circuits, the D-algorithm—developed by J.P. Roth and his colleagues at IBM Corp. almost 20 years ago—remains the prototype for most commercially feasible algorithms. The algorithm takes its names from the character "D" that is used by test engineers as a variable to show whether a circuit node is affected by a fault (D = 0) or not (D = 1).

To produce a set of test vectors, engineers reproduce all possible stuck faults on a computer-simulated circuit, and for each fault they invoke the D-algorithm to establish the appropriate value of D. This is repeated until a path is formed from the node of the circuit where the fault exists to an output pin of the chip. The term "sensitized" refers, in this case, to the observation of the test signal at the location of the fault, which the engineer obtains by manipulating the signals to the logic gates extraneous to the signal path. The D-algorithm is a recursive search procedure—advancing one gate at a time and repeating itself until the fault is detected.

As a path is advanced from an input to the output of a gate, values of other inputs to the gate may have to be set to a constant to allow the selected input to control the output—that is, to sensitize the path. These line values may, in turn, change the values of the inputs and outputs of other gates to which they are directly connected. Another recursive step is necessary to take into account all the implications of advancing the sensitized path through one gate. Inconsistencies caused by earlier assignments of gate inputs are discovered at this point. At any juncture, several alternatives might be available, of which the algorithm chooses one arbitrarily and records it in a stack. If the algorithm runs into a dead end, it retraces its steps by reading values off the stack and trying another alternative. This procedure is repeated until a consistent and sensitized path is found from the fault location to an output pin, which constitutes a valid test for one fault.

Clearly, the D-algorithm may involve a great deal of backtracking. In the worst case, it may have to examine all sensitized paths not only one at a time but in all possible combinations as well, because for some single faults it is necessary to sensitize several paths. In practice, the expected number of choices actually examined may be reduced by using heuristics, a method of ordering the choices that the D-algorithm

Scan design makes the generation of tests for sequential circuits easier, and it greatly reduces the number of transitions in the state-transition table that must be verified, thus reducing the task to manageable size. In addition, computer programs have been developed at AT&T Bell Laboratories and elsewhere in the last few years to automate the generation of test vectors for circuits using scan design.

The price that designers pay for using scan design is a requirement for additional logic in a circuit. The precise area needed for the additional circuitry is a matter of dispute, but most estimates fall between 10 and 20 percent of the chip size. This overhead, which degrades performance of the chip somewhat, may seem a high price to pay, but it results in much quicker test generation than most alternative ad hoc methods.

Scan design is finding acceptance in the industry for semicustom circuits such as gate arrays. Since the extensive automation in semicustom-circuit design makes the design process quicker than for handcrafted circuits, the time for generating test vectors must be held to a minimum; scan design can be implemented quickly by computers, and test vectors can be generated automatically. Scan design also eases systems testing for some manufacturers; hierarchical scan design, in which a scan path can be made from the box to the printed-circuit boards and down to individual chips, is not uncommon.

Mainly for economic reasons, scan design has not caught on in so-called commodity circuits, which are manufactured in high volumes for off-the-shelf use. Since commodity circuits, such as advanced microprocessors and other general-purpose chips, are mass-produced, manufacturers are willing to devote considerable resources to handcrafting the design of the chips to get the most yield from their wafers. Unlike semicustom designers, who use computer-aided design (CAD) to automate designs and layouts, the commodity-circuit manufacturers tend to use CAD to aid in hand designing. Since much time and money are spent simulating commodity-circuit designs, the manufacturers generate extensive data about the circuits that are useful for devising

tests. They also use many custom techniques to obtain chip tests that cannot be computer-automated.

Furthermore, commodity-circuit manufacturers are entirely unlike semicustom manufacturers in their production test strategy, which does not favor scan-design techniques. Instead, they tend to rely on functional tests. For example, the 30 000-gate 32-bit microprocessor developed at Bell Labs is tested solely with functional techniques that execute the microprocessor instructions instead of finding stuck faults. The lifetime of a commodity chip, which may be five or more years, gives the manufacturers two advantages that negate some of the benefits of scan design: (1) they can afford to spend more time and effort to reduce the overhead for making the chip testable; and (2) they can refine the production test based on the chip failures reported by users of preproduction samples, usually original-equipment manufacturers. Semicustom designers, whose chips have relatively short production lifetimes, cannot rely as heavily on production experience to ensure chip quality.

Divide and conquer

Another design-stage technique for reducing the time and cost of testing large circuits is the "divide and conquer" approach. Often used in conjunction with other techniques, such as scan design, it requires no special circuitry. Rather than being designed as a monolith, a complex circuit is designed as an interconnection of modules, which may be further partitioned into submodules. This method is similar to the structural design of computer programs.

Ideally, a partitioned circuit would be designed with a test mode that would connect the inputs and outputs of each partitioned block to the output pins of the chip, so that the block could be observed. Test vectors would be multiplexed in the test mode through a set of input/output pins. The I/O pins would be used for each block in succession until the entire chip was tested.

Partitioning looks promising. However, the technique has not been widely adopted because the chip under test must be designed with independently testable partitions. So far, partitioning has been used mainly in circuits, such as microprocessors, that have architectures with natural partitions. At present, there is no economical way of imposing partitions on otherwise unstructured circuits.

However, partitioning is one element of two recently developed techniques that are proving quite useful in reducing costs: built-in testing and random testing.

The built-in self-testing (BIST) approach calls for partitioning a circuit into blocks during design; after the chip is fabricated, each block is exhaustively tested with a built-in pattern generator. The response to the pattern from the generator, which may run into millions of bits, is compressed into a "signature" of a relatively small number of bits. A multiple-input linear feedback shift register is used for this purpose, with feedback lines chosen carefully to ensure to a high degree of confidence that the signature is unique. An external control signal is introduced, as in scan design, to put the circuit into a test mode and to start the pattern generator. When the pattern ends, the contents of all the signature registers are compared with signatures stored in a read-only memory (ROM).

After the signatures in the different blocks are scanned with one output pin, the result is an indication that the circuit is either good or faulty.

The scan and BIST design methods complement each other and are often used in conjunction. Scan design solves test problems arising from the sequential nature of a circuit; BIST lessens the burden of generating and storing tests for complex combinational blocks of circuitry.

Random testing is useful for certain exceptional cases in which logic partitioning is not feasible, including gate arrays and other unstructured designs. Exhaustive testing of such circuits is impractical because of the large number of circuit inputs. Consider combinational logic implementing 32-bit multiplication:

makes at each circuit node.

The D-algorithm can be extremely time-consuming for deep circuits—large circuits in which a typical fault path would wind through 15 to 20 gates. In practice, the length of time for running a D-algorithm increases by $n^{1.8}$, where n equals the number of gates in the circuit.

The D-algorithm performs particularly poorly for circuits containing "exclusive-or" gates arranged in a tree structure, which is commonly found in circuits that check the parity of signals. If many bits are fed in parallel into a large exclusive-or gate, the gate will detect the occurrence of an error on any one of the inputs. In practice, a tree of double-input exclusive-or gates is often used instead of multi-input gates. The degradation in performance occurs because a very large number of possibilities may have to be examined for each gate in the recursive step to check the consistency of the process.

This shortcoming is counteracted, however, by other algorithms. The algorithm called Podem (path-oriented decision making) has been designed to minimize backtracking. For a 64-bit arithmetic-logic unit with about 2000 gates, for example, the D-algorithm takes 45 seconds for each test vector on a VAX 11/780 computer. Podem is six times faster. A further enhancement called Fan (for fan-out-oriented test-generation algorithm) is five times faster than Podem.

Even so, the fastest reported algorithms would typically consume 1500 seconds of CPU time on a VAX 11/780 computer to detect all the faults on a 3000-gate arithmetic and logic unit. For VLSI circuits with about 30 000 gates, test-vector-generation algorithms would take about 40 hours, which is not acceptable.   —S.C.S. and V.D.A.

since a 32-bit multiplier has a total of 64 inputs, exhaustive testing would require 2^{64} test vectors—an astronomical number.

Recent analyses show that very high fault coverage can be attained by nonexhaustive random testing, in which test patterns are random bit patterns. Further, computational algorithms, for which execution times increase linearly with circuit size, can identify those faults not likely to be covered by random testing. Such faults can then be eliminated by redesigning the chip. Alternatively, BIST patterns may be generated and stored in a ROM to catch the remaining faults.

BIST techniques have not yet caught on in many areas of IC manufacturing because of the additional chip area, or overhead, occupied by the partitioning and the logic for internal testing.

The techniques are useful primarily for more complex circuits, such as the 200 000-transistor 68020 microprocessor of the Motorola Corp. Many engineers say that BIST will become more widespread when circuits with at least 100 000 gates become more common, for which about 5 million test vectors would probably be required. Motorola uses built-in testing in its 8-bit 6804P2 microcomputer, which has 17 800 transistors. About 5 percent of the total area of the chip is occupied by a 288-byte ROM to store test programs and a register to detect the signature.

Testing the tests to save time

An estimate of the number of faults that will be uncovered by a chip test goes a long way toward reducing the time needed to generate tests. The overall process of generating a test program for a chip is like shooting at a progressively smaller target. The first set of patterns may test, say, 30 percent of the possible stuck faults of a circuit. An additional set of vectors to test another 30 percent of the chip would increase the total coverage to about 50 percent, after allowance is made for a 10 percent overlap. As the coverage increases, the value of each additional test decreases. At roughly 70 to 80 percent fault coverage, the test strategy is usually changed; at this point, specific nodes of the circuit that have not yet been tested are targeted with special algorithms for test generation and fault simulation. They push the fault coverage to 90 or 95 percent.

The key to estimating fault coverage in this way is computer simulation; only by simulating a circuit can the fault coverage of test vectors be evaluated. The test engineer simulates each possible stuck fault in a circuit to determine whether that fault was uncovered by the test. This indicates the fault coverage of the test vectors. Although the basic principles of production-quality fault simulators have been unchanged since the advent of LSI circuits, various techniques have greatly increased the speed of simulators.

The computation time of commercial simulators has been greatly reduced by simulating more than one fault for each input pattern. The simplest and most widely used technique is parallel fault simulation; for each input pattern, each bit of a computer word simulates a different fault.

Deductive fault simulators have further reduced the number of calculations. With such simulators, each line of logic gates is associated with a list of those faults that are sensitized to it—that is, the faults detected up to that point. The simulator refers to the list of faults already sensitized to primary outputs and then computes the fault coverage.

Even these advances in fault simulators have not completely solved the problem of pushing fault coverage to 70 to 80 percent without exorbitant computer simulation costs. The cost of network simulation has been estimated to grow at a rate proportional to the cube of the number of gates in a circuit for parallel fault simulations, and to the square of the number of gates for deductive simulation. The concurrent simulator, a refinement of the deductive simulator, takes 7.4 seconds of central-processing-unit time for each test pattern on a VAX11/780 system for a MOS circuit with 505 transistors. With a quadratic rise in simulation time, a 50 000-transistor circuit would require over 20 hours of simulation time for each test pattern on the same machine.

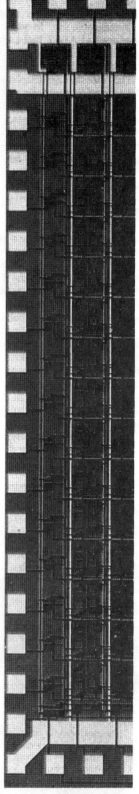

[3] Four methods of VLSI chip testing are gaining acceptance in the electronics industry. Testability analysis programs (A) allow designers to improve the planning of test strategies during the design of the chip. The other three—scan design (B), partitioning (C), and built-in self-test (D)—entail modifications in the chip design.

Fixed-purpose simulation engines, which have been announced recently, greatly reduce the simulation time for specific circuits by using hardware to concurrently execute different steps of simulation algorithms. What they sacrifice in flexibility, they gain in speed. One such system, the Logic Evaluator made by Zycad Corp., of St. Paul, Minn., has 16 hardware units, which can simulate 60 million active logic gates per second.

By using parallel execution techniques, fixed-purpose systems solve the speed problem for the short term. However, they use algorithms for which the execution times tend to increase as the cube of the number of gates in the circuit being simulated. For this reason, the cost of testing denser chips will increase quickly. Ultimately, test strategies will combine the use of such high-speed simulators with the other techniques described here.

Test engineers have a third way of measuring fault coverage of test vectors before fabrication, in addition to design-for-testability techniques (such as scan design) and special-purpose hardware simulators. The third approach is statistical fault sampling, rather than deterministically checking each one.

Only a fraction of the possible faults are simulated in a statistical sampling technique to estimate fault coverage. The method is analogous to public opinion polls: randomly sampled faults are simulated, and the percentage of these faults that are detected by the set of test vectors is used as an estimate of the overall fault coverage.

The confidence range of these estimates gets narrower as the estimate of the fault coverage approaches 100 percent. For a sample of 1000 faults, an estimate of 50 percent fault coverage is accurate to within ±5 percent, whereas an estimate of 95 percent is accurate to within ±2 percent. Nevertheless, statistical sampling can effectively estimate any fault coverage.

Not perfect

Regardless of whether stuck faults are simulated exhaustively or statistically sampled, the estimated fault coverage is only an

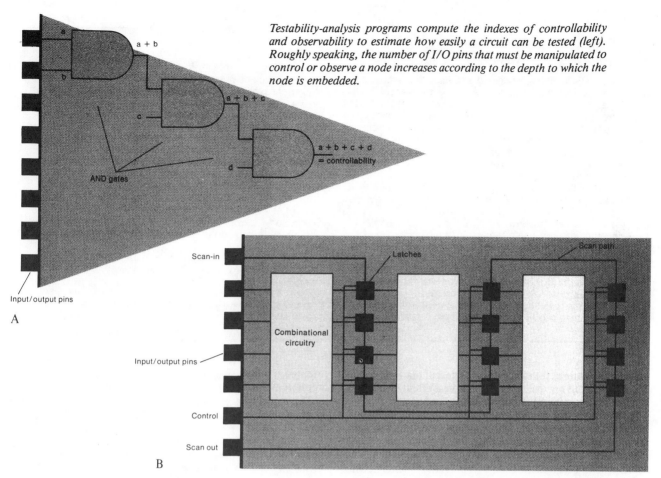

Testability-analysis programs compute the indexes of controllability and observability to estimate how easily a circuit can be tested (left). Roughly speaking, the number of I/O pins that must be manipulated to control or observe a node increases according to the depth to which the node is embedded.

Scan design simplifies the testing of sequential circuits by breaking them into blocks of combinational circuitry (above). When the circuit is placed in a "scan" mode, D flip-flops are linked so that test vectors can be inserted into embedded circuitry through the I/O pins.

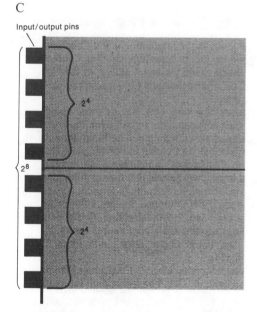

Partitioning simplifies the testing of large blocks of circuitry by dividing them into smaller blocks that can be tested independently. For example, if 2^8 patterns must be generated to test one block of circuitry, only 2^4 patterns are needed if the block is divided in half.

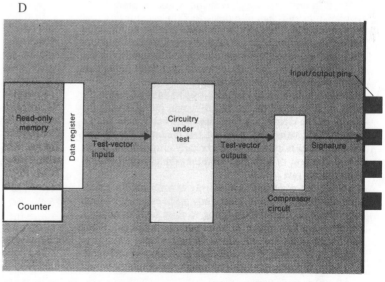

For built-in self-testing, a test-program generator is embedded in a circuit. The common type of generator here uses a ROM to store test vectors and a simple circuit for compressing the response into a signature, which is read through one or more I/O pins. Other types include random-number generators.

Integrated-circuit chips undergo a series of tests that add to the costs. The final production test is the one that causes the greatest increase in chip costs, mainly because it is the most thorough. It caps a long and complicated test process that varies widely from one type of circuit to another and from one manufacturer to another. However, because of the high number of internal devices on current VLSI chips, production test programs are becoming too time-consuming and too costly to devise and run.

Chip testing begins when the chips are still part of a wafer. Parametric tests—which determine electrical properties such as gate threshold, polysilicon resistance, and diffusion resistance—are usually performed on four specially designed chips on a wafer. The results are used in one of two ways: (1) if the measured values are not within satisfactory ranges, the wafer is either scrapped or recycled with no further testing; or (2) changes in the fabrication process to maintain its integrity may be indicated. Such tests are essentially the same as when LSI chips were introduced.

Next is the wafer-sort test, which is usually inexpensive compared with the final production test; it is designed to screen out chips that have gross faults before they undergo the rather expensive packaging operation. However, in recent years the wafer sort has taken on some of the burden of the final test. A computer-controlled tester applies a series of functional tests to each chip on the wafer. These tests are similar to the final test in that they check the internal gates of a circuit using a set of test vectors that cover the inputs and outputs of a properly working chip. In some cases, the wafer sort can achieve a fault coverage as high as 80 percent—meaning that 80 percent of the possible faults are detected. The final test, which typically has 95 percent fault coverage, often uses the same vectors as the functional test in the wafer sort. However, these vectors are applied under wider variations in conditions such as temperature, voltage, and speed.

Other tests following the wafer sort are as important as the functional tests in ensuring quality. In recent years, tests have become much more rigorous in such areas as checking the contacts between test probes and chip pads, applying heat stress to accelerate latent defects, and measuring the power dissipation. —*S.C.S. and V.D.A.*

---

imperfect measure of the effectiveness of a set of test vectors. For this reason, VLSI test engineers rely to a great extent on their experience to determine what fault coverage is adequate.

A fault simulator cannot evaluate the coverage of physical faults that are not covered in the stuck-fault model, such as short circuits or open circuits in metal, diffusion, or polysilicon; shorts between semiconductor layers; or parametric irregularities. The simultaneous occurrence of two or more faults is also not simulated because of the very large number of possible fault combinations, even though a processing defect is quite likely to lead to multiple faults, especially with small circuit geometries.

The real value of estimating the fault coverage of a set of test vectors may also depend on the simulator used, since simulators incorporate criteria for detecting specific faults other than stuck ones—fault-induced races and oscillations, for example.

Redundant circuits can also throw off the accuracy of fault-coverage simulation. They give rise to faults that are not detected in a test because the faults do not cause a circuit to work improperly. In addition, simulators have no way of distinguishing between faults hidden by redundant circuits and valid faults that the test program simply cannot identify.

Redundant faults are not identified by simulators because the computer time required to do the job would increase with the complexity of the circuit at a rate that is always greater than a polynomial. This means that even if a test method were devised to keep the cost of testing the circuit linearly proportional to the circuit size, the cost of locating redundant faults would still increase at a faster rate.

At present, test engineers have no way of knowing the extent to which redundant faults influence any given estimate of fault coverage. Time is often wasted trying to raise fault coverage a few percentage points above 90 when perhaps 5 percent of the possible circuit faults are redundant. In such a case, a test program might in fact have 95 percent fault coverage—usually considered adequate for most chips—although the simulator would show only 90 percent fault coverage.

Despite the drawbacks of the current measures of fault coverage by simulators, this method continues to be relied upon as the figure of merit for a test vector set. One may rightfully ask how this figure of merit relates to the quality of the tested chips. A quantitative answer can be given, based on a model of the fault distribution on the chip. It is assumed in such a model that a random number of logical faults are caused by each physical defect on a chip. Since the physical defects themselves are randomly dis-tributed, a compound distribution can be used to describe the occurrence of logical faults.

The model of the fault distribution predicts that for denser chips, a lower fault coverage is needed to obtain the same quality level. In smaller geometries, a defect caused by a dust particle, for example, will damage more gates, because the particle will be larger relative to the gates. Since more gates will thus be affected by a single particle, there will be more faults to flag the effects it causes. Although other problems will certainly arise in testing even more complex chips, this is at least one encouraging sign, especially in view of the disproportionately high cost of increasing fault coverage.

To probe further

Recent analyses showing that a high fault coverage can be obtained by nonexhaustive random testing are reported in "On random test," a paper given at the International Test Conference in 1983 and available in the proceedings of that conference. Another paper, "When to use random testing," in the November 1978 issue of *IEEE Transactions on Computers*, pp. 1054–55, also discusses this issue.

Several conferences now deal with one or more aspects of VLSI chip testing, including computer software for implementing many of the techniques described here. The International Test Conference 1985 will be held in October in Philadelphia, Pa. The Design Automation Conference, which has dealt increasingly with testing-related topics, will be held this June in Albuquerque, N.M. Registration information for both conferences may be obtained by writing to the IEEE Computer Society, 1109 Spring St., Suite 300, Silver Springs, Md. 20910; telephone 301-589-8142. To order the proceedings of last year's conferences on VLSI chip testing, write to the IEEE Order Dept., 445 Hoes Lane, Piscataway, N.J. 08854.

The IEEE Custom Integrated Circuits Conference 1985 will be held May 20–23 in Portland, Ore. For registration information, write to Laura Silzars, 6900 South Canyon Drive, Portland, Ore. 97225; telephone 503-292-6374. To order last year's proceedings, write to the IEEE Order Dept. at the address above.

The eighth annual Design for Testability Workshop will be held April 23–25 in Beaver Creek, Colo. For information, write to Thomas Williams, IBM Corp., P.O. Box 1900, Boulder, Colo. 80302.

The IEEE Instrumentation and Measurement Society sponsored its second annual Instrumentation and Measurement Technology Conference last March in Tampa, Florida. For a copy of the proceedings, write to Robert Myers, Conference Coordinator, 1700 Westwood Blvd., Los Angeles, Calif. 90024; telephone 213-475-4571.

Many of the topics covered in this article were touched upon in "The one-month chip: testing," by Fred Guterl, which appeared in the September 1984 issue of *Spectrum*, p. 40, as part of a five-part report. Another article on printed-circuit-board testing, dealing with issues similar to those discussed in this article, is "Automated board testing: coping with complex circuits," by Rodham E. Tulloss, in the July 1983 issue of *Spectrum*, p. 38.

A variety of automatic test systems for test applications are described by W.G. Fee in *Tutorial—LSI Testing*, second edition, IEEE Computer Society, Long Beach, Calif. (catalog no. EHO 122.2).

For information on stuck-type and nonclassical faults in MOS circuits, see "A Fault Simulator for MOS LSI Circuits," A.K. Bose et al., *Proceedings* of the 19th Design Automation Conference, pp. 400–409, June 1982. Nonclassical faults are also described in "Fault Modeling and Simulation of CMOS and MOS Integrated Circuits," R.L. Wadsack, *Bell System Technical Journal*, Vol. 57, pp. 1449–1472, May–June 1977. The inadequacy of stuck-type faults at the gate level for MOS circuits is discussed in "Physical vs. Logical Fault Models of MOS LSI Circuits: Impact on Their Testability," J. Galiay, Y. Crouzet, and M. Vergniault, *IEEE Transactions on Computing*, C-29, pp. 527–31, June 1980.

The D-algorithm is described in "Programmed Algorithms to Compute Tests and to Detect and Distinguish Between Failures in Logic Circuits," J.P. Roth, W.G. Bouricius, and P.R. Schneider, *IEEE Transactions on Electrical Components*, EC-19, pp. 567–80, October 1967. The Podem enhanced algorithm for test generation is described in "An Implicit Enumeration Algorithm to Generate Tests for Combinational Logic Circuits," P. Goel, *IEEE Transactions on Computing*, C-30, pp. 215–22, March 1981. The FAN enhanced algorithm is examined in "On the Acceleration of Test Generation Algorithms," H. Fujiwara and T. Shimono, *IEEE Transactions on Computing*, C-32, pp. 1137–44, December 1983.

The Scoap testability measure of L.H. Goldstein is the subject of "Controllability/Observability Analysis of Digital Circuits," *IEEE Transactions on Circuit and Systems*, CAS-26, pp. 685–93, September 1979. For applications of testability measures and their accuracy, a useful work is "Testability Measures—What Do They Tell Us?" V.D. Agrawal and M.R. Mercer, *Digest of Papers*, International Test Conference, pp. 391–96, 1982.

A scan-design method is described in "Logic Structure for LSI Testability," E.B. Eichelberger and T.W. Williams, *Journal of Design Automation and Fault Tolerant Computing*, Vol. 2, pp. 165–78, May 1978. A proposal for logic partitioning and multiplexer logic for observing internal logic blocks is made by E.J. McCluskey and S. Bozorgui-Nesbat in "Design for Autonomous Test," *IEEE Transactions on Computing*, C-30, pp. 866–75, November 1981.

Built-in self-testing (BIST) is an active area of research. A primary forum for exchange of ideas is the annual BIST Workshop, the third of which was held in March 1985 at Kiawah Island (Charleston), S.C., under the chairmanship of Richard M. Sedmak, Self-Test Services, Maple Glenn, Pa. At the 1984 International Test Conference in Philadelphia, a tutorial on BIST was organized by P.H. Bardell of IBM Corp., Poughkeepsie, N.Y. 12602.

Methods of fault simulation are described by M.A. Breuer and A.D. Friedman in *Diagnosis and Reliable Design of Digital Systems*, Computer Science Press, Rockville, Md., 1976. Test-generation and fault-simulation costs are the subject of "Test Generation Costs Analysis and Projection," P. Goel, *Proceedings* of the 17th Design Automation Conference, pp. 77–84, June 1980.

The use of sampling techniques in evaluating fault coverage is discussed by V.D. Agrawal in "Sampling Techniques for Determining Fault Coverage in LSI Circuits," *Journal of Digital Systems*, Vol. 5, pp. 189–202, 1981. A relationship between fault coverage and product quality is derived by V.D. Agrawal, S.C. Seth, and P. Agrawal in "LSI Product Quality and Fault Coverage," *Proceedings* of the 18th Design Automation Conference, pp. 196–203, 1981. This is further refined by S.C. Seth and V.D. Agrawal in "Characterizing the LSI Yield Equation from Wafer Test Data," *IEEE Transactions on Computer Aided Design*, CAD-3, April 1984.

About the authors

Sharad C. Seth (SM) is a professor of computer science at the University of Nebraska in Lincoln, where he joined the faculty in 1970. He held visiting positions at the Indian Institute of Technology in Kanpur, India, in 1974–75 and 1982–83 and worked at the AT&T Bell Laboratories in Murray Hill, N.J., during the summers of 1980 and 1982. His current research interests are in the areas of VLSI testing and design and reliability analysis of fault-tolerant systems. He holds a bachelor of engineering degree in electronics and telecommunications from Jabalpur University in India, a master of technology degree in electrical engineering from the Indian Institute of Technology in Kanpur, and the Ph.D. in electrical engineering from the University of Illinois in Urbana.

Vishwani D. Agrawal (SM) is supervisor of the test-aids group at Bell Laboratories in Murray Hill. Before joining Bell Labs, he worked at TRW Defense and Space Systems Group in California and as assistant professor at the Indian Institute of Technology in New Delhi. He holds a bachelor's degree in telecommunication engineering from the University of Roorkee in India, a master's degree in engineering from the Indian Institute of Science in Bangalore, and a Ph.D. from the University of Illinois in Urbana. The author of more than 60 papers, he won the best-paper award at the 1982 International Test Conference in Philadelphia. He is vice chairman of the Design Automation Standards Subcommittee of the IEEE and is a member of the editorial board of *IEEE Design and Test Magazine*. He is a fellow of the Institution of Electronics and Telecommunication Engineers of India. ◆

A grab bag of methods for designing testable chips

Method	Advantages	Disadvantages
Testability analysis: computer programs for evaluating how easily a circuit design can be tested	Easy to use; executes quickly; useful for all kinds of circuits	Inaccurate for particular nodes
Scan design: a method of converting sequential circuitry into combinational circuitry for testing	Allows automation of test generation; simplifies test program; good for semicustom circuits (fast turnaround)	Overhead in chip area degrades performance
Partitioning: dividing a circuit into sections that can be tested independently	Moderate overhead	Largely experimental; used only in conjunction with other methods
Built-in self-test: execution of test programs by circuits built into the circuit that is subject to testing	Reduces task of automatic production testers	Gives only a 'go–no go' indication; poor for diagnostics
Random testing: use of random signals to yield a probable fault coverage	Less time-consuming than exhaustive tests; easy to implement on the test chip (as with built-in self-test)	Can't predict coverage of particular faults

Chapter II: Fault Modeling

Just like any other analysis, fault analysis requires modeling (or abstraction). Fault models serve two purposes. First, they help generate tests, and, second, they help evaluate test quality defined in terms of coverage of modeled faults. A good fault model is one that is simple to analyze and yet closely represents the behavior of physical faults in the circuit.

Fault modeling is strongly related to circuit modeling. Digital circuits are commonly described as an interconnection of logic gates. Even a moderate amount of imagination provides numerous fault possibilities, for example, missing gates, wrong gate types, missing interconnections, added interconnections, shorted interconnections, etc. Most of these faults, although physically real, are too complex to model. The faults most commonly modeled are *stuck faults*.

1: Stuck Faults

Stuck faults are not only the simplest faults to analyze, but they also have proved to be very effective in representing the faulty behavior of actual devices. The simplicity of stuck faults is derived from their logical behavior; so these faults are often referred to as *logical faults*. One of the earliest discussions on stuck faults was given by Poage [Poag63].

Stuck faults are assumed to affect only the interconnections (or lines) between the gates. Each line can have two types of stuck faults: stuck-at-1 and stuck-at-0. Thus, a line with a stuck-at-1 fault will always have a logical value 1 irrespective of the correct logical output of the gate driving it.

In general, several stuck faults can be assumed to be simultaneously present in a circuit. A circuit with n lines can have $3^n - 1$ possible stuck line combinations. This is because each line can be in any one of the three states: stuck-at-1, stuck-at-0, or fault-free. All combinations except the one with all lines in the fault-free state are counted as faults. It is easy to realize that even with moderate values of n, the number of multiple stuck faults will be very large; therefore, in practice, we only analyze *single* stuck faults. An n-line circuit will have $2n$ single stuck faults, a number that can be further reduced by *fault collapsing*. This technique is applicable to multiple faults as well.

2: Fault Collapsing

Two faults are called *equivalent* if their effect is indistinguishable at the outputs of a circuit, which means that any test detecting one of them will also detect the other. Selecting one representative fault from each class of equivalent faults is called *equivalence fault collapsing*. Computationally, this is an intractable problem in its general form. In practice, incomplete yet substantial fault collapsing may be possible with little computational effort. A good example is the collapsing of faults associated with the inputs and the output of a logic gate. Consider an n-input AND gate with none of the inputs directly observable. It is easy to see that an input stuck-at-0 (it is a common practice to write *a stuck-at-i* as *a s-a-i*) is equivalent to the output s-a-0; there is no way to distinguish the two from the inputs and outputs of the circuit. For the purpose of test generation, therefore, we only consider $n+2$ of the $2n+2$ faults associated with the AND gate: s-a-1 on each input and s-a-1 and s-a-0 on the output. Similarly, in an n-input OR gate, we test for s-a-0 on each input and s-a-1 and s-a-0 on the output. Testing considerations for NAND and NOR gates are similar.

A three-value logic simulator is effective in finding equivalent faults that may be separated by several gates in a circuit. The three values used in simulation are 0, 1, and X ≡ *unknown or don't care*. Consider the circuit of Figure 2.1. A value 0 on line *a* uniquely (i.e., irrespective of the other inputs of the NAND gate) forces a 1 on line *e*, and, thereby, forces a 1 on line *h*. This is easily checked by setting *don't care* values on all other input lines and noticing that the values of lines *e* and *h* are still unique. Thus, the faults, *a stuck-at*-0, *e stuck-at*-1, and *h stuck-at*-1, are equivalent.

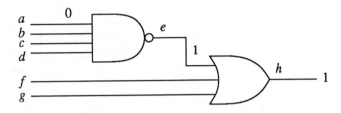

Figure 2.1: Collapsing of stuck faults.

The illustration above can be generalized. To find if a fault, say *a* $s-a-i$ can be collapsed with another fault, we carry out three-value simulation after initializing line *a* to *i* and all other lines to *X*. If, as a result of simulation, another line, say *b*, is forced to a binary value *j*, then the fault *a* $s-a-i$ is equivalent to *b* $s-a-j$. This simple procedure has been used in an MOS* simulator where the circuit is described as an interconnection of transistors [Lo87].

In equivalence fault collapsing we only collapse the faults that are indistinguishable. If we are prepared to give up on diagnostic resolution (ability to distinguish between faults), more collapsing is possible. This is accomplished by using the concept of *fault dominance* as explained next. In very large scale integration (VLSI) circuits, where coverage of faults rather than their exact location is the overriding consideration, *dominance fault collapsing* may be desirable.

Consider two faults f_1 and f_2. Suppose all tests for f_1 also detect f_2 but only some of the tests for f_2 detect f_1. Then f_2 is said to *dominate* f_1. This definition of dominance, originally given by Poage

---

* MOS refers to the Metal Oxide Semiconductor technology which derives its name from the type of semiconductor devices used on chips [Eins85]. Two types of devices are common. These are called the n-channel (NMOS) and the p-channel (PMOS) transistors. A popular integrated circuit technology, known as Complementary MOS (CMOS), employes both types of transistors.

[Poag63], also appears in text books [Breu76]. However, some authors have used the term dominance in an opposite sense [Abra86a]. If we had to pick one to detect, obviously, we are safer to take f_1. Even though, at times, it may be a little harder to find a test for f_1, this test is guaranteed to cover f_2.

In an AND gate, the output $s-a-1$ dominates any input $s-a-1$. Thus if we desire dominance fault collapsing, then for an *n*-input AND gate we need to consider only *n*+1 faults.

Equivalence and dominance fault collapsing may be used to reduce the number of faults that must be considered for detection. In the AND-gate example above, we found that the two stuck faults on the output line can be collapsed with appropriate input-line faults. This type of collapsing can be repeatedly used until one arrives at a *checkpoint* defined as either as a primary input or a fan-out branch [Breu76]. It has been shown that it is sufficient to consider single faults on the checkpoints in a circuit as long as all such faults are detectable. In actual circuits, however, there can be a small number of faults, referred to as *undetectable* or *redundant* faults, that are not detected by any test. The presence of such faults, by definition, does not cause malfunction in the circuit. If any checkpoint fault is undetectable, then additional faults must be considered [Abra86b]. Finding checkpoints in sequential circuits requires further analysis [Chan81].

In sequential circuits, fault collapsing is often accomplished through multiple passes. More details may be found in [McCl71, Sche72]. In other related work, fault set reduction algorithms have been reported by Goel [Goel73] and Cha [Cha79].

3: Transistor Faults

Today's VLSI devices often consist of MOS transistors that functionally behave like ideal switches. In 1978, Wadsack [Wads78] discovered that digital circuits implemented in CMOS technology could also display fault modes other than stuck-at faults. What was worse, tests written for stuck faults could, at times, be ineffective in detecting these other faults often referred to as *nonclassical faults*.

Considering MOS transistors as ideal switches, the nonclassical faults correspond to a transistor being permanently *stuck-open* or permanently *stuck-short*. Figure 2.2 shows a NOR gate implemented in CMOS technology. $P1$ and $P2$ are PMOS transistors that will be shorted when their gate inputs, A and B, respectively, are 0. The same values on the gate inputs make the NMOS transistors, $N1$ and $N2$, open. Thus, $A = B = 0$ will connect the output C to VDD while isolating it from VSS. Either $A = 1$ or $B = 1$ will connect C to VSS and isolate it from VDD. Now consider the fault $P1$ stuck-open. If we apply inputs, $A = 0$ and $B = 0$, then only $P1$ and $P2$ are shorted. As a result, the output $C = 1$. When $P1$ is stuck-open, the output C will be connected neither to VDD nor to VSS. This is called a *floating or high-impedance* state. If the output has a capacitive load (i.e., input of another CMOS gate), then any voltage on it will be retained for a long time. Only if the output was set to 0 before applying the 00 input, will the fault produce an error. To ensure that the fault is detected, we precede a 00 input by a 10 input which initializes the output to 0 irrespective of the fault. Notice that for A $s-a-1$ fault, the 00 pattern would have been a sufficient test. A transistor stuck-open fault, in general, requires a two-pattern test sequence. Similarly, testing of stuck-short faults also requires considerations that are different from line-stuck fault testing. In general, the tests that are generated specifically to cover line-stuck faults will have somewhat lower (10-15 percent) coverage on transistor faults [Seth85].

CMOS is emerging as a dominant technology. Modeling of transistor faults in CMOS circuits is, therefore, important. Fortunately, these faults can also be modeled as line stuck faults. Notice that a stuck fault on line A (before it fans out) in Figure 2.2 corresponds to two simultaneous transistor faults. For example, A $s-a-1$ has the same effect as that of the simultaneous presence of $P1$ *stuck−open* and $N1$ *stuck−short*. Observing this equivalence, Jain and Agrawal [Jain85, Redd84] proposed a logic model for transistor networks. In their model, the gate terminal of a transistor becomes an input to a logic gate. Gate inputs to PMOS devices are inverted and those to NMOS devices are used without inversion. Series connected transistors are replaced by AND gates and parallel transistors are replaced by OR gates. A CMOS gate consists of a cluster of PMOS devices and another cluster of NMOS devices. The outputs

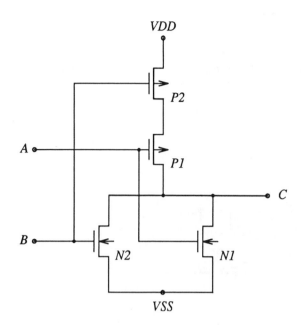

Figure 2.2: A CMOS NOR gate.

of these clusters are combined in a special logic element called the *B-block*. The logic circuit for the NOR gate of Figure 2.2 is shown in Figure 2.3. When the output $C1$ from the PMOS cluster is true, the gate output C becomes 1. Similarly, when the output $C2$ of the NMOS cluster is true, the output is set to 0. When both outputs, $C1$ and $C2$, are false, C retains its previous value as indicated by M (memory) in the truth table for the B-block shown in Figure 2.3. In CMOS circuits where the PMOS and the NMOS clusters realize complementary functions, this state will not occur. However, this state can occur in a faulty circuit. Another faulty condition with both outputs true can be set to 0 or X (unknown) depending upon specific technology.

In this model, every line-stuck or transistor fault is represented as a simple line-stuck fault. For example, $P1$ stuck open is represented as $A1$ $s-a-1$. Test generation with this model will be discussed in the next chapter.

It should be noticed that the logic circuit of Figure 2.3 contains more lines than the corresponding CMOS implementation shown in Figure 2.2. To account for all line and transistor faults, stuck faults only on the input lines A and B, their fanout lines $A1$, $A2$, $B1$, and $B2$, and the output line C should be considered. Faults on the internal lines $C1$ and $C2$ that do not correspond to any specific faults in the CMOS circuit need not be considered. Also,

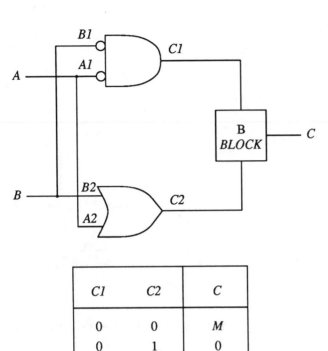

C1	C2	C
0	0	M
0	1	0
1	0	1
1	1	X

Figure 2.3: Logic model for CMOS NOR gate.

normal fault collapsing algorithms, like the one described previously, can be applied.

There are several ways of dealing with transistor faults in practice. First, using circuit-level *design for testability,* possible transistor faults can be made detectable by the normal tests for stuck faults [Redd86, Liu87]. The second alternative is to generate and to evaluate tests for transistor faults, which will be discussed in Chapters III and IV, respectively.

4: Other Faults

There are circuits in which faults other than those just described must be considered. We can divide faults into two classes: (1) functional and (2) physical. Line-stuck faults are functional faults in the signals of a logic circuit. Transistor-stuck faults are functional faults in MOS devices. Higher level functional faults are usually suitable for memories and microprocessors, while physical faults are normally modeled in devices like Programmable Logic Arrays (PLA) where the layout is well defined. Yet

another example of a physical fault is the variation of gate to source resistance of a transistor or the leakage current in its off state.

4.1: Memory Faults

With higher levels of integration, more and more chips are combining logic and memory blocks. It is, therefore, advantageous for a logic chip designer to be familiar with memory testing methodology. Semiconductor memories differ from random logic implemented on a VLSI chip. Layout of a memory is, in general, more densely packed. In order to thoroughly test a memory, one may have to test multiple faults of various types. This will increase test complexity and make test generation almost impossible.

Fortunately, memories perform simple and well-defined functions. Faults can be easily modeled at a functional level. Two types of faults are tested in memories: (1) parametric faults and (2) functional faults.

Parametric faults include unacceptable output levels, too high power consumption, inadequate fanout driving capability, impropernoise margins, too small data retention time, etc. Specific nature of parametric faults depends upon the technology and the manufacturing process used.

A functional block diagram of a memory is shown in Figure 2.4. Its basic functions are writing, storing, and reading data to or from any arbitrary cell. Since a Random Access Memory (RAM) is designed to hold any arbitrary data pattern in its cells, ideally, the functioning of each cell should be checked for all possible data patterns in the remaining cells. Even for a memory of moderate size, this will amount to too many faults. However, several of these faults are very unlikely to occur in practice. Fault models that are commonly used are given below [Abad83].

Stuck-at faults: These faults correspond to one or more memory cells being *stuck-at*-1 *or* -0. Stuck faults are also modeled in the logic of address and data registers, and address decoder.

Coupling faults: Two memory cells are assumed to be coupled if a state change in one cell causes a state change in the other. A special case of these faults is the coupling between two cells that are physically *adjacent.*

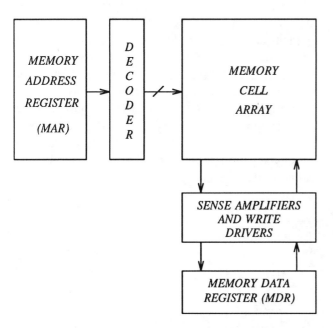

Figure 2.4: Functional block diagram of RAM.

Pattern-sensitive faults: A fault that alters the state of a memory cell as a result of certain patterns of zeros, ones, 0-to-1 transitions, and/or 1-to-0 transitions in other cells is called a pattern-sensitive fault. Failure of a read or write operation on a cell when certain data pattern is stored in other cells is also a pattern-sensitive fault. Since the number of such faults can be very large, in practice only a subset is considered.

4.2: PLA Faults

A PLA is a two-level implementation of a logic function. PLAs are easy to design and can be efficiently implemented in MOS technologies. It is quite common to use PLAs to implement large blocks of combinational logic on a VLSI chip. Since PLAs are laid out as regular structures, it is possible to consider fault models that are related to their physical geometry.

Consider the PLA implementation of two functions f_1 and f_2 as shown in Figure 2.5. The left part of the PLA generates three product terms, p_1, p_2, and p_3 from the input variables x_1 through x_4. This portion of PLA is called the AND matrix. The vertical lines in this matrix carry the input variables in true or complementary form. The three horizontal lines carry the product term signals. A solid dot in this matrix indicates the presence of an MOS

device (transistor). Crossing lines without a solid dot are crossing but electrically isolated signals. Thus p_1 is the product term $x_1 x_3$. The three product terms are shown in the Karnaugh map in Figure 2.5. The right portion of PLA, which produces the two output functions, is called the OR matrix. Dots again represent MOS devices. Thus, the function f_1 contains product terms p_1 and p_2 but does not contain p_3.

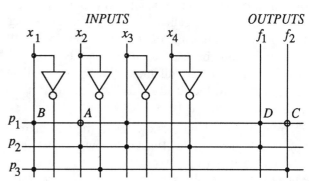

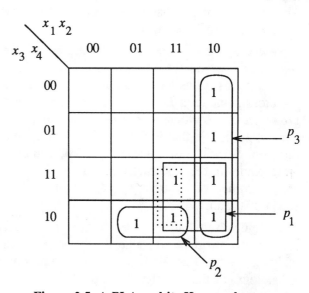

Figure 2.5: A PLA and its Karnaugh map.

A simple implementation of a PLA contains horizontal and vertical conducting paths with devices placed at appropriate *cross-points*. PLA geometry thus resembles its symbolic representation. The following faults are considered relevant in PLAs:

- Stuck faults – Stuck at 1 and 0 on the inputs, input inverters, product lines, and outputs.

- Cross-point faults – A single missing or additional device in either the AND or the OR matrix. These faults are also referred to as *contact faults*.

- Bridging faults - A short between any two adjacent parallel signal lines (inputs, products, outputs).

These faults have been extensively studied in the literature [Bose82]. For illustration, consider the fault due to an additional device at the point A in Figure 2.5. The effect of this fault is to modify the product term p_1, as shown on the Karnaugh map, to the one shown by the dotted line. Added cross-points in the AND matrix always shrink the product terms, and they are called *shrinkage faults*. Notice that the two minterms of p_1 that the fault left uncovered could be used as tests for this fault. A test of 1011 or 1010 will make the output f_1 0 in the presence of the fault. Also notice that if f_1 included p_3, then this fault would be undetectable.

Similarly, an added cross-point in the OR matrix, say, C in Figure 2.5, will cause a new product term to be added to an output function. In this case, p_1 is added to f_2. This is called an *appearance fault*. Any minterm of p_1 that is not covered in f_2 will test for the appearance of p_1 in f_2.

Now suppose the cross-point B is missing. This changes the product term p_1 to expand to include four minterms on its left on the map. Thus, a missing cross-point fault in the AND matrix is called a *growth fault*. A minterm of the expanded product term (e.g., 0011), that is not included in the output function f_1 will test this fault. Last, a missing cross-point in the OR matrix, such as D, causes *disappearance* of p_1 from f_1. An input 1111 will detect this fault.

Bridging faults, that cause shorting of adjacent lines, force an identical value on the shorted lines which is an AND or OR function (depending on the technology) of the two signals on the lines.

What is described above is functional modeling of PLA faults. Efficient algorithms are possible for generating tests, simulating faults, and detecting redundant faults. There are difficulties, however, in using these methods when PLA is embedded in the logic of a chip. A simple and popular way of modeling PLAs is by means of logic gates. This model was first used to study multiple faults in PLAs [Agar80]. A two-level AND-OR model has all stuck faults. Such a model for the PLA of Figure 2.5 consists of two OR gates, three AND gates, and two inverters. These gates are shown in Figure 2.6 without the marking of 'M.' The gates marked

with 'M' are added for modeling cross-point faults. For example, missing cross-point B is represented as an input stuck-at-1 on an OR gate feeding into the gate producing p_1. One input of this OR gate is set to logical 0 and the other input is x_1. Notice that when the logical 0 input is stuck-at-1, as indicated by (B) on Figure 2.6, the variable x_1 will be missing from product term p_1. Similarly, cross-point faults A, C, and D of Figure 2.5 are modeled by stuck-type faults shown on Figure 2.6 as (A), (C), and (D), respectively.

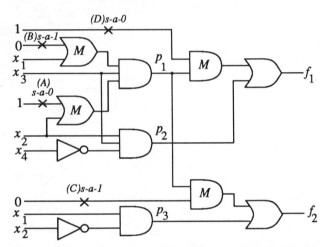

Figure 2.6: A Logic model for PLA cross-point faults.

If the number of inputs, outputs, and product terms is I, O, and P, then considering the input inverters, the basic logic model (with stuck faults only) contains at most $I+P+O$ gates. This model can be used for fault simulation and test generation when the PLA is embedded in the logic of a chip. The maximum number of cross-point faults will be $(2I+O) \times P$ and their modeling will require one gate for each fault.

Additional gates can be similarly added to model bridging faults [Agra86]. In general, however, only cross-point faults are modeled in practice. The reasons are as follows:

- A large number of stuck faults and bridging faults (in access of 80 percent) are also tested by the same tests that cover cross-point faults.

- Bridging faults increase the complexity of a model very significantly.

- Actual bridging faults, which can occur in a PLA, are only determined after the layout of PLA is completed.

While logic modeling of PLA faults is useful in the context of the present design methodologies and computer-aided design (CAD) tools, functional models are likely to provide more efficient modeling in the future.

4.3: Functional Faults

We supplied glimpses of functional faults in the context of memory and PLA. For other circuits, the usefulness of functional faults is not proven.

The most significant work on functional faults was reported by Thatte and Abraham [That80]. They developed fault models for microprocessors based entirely on the functional description like its architecture and the instruction set. Faults in (1) register address decoding, (2) instruction decoding, (3) data storage, (4) data transfer, and (5) data manipulation are considered. For example, a register address decoding fault will choose a wrong register for any operation. An instruction decoding fault will cause execution of wrong instruction.

When tests were generated for an 8-bit microprocessor, it was found that these tests detected 96 percent of single stuck faults in one particular implementation. One problem with Thatte and Abraham's approach is that it is clearly understood only for microprocessors.

The functional description of a circuit is, in general, much compact when compared with the gate level description. Techniques for function-level test generation and fault simulation applicable to general circuits (not just microprocessors) hold promise for the future.

4.4: Multiple Stuck Faults

It is quite possible that a circuit under test has more than one fault. Multiple stuck faults were analyzed by Bossen and Hong [Boss71]. Intuitively, one might feel that tests derived for single faults should be effective for multiple faults as well. However, the fault effect produced by the test of one fault can be masked by another fault. Considering such masking, lower bounds on the multiple fault coverage of single fault tests have been derived [Agar81]. Even though the lower bound appears to be, in some cases, as much as 20 percent below the single fault coverage, our simple intuition does work for VLSI chips where fault location is often

not desired. According to Breuer and Friedman [Breu76], single fault tests are relatively good for the *detection* of multiple faults but are not as good for the *location* of multiple faults.

In more recent work, Hughes and McCluskey [Hugh86] found that in a 4-bit arithmetic logic circuit any complete single stuck fault test vector set can detect more than 99.96 percent of the double stuck faults. This result is analytically explained by Jacob and Biswas [Jaco87]. They showed that at least 99.67 percent of all multiple faults in any circuit are detected by any single fault detection test set if the number of observable outputs in the circuit is three or more.

One might feel that a large circuit is more likely to have multiple faults. Fortunately, in CMOS circuits, the coverage of single fault tests over multiple faults improves as the circuit becomes large. To show this, Jha [Jha86] has developed an analysis. He defined *n-dominance* as the n-type network of a CMOS gate having a much lower on-impedance than the on-impedance of the p-type network. Under n-dominance the single fault test coverage of multiple faults in a CMOS NAND gate is 99.6 percent. As the complexity of the gate increases, this coverage tends toward 100 percent.

4.5: Miscellaneous Fault Models

There is a wide range of possible fault models that we have not touched upon either in this chapter or in the included reprints. Some of these may be useful in specific applications. We briefly discussed *bridging faults* of PLAs in Section 4.2. A detailed discussion of bridging faults in general logic circuits is given by Mei [Mei74]. In fast MOS technologies, *delay faults,* that cause the delay of combinational paths to exceed the clocking constraints of the circuit, may be significant. An interested reader is referred to recent papers by Smith [Smit85] and Lin and Reddy [Lin86]. Simulation of delay faults in scan circuits is discussed by Waicukauski *et al.* [Waic87]. Also, a discussion on delay faults in CMOS logic is given by Koeppe [Koep86].

Another fault mode, known as *intermittent faults,* can be important in certain applications. Even though an intermittent fault may influence the circuit behavior in much the same way as a stuck fault, it can evade detection if it is not active at the time of testing [Kama74]. These faults are normally characterized by probabilistic models [Savi80]. *Parametric faults,* which often modify the analog behavior of devices on a chip, are caused by imperfections in processing [Beck85]. Recent theoretical studies have attempted to relate processing faults to the logical behavior of the circuit [Shen85].

5: Conclusion

In VLSI technology today, the stuck-fault model continues to be the *standard*. The algorithms and CAD tools described throughout this book support this standard. In this chapter, we have given some basic essentials of fault modeling. An obvious stronger emphasis on stuck faults should satisfy the needs of a practicing engineer. Also essential in todays design environment is the knowledge of memory faults [Abad83] since many VLSI chips are designed with embedded RAM and read-only memory (ROM) blocks.

The future of fault modeling presents a dilemma. Complexity of circuits with 100,000 or a million gates will make it almost impossible to model stuck faults with the present CAD tools and computers. Researchers are, therefore, trying to elevate to functional level where the complexity is more manageable. Concern for the quality of the manufactured device, on the other hand, forces us to move in the opposite direction to look inside logic gates for technology-dependent faults.

6: Selected Reading

Early work on stuck faults has appeared in a book by Chang, Manning, and Metze [Chan70]. For a more recent survey, readers are referred to an article by Abraham [Abra86a].

Satisfying practicing engineers as well as researchers are two conflicting goals. In this tutorial, we have leaned toward current practices. For a detailed study, we recommend seven papers. Of these, four are reprinted in this chapter and the remaining three can be found in the next chapter on test generation.

The first paper by Schertz and Metze [Sche72] is one of the classical articles on stuck-type faults. The second paper [Wads78] records experimental work leading to the discovery of *non-classical*

CMOS faults. The third paper [Redd84] describes logical modeling of non-classical faults. The fourth paper [Shen85] investigates MOS technologies to relate layout-level fabrication defects to higher level fault models.

Our selection of papers on function-level fault models consists of three papers on memories [Abad83], PLAs [Bose82], and microprocessors [That80], respectively. Since these papers also deal with test generation, they have been included in the next chapter.

7: References

[Abad83] M. S. Abadir and H. K. Reghbati, "Functional Testing of Semiconductor Random Access Memories," *ACM Computing Surveys*, Vol. 15, pp. 175-198, September 1983, **see reprint in Chapter III**.

[Abra86a] J. A. Abraham, "Fault Modeling in VLSI," in *VLSI Testing*, ed. T. W. Williams, North-Holland, Amsterdam, The Netherlands, 1986.

[Abra86b] M. Abramovici, P. R. Menon, and D. T. Miller, "Checkpoint Faults Are Not Sufficient Target Faults for Test Generation," *IEEE Trans. on Computers*, Vol. C-35, pp. 769-771, August 1986.

[Agar80] V. K. Agarwal, "Multiple Fault Detection in Programmable Logic Arrays," *IEEE Trans. Computers*, Vol. C-29, pp. 518-522, June 1980.

[Agar81] V. K. Agarwal and A. S. F. Fung, "Multiple Fault Testing of Large Circuits by Single Fault Test Sets," *IEEE Trans. Computers*, Vol. C-30, pp. 855-865, November 1981.

[Agra86] V. D. Agrawal and D. D. Johnson, "Logic Modeling of PLA Faults," *Proc. Int. Conf. on Computer Design (ICCD-86)*, Port Chester, NY, pp. 86-88, October 1986.

[Beck85] C. A. Becker, "Testing of VLSI Parametrics," pp. 515-526 in *VLSI Handbook*, ed. N. G. Einspruch, Academic Press, Orlando, FL, 1985.

[Bose82] P. Bose and J. A. Abraham, "Test Generation for Programmable Logic Arrays," *Proc. ACM/ IEEE Design Automation Conf.*, Las Vegas, Nevada, pp. 574-580, June 1982, **see reprint in Chapter III**.

[Boss71] D. C. Bossen and S. J. Hong, "Cause-Effect Analysis for Multiple Fault Detection in Combinational Networks," *IEEE Trans. Computers*, Vol. C-20, pp. 1252-1257, November 1971.

[Breu76] M. A. Breuer and A. D. Friedman, *Diagnosis & Reliable Design of Digital Systems,* Computer Science Press, Rockville, MD, 1976.

[Cha79] C. W. Cha, "Multiple Fault Diagnosis in Combinational Networks," *Proc. 16th Des. Auto. Conf.,* San Diego, CA, pp. 149-155, June 1979.

[Chan70] H. Y. Chang, E. G. Manning, and G. Metze, *Fault Diagnosis of Digital Systems,* Wiley-Interscience, New York, 1970.

[Chan81] S. J. Chang and M. A. Breuer, "A Fault-Collapsing Analysis in Sequential Logic Networks," *Bell Syst. Tech. Jour.,* Vol. 60, pp. 2259-2271, Nov. 1981.

[Eins85] N. G. Einspruch, *VLSI Handbook,* Academic Press, Orlando, FL, 1985.

[Goel73] P. Goel, "The Feed Forward Logic Model in the Testing of Large Scale Integrated Logic Circuits," *Ph.D. Dissertation,* Carnegie-Mellon University, Pittsburgh, PA, September 1973.

[Hugh86] J. L. A. Hughes and E. J. McCluskey, "Multiple Stuck-at Fault Coverage of Single Stuck-at Fault Test Sets," *Proc. Int. Test Conf.,* Washington, D.C., pp. 368-374, September 1986.

[Jaco87] J. Jacob and N. N. Biswas, "GTBD Faults and Lower Bounds on Multiple Fault Coverage of Single Fault Test Sets," *Proc. Int. Test Conf.,* Washington, D.C., pp. 849-855, September 1987.

[Jain85] S. K. Jain and V. D. Agrawal, "Modeling and Test Generation Algorithms for MOS Circuits," *IEEE Trans. Computers,* Vol. C-34, pp. 426-433, May 1985, Also see, Correction, in *IEEE Trans. Computers,* Vol. C-34, p. 680, July 1985.

[Jha86] N. K. Jha, "Detecting Multiple Faults in CMOS Circuits," *Proc. Int. Test Conf.,* Washington, D.C., pp. 514-519, September 1986.

[Kama74] S. Kamal and C. V. Page, "Intermittent Faults: A Model and a Detection Procedure," *IEEE Trans. Computers,* Vol. C-23, pp. 713-719, July 1974.

[Koep86] S. Koeppe, "Modeling and Simulation of Delay Faults in CMOS Logic Circuits," *Proc. Int. Test Conf.,* Washington, D.C., pp. 530-536, September 1986.

[Lin86] C. J. Lin and S. M. Reddy, "On Delay Fault Testing in Logic Circuits," *Proc. Int. Conf. on CAD (ICCAD-86),* Santa Clara, CA, pp. 148-151, November 1986.

[Liu87] D. L. Liu and E. J. McCluskey, "Designing CMOS Circuits for Switch-Level Testability," *IEEE Design & Test of Computers,* Vol. 4, pp. 42-49, August 1987.

[Lo87] C. Y. Lo, H. N. Nham, and A. K. Bose, "Algorithms for an Advanced Fault Simulation System in MOTIS," *IEEE Trans. CAD,* Vol. CAD-6, pp. 232-240, March 1987, **see reprint in Chapter IV.**

[McCl71] E. J. McCluskey and F. W. Clegg, "Fault Equivalence in Combinational Logic Networks," *IEEE Trans. Computers,* Vol. C-20, pp. 1286-1293, November 1971.

[Mei74] K. C. Y. Mei, "Bridging and Stuck-at-Faults," *IEEE Trans. Computers,* Vol. C-23, pp. 720-727, July 1974.

[Poag63] J. F. Poage, "Derivation of Optimum Tests to detect Faults in Combinational Circuits," pp. 483-528 in *Proc. Symp. on Mathematical Theory of Automata (April 1962),* Polytechnic Press, New York, 1963.

[Redd86] M. K. Reddy and S. M. Reddy, "Detecting FET Stuck-Open Faults in CMOS Latches and Flip-Flops," *IEEE Design & Test of Computers,* pp. 17-26, October 1986.

[Redd84] S. M. Reddy, V. D. Agrawal, and S. K. Jain, "A Gate Level Model for CMOS Combinational Logic Circuits with Application to Fault Detection," *Proc. 21st Des. Auto. Conf.,* Albuquerque, NM, pp. 504-509, June 1984, **see reprint in this chapter.**

[Savi80] J. Savir, "Testing of Single Intermittent Failures in Combinational Circuits by Maximizing the Probability of Fault Detection," *IEEE Trans. Computers,* Vol. C-29, pp. 410-416, May 1980.

[Sche72] D. R. Schertz and G. Metze, "A New Representation for Faults in Combinational Digital Circuits," *IEEE Trans. Computers,* Vol. C-21, pp. 858-866, August 1972, **see reprint in this chapter.**

[Seth85] S. C. Seth and V. D. Agrawal, "A Review of Testing of Digital VLSI Devices," *IETE Technical Review,* Vol. 2, pp. 363-374, November 1985.

[Shen85] J. P. Shen, W. Maly, and F. J. Ferguson, "Inductive Fault Analysis of MOS Integrated Circuits," *IEEE Design & Test of Computers,* Vol. 2, pp. 13-26, December 1985, **see reprint in this chapter.**

[Smit85] G. L. Smith, "Model for Delay Faults Based on Paths," *Proc. Int. Test Conf.,* Philadelphia, PA, pp. 342-349, November 1985.

[That80] S. M. Thatte and J. A. Abraham, "Test Generation for Microprocessors," *IEEE Trans. Computers,* Vol. C-29, pp. 429-441, June 1980, **see reprint in Chapter III.**

[Wads78] R. L. Wadsack, "Fault Modeling and Logic Simulation of CMOS and MOS Integrated Circuits," *Bell Syst. Tech. Jour.*, Vol. 57, pp. 1449-1474, May-June 1978, **see reprint in this chapter**.

[Waic87] J. A. Waicukauski, E. Lindbloom, B. K. Rosen, and V. S. Iyengar, "Transition Fault Simulation," *IEEE Design & Test of Computers*, Vol. 4, pp. 32-38, April 1987.

A New Representation for Faults in Combinational Digital Circuits

DONALD R. SCHERTZ, MEMBER, IEEE, AND GERNOT METZE, MEMBER, IEEE

Abstract—A new representation for faults in combinational digital circuits is presented. Faults that are inherently indistinguishable are identified and combined into classes that form a geometric structure that effectively subdivides the original circuit into fan-out-free segments. This fan-out-free characteristic allows a simplified analysis of multiple fault conditions. For certain circuits, including all two-level single-output circuits, it is shown that the detection of all single faults implies the detection of all multiple faults.

The behavior of any circuit under fault conditions is represented in terms of the classes of indistinguishable faults. This results in a description of the faulty circuit by means of Boolean equations that are readily manipulated for the purpose of fault simulation or test generation. A connection graph interpretation of this fault representation is discussed. Heuristic methods for the selection of efficient tests without extensive computation are derived from these connection graphs.

Index Terms—Combinational logic, digital systems, fault detection, fault diagnosis, fault models, multiple faults.

INTRODUCTION

THE detection and location of failures in digital systems has been the subject of a number of investigations [1]–[3], [7]. These investigations have been directed primarily toward the development of algorithms for the derivation of testing procedures for specific systems. In this paper, the same problem is approached from a more theoretical standpoint. Here the emphasis is on making *a priori* statements about the relative detectability of various system failures rather than making *a posteriori* statements based on the reduction of a fault table.

A system failure may be thought of as a transformation of the desired system into some other system. If the faulty system has a response that differs from that of the fault-free system under at least one set of input conditions, then the failure is said to be *detectable*. If the transformed systems resulting from two distinct failures have different responses for at least one set of input conditions, then the two failures are said to be *distinguishable*.

In this paper, the fault model used to represent circuit failures will be a "line stuck-at-1, line stuck-at-0" model. If a line is stuck-at-1 (s-a-1), it is considered to be permanently tied to the logical 1 level. Similarly, a line stuck-at-0 (s-a-0) is considered to be permanently tied to the logical 0 level. It is further assumed that either of the faults (s-a-1 or s-a-0) can occur at any gate input or output or at a primary input or output of the circuit. It is henceforth assumed that any physical failure in a system has been represented in terms of the appropriate fault model. While some physical failures cannot be represented as single line faults, it may be shown that nearly all failures other than certain shorts between lines may be adequately represented by single or multiple line faults of the type described [4]. A shorthand notation is used for the fault model; the fault "line i s-a-1" is written $i/1$, and the fault "line i s-a-0" is written $i/0$.

FAULT COLLAPSING

Minimization techniques for the selection of efficient sets of diagnostic tests for combinational circuits normally begin with the consideration of a fault table $[T_{ij}]$ in which each test is represented by a row and each fault by a column. The entry t_{ij} in the ith row and jth column is 1 if and only if test i detects fault j. Selecting a minimal set of tests having the desired fault diagnosis properties is a covering problem analogous to finding a minimum set of prime implicants for a combinational switching function. As in the prime implicant covering problem, the fault table can be reduced by means of row and column dominance conditions before test selection begins. The type and extent of the reduction depends on the desired resolution of the test set, that is, fault detection, or fault location to within some unit. It will be shown that much of this reduction may be carried out prior to the derivation of tests rather than after, thus simplifying the process of test generation.

Column dominance as applied to a complete fault table is related to the relative detectability of faults. Column j dominates column k if for every 1 in column k there is also a 1 in column j. If the two columns of the table are identical then each dominates the other and the faults corresponding to these two columns are indistinguishable. In this case, any test which detects one fault will also detect the other and a bidirectional implication relationship exists between the detection of one fault and the detection of the other. If one column dominates another but is not identical to it, then the faults

Manuscript received May 20, 1970; revised February 22, 1972. This work was supported in part by the Joint Services Electronics Program under Contract DAAB-07-67-C-0199 and in part by NSF Grant GK-1663.

D. R. Schertz was with the Coordinated Science Laboratory, University of Illinois, Urbana, Ill. He is now with the Department of Electrical Engineering and Electrical Engineering Technology, Bradley University, Peoria, Ill. 61606.

G. Metze is with the Coordinated Science Laboratory and the Department of Electrical Engineering, University of Illinois, Urbana, Ill. 61801.

EH0278-2/88/0000/0025$01.00 © 1972 IEEE

25

corresponding to these two columns are distinguishable. In this case, one fault is more readily detected than the other and the implication relationship is unidirectional.

Fault collapsing [4] is the process of combining faults by means of implication relationships derived from a study of the network concerned. These relationships form a partial ordering relative to the detection of faults. Classes of indistinguishable faults are found before deriving diagnostic tests rather than after, and only one fault from each class need then be considered.

Three separate stages of fault collapsing may be defined corresponding to three different types of implication relationships. "First-stage" techniques of fault collapsing correspond to the case of identical columns in the fault table, that is, to indistinguishable faults. "Second-stage" techniques correspond to the case of unequal columns, that is, to situations where one fault is more readily detected than the other. "Third-stage" techniques concern the relationships between single and multiple faults and therefore have no direct analogy in the single fault covering table problem.

The various fault collapsing techniques will be discussed with the aid of the circuit of Fig. 1. It is assumed that a fault can occur at any lettered position in the circuit. Fault collapsing as applied to the AND gate will be discussed first. "First-stage" techniques apply to the four s-a-0 faults for this gate. In order to detect the fault $d/0$, the circuit inputs must be such that line d will be in the 1 state if the circuit is fault free. For the AND this means that all inputs must be set to 1. Such a set of inputs will also detect the fault condition of any input line s-a-0. Conversely, any set of inputs that detects an input line s-a-0 will also detect the output line s-a-0. The faults $a/0$, $b/0$, $c/0$, and $d/0$ are thus indistinguishable for this circuit. The "first-stage" implication relationships for this gate are written symbolically as

$$a/0 \Leftrightarrow b/0 \Leftrightarrow c/0 \Leftrightarrow d/0.$$

"Second-stage" analysis of the same circuit deals with the remaining single faults for the gate. In this case, any test which detects one of the input lines s-a-1 will also detect the output line s-a-1. The "second-stage" implication relationships for this gate are thus written

$$a/1 \Rightarrow d/1$$
$$b/1 \Rightarrow d/1$$
$$c/1 \Rightarrow d/1.$$

"Third-stage" analysis of the AND circuit is concerned with multiple faults. The multiple fault consisting of all input lines s-a-1 is indistinguishable from the single fault corresponding to the output line s-a-1. The "third-stage" implication relationship is thus written

$$d/1 \Leftrightarrow (a/1, b/1, c/1).$$

The foregoing analysis may be repeated for OR, NAND, and NOR gates with s-a-0 and s-a-1 interchanged where

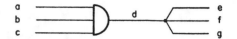

Fig. 1. Circuit for fault collapsing definitions.

appropriate. The case of the NOT gate is seen to be identical to that of a one-input NAND or one-input NOR.

Fault collapsing techniques may also be applied at a fan-out point in a circuit. "First-stage" analysis is applicable only to the trivial case of a single line, that is, a line having a fan-out of 1. In this case, we find that a fault at the origin of the line is indistinguishable from the corresponding fault at the destination of the line.

Before attempting to apply "second-stage" analysis to a fan-out point, the types of fan-out must be classified. *Reconvergent fan-out* describes a structure in which more than one directed path may be traced from one line to another in the circuit. That is, once a line has been split by fan-out, the new lines reconverge at the input to some gate further along in the circuit. *Nonreconvergent fan-out* is defined in a complementary manner.

In the case of nonreconvergent fan-out, faults at the fan-out point may be collapsed because any test that detects a fault along one of the destination lines from the fan-out point will also detect the corresponding fault on the origin line of the fan-out point. Thus, if lines e, f, and g in Fig. 1 do not later reconverge, we have the "second-stage" implication relationships

$$e/1 \Rightarrow d/1, \qquad e/0 \Rightarrow d/0$$
$$f/1 \Rightarrow d/1, \qquad f/0 \Rightarrow d/0$$
$$g/1 \Rightarrow d/1, \qquad g/0 \Rightarrow d/0.$$

The foregoing is not necessarily true in the case of reconvergent fan-out as the reconverging branch may interfere with the propagation of the fault to a primary output.

"Third-stage" analysis is also applicable at a fan-out point in the circuit. In this case, the multiple fault consisting of all destination lines s-a-1 (s-a-0) is indistinguishable from the single fault corresponding to the origin line s-a-1 (s-a-0). The "third-stage" relationships for Fig. 1 are thus written

$$d/1 \Leftrightarrow (e/1, f/1, g/1)$$
$$d/0 \Leftrightarrow (e/0, f/0, g/0).$$

The fault collapsing techniques presented are summarized in Table I. In this table, each relationship is presented in a generalized form which does not use specific line numbers. "First-stage" techniques may always be applied whether the objective of the analysis is fault detection or fault location. "Second-stage" techniques are useful when detection only and not location is desired. "Third-stage" techniques may be used in cases where all multiple faults are to be considered.

The circuit of Fig. 2 will be used as an example to

TABLE I
Summary of Fault Collapsing Techniques

First Stage

Type	Description	
fan-out of 1	origin s-a-1	⇔ destination s-a-1
	origin s-a-0	⇔ destination s-a-0
AND	any input s-a-0	⇔ output s-a-0
OR	any input s-a-1	⇔ output s-a-1
NAND	any input s-a-0	⇔ output s-a-1
NOR	any input s-a-1	⇔ output s-a-0
NOT	input s-a-1	⇔ output s-a-0
	input s-a-0	⇔ output s-a-1

Second Stage

Type	Description	
nonreconvergent	any destination s-a-1	⇒ origin s-a-1
fan-out	any destination s-a-0	⇒ origin s-a-0
AND	any input s-a-1	⇒ output s-a-1
OR	any input s-a-0	⇒ output s-a-0
NAND	any input s-a-1	⇒ output s-a-0
NOR	any input s-a-0	⇒ output s-a-1

Third Stage

Type	Description	
fan-out	origin s-a-1	⇔ all destinations s-a-1
	origin s-a-0	⇔ all destinations s-a-0
AND	output s-a-1	⇔ all inputs s-a-1
OR	output s-a-0	⇔ all inputs s-a-0
NAND	output s-a-0	⇔ all inputs s-a-1
NOR	output s-a-1	⇔ all inputs s-a-0

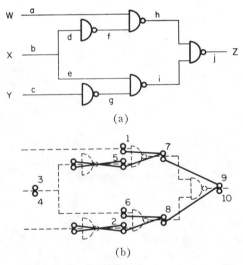

(a)

(b)

Fig. 2. (a) Example circuit. (b) Fault class structure (upper circle: s-a-1 fault; lower circle: s-a-0 fault).

illustrate the usefulness of fault collapsing. This circuit represents the single-output three-variable function

$$Z = W\overline{X} + X\overline{Y}.$$

The ten distinct lines in the circuit are labeled $a, \cdots, j$ where lines a, b, c are primary inputs and line j is a primary output. The circuit contains 20 single faults and a total of $3^{10} - 1$ multiple faults. The number of multiple faults contained in even this small circuit is so large as to make any exhaustive analysis of multiple faults unthinkable.

"First-stage" fault collapsing techniques are applied

TABLE II
Fault Classes for Example Circuit

Class	Faults
1	$a/1$
2	$c/0, g/1$
3	$b/1$
4	$b/0$
5	$d/0, f/1$
6	$e/1$
7	$a/0, d/1, f/0, h/1$
8	$c/1, e/0, g/0, i/1$
9	$h/0, i/0, j/1$
10	$j/0$

to the two inverters and the three NAND gates. The resulting implication relationships are combined by transitivity to arrive at the ten classes of indistinguishable faults listed in Table II. "First-stage" analysis thus reduced the number of single faults to be considered from 20 to 10. The faults are shown in Fig. 2(b) with those in the same class linked together. In this figure, each pair of faults is drawn in the same relative position as the corresponding line in the circuit diagram. The upper fault represents the line s-a-1 in each case. This graphical representation of the faults is referred to as the *fault class structure*.

If fault detection only rather than fault location is desired, "second-stage" fault collapsing techniques may be applied to further reduce the number of faults to be detected. The appropriate rules in this case may be applied to the three NAND gates. Since each case of fan-out in this circuit is reconvergent no fan-out collapsing is applicable. "Second-stage" analysis allows the removal of classes 9 and 10 from the list leaving only eight fault classes to be considered for detection.

If multiple faults are to be considered, "third-stage" fault collapsing techniques may be applied to the three NAND gates and to the fan-out point in the circuit. The only useful relationships are those that result from the fan-out of line b. These relationships may be used to remove fault classes 3 and 4 from consideration. This leaves a total of six fault classes as the basis for all multiple faults in this circuit and therefore the total number of multiple faults to be considered is $2^6 - 1$. This is considerably smaller than the $3^{10} - 1$ multiple faults identified in the original circuit. It will be shown in the next section that even further reduction is possible for many circuits.[1]

Consequences of Fault Collapsing

The application of first-stage techniques of fault collapsing to a circuit consists of forming all possible expressions like those of Table I and combining these expressions by means of transitivity. The resulting classes of indistinguishable faults are combined into structures such as the one of Fig. 2(b). That the resulting fault

[1] Since the writing of this paper, other types of fault indistinguishabilities have been described [9], [10].

classes are tree-like in form may be seen by considering the segment of the circuit covered by a single class. One or more faults lie on lines which carry information into the segment and a single fault lies on the line which carries information out of the segment. These faults are referred to, respectively, as *initial* and *final* faults for the class. (In a class consisting of a single fault, that fault is both initial and final.) A class that has two or more initial faults is always formed from the bidirectional implication relationships between the input and output faults for a combinational gate. Such a class is said to *span* the gate.

Neighboring fault classes may be situated so that the final fault in one class is at the same line position as one of the faults of another class. In this case, the two classes are said to be *strongly connected*. For example, classes 7 and 9 in Fig. 2(b) are strongly connected. If two classes are situated such that a chain of strongly connected classes exists between them, they are said to be *connected* or to form a *connected set*. This definition of "connected" should not be confused with the sequential circuit concept of a connected machine. In Fig. 2(b), there are two connected sets, one consisting of classes 3 and 4, and the other consisting of all remaining classes.

The tree-like characteristic of fault classes carries over to connected sets. Progressing through a connected set in the forward direction, paths may converge but will never diverge. This is another way of saying that the portion of the original circuit that is represented by a connected set contains no fan-out point. The connected set representation thus subdivides a circuit into fan-out-free or tree-like segments.

Since the connected set corresponds to a fan-out-free segment of the circuit, it has a single output line. If the connected set contains more than two classes, then one of the classes having its final fault on this output line spans a gate. The class on this line that does not span a gate is the *final class* in the connected set. The *initial classes* for a connected set are defined in an analogous manner. (If the connected set consists of only two classes, then the choice of final class is arbitrary.)

It is desirable from the standpoint of multiple fault analysis to introduce a restriction on the size of connected sets considered. That is, if a fan-out-free segment of a circuit does not exceed a particular size then general statements may be made about the detection of multiple faults within the connected set that represents the given circuit segment. The restriction on size may be stated in terms of the paths which are traced going backward through each input of a class which spans a gate [4]. A useful working definition for this size restriction is the following. A *restricted connected set* is a set that does not contain the connected set of Fig. 3 as a subset.

For any multiple fault in a restricted connected set, it is possible to identify a single component fault such that any test which detects that single fault will also detect the multiple fault from which it was selected [4].

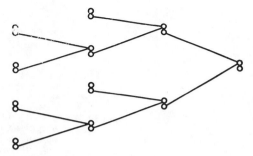

Fig. 3.   The minimal nonrestricted connected set.

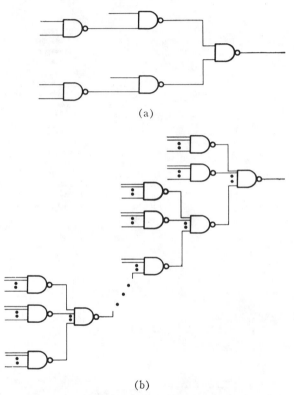

(a)

(b)

Fig. 4.   (a) Circuit segments represented by nonrestricted connected sets. (b) Circuit segments represented by restricted connected sets.

Since this holds for every multiple fault, it is seen that any test set which detects every single fault within a restricted connected set also detects every multiple fault within that restricted connected set.

The circuit of Fig. 4(a) leads to the fault class structure of Fig. 3. Thus any fan-out-free circuit segment which contains this circuit as a subcircuit does *not* fit the size restriction just presented. Note that although the circuit of Fig. 4(a) contains NAND gates, it is the circuit size alone that determines whether or not the resulting connected set is a restricted connected set. For example, if all gates in Fig. 4(a) were replaced by NOR gates, the same fault class structure would result. The most general fan-out-free NAND circuit segment which leads to a restricted connected set is shown in Fig. 4(b). This circuit is essentially a cascade with additional input gates at each level. Since any subcircuit of this circuit obviously also leads to a restricted connected set, all cascade networks obey the size restriction. In particular, any two-level circuit, such as a standard sum-of-products or product-of-sums realization of a combinational switching function, is a cascade of this type and therefore leads to a restricted connected set.

Consider a two-level single-output circuit. Since there is a single gate at the second level preceded by one or more gates at the first level, there can be no fan-out between the first and second levels. However, there may be fan-out associated with one or more input lines. The fault class structure resulting from such a circuit is a single large restricted connected set possibly preceded by one or more connected sets consisting of only two fault classes. An example of this type of circuit and the corresponding fault class structure are shown in Fig. 2.

"Third-stage" fault collapsing techniques relate the individual faults on the origin line of a fan-out point to multiple faults on the destination lines following the fan-out point. Thus the faults on the origin line may be ignored if multiple faults on the destination lines will be considered. This allows the elimination of the small connected sets such as the one containing classes 3 and 4 in Fig. 2(b) and leaves only multiple faults in a single restricted connected set to be considered. However, since any test set that detects all single faults in a restricted connected set also detects all multiple faults in that same connected set, all multiple faults in the entire circuit are also detected. Furthermore, since any test set that detects all single faults in the entire circuit must also detect all single faults in the restricted connected set, any test set that detects all single faults in a two-level single-output circuit also detects all multiple faults in that circuit. This result also applies to the more general NAND cascade of Fig. 4(b) [5].

By contrast, the circuit of Fig. 4(a) is the smallest NAND circuit for which it cannot be guaranteed that any test set that detects all single faults also detects all multiple faults.

Representation in Terms of Fault Classes

The total state of a combinational circuit in the presence of faults could be fully specified by giving the logic level carried on each line in the circuit. The theoretical evaluation of the state of any line under fault conditions would have to include the effects of the faults corresponding to that line. Unfortunately, the three-valued nature of the condition of a line (normal, s-a-1, s-a-0) makes such an evaluation relatively complicated if the effects of several faults are to be considered simultaneously [6].

The difficulty in the fault representation is resolved by the use of fault classes rather than lines as coordinates for the representation of the total state of a circuit. The line value associated with the final fault in a class is used to represent the class. The line on which the final fault is located may carry the logic value corresponding to that fault either as a result of the occurrence of a fault in the class or as a result of conditions on other lines which affect the logic value of the line considered.

The total state of the circuit is represented by the binary state vector S where $S_i = 1$ whenever the line on which the final fault of class i is located carries the value corresponding to that fault. Similarly, the fault condition in the circuit is represented by a binary fault vector F where $F_i = 1$ whenever a fault in class i occurs. The fault functions are defined so that they model the actual circuit failure considered. The state functions, however, are also partially determined by the signals applied to the circuit inputs. Thus S_i may be 1 either because a fault in class i occurred ($F_i = 1$) or because other conditions in the circuit cause the line to take on the representative value. It is obvious from consideration of the direction of information flow in the original circuit that S_i depends on conditions in the part of the circuit which lies between class i and the primary inputs and thus must be expressed in terms of the state functions for classes in this part of the circuit. In order to avoid circular definitions, S_i should be expressed in terms of the fault function for class i and the state functions for classes which immediately precede class i.

This technique of state representation is probably best developed by means of a simple example. The circuit of Fig. 2(a) which realizes the function $Z = W\overline{X} + X\overline{Y}$ was found to have the fault class structure of Fig. 2(b) consisting of two connected sets. The fault classes are listed in Table II. The final fault class is class 10 which contains the single fault $j/0$. The state function corresponding to class 10 must thus represent the condition "line j carries logic value 0." This condition can hold either because fault $j/0$ occurs or because the line is given that value by conditions in the remainder of the circuit. A 0 on line j is the complement of a 1 on line j, and a 1 on line j is the condition for the state function corresponding to class 9. (Fault $j/1$ is the final fault, and hence the representative fault, of class 9.) Therefore, the state function for class 10 can be written as

$$S_{10} = F_{10} + \overline{S_9}.$$

As was stated above, the state function for class 9 represents the condition "line j carries logic value 1." This can occur either as a result of a fault in class 9 or as a result of conditions in the circuit between class 9 and the primary inputs. Consideration of the original circuit shows that line j will carry logic value 1 whenever either line h or line i carries logic value 0. The latter conditions are the complements of the conditions for the state functions corresponding to classes 7 and 8, hence

$$S_9 = F_9 + \overline{S_7} + \overline{S_8}.$$

In a similar manner, the state functions for class 7 and 8 are found to be

$$S_8 = F_8 + \overline{S_2} + \overline{S_6}$$
$$S_7 = F_7 + \overline{S_1} + \overline{S_5}.$$

Classes 5 and 6 represent faults on destination lines from a fan-out point. The state function for class 6 represents the condition "line e carries logic value 1." Line e will carry logic value 1 whenever line b carries logic value 1. However, the state function for class 4 represents the condition "line b carries logic value 0." The appropriate definition for the state function for class 6 becomes

$$S_6 = F_6 + \overline{S_4}.$$

Similarly, the state function for class 5 is

$$S_5 = F_5 + S_4.$$

Class 4 may be treated in a manner analogous to that of class 10. The state function in this case is

$$S_4 = F_4 + \overline{S_3}.$$

The three remaining classes represent classes on primary input lines. Class 3 represents the condition "line b carries logic value 1." This condition may be caused by a fault in class 3 or by the input condition "input X is 1." Thus, the state function for class 3 is

$$S_3 = F_3 + X.$$

Similarly, the state functions for classes 1 and 2 are

$$S_2 = F_2 + \overline{Y}$$
$$S_1 = F_1 + W.$$

The output function Z may be related to the state function for the final class of the connected set closest to the output by noting that the state function corresponds to logic value 0 on line j. Therefore, the desired functional relationship is

$$Z = \overline{S_{10}}.$$

The rules for evaluating state functions may be summarized quite simply. The state function is always of the form

$$S_i = F_i + G_i$$

where F_i is the fault function for class i and G_i is a term obtained as follows, depending on whether or not the class is an initial class.

1) For any class i except an initial class in a connected set, G_i is the disjunction of the complements of the state functions for all classes strongly connected to the given class at its initial faults.

2) For an initial class i which: a) lies on primary input line X_j, G_i is X_j ($\overline{X_j}$) if the initial fault of the initial class represents a line s-a-1 (s-a-0); b) does not lie on a primary input line (i.e., lies on a destination line from a fan-out point where the final class of the connected set which precedes the fan-out point is class j), G_i is S_j ($\overline{S_j}$) if the initial fault of class i and the final fault of class j represent lines stuck at the same (opposite) logic values.

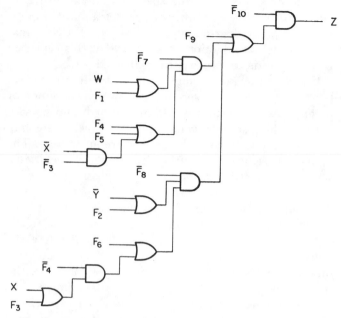

Fig. 5. Fault injection circuit for example circuit of Fig. 2(a).

These cases cover all fault structures resulting from combinational circuits except for a special case which arises in circuits containing successive gates of the same logic type (AND feeding AND, OR feeding NOR, etc.). The treatment of this special fault class structure is presented elsewhere [4].

Returning to our example, the equations found for the state functions may be combined. Successive substitution of the definition for each state function leads to an expression for the circuit output which involves only fault functions and primary inputs. This expression is

$$Z = \overline{F_{10}}(F_9 + \overline{F_7}((F_1 + W)(F_5 + F_4 + \overline{F_3}\overline{X}) + \overline{F_8}((F_2 + \overline{Y})(F_6 + \overline{F_4}(F_3 + X))))).$$

Thus the behavior of the circuit under all fault conditions is described by means of a Boolean equation rather than by means of an equation involving three-valued terms as was the case in Poage's treatment [6]. This equation may be manipulated to generate tests for faults or to simulate the effect of faults on the circuit behavior.

In addition to the advantages for direct manipulation, two other interpretations of the output expression are useful. The first interpretation deals with the relationship between the original circuit with its various possible faults and a realization of the Boolean output function as a fault-free circuit whose inputs are the original primary inputs as well as inputs for the fault function variables. Each single or multiple fault in the original circuit can be represented by proper assignment of values to the fault function variables. Such a circuit is called a *fault injection circuit* and may be used for purposes of fault simulation.

The fault injection circuit corresponding to our example is shown in Fig. 5. Any single or multiple fault in the circuit of Fig. 2(a) may be represented by the proper assignment of the fault function variables F_i to the fault vector $\mathbf{F} = (F_1, F_2, \cdots, F_{10})$. For example, the sing! fault "line f s-a-1" is represented by the binary fault vector $\mathbf{F} = (0, 0, 0, 0, 1, 0, 0, 0, 0, 0)$ and the multiple fault "line d s-a-1 and line c s-a-0" by $\mathbf{F} = (0, 1, 0, 0, 0, 0, 1, 0, 0, 0)$. In either case, if these inputs are applied to the fault function inputs of the fault injection circuit of Fig. 5, then that circuit will respond to any primary input pattern in the same manner as would the circuit of Fig. 2(a) with the appropriate fault. The simulation problem for any circuit is thus transformed from a circuit involving faults to a somewhat larger but fault-free circuit.

The second interpretation of the output equation corresponds to a connection graph. This interpretation is the topic of the following section.

CONNECTION GRAPHS

Any Boolean function may be represented as a connection graph which is isomorphic to a contact network that realizes the given function. For each appearance of a literal in the function to be represented, the graph has one edge whose weight is that literal. In the case of the fault expression for the circuit output, one edge is present for each occurrence of a fault function. An edge forms a connection if and only if its weight is 1. The value of the output function is 1 if and only if a path is formed between the two terminal nodes of the graph [8].

The dual graph with corresponding edge weights complemented represents the complemented output function. The two graphs may be used in conjunction for the derivation of diagnostic tests. If the circuit has more than one output, a pair of dual graphs is used for each output line.

A fault is detected by a test if the circuit output in the presence of the fault differs from that of the good circuit. Every test completes a path between the terminal nodes in one of the two output graphs. When a test is applied to a fault-free circuit, all edges corresponding to complemented fault functions are shorted and all edges corresponding to uncomplemented fault functions are open. The edges corresponding to circuit inputs are open or shorted in accordance with the value of the test input. Any path that is formed is thus made up of edges corresponding to complemented fault functions and to input variables. Any edge whose weight is 0 does not form a connection and may be removed from the graph.

If a single path is completed, then the removal of any edge in the path separates the two terminal nodes. An edge having weight $\overline{F_j}$ is removed if a fault in class j occurs. However, the occurrence of this fault may add or remove more than one edge (the literals $\overline{F_j}$ and F_j may appear more than once in the output function). A test which completes a path between terminal nodes thus *detects* a fault in class j if and only if the removal of all edges corresponding to $\overline{F_j}$ and the simultaneous addition of all edges corresponding to F_j breaks every path between terminal nodes, in either of the dual graphs.

For multiple faults, one need only consider the simul-

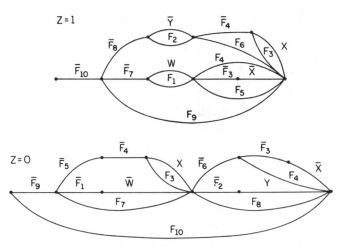

Fig. 6.   Complete connection graphs for example circuit of Fig. 2(a)

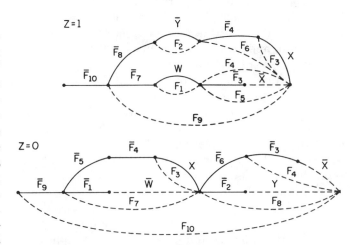

Fig. 7.   Connection graphs for example circuit with input assignment (1, 1, 0).

taneous addition and removal of edges corresponding to each class involved.

In a similar manner, fault location is concerned with the separation of faults in different classes. A test *distinguishes* between a fault in class j and a fault in class k if and only if the test fulfills the conditions for the detection of fault class $j(k)$ but not for the detection of fault class $k(j)$.

The application of connection graphs to diagnosis will be illustrated with the aid of the graphs of Fig. 6 which represent the circuit of Fig. 2(a). It should be noted that each graph contains a single edge corresponding to each fault class in the connected set nearest the output, but contains multiple edges corresponding to those fault classes which precede a fan-out point.

The test input (1, 1, 0) is a true vector for the circuit considered. The graphs of Fig. 6 are redrawn in Fig. 7 with open edges dotted in accordance with this input pattern and assuming fault-free behavior. The test completes a single path through the graph for $Z = 1$ and separates the terminal nodes in the graph for $Z = 0$. In the graph for $Z = 1$, complemented fault functions $\overline{F_4}$, $\overline{F_8}$, and $\overline{F_{10}}$ appear along the completed path so if a fault in one of these classes occurs, that path will be broken, and since the literals F_8 and F_{10} appear only in complemented form the test detects faults in these two classes, that is, faults $c/1$, $e/0$, $g/0$, $i/1$, and $j/0$. However, the detection of faults in class 4 is blocked since the graph for $Z = 1$ also contains an edge corresponding to the uncomplemented fault function F_4 and the addition of this edge completes a new path between the terminal nodes. It should be noted that the removal of any edge which breaks the original path causes the addition of a corresponding edge in the dual graph and thus completes a path there.

Test $(0, 1, 0)$ completes the same path as test $(1, 1, 0)$ in the graph for $Z = 1$ but does not complete the edge corresponding to input W. This change does not affect the detection of faults in classes 8 and 10 but does now allow the detection of faults in class 4 since the addition of the edge corresponding to the uncomplemented fault function F_4 no longer completes a new path through the graph. Test $(0, 1, 0)$ thus detects all faults detected by test $(1, 1, 0)$ and in addition detects another fault. Thus $(0, 1, 0)$ is in some sense a "better" test than $(1, 1, 0)$ for fault detection. This phenomenon will be investigated more fully after considering other test inputs.

The test input $(0, 0, 1)$ is a false vector of the original circuit. This test completes a path through the fault-free graph for $Z = 0$. Complemented fault functions $\overline{F_1}$, $\overline{F_2}$, $\overline{F_3}$, $\overline{F_6}$, and $\overline{F_9}$ lie on the path; however, those edges resulting from classes 2, 3, and 6 lie in parallel segments of the graph and thus removal of any one of these edges does not break the path. Removal of the edge resulting from either class 1 or class 9 breaks the original path and since the fault functions F_1 and F_9 do not appear in uncomplemented form in the graph, the test detects faults in these classes; that is, faults $a/1$, $h/0$, $i/0$, and $j/1$.

Test input $(0, 0, 0)$ completes a single path between terminal nodes in the graph for $Z = 0$. Complemented fault functions $\overline{F_1}$, $\overline{F_3}$, $\overline{F_6}$, $\overline{F_9}$ lie on this path and it is seen that this test detects faults in all four of these classes. That this is so is seen by considering the only class of these four that appears in both complemented and uncomplemented form, class 3. The edge corresponding to the uncomplemented fault function F_3 does not inhibit the breaking of the path by the removal of the edge corresponding to $\overline{F_3}$. Test $(0, 0, 0)$ thus detects all faults detected by test $(0, 0, 1)$ and in addition detects others. Thus $(0, 0, 0)$ is in some sense a "better" test than $(0, 0, 1)$ for fault detection.

Two separate cases where one test proved superior to another have been investigated. In one case, a test was inefficient because it completed multiple paths and in another it was inefficient because it completed a partial path in addition to the path between terminal nodes. These simple examples suggest the following more general criterion for the selection of tests. As a primary objective, the test should form a single path between terminal nodes of the graph. If multiple paths are formed by the test, the parallel sections should be as short as possible. (In some graphs representing re-

dundant circuits it is not possible to complete only single paths.) As a secondary objective, as few extra edges as possible should be completed by the test.

In the case of multiple faults, one fault inhibits the detection of a second fault by completing a secondary path in parallel to the original path. This suggests that if a selected fault is to be detected in the presence of other faults, the primary and secondary objectives stated above should be interchanged.[2]

It may happen that the assignment of every input variable is necessary for the completion of some path through a graph. In this case, the necessary assignment is the only test which completes the given path. If a complemented fault function along this path does not appear complemented at any other position in either of the graphs, then this test is the only test which can detect that fault class. On the other hand, if a partial assignment of input variables is sufficient to complete a path, then the remaining input variables may be assigned in different ways to give different complete assignments, each of which detects some or all of the faults along the path.

Analyses such as those of the preceding paragraphs may be used for the heuristic selection of tests. For example, a test which uniquely completes a path is a good candidate for selection because it is likely to be the only test that detects some fault class (and is an essential test whenever no other path can be completed through that fault class).

The application of connection graphs to the generation of tests to detect all faults in a combinational circuit will be illustrated for the circuit of Fig. 2(a). This circuit is a two-level circuit and by the result stated previously any set of tests which detects all single faults also detects all multiple faults. This allows the use of both second- and third-stage fault collapsing techniques to reduce the number of fault classes to be considered. Specifically, fault classes 3, 4, 9, and 10 may be removed from consideration. Since these classes need not be considered in the derivation of tests, edges corresponding to them may be removed from the connection graphs. Edges corresponding to uncomplemented fault functions are simply removed and edges corresponding to complemented fault functions are replaced by short circuits. The resulting connection graphs are shown in Fig. 8. Note that these graphs are considerably simpler than the original graphs shown in Fig. 6.

Any test selected completes a path through one of the two graphs. It should be noted that, in the graphs of Fig. 8, each complemented fault function appears only once and that the same fault function does not appear in the same graph in uncomplemented and complemented form. This means that the process of test generation reduces to the problem of completing a path through each complemented fault function. In

[2] Since the writing of this paper, several other approaches to the generation of multiple fault tests have appeared in the literature [11]–[13].

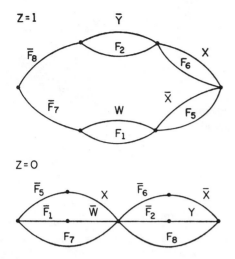

Fig. 8. Reduced connection graphs for example circuit.

the graph for $Z = 1$, the upper path consisting of edges $\overline{F}_8$, $\overline{Y}$, and X is completed by test $(-, 1, 0)$. The variable W is assigned by means of the secondary objective stated earlier: $W = 0$ is chosen so as not to complete a partial path. This leads to test $(0, 1, 0)$ which detects fault class 8 (also fault classes 4 and 10). In a similar manner, the lower path in the graph for $Z = 1$ is completed by test $(1, 0, 1)$. In the graph for $Z = 0$ any path through $\overline{F}_5$ must also pass through edge X. This implies that the edge corresponding to $\overline{X}$ must be open. The path through edge $\overline{F}_5$ must then be completed through $\overline{F}_2$ and Y. W must be set to 1 to avoid a parallel path thus leading to test $(1, 1, 1)$. In a similar manner, test $(0, 0, 0)$ completes a path through $\overline{F}_1$ and $\overline{F}_6$. These four tests detect all single and thus all multiple faults in the circuit of Fig. 2(a). They are, in fact, one of four possible minimal test sets for this circuit.

CONCLUSIONS

The techniques of fault collapsing have been shown to permit a reduction in the number of faults to be considered in combinational networks. The three "stages" of fault collapsing were seen to be applicable to different diagnosis objectives, i.e., fault detection or location. The fault class structure which resulted from the application of fault collapsing techniques resulted in a division of the circuit into fan-out-free segments.

The detection of all single faults within a restricted connected set implies the detection of all multiple faults within that connected set. This result was combined with "third-stage" fault collapsing to show that any test set which detects every single fault in a two-level single-output combinational circuit also detects every multiple fault in the circuit.

The behavior of a circuit under fault conditions was represented using the classes of indistinguishable faults rather than the actual circuit lines as a basis for the representation. This lead to a two-valued Boolean expression rather than an expression involving three-valued variables. Such an expression may be readily manipulated for the purpose of fault diagnosis.

A particularly useful interpretation of this circuit information takes the form of a connection graph. A number of heuristic rules for choosing diagnostic tests based on this graph is suggested. The advantage of this technique is that "good" diagnostic tests may be selected with a minimum of processing time.

REFERENCES

[1] S. Seshu and D. N. Freeman, "The diagnosis of asynchronous sequential switching systems," *IEEE Trans. Electron. Comput.*, vol. EC-11, pp. 459–465, Aug. 1962.
[2] D. B. Armstrong, "On finding a nearly minimal set of fault detection tests for combinational logic nets," *IEEE Trans. Electron. Comput.*, vol. EC-15, pp. 66–73, Feb. 1966.
[3] J. P. Roth, W. G. Bouricius, and P. R. Schneider, "Programmed algorithms to compute tests to detect and distinguish between failures in logic circuits," *IEEE Trans. Electron. Comput.*, vol. EC-16, pp. 567–580, Oct. 1967.
[4] D. R. Schertz, "On the representation of digital faults," Coord. Sci. Lab., Univ. Illinois, Urbana, Rep. R-418, May 1969.
[5] D. R. Schertz and G. A. Metze, "On the indistinguishability of faults in digital systems," in *Proc. 6th Annu. Allerton Conf. Circuit and System Theory*, Oct. 1968, pp. 752–760.
[6] J. F. Poage, "Derivation of optimum tests to detect faults in combinational circuits," in *Mathematical Theory of Automata*. Brooklyn, N. Y.: Polytechnic Press, 1963, pp. 483–528.
[7] H. Y. Chang, E. G. Manning, and G. Metze, *Fault Diagnosis of Digital Systems*. New York: Wiley-Interscience, 1970.
[8] D. R. Schertz and G. Metze, "The use of connection graphs for the detection of digital faults," in *Proc. 7th Annu. Allerton Conf. Circuit and System Theory*, Oct. 1969, pp. 261–271.
[9] E. J. McCluskey and F. W. Clegg, "Fault equivalence in combinational logic networks," *IEEE Trans. Comput.*, vol. C-20, pp. 1286–1293, Nov. 1971.
[10] J. P. Hayes, "A NAND model for fault diagnosis in combinational logic networks," *IEEE Trans. Comput.*, vol. C-20, pp. 1496–1506, Dec. 1971.
[11] A. R. Klayton and A. K. Susskind, "Multiple-fault-detection tests for loop-free logic networks," in *Dig. 1971 IEEE Int. Comput. Soc. Conf.*, Sept. 1971, pp. 77–78.
[12] M.-W. Du and C. D. Weiss, "Circuit structure and switching function verification," in *Proc. 9th Annu. Allerton Conf. Circuit and System Theory*, Oct. 1971, pp. 122–130.
[13] D. C. Bossen and S. J. Hong, "Cause-effect analysis for multiple fault detection in combinational networks," *IEEE Trans. Comput.*, vol. C-20, pp. 1252–1257, Nov. 1971.

Copyright © 1978 American Telephone and Telegraph Company
THE BELL SYSTEM TECHNICAL JOURNAL
Vol. 57, No. 5, May–June 1978
Printed in U.S.A.

Fault Modeling and Logic Simulation of CMOS and MOS Integrated Circuits

By R. L. WADSACK

(Manuscript received October 10, 1977)

This paper addresses the simulation and detection of logic faults in CMOS integrated circuits. CMOS logic gates are intrinsically tri-state devices: output low, output high, or output open. This third, high-impedance condition introduces a new, nonclassical logic fault: the "stuck-open." The paper describes the modeling of this fault and its complement, the stuck-on, by means of gate-level networks. In addition, this paper provides a methodology for creating simulator models for tri-state and other dynamic circuit elements. The models are gate-level in structure, provide for both classical and stuck-open/stuck-on faults, and can be adopted for use on essentially any general purpose logic simulator.

I. INTRODUCTION

The challenge of testing silicon integrated circuits (ICs) is becoming more formidable with the rapidly expanding production of large-scale integrated (LSI) circuits. Increased gate-count, increased pin-count, smaller feature size, higher performance, and higher complexity all contribute to a mounting "testability" problem. Furthermore, there is considerable evidence that the economic requirements to meet that challenge will continue to grow at a rate markedly greater than that of circuit size alone.

As a further dimension to the challenge, IC tests must be specifically designed to recognize failure-mode dependence upon circuit configuration, processing parameters, and the overall technology (TTL, ECL, PMOS, CMOS, etc.). That is, a Boolean network realized in one technology can have a strikingly different implementation in another. Consequently, logic tests must be created which exercise not only the gross functional behavior of the IC but also the structure used for that function. However, for large-scale ICs, internal circuit structure and complexity are increasing at a much more rapid rate than is the number of access terminals.

The rising use of MOS technology for LSI circuits has introduced a number of circuit elements whose logical behavior and faults are gen-

erally not treated by existent logic simulators.[1] These include, for example, transmission gates, tri-state inverters, and bidirectional buses. Furthermore, the failure modes of such circuits and even those of ordinary combinational logic gates can introduce nonclassic logic faults. That is, they possess a faulted behavior for which test coverage would not be verified on a conventional fault simulator.

The focus of this paper will be centered upon fault modeling and logic simulation of CMOS digital integrated circuits. The motivation for this direction is the recent emergence of CMOS as a mature technology for the design of densely-packed, low-power digital LSI circuits.[2] Secondly, CMOS is intrinsically a three-state logic technology. Consequently, it readily lends itself both to the illustration of the new, nonclassical logic faults and to a methodology for modeling the dynamic nature of MOS circuits.

II. CMOS LOGIC FAULTS

2.1 CMOS logic gates

Figure 1 shows a two-input CMOS NOR gate: the output is high if and only if $A = B = 0$. The realization of the NOR function shows the series/parallel complementary nature of CMOS logic gates: $F = \overline{A} \cdot \overline{B}$ and $\overline{F} = A + B$ where the Boolean function $\overline{A} \cdot \overline{B}$ connects the output to the "1" level and the function $A + B$ connects the output to the "0" level. Each is the complement of the other and is implemented, respectively, with p-channel FETs and n-channel FETs.

The NOR circuit is a specific example of the general CMOS characteristic of complementary pull-up/pull-down networks. The only two steady-state logic outputs are 0 and 1. The former arises when the pull-down network is conducting and the pull-up network is nonconducting. The latter, $F = 1$, occurs when the two networks reverse their conductivity states. Consequently, there is no static current path between VDD and VSS, and CMOS ICs therefore dissipate power only to charge and discharge circuit capacitance.

On the other hand, there are two common situations which can lead to a third logic state. This third condition is the "open" or high-impedance state.[3] One source of the "open" state is the presence of a logic fault which prevents one network from conducting when the other is in a nonconductive state. A second cause is the legitimate use of a high-impedance state in dynamic circuits or tri-state buffers, for example. In each instance the output retains the logic value of the previous output

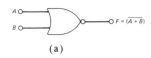

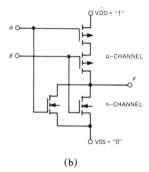

(a)

(b)

Fig. 1—The CMOS two-input NOR gate: (a) logic symbol and transfer function, and (b) FET realization.

Table I — CMOS two-input NOR gate: truth table

A	B	F	F (0)	F (1)	F (A)	F (B)	F (ASOP)	F (BSOP)	F (VDDSOP)
0	0	1	0	1	1	1	1	1	4
0	1	0	0	1	0	1	0	4	0
1	0	0	0	1	1	0	4	0	0
1	1	0	0	1	0	0	0	0	0
	normal			classical faults				nonclassical faults	

4 = previous output state
$F(A) = F(\text{IOFA})$
$F(B) = F(\text{IOFB})$

included to represent the undesired, high-impedance state caused by a faulty pull-up or pull-down network. For the two-input NOR gate of Fig. 1, there are three such stuck-open (S-OP) faults: ASOP, BSOP, and VDDSOP. The first, ASOP, is caused by an open, or missing, n-channel A-input pull-down FET. The second, BSOP, is caused by an open, or missing, B-input pull-down FET. The third, VDDSOP, is caused by an open anywhere in the series, p-channel pull-up connection to VDD.

Table I shows the truth table for the two-input CMOS NOR gate for both the fault-free and the seven faulted conditions. For example, the fault-free gate obeys

$$F = \overline{(A + B)}$$

whereas

$$F(\text{IOFB}) = \overline{A}$$

and

$$F(\text{ASOP}) = \overline{A} \cdot \overline{B} + 4 \cdot A \cdot \overline{B},$$

where "4" denotes the previous state of F. [Using the notation of sequential circuit design, the latter equation would read $F_{n+1}(\text{ASOP}) = \overline{A} \cdot \overline{B} + F_n \cdot A \cdot \overline{B}$. The use of a "4" to symbolize F_n is a convention adopted to describe the effect of S-OP faults.]

How are the seven NOR gate logic faults related to actual physical flaws in the IC? The SA0, SA1 faults correspond to a low-impedance "short" to VSS or VDD, respectively. The IOF faults are caused by an open input to the *logic gate* as a whole. In addition to being open, the input is in a charged condition which is recognized as a logic 0. (An IOF fault in a NOR gate is an SA0, by definition; in a NAND gate the analogous fault would be an SA1, of course.) That is, both the p-channel and the n-channel FETs have a 0 applied to them. On the other hand, the nonclassical S-OP faults arise from a missing connection to the gate of *individual* FETs, for example, with the gate in a charge state such that the FET is nonconducting. Another cause of an S-OP fault is an open, or missing, connection to either the source or the drain of an FET.

state. This is true because the gates are loaded with capacitance only. The length of time the state is retained, however, is determined by the leakage current at the node.

Conceptually, a fourth state could exist: both networks conducting. However, this represents a logical inconsistency, i.e., the output cannot simultaneously be both high and low. Such a fault is more analog in nature because the output voltage lies somewhere between VDD and VSS. The actual value is determined by the impedance ratios of the networks and the associated fault. For the most part these failures will not be treated as logic faults.

There are two kinds of *classical* logic faults: stuck-at-one (SA1) and stuck-at-zero (SA0). These faults may occur at either an input or an output of a logic gate. On the other hand, a gate with n inputs can have only $n + 2$ distinct classical faults. Input faults must be stuck in the "nondominant" state to be distinguishable from an output stuck-at fault. For AND/NAND gates and OR/NOR gates such nondominant faults are SA1's and SA0's, respectively. These faults are sometimes called "input-open-from" faults and will be denoted as IOF faults in this paper. The two-input NOR gate of Fig. 1 has the four classical faults: SA0, SA1, IOFA, and IOFB. These are also symbolized as $F(0)$, $F(1)$, $F(A)$, and $F(B)$, respectively.

For CMOS logic gates the nonclassical "stuck-open" faults must be

Table II — CMOS two-input NOR gate: fault detection
(test sequence: AB = 00,01,00,10)

	A	B	F	F(0)	F(1)	F(A)	F(B)	F(ASOP)	F(BSOP)	F(VDDSOP)
1	0	0	1	0*	1	1	1	1	1	3
2	0	1	0	0	1*	0	1*	0	1*	0
3	0	0	1	0	1	1	1	1	1	0*
4	1	0	0	0	1	1*	0	1*	0	0
	normal			classical faults				nonclassical faults		

3 = unknown output state (0 or 1).
* Vector at which simulator detects the fault.

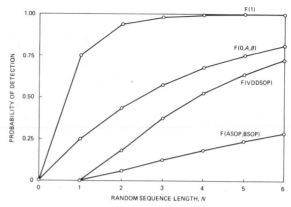

Fig. 2—The CMOS two-input NOR gate: probability of fault detection (for a simulator) versus the length N of a sequence of random input vectors.

In this context an "open" denotes an undesired high impedance at either the gate, the source, or the drain of an FET. Of course, any residual capacitive or resistive coupling must be negligibly small for a high-impedance fault to be regarded as a true "open." In addition, the actual occurrence of such faults depends on the specific topology of the logic gate.

The truth table of Table I shows that S-OP faults create sequential circuits where only a combinational circuit existed for the fault-free gate. This increases the difficulty of both testing the circuit and designing a set of input test "vectors" to achieve a high percentage of fault coverage. For example, the four input states of Table I, if applied in that order, will detect only 5 out of the 7 logic faults. ASOP and VDDSOP will be undetected. The ASOP fault is not detected because F(10) = "4" = 0 which is the correct output for the "10" input vector. The VDDSOP fault will not necessarily be detected because of the chance that the gate powers up with the output in the high (but correct) state for the "00" input vector.

The primary reason that the above two faults were undetected is that the corresponding circuit paths (devices) were not tested to determine whether they fulfilled their most basic function. For example, to test the A-input n-channel *pull-down* FET, the output node must first be driven high and then that FET, and it alone, must be capable of pulling the node low. The sequence of inputs in Table I did not meet that condition.

A set of vectors which detects all 7 faults is the following: 00,01,00,10. Table II shows the response of the 8 circuits (the good circuit and the 7 faulty ones) to the above input sequence. The * symbol designates the vector at which each fault is first detected by the *simulator*. The "3" denotes an unknown state (either a 1 or a 0), caused by the VDDSOP fault as described previously. Depending upon the actual state of the circuit at power-up, the VDDSOP fault may, therefore, be detected at either vector 1 or 3.

The influence of CMOS faults on fault coverage is shown in Fig. 2. The probability of detection for random vector sequences is given for each of the 7 faults in Table I. The probability is that which would prevail for a logic simulation of a two-input NOR gate subjected to random vector sequences of length N. The output SA1 fault (F(1)) has a probability of detection of nearly unity for sequences of length greater than three. The two pull-down stuck-open faults have the lowest probability, reaching only 0.29 for sequences 6 vectors long (45 vectors are required to reach 0.95). Note also the similarity between the VDDSOP fault and the output SA0 fault (F(0)). Further, the lag for all three CMOS faults is evident.

In addition to increasing the number and complexity of CMOS logic faults, stuck-open faults are also timing-sensitive. Specifically, the above set of input vectors will detect three S-OP faults of the NOR gate only if they are applied to the gate at a rate more rapid than that associated with leakage current time-constants. A rate significantly slower than, say, 10 kHz may allow some faulty devices to charge to the correct state before the output is sampled by the test set. Truth-table testing at quasi-dc rates is inadequate. Conversely, an ill-chosen vector set, such as the binary sequence of Table I, may not detect S-OP faults no matter how fast it is applied to the device under test. Note also that the sequence of Table I is "exhaustive," but does not achieve 100 percent fault coverage.

Another aspect of stuck-open faults is that of long-term reliability. A fault caused by a missing connection to the gate of an individual FET may cause that FET to be open and yet remain undetected during production testing if the test vector set has less than 100 percent fault coverage. Later, however, under actual operating conditions the FET gate may acquire charge of the opposite polarity and become conducting or "stuck-on." CMOS S-OP field failures have been observed.[4]

2.2 Modeling CMOS logic faults

The design of a set of vectors to achieve 100 percent fault coverage for small-scale integrated (SSI) circuits such as NAND and NOR gates is trivial and can be done by inspection. However, for complex high gate-count circuits such as medium- and large-scale ICs (MSI, LSI), the use of computer-based logic simulators is a necessity. To meet this need the simulation of both stuck-open faults and dynamic logic elements has been approached from the standpoint of circuit modeling. The models represent circuit elements both in their fault-free condition and in high-impedance state(s), if any. Combinational "static" gates (e.g., NAND or NOR) enter the high-impedance condition only in the presence of S-OP faults. Dynamic or tri-state logic elements, however, can intentionally be placed into a high-impedance state by auxiliary, or control, inputs.

The models presented in this paper are gate-level oriented because no other method generally exists for simulating nonclassical logic faults. On the other hand, the logical behavior of the models can be incorporated into a higher-level functional description if that capability is available on the logic simulator. On the LAMP system[1] the Function Description Language (FDL) is being modified to include such "internal faults."[5] Although the models in this paper are implemented in terms of NAND/NOR logic, they do have the advantage of being simulator independent. That is, they will correctly model fault-free and faulted logic networks regardless of the particular simulator chosen. The specific illustrations, however, are taken from the author's experience with LAMP.

Existent machine aids simulate for the most part only the classical SA0/SA1 faults and not the "stuck-open" faults. One possible solution to the problem is to use a network of conventional gates (NOT, NAND, NOR, etc.) to form a model which duplicates both the normal and the faulted behavior of a single CMOS gate. One of the basic properties of the model is that it must possess the capability of passing 0/1 data from input to output in accordance with the fault-free logic function of the gate. Second, when there is an S-OP fault, it must retain the previous state in the presence of the "provoking" input (see Table I). This suggests the use of gated latch.

The general approach to modeling either stuck-open (S-OP) faults or dynamic gates is shown in Fig. 3. The "gated latch" represents the nodal capacitance associated with the logic function. For $T = 1$, the output equals the input ($Z = D$); the $T = 0$, the output latches and stores the previous state ($Z = $ "4"). The "node faults gate" has been added to introduce the two classical SA0 and SA1 (stuck-at) faults. The gate is not

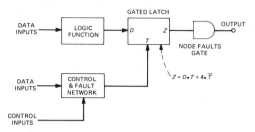

Fig. 3—Block diagram: the general approach for stuck-open/dynamic gate models.

necessary if those faults are incorporated within the "logic function" network. The latter represents the actual logical operation being modeled (NAND, NOR, etc.). The "control and fault network" establishes whether the output of the "logic function" is to be transmitted to the gates driven by the "output." In the case of static gates, there are no "control inputs" to that network. Only the presence of S-OP faults would cause $T = 0$ (i.e., no transmission). Dynamic circuit elements have "control inputs" which can cause $T = 0$ in the absence of faults. Classical faults generated in the "logic function" network at input D will, of course, propagate through the latch (and not through the S-OP fault generating network).

III. SPECIFIC MODELS

3.1 The NOR gate

The model for the two-input CMOS NOR gate is shown in Fig. 4. The NOR gate named GATE has zero delay but is faulted (i.e., the fault simulator will simulate faults for this gate) so as to introduce all the classical faults of a two-input NOR gate. Of course, GATE represents the modeled logic function. All other gates in Fig. 4 compose the fault-generating network which sets $T = 0$ in the presence of an S-OP fault *and* the "provoking" input for that fault.

The model functions as follows: If there are no faults in the circuit, then $F = \overline{(A + B)}$. If there are only classical faults (from GATE), then $T = 1$ and those faults propagate through GL. If there is an S-OP fault in the gate, than $T = 0$ for the provoking vector and $F = 4$ as required from Table I. For example, because its input is grounded the only fault that the simulator assigns to the gate ASOP is an SA1. Therefore, in the presence of the fault ASOP(1) and when $AB = 10$, then $T = 0$ and the GL latch holds the output equal to the previous value. Similarly the output F will be stuck-open in the presence of the VDDSOP(1) fault if and only if $AB = 00$.

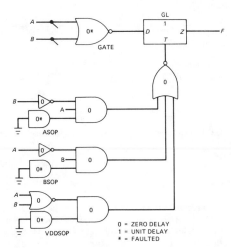

Fig. 4—The CMOS two-input NOR gate model, NR2. The block labeled GL is the gated latch circuit of Fig. 3. Only those gates marked * are faulted by the simulator. Propagation delays are denoted by either 0 or 1.

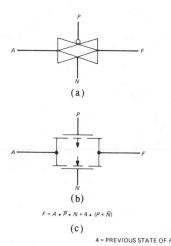

$$F = A \cdot \bar{P} \cdot N + 4 \cdot (P + \bar{N})$$

(c)

4 = PREVIOUS STATE OF F

Fig. 5—The CMOS transmission gate: (a) logic symbol, (b) FET realization, and (c) the static, unilateral logic transfer function.

The NOR gate model of Fig. 4 has been designed to yield the correct logic behavior of the two-input CMOS NOR gate in the absence of faults. Secondly, it correctly models all 7 logic faults: SA0, SA1, IOFA, IOFB, ASOP, BSOP, and VDDSOP. Thirdly, it generates no spurious faults associated with the modeling, nor does it have a propagation delay other than the one unit that would be expected from a single NOR gate. Finally, the nature of the fault-generating network prevents the spurious propagation of faults from other gates connected to the inputs of the gate in question.

The names of the gates in the model have been chosen to provide ease of use during simulation. Specifically, if a circuit contained a two-input CMOS NOR gate with the name NOR17, then the LAMP simulator would assign the following fault list to it:

NOR17.GATE(0)
NOR17.GATE(1)
NOR17.GATE(A)
NOR17.GATE(B)
NOR17.ASOP(1)
NOR17.BSOP(1)
NOR17.VDDSOP(1)

Consequently, the test engineer can determine at a glance the nature of a fault and where it is located. In addition, in the LAMP system all S-OP faults can be globally nonfaulted (or faulted) because they arise from gates ending in the string "SOP." This nonfaulting capability is useful in determinations of relative fault coverage.

3.2 The transmission gate

MOS technology possesses an interesting circuit element with both digital and analog capability: the transmission gate. The CMOS transmission gate is shown in Fig. 5.[6] It is a *bilateral* device with a conducting mode for PN = 01 and a nonconducting state for PN = 10. A problem occurs for the two other vectors PN = 00 and PN = 11. In each case either the p-channel or the n-channel FET will be on, but not both. Low-to-high transitions (open p-FET) or high-to-low transitions (open n-FET) will be attenuated as they pass through the transmission gate. In addition, there will be an accompanying speed degradation caused by the higher impedance of the single FET path.

Although the two input vectors 00 and 11 apply abnormal conditions to the transmission gate, the choice of whether to regard the gate as a whole as either "on" or "off" is somewhat arbitrary. For these particular

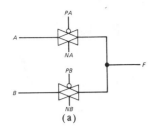

(a)

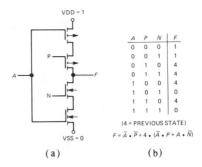

A	P	N	F
0	0	0	1
0	0	1	1
0	1	0	4
0	1	1	4
1	0	0	4
1	0	1	0
1	1	0	4
1	1	1	0

(4 = PREVIOUS STATE)

$$F = \overline{A} \cdot \overline{P} + 4 \cdot (\overline{A} \cdot P + A \cdot \overline{N})$$

(a)   (b)

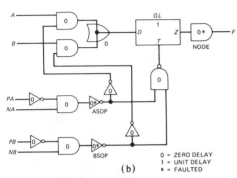

0 = ZERO DELAY
1 = UNIT DELAY
* = FAULTED

(b)

Fig. 6—The CMOS two-channel transmission gate node, XG2: (a) logic symbol and (b) a gate-level model which exhibits both the fault-free and the faulted behavior of the XG2 element. Signal flow is unilateral: from A and B to F. Normally only one channel is enabled at one time.

(c)

Fig. 7—The CMOS tri-state inverter: (a) the FET realization, (b) the truth table, and (c) the logic symbol.

models the worst-case logic behavior of the gate has been taken to be

$$F = A \cdot \overline{P} \cdot N + 4 \cdot (P + \overline{N})$$

where "4" represents the previous state of the output. The above expression can be rewritten as

$$F = D \cdot T + 4 \cdot \overline{T}$$

where $T = \overline{P} \cdot N$ and $D = A$. This is just the equation for the gated latch of Fig. 3, i.e., the gated latch is equivalent to a nonfaulted transmission gate.

Functionally, transmission gates generally occur in groups of two, three, four, etc. Hence, they can be regarded as multiplexing nodes at which usually only one of the gates is conducting at a time. The model for the CMOS two-channel transmission gate node, used in the above sense, is shown in Fig. 6. The gate named SUM is a zero-delay nonfaulted tied-OR node (TOR). The purpose of the gate labeled NODE is to provide the two classical faults SA0, SA1 associated with the node F. The nonclassical faults generated by this network are four in number: ASOP(0), ASOP(1), BSOP(0), and BSOP(1). As usual, ASOP(1) means that the A-channel is stuck-open and, conversely, ASOP(0) means that it is "stuck-on" (S-ON). For the latter fault, $F = A + B \cdot (\overline{PB}) \cdot (NB)$. Here, the stuck-on has been treated as a legitimate logic fault whose presence induces a "1-dominant" short, i.e., the spurious A-input is ORed with the correct B-channel response. Of course, there may be no technological reason to assign a S-ON fault as either 1-dominant or 0-dominant. In that case, the model in Fig. 6 (and others) can easily be recast to exhibit only S-ON nonclassical faults.

Stuck-open faults in a CMOS transmission gate are also timing-sensitive as in NAND and NOR gates, but in a different manner. Specifically, even with one FET of the pair open, the other can provide nearly a complete logic transition but at a higher average impedance level. Consequently, 0/1 data will propagate through the gate but at slightly slower speeds. However, the reduction in speed is much smaller than that caused by S-OP faults in NAND or NOR gates. Therefore, an S-OP fault in a transmission gate may be intrinsically undetectable even at the highest data rates that occur at a particular gate.

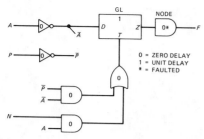

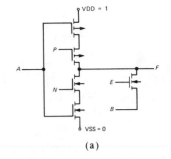

(a)

Fig. 8—The CMOS tri-state inverter model. Only the gate marked * is faulted by the simulator. Propagation delays are denoted by either 0 or 1.

A	P	N	E = 0 F	B = 0 F	B = 1 F
0	0	0	1	3	1
0	0	1	1	3	1
0	1	0	4	0	1
0	1	1	4	0	1
1	0	0	4	0	1
1	0	1	0	0	3
1	1	0	4	0	1
1	1	1	0	0	3

E = 1

(3 = UNKNOWN STATE)
(4 = PREVIOUS STATE)

(b)

3.3 The tri-state inverter

The FET implementation of the CMOS tri-state inverter is shown in Fig. 7(a). In this case P and N are control leads that determine whether the circuit inverts the input A or remains in the high-impedance ("4") state. For the latter condition, the nodal capacitance retains the value of the previous state ("0," "1," or "3"). The truth table is given in Fig. 7(b) and leads to the transfer function: $F = \overline{A} \cdot \overline{P} + 4 \cdot (\overline{A} \cdot P + A \cdot \overline{N})$. The logic symbol is shown in Fig. 7(c).

The model for the tri-state inverter is given in Fig. 8. Here, only the two classical faults $F(0)$ and $F(1)$ have been assigned to the model because of the similarity of VDDSOP/VSSSOP faults to $F(0)$ and $F(1)$ faults, respectively. The S-OP and S-ON faults could be modeled, of course, but the added complexity does not warrant separate treatment.

The relation of the model network to the truth table is perhaps more obvious if the transfer function is written as

$$F = 1 \cdot \overline{A} \cdot \overline{P} + 0 \cdot A \cdot N + 4 \cdot (\overline{A} \cdot P + A \cdot \overline{N}).$$

The terms $\overline{A} \cdot \overline{P}$ and $A \cdot N$ then compose the transmit (T) function: $T = \overline{A} \cdot \overline{P} + A \cdot N$. Therefore, when $T = 0$ then $F = $ "4." That is, the output latches (or stores) the previous state.

3.4 Modified tri-state inverter

The addition of an n-channel transmission gate FET to the output of the tri-state inverter forms a "modified" inverter of Fig. 9(a). (This circuit element forms one half of a gated sense amplifier.) The resultant truth table is shown in Fig. 9(b). The "3" (unknown 0 or 1) state occurs whenever $A = B$ and both the inverter and the transmission gate are enabled. In other words, whenever each attempts to drive the node F to

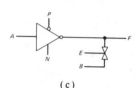

(c)

Fig. 9—The CMOS modified tri-state inverter: (a) the FET realization, (b) the truth table where 3 indicates an unknown 0 or 1 state and 4 symbolizes the previous state of F, and (c) the logic symbol for the combination tri-state inverter and n-channel FET.

opposing logic states, the output is indeterminate ("3"). The high impedance "4" state occurs whenever both channels are disabled.

The model for the modified tri-state inverter can be developed by noting that the Boolean expression that selects the $\overline{A}$ channel is $\overline{P} \cdot A + N \cdot A$ and the term that selects the B channel is E [see Fig. 9(a)]. Therefore, define SA $= \overline{P} \cdot A + N \cdot A$ and SB $= E$. Then, $T = $ SA $+$ SB or $T = \overline{\text{SA} \cdot \text{SB}}$. Therefore,

$$F = \overline{A} \cdot \text{SA} \cdot \overline{\text{SB}} + B \cdot \overline{\text{SA}} \cdot \text{SB} + 3 \cdot \text{SA} \cdot \text{SB} + 4 \cdot \overline{\text{SA}} \cdot \overline{\text{SB}}$$

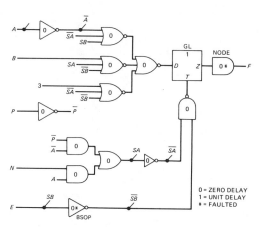

Fig. 10—The CMOS modified tri-state inverter model.

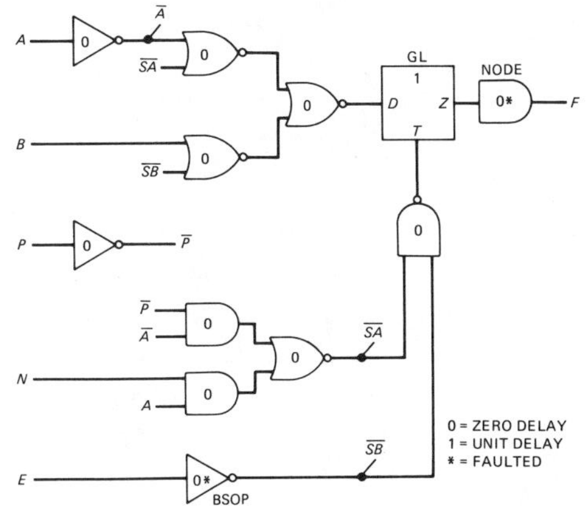

Fig. 11—The CMOS modified tri-state inverter model: reduced version. The unknown 3 condition has been ignored and replaced by a 0-dominant short assignment.

or

$$F = (\overline{A} + \overline{SA} + SB) \cdot (B + SA + \overline{SB}) \cdot (3 + \overline{SA} + \overline{SB}) \cdot (4 + SA + SB).$$

The model corresponding to the latter expression for F is shown in Fig. 10. The model has four faults assigned to it: two classical faults NODE(0,1), and two CMOS faults BSOP(0,1). For example, the fault BSOP(1) means that the B-channel transmission gate is stuck-open and nonconducting. S-OP faults in the inverter itself are ignored (see Section 3.3, above).

The model of Fig. 10 produces a "3" output whenever conflicting output conditions are generated by the simultaneous selection of both the A channel and the B channel. The "3" capability may be important during design verification of the fault-free circuit behavior. On the other hand, if it is known that mis-selection is unimportant or not possible, then the model can be reduced to that shown in Fig. 11.

It would be pointless to introduce into either model a fault whose sole effect would be the generation of a "3" output. For fault simulations "3" outputs are effectively ignored. A fault whose only result is to produce a "3" would be undetectable on a logic simulator.

3.5 Input/output port

Some integrated circuits contain pins which can serve as both input and output ports. Figure 12(a) shows the physical structure of one such pin. IOPIN is the actual connection to the external world, FO represents all fan-out loads from the node, and FI represents all fan-in (tri-state) devices at the node. The modeled structure is shown in Fig. 12(b) where the IOPIN has been divided into separate IN and OUT functions. The D and E variables have been introduced as the control inputs which define the state of the input driver and the FI branch, respectively.

The truth table of Fig. 12(c) defines the relation between D, E, and OUT. Note that the impedance of the input driver (of the test set) is taken to be much less than that of the FI branch. Consequently, whenever the node is driven from an external source ($D = 1$), the logical state of the driver overrides that of FI.

Under the above assumptions the gate-level model for the I/O port can be constructed as shown in Fig. 13. The model has been assigned four faults: the usual output SA0, SA1 faults and two S-OP/S-ON faults associated with the FI branch. Ideally each fan-in branch at the node would have two such faults. However, in the absence of a detailed knowledge of the fan-in network, just two faults have been indicated.

3.6 Tri-state bilateral buses joined by a transmission gate

The characteristics of the simple I/O port described above can be extended to more complex networks. One example is shown in Fig. 14. Two tri-state bilateral buses are connected by a bilateral transmission gate. All the data sources ("talkers") are grouped on the left and all data

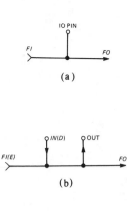

(a)

(b)

D	E	OUT = FO
0	0	4
0	1	FI
1	0	IN
1	1	IN

$$OUT = IN \cdot D + FI \cdot \overline{D} \cdot E + 4 \cdot \overline{D} \cdot \overline{E}$$

(c)

Fig. 12—Input/output port: (a) physical structure, (b) modeled structure, and (c) truth table. IOPIN is the actual connection to the outside world, FO represents all fan-out loads, and FI represents all fan-in (tri-state) devices. D and E define the state of the input driver and the FI branch, respectively. The symbol 4 denotes the previous state of OUT.

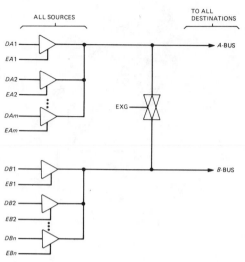

Fig. 14—Two bilateral tri-state buses connected by a transmission gate. All data sources (drivers) are grouped on the left. All data sinks (gate inputs) are to the right.

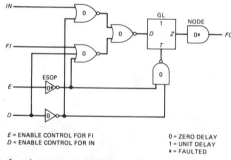

E = ENABLE CONTROL FOR FI
D = ENABLE CONTROL FOR IN

0 = ZERO DELAY
1 = UNIT DELAY
* = FAULTED

Fig. 13—Input/output port model. Only gates marked * are faulted, 0 and 1 denote delays, and D and E are enable controls for IN and FI, respectively. FI = fan-in; FO = fan-out.

sinks ("listeners") on the right. A device that can be both send and receive would be represented once in each group.

The models described previously in this paper have all been independent of each other. Therefore, they can be organized as a library of subnetwork building blocks. Consequently, it would be tempting to model the network of Fig. 14 as an interconnection of three independent models: one for the A-bus, one for the B-bus, and one for the bilateral transmission gate. However, in this instance, that is not possible. A successful model must incorporate features from all three to correctly represent the true bilateral interactions between each bus by way of the transmission gate.

The model for the fault-free behavior of the A-bus output is shown in Fig. 15. The interbus coupling is modeled by means of the EXG·EB AND gate and the B·SB AND gate. For example, if the A-bus driving sources are in the high-impedance state (EA = 0) and the B-bus is in the low-impedance sourcing mode (EB = 1), then when the transmission gate is enabled (EXG = 1), the A-bus output takes the same value as that present on the B-bus. Conversely, information can travel from the A-bus to the B-bus. The model for the B-bus output has not been shown because it is analogous to that of the A-bus: In Fig. 15, wherever the symbol A appears substitute B and vice versa. The fault-free behavior of the bus model as compared to that of the "actual" buses is given in Table III.

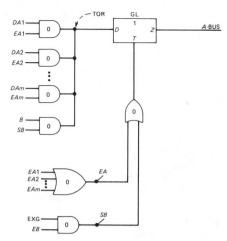

Fig. 15—The A-bus fault-free model. The unknown 3 condition is ignored here. The B-bus model is analogous.

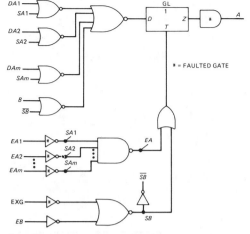

Fig. 16—The A-bus faulted model. Only gates marked * will be faulted by the simulator. Two SA0/SA1 node (pin) faults and $m + 1$ pairs of stuck-open/stuck-on faults have been assigned. The B-bus faulted model is analogous.

Table III — Fault-free behavior of the coupled buses and their model

			Model		Actual Buses	
EXG	EA_i	EB_j	A	B	A	B
0	0	0	4	4	4	4
0	0	1	4	DB_j	4	DB_j
0	1	0	DA_i	4	DA_i	4
0	1	1	DA_i	DB_j	DA_i	DB_j
1	0	0	4	4	*	*
1	0	1	DB_j	DB_j	DB_j	DB_j
1	1	0	DA_i	DA_i	DA_i	DA_i
1	1	1	$DA_i + DB_j$	$DA_i + DB_j$	*	*

*	A	B	A	B
	0	0	0	0
	0	1	3	3
	1	0	3	3
	1	1	1	1
	present		next	

EXG, EA_i, EB_j = enable control inputs
DA_i, DB_j = data inputs
A, B = bus outputs
3 = unknown 0 or 1

One possible faulted model for the A-bus is shown in Fig. 16. For multiple selections among the DAj and B the response is that of a 0-dominant short. The "3" output could be substituted, however. All elements are zero delay except the gated latch. The usual faults have been assigned to the model: two SA0/SA1 classical "pin" faults and $m + 1$ pairs of S-OP/S-ON faults. As before, the faulted model for the B-bus output is obtained by the symbolic interchange of As and Bs.

3.7 The programmable logic array (PLA)

The programmable logic array (PLA) is a simple method for implementing "random" combinational logic networks. An example of a three-variable, three output PLA is pictured in Fig. 17. The circuit is implemented in dynamic "pseudo NMOS."[7] That is, only the pull-up, or precharge, FETs are PMOS; all others are NMOS.

Clock $\Phi1$ precharges the word and bit lines to the 1 state. Next, clock $\Phi2$ causes the input signals x, y, z to propagate to the output terminals $W1$, $W2$, $W3$. (Although the two clock waveforms are essentially in phase, they are applied to PMOS and NMOS FETs, respectively, and the resulting conduction modes are 180° out of phase.)

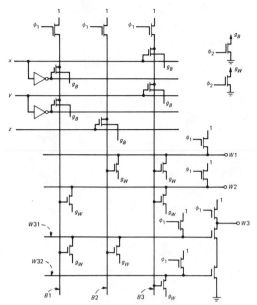

Fig. 17—Dynamic pseudo NMOS programmable logic array (PLA). There are three input variables (x, y, z) and three outputs ($W1$, $W2$, $W3$). Pull-up FETs are PMOS; all others are NMOS.[7]

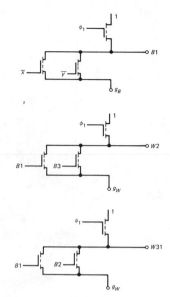

Fig. 18—Subcircuit portions of the PLA of Fig. 17.

The steady-state transfer functions are:

$$B1 = x \cdot y, \quad B2 = \bar{z}, \quad B3 = \bar{x} \cdot \bar{y},$$

$$\overline{W1} = B2 + B3, \quad \overline{W2} = B1 + B3, \quad \overline{W3} = W31 \cdot W32,$$

$$\overline{W31} = B1 + B2, \overline{W32} = B3.$$

Therefore,

$$\overline{W1} = \bar{z} + \bar{x} \cdot \bar{y},$$

$$\overline{W2} = x \cdot y + \bar{x} \cdot \bar{y},$$

$$\overline{W3} = \bar{x} \cdot y \cdot z + x \cdot \bar{y} \cdot z.$$

Models for the example PLA can be constructed by noting that the relation between inputs and bit lines and between bit lines and word lines is essentially that of a dynamic NOR gate. Figure 18 shows several "subcircuit" portions of the PLA. Figure 19(a) gives the model for one typical subcircuit, $W2$. Figure 19(b) gives the model for the more complex $W3$ output. By this method the characteristics of any PLA, including dynamic properties, can be represented as a sum of simpler subcircuit models.

IV. THE GENERAL CASE

The preceding examples are particular illustrations of a more general configuration, shown in Fig. 20. The capacitance implicitly associated with the node F will be in one of four possible states: (*i*) low-impedance 0, (*ii*) low-impedance 1, (*iii*) high-impedance 0, or (*iv*) high-impedance 1. The first two conditions occur whenever one of the four input channels are enabled (conducting). The latter two cases arise when no circuit is enabled and the output is the resultant high-impedance state ($F = 4$).

In terms of the model, the logic state of the network is "transferred" to node F if and only if $T = 1$ where

$$T = \sum_i EX_i \cdot \overline{EXSOP}_i.$$

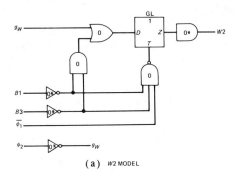

(a) W2 MODEL

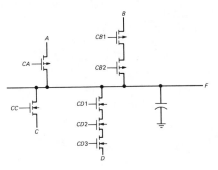

$$T = EA \cdot \overline{EASOP} + EB \cdot \overline{EBSOP} + EC \cdot \overline{ECSOP} + \cdots$$

WHERE $EA = \overline{CA}, EB = \overline{CB1} \cdot \overline{CB2}$
$EC = CC, ED = CD1 \cdot CD2 \cdot CD3$

Fig. 20—The general case: multiple series/parallel combinations driving one node. FETs on the upper side are p-channel; those below are n-channel.

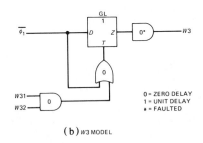

(b) W3 MODEL

0 = ZERO DELAY
1 = UNIT DELAY
* = FAULTED

Fig. 19—PLA subcircuit models. Gates marked * are faulted by the simulator, and 0 and 1 denote delays.

a clear choice, stuck-on logic faults should generally be disregarded. Nodes at which several tri-state elements connect can be assigned the two SA0/SA1 classical faults and one S-OP fault per channel. Fault conditions producing the unknown "3" state should not be modeled. On the

That is, at least one of the input circuits must be enabled (EXj = 1) and that circuit must not be stuck-open, i.e., EXSOPj = 0. Otherwise, $T = 0$ and $F = 4$.

If two channels, A and B, are simultaneously enabled ($A\&B$), then the result is said to be a 0-dominant short if $A\&B = A \cdot B$. For the 1-dominant short, $A\&B = A + B$. These two cases are shown in Figs. 21 and 22, respectively. Of course, if stuck-on faults are ignored entirely, then the network for T is represented by the summation immediately above.

Logic faults are assigned in the following manner. Simple n-input combinational gates are given the usual $n + 2$ stuck-at faults. In addition, one stuck-open fault is associated with each parallel branch of the pull-up/pull-down networks. Stuck-opens in strictly series paths to either VDD or VSS are ignored because of their similarity to SA0/SA1 faults, respectively. Unless the details of circuit technology and design dictate

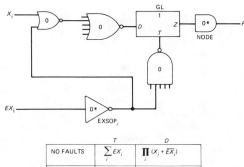

NO FAULTS	$\sum\limits_{i} EX_i$	$\prod\limits_{i} (X_i + \overline{EX_i})$
$EXSOP_j(1)$	$\sum\limits_{i \neq j} EX_i$	$\prod\limits_{i \neq j} (X_i + \overline{EX_i})$
$EXSOP_j(0)$	1	$X_j \cdot \prod\limits_{i \neq j} (X_i + \overline{EX_i})$

Fig. 21—The general case: S-OP and S-ON faults (0-dominant).

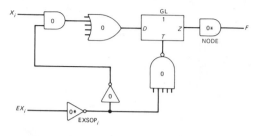

	T	D
NO FAULTS	$\displaystyle\sum_i EX_i$	$\displaystyle\sum_i X_i \cdot EX_i$
$EXSOP_j$ (1)	$\displaystyle\sum_{i \neq j} EX_i$	$\displaystyle\sum_{i \neq j} X_i \cdot EX_i$
$EXSOP_j$ (0)	1	$\displaystyle X_j + \sum_{i \neq j} X_i \cdot EX_i$

Fig. 22—The general case: S-OP and S-ON faults (1-dominant). This is a variant of the model of Fig. 21 except that the S-ON fault is 1-dominant.

REFERENCES

1. "LAMP: Logic Analyzer for Maintenance Planning," B.S.T.J., *53*, No. 8 (October 1974), pp. 1431–1555.
2. T. G. Athanas, "Development of COS/MOS Technology," Solid State Tech., *17*, No. 6 (June 1974), pp. 54–59.
3. H. Rombeek and P. Wilcox, "Interactive Logic Simulation and Test Pattern Development for Digital Circuitry," Electro 76, Paper 26.2, April 1976.
4. R. H. Krambeck, private communication.
5. The first successful demonstration of the FDL capability was performed for the NOR gate faults in Table I, R. E. Strebendt, private communication.
6. The logic symbol was suggested to the author by D. L. Kushler.
7. J. A. Cooper, J. A. Copeland, R. H. Krambeck, D. C. Stanzione, and L. C. Thomas, "A CMOS Microprocessor for Telecommunications Applications," ISSCC 77, Paper THPM 12.3, February 17, 1977.

other hand, simulation models for design verification ("true value" simulation) can include the "3" state as an indication of erroneous tri-state selection as in bus-oriented circuits.

V. SUMMARY

This paper has described a procedure for modeling faults which are a peculiarity of CMOS digital integrated circuits. Furthermore, the resultant methodology was also utilized to provide simulator models for complex MOS dynamic circuit topologies. The models are gate-level in structure and can be adapted for use on essentially any general purpose logic simulator. In addition, the models have been chosen to avoid faults which are artifacts of the model and which do not represent physically likely logic defects. The models have also been structured to preserve the distinction between classical and nonclassical faults. In addition, all models are designed to avoid races and circuit oscillations.

From the examples in this paper, it can be seen that there are a number of choices that can be taken for modeling a given logical function. In addition, a particular function may well be reduced in gate-count from the examples and the "general" realizations shown in this paper. That is, depending upon the selection of characteristics most important to the user, different models will result. In that spirit, the illustrations used above were selected to demonstrate the principles of modeling in a clear, straightforward manner.

A GATE LEVEL MODEL FOR CMOS COMBINATIONAL LOGIC CIRCUITS WITH APPLICATION TO FAULT DETECTION

Sudhakar M. Reddy

Department of Electrical and Computer Engineering
University of Iowa, Iowa City, Iowa 52242

Vishwani D. Agrawal
Sunil K. Jain
AT&T Bell Laboratories
Murray Hill, New Jersey 07974

ABSTRACT - A procedure to derive gate level equivalent circuits for CMOS combinational logic circuits is given. The procedure leads to a model containing AND, OR and NOT gates. Specifically it does not require memory elements as does an earlier model and also uses fewer gates. It is shown that tests for classical stuck-at-0 and stuck-at-1 faults in the equivalent circuit can be used to detect line stuck-at, stuck-open and stuck-on faults in the modeled CMOS circuit.

I. INTRODUCTION

CMOS technology is expected to be a dominant (if not the dominant) technology for VLSI [1]. Several researchers have studied the problems of modeling failures and deriving tests for CMOS logic circuits [2-10]. Classical line stuck-at models are known to be inadequate to model faults occurring in VLSI circuits [2,3]. The class of faults that appear to be essential to model most probable failures in CMOS logic circuits include line stuck-at faults, transistor stuck-open and stuck-on faults, shorts between lines of the logic circuits, and open lines [2-9]. In this paper we derive a gate level logic model to represent combinational logic circuits consisting of an important class of CMOS logic gates.

Our aim is to provide, for a given CMOS combinational logic circuit, an *equivalent* gate level logic circuit, that is less complex than a similar model proposed earlier by Jain and Agrawal [8]. Furthermore, we will establish that tests for faults in the modeled CMOS logic circuits can be readily derived by deriving tests for the equivalent gate level logic circuits.

II. PRELIMINARIES

A CMOS combinational logic circuit is constructed by interconnecting CMOS gates. A block diagram of a CMOS gate is shown in Figure 1 and two example gates are given in Figure 2(a) and 2(b). As illustrated, CMOS gate consists of a network of p-channel FETs (often called load network) and a network of n-channel FETs (often called driver network). Using positive logic, a PFET (NFET) conducts when its gate is at logic 0 (1).

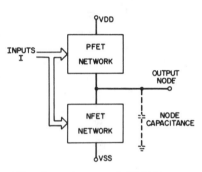

Fig. 1   A general CMOS gate.

Normally the output of a CMOS gate is 1 (0) if and only if the combination of inputs is such that a conducting path from $V_{DD}(V_{SS})$ to the output node is established (by turning on the FETs in the load (driver) network) and no conducting path from $V_{SS}(V_{DD})$ to the output node is established. Most CMOS gates used in a logic circuit are what may be referred to as *fully complementary MOS (FCMOS) gates*. In a FCMOS gate, (i) each gate input is connected to the gate terminals of a PFET and an NFET and (ii) for each input combination a conducting path either in the load or the driver network (but not in both networks) is established such that the output of a fault-free gate is 1 or 0, respectively. Figure 2(a) is an example of a FCMOS gate, while the CMOS gate in Figure 2(b) is not a FCMOS gate (for example when A=1, B=0 the output of the gate in Figure 2(b) is in high impedance state, because a conducting path cannot be established either through the driver or the load network under these input conditions). Gates that are not FCMOS gates are often used as I/O buffers and in busses. *In this paper we will consider combinational logic circuits constructed from FCMOS gates and for this reason, in the sequel whenever we say CMOS gate we mean FCMOS gates.*

It can be noticed that a single CMOS gate can realize all combinational switching functions if we assume variables and their complements are available. Simple gates NAND, NOR, AND, OR and NOT are called *primitive gates* in this paper. Recent published works [6,7,8] have provided the following results:

Reprinted from *Proceedings of the 21st Design Automation Conference,* 1984, pages 504-509. Copyright © 1984 by The Institute of Electrical and Electronics Engineers, Inc. All rights reserved.

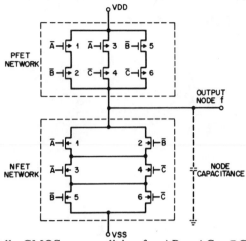

(a) A fully CMOS gate realizing f = AB + AC + BC.

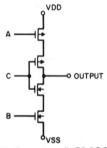

(b) A "non-true" CMOS gate.

Fig. 2 Examples of CMOS gates.

(i) test procedures to detect single line stuck-at and single FET stuck-open or stuck-on faults in CMOS combinational logic circuits consisting of primitive gates [6],

(ii) a graph model for CMOS combinational logic circuits to derive test procedures to detect single FET stuck-open and stuck-on faults [7], and

(iii) a method to derive a gate level equivalent circuit model for a class of CMOS combinational logic circuits and procedures to derive tests for the faults considered in (i) above [8].

The results in [6] lack generality. The procedure in [7] requires complex analysis and is probably impractical for large circuits. The gate level model in [8] is applicable only to series-parallel CMOS gates and has the further disadvantage that the equivalent circuit has twice as many gates as needed and a memory element per gate that is not needed (this will be shown in the next section). Our aim, in this paper, is to provide a simpler gate level equivalent circuit and investigate the problem of detection of single line stuck-at and FET stuck-open or stuck-on faults.

III. GATE LEVEL EQUIVALENT CIRCUIT

In this section we give a procedure to derive a gate level equivalent circuit for a given combinational CMOS logic circuit consisting of FCMOS gates. The gate level

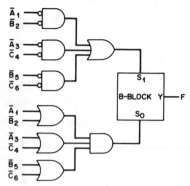

(a) Logic equivalent. Inputs are subscripted by the number of the corresponding FET in the modeled circuit.

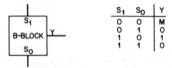

(b) Truth table of B-block. M represents the high impedance state. For $S_1 = S_0 = 1$, $Y = 0$ represents 0 as the dominating logic.

Fig. 3 Equivalent circuit of the CMOS gate in Fig. 2(a).

circuit to be developed will contain NOT, AND and OR gates only. This procedure can be viewed as an augmentation and refinement to the procedure given by Jain and Agrawal [8]. For this reason a brief review of the procedure in [8] is given next.

The derivation of the model of a CMOS combinational logic circuit using the procedure given by Jain and Agrawal [8] requires that:

(i) each CMOS gate in the circuit be replaced by a network consisting of a B block (the memory element shown in Figure 3(b)) driven by two networks constructed from AND, OR, NOT gates, and

(ii) the gate networks driving the S_1 (S_0) input of the B block are obtained by iteratively replacing series connections of PFETs (NFETs) by AND gates and parallel connections of PFETs (NFETs) by OR gates and finally applying the inputs to PFETs (NFETs) as inputs to the gate network driving S_1 (S_0) input through inverters (straight connections).

This procedure is applied to the circuit of Figure 2(a) for obtaining the circuit of Figure 3(a). Notice that the S_1 (S_0) input of the B block takes the value of 1 whenever the combination of inputs is such that a conducting path from V_{DD} (V_{SS}) to the output node occurs. The truth table for B block indicates the logic operation occurring at the output node of the gate. When the input combination does not create a conducting path from V_{DD} or V_{SS} to the output node, then $S_1 = S_0 = 0$ and the truth table indicates that the output is M or memory state, which implies that the

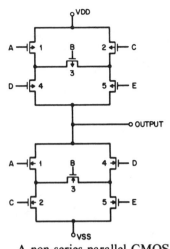

Fig. 4   A non-series-parallel CMOS gate.

output node is in high impedance state and the logic value at the output node is the same as the output value due to the previous input. The reason for indicating the memory state rather than high impedance is that, when the output of a gate is driven to a high impedance state, the previous value of the output is retained by the capacitor at the output node.

It should be pointed that the procedure proposed in [8] and described above, models only series-parallel type of gates. For example the CMOS gate of Figure 4 cannot be modeled by straight forward application of the procedure in [8]. This is due to FETs numbered 3 in Figure 4. This deficiency and the need for B block of the equivalent model are removed in the procedure given here. Furthermore, the proposed procedure will use half as many gates as the model derived by the procedure in [8]. The procedure to derive the equivalent circuit uses only the PFET or load network of the CMOS gate and has two steps; in Step 1 each gate of the given CMOS logic circuit is reduced to a special irreducible form and all paths between a pair of nodes in this irreducible form are determined and in Step 2 the procedure of [8] is applied to each element in the reduced network and the equivalent circuit is derived from these elemental circuits and the paths generated in Step 1. The procedures are formally stated next and are illustrated by an example.

Step 1:   Apply procedure REDUCE, given below, to the PFET network of each gate of the given CMOS combinational logic circuit.

PROCEDURE REDUCE:

1. Associate a unique index (number) with each PFET in the PFET network.

2. Replace each series connection of PFETs by a single PFET and associate a set of indices with it. This set of indices is the union of the sets of indices of the replaced FETs.

3. Replace each parallel connection of PFET with a single PFET. The index set of the new PFET is derived as in step 2.

4. Repeat (2) and (3) until no reduction is possible.

5. Label V_{DD} node V and the output node 0. Identify and label all nodes of the reduced network by positive integers and the FETs by letters. (The reduced network can be regarded as a graph with PFETs as the edges.)

6. Find all loop-free paths between nodes V (V_{DD}) and 0 (output). Express these paths as a product (AND) of the labels of the PFETs in the paths.

7. Write a gate function G_f as a sum of products expression, where the products are the products associated with each path between V and 0.

Step 2:   Apply Procedure EQUIVALENT to the reduced networks obtained in (5) of Procedure REDUCE.

PROCEDURE EQUIVALENT:

(i)   For each PFET, say P, in the reduced network of each gate, derive, by the procedure in [8] (only step (ii) of this procedure for PFET network is to be applied), the equivalent circuit of the PFET network represented by the index set of P and label the output of the equivalent circuit by P.

(ii)   Using AND gates and one OR gate connect the outputs of the equivalent circuits derived in (i) to realize the gate function G_f obtained in (7) of Procedure REDUCE.

The derivation of equivalent circuit is illustrated by considering the gate of Figure 5. Note that in Figure 5 only the PFET network of the CMOS gate is given. The reduced network, the paths from V_{DD} to output node and the gate function obtained by applying Procedure REDUCE to the gate of Figure 5 are given in Figure 6. The equivalent circuits derived by procedures in [8] for each PFET in Figure 6 and given in Figure 7. The complete equivalent circuit of the CMOS gate in Figure 5 is given in Figure 8.

The proof that steps 1 and 2 of the procedure given above yield a logic circuit that is *functionally equivalent* to the modeled CMOS logic circuit follows. The output of the modeled CMOS gate is a one if and only if there is a conducting path through the load network (PFET network) from V_{DD} to output. This is true if and only if there is a conducting path in the reduced network obtained at (5) of Procedure REDUCE. Since G_f contains AND terms for all paths in the reduced network, for every

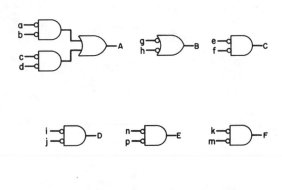

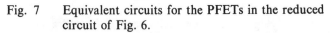

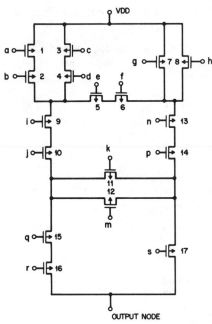

Fig. 5   PFET network of a CMOS gate.

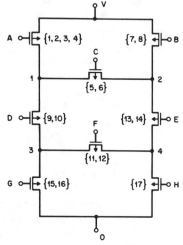

Fig. 6   Reduced network of the CMOS gate of Fig. 5. Paths from V to O are V13O, V134O, V124O, V12430, V24O, V2430, V2130, V21340. G_f = ADG + ADFH + ACEH + ACEFG + BEH + BEFG + BCDG + BCDFH.

conducting path the corresponding AND gate in G_f takes the value 1 forcing the output of the equivalent circuit to take the value of 1. Similarly, for inputs which produce a 0 output, no conducting PFET paths are created between V_{DD} and the output node of the modeled CMOS gate. This implies that for such inputs at least one input to each AND gate in the network realizing G_f is 0 and hence G_f takes the value 0.

The next question to be asked is for line stuck-at, FET stuck-open and FET stuck-on faults in the modeled CMOS circuit, what are the corresponding faults in the equivalent circuit? It is known that to detect FET stuck-open faults two pattern tests are needed [3-9]. First let us formally define the faults (it is assumed that the reader is familiar with classical line stuck-at-0 and stuck-at-1 faults [2]).

Fig. 7   Equivalent circuits for the PFETs in the reduced circuit of Fig. 6.

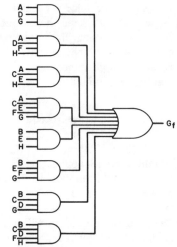

Fig. 8   Logic circuit realizing the function of G_f of the reduced circuit in Fig. 6. The inputs A through H are obtained in Fig. 7.

Definition 1:   A *single stuck-open fault* in a CMOS logic gate G is any failure that permanently leaves a series connection of FETs in G in a non-conducting state.

Definition 2:   A *single stuck-open fault* in a CMOS logic circuit is a failure that causes a stuck-open fault in at most one gate in the circuit.

Definition 3:   A *single stuck-on-fault* in a CMOS logic gate G is any failure that permanently leaves a FET in G in a conducting state.

Definition 4:   A *single stuck-on fault* in a CMOS logic circuit is a failure that causes a stuck-on fault in at most one gate in the circuit.

Note that if an input to a CMOS gate is stuck-at-0 (1) then it is equivalent to both a PFET stuck-on and an NFET stuck-open simultaneously [7]. However, the equivalent circuit in that paper was derived using only the load or PFET network of FCMOS gates. Therefore, we need to show that the tests to detect line stuck-at faults as well as the stuck-open and stuck-on faults in the NFET network of the modeled CMOS gate can be derived by considering faults in the equivalent circuit. Since our equivalent circuit is a gate network, clearly we need to model the faults by equivalent stuck-at-0 and stuck-at-1 faults. We provide a sketch of the proof that tests for faults in the modeled CMOS circuit can be derived by deriving tests for line stuck-at faults in the equivalent circuit.

Let E_G be the equivalent circuit, derived by the procedure given above, of a CMOS gate G in the given CMOS network N and let E_N be the equivalent network for N. As indicated earlier two pattern tests are required to detect stuck-open faults. The first part of the two-pattern test is an initializing input that initializes the output of the faulty gate to a known value. The second input pattern in the two pattern test is the test input that will force the output of the faulty gate to an erroneous value (because of the initialized output) and simultaneously propagate the effect of this erroneous value to an observable output (actually under the test the output of the faulty gate in the modeled CMOS circuit goes into an high impedance state). In the gate equivalent circuit derived by the procedure given in this paper the initializing input should make the output of E_G, under the test input among the two patterns, complement of the output of E_G when it is fault-free. We assume that such initializing inputs are applied prior to *every test* for the faults in the equivalent circuit E_N. With this assumption (incidently this assumption does not necessarily lead to longer overall test lengths, as explained later) we need only consider the problem of generation of the tests.

The first observation that can be made is that since the equivalent circuit is functionally equivalent to the modeled circuit, on a gate by gate basis, a test, say T, that will sensitize a fault to the output of a faulty gate equivalent circuit, say E_G, and propagate it to an observable output in the complete equivalent circuit, will also be a test for every fault in the modeled FCMOS circuit, for which it can be shown that the test T does sensitize it to the output of the modeled gate G. However, to derive a complete test set for the modeled CMOS circuit, it is not necessary to generate tests for stuck-at faults on all lines in the equivalent circuit. The "check points" [6,11] for which tests need to be derived are formally given below.

Theorem 1: If a test set T detects all single stuck-at-0 and stuck-at-1 faults on the external inputs, the outputs (and their fanout branches) of the gates realizing G_f in E_N and the primary inputs to the network E_N, then T together with appropriate initializing inputs detects all single stuck-at-0, stuck-at-1, stuck-open faults in the modeled CMOS combinational logic network N.

The check points of the equivalent circuit of Figure 8 are indicated by marking with X in Figure 9. The tests for E_N can be found by any method available to detect line stuck-at faults in E_N [11].

The correspondence between the faults in the modeled circuit N and the model E_N is given in Theorem 2.

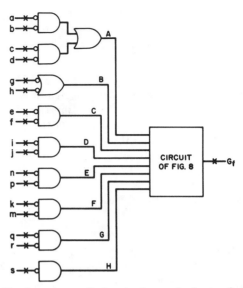

Fig. 9   Check points of the logic equivalent of the CMOS gate of Fig. 5.

Theorem 2: Let I be an input to a first level gate of an equivalent circuit E_G in E_N of a FCMOS gate G in N and Z be its output. The tests for stuck-at-0(1) on Z and its fan-out branches are tests for stuck-at-0(1) on the output of the modeled gate and its fan-out branches. A test to detect stuck-at-0(1) on I in E_N is a test to detect stuck-at-0(1) on the line corresponding to I in N, stuck-open fault on the NFET(PFET) and stuck-on fault on the PFET(NFET) in N, whose device gates are connected to the line corresponding to I in N.

A point should be made about stuck-on faults. A test to detect a stuck-on fault will create, in the presence of the fault, conducting paths, simultaneously, from V_{DD} and V_{SS} to the output node. That is, *a conducting path between V_{DD} and V_{SS} will be created.* the logic value at the output of the faulty gate would then depend on the relative resistances of the conducting paths to V_{DD} and V_{SS} from the output node. It may then be necessary to monitor the steady state supply current to detect the fault.

Earlier it was shown that tests for stuck-open faults may be invalidated by delays in the circuit under test [8,12]. Procedures to derive robust tests that will remain valid in the presence of arbitrary delays in the circuit under test are given in [10].

IV. CONCLUSIONS

In this paper we have given a gate level model, for CMOS combinational logic circuits constructed out of FCMOS gates. For circuits containing CMOS gates that are not fully complementary, the non-FCMOS gates could be modeled by the procedures given earlier in [8]. We earlier noted that assuming that a proper initializing input is added to every test might mean longer than necessary test lengths. However by cleverly sequencing tests one can reduce the overall test lengths (i.e. by obtaining initialization through tests for other faults). This approach is well exploited in [6] and similar procedures can be adopted for the equivalent circuit given in this paper.

It is necessary to apply Procedure REDUCE only to gates that are not series parallel. Non-series-parallel gates are often used to reduce the number of FETs. Classic examples of such circuits are the circuits that realize all symmetric functions [13].

Acknowledgment - The research of S. M. Reddy was supported in part by the U.S. Army Research Office Contract No. DAAG29-84-K-0044.

REFERENCES

[1] D. L. Wollesen, "CMOS LSI - The Computer Component Process for the 80's", *IEEE Computer*, pp. 59-62, February 1980.

[2] J. Galiay, Y. Crouzet and M. Vergniault, "Physical Versus Logical Fault Models in MOS LSI Circuits: Impact on their Testability", *IEEE Trans. Comp.*, vol. C-29, pp. 527-531, June 1980.

[3] R. L. Wadsack, "Fault Modeling and Logic Simulation of CMOS and MOS Integrated Circuits", *Bell Syst. Tech. J.*, vol. 57, pp. 1449-1474, May-June 1978.

[4] Y. M. El-Ziq, "Automatic Test Generation for Stuck-Open Faults in CMOS VLSI", *Proceedings of the Eighteenth Design Automation Conference*, Nashville, TN, June 1981, pp. 347-354.

[5] Y. M. El-Ziq and R. J. Cloutier, "Functional-Level Test Generation for Stuck-Open Faults in CMOS VLSI", *International Test Conference*, Philadelphia, PA, October 1981, pp. 536-546.

[6] R. Chandramouli, "On Testing Stuck-Open Faults", *International Fault-Tolerant Computing Symposium*, Milano, Italy, June 28-30, 1983.

[7] K. W. Chiang and Z. G. Vranesic, "On Fault Detection in CMOS Logic Networks", *Proceedings of the Twentieth Design Automation Conference*, Miami Beach, FL, June 1983, pp. 50-56.

[8] S. K. Jain and V. D. Agrawal, "Test Generation for MOS Circuits Using D-Algorithm", *Proceedings of the Twentieth Design Automation Conference*, Miami Beach, FL, June 1983, pp. 64-70.

[9] E. J. McCluskey and S. Borzorgui-Nesbat, "Design for Autonomous Test", *IEEE Trans. on Comp.*, vol. C-30, pp. 866-874, November 1981.

[10] S. M. Reddy, M. K. Reddy and V. D. Agrawal, "Robust Tests for Stuck-Open Faults in CMOS Combinational Logic Circuits", *Fourteenth International Fault-Tolerant Computing Symposium*, Kissimmee, Florida, June 20-22, 1984.

[11] M. A. Breuer and A. D. Friedman, *Diagnosis and Reliable Resign of Digital Systems*," Rockville, MD: Computer Science Press, 1976.

[12] S. M. Reddy, M. K. Reddy, and J. G. Kuhl, "On testable design for CMOS logic circuits," *International Test Conference*, Philadelphia, PA, October 1983, *Digest of papers,* pp. 435-445.

[13] Z. Kohavi, "*Switching and Finite Automata Theory*", New York: McGraw Hill, 1970.

Inductive Fault Analysis of MOS Integrated Circuits

John P. Shen, W. Maly and F. Joel Ferguson
Carnegie-Mellon University

Inductive Fault Analysis (IFA) is a systematic procedure to predict all the faults that are likely to occur in a MOS integrated circuit or subcircuit. The three major steps of the IFA procedure are: (1) generation of physical defects using statistical data from the fabrication process; (2) extraction of circuit-level faults caused by these defects; and (3) classification of fault types and ranking of faults based on their likelihood of occurrence.

Hence, given the layout of an IC, a fault model and a ranked fault list can be automatically generated which take into account the technology, layout, and process characteristics. The IFA procedure is illustrated by its application to an example circuit. The results from this sample led to some very interesting observations regarding nonclassical faults.

The current difficulty of testing VLSI circuits can be attributed to the tremendous increase of chip complexity and the inappropriateness of traditional models. With increased chip complexity, both test generation and test evaluation become very cumbersome, and at times even computationally infeasible.

Both the suitability and effectiveness of the traditional fault model and associated testing techniques for contemporary VLSI technologies is unclear. Most of the existing testing methodologies and associated software tools were originally developed for testing printed-circuit boards containing TTL SSI/MSI components. Most of the traditional and existing techniques share the following three characteristics.

Single-level or "flat" approach: Most of the existing testing techniques assume a logic gate-level model. Although MSI-level macros are often used in logic simulators, most systematic test generation algorithms require a gate-level representation.

Technology-independent fault model: Regardless of the technology used in the actual implementation, the logical line stuck-at-0/1 fault model is frequently used. In fact, the single line stuck-at fault model is the most widely used fault model.

Unranked fault list: The fault list used for test generation and fault simulation is usually unranked. In other words, the relative importance of different faults is not emphasized.

Reprinted from *IEEE Design & Test of Computers,* Volume 2, Number 12, December 1985, pages 13-26. Copyright © 1985 by The Institute of Electrical and Electronics Engineers, Inc. All rights reserved.

December 1985

EH0278-2/88/0000/0053$01.00 © 1985 IEEE

A new test methodology

It is our belief that these three characteristics are incompatible with the current technology and that a new methodology and associated software tools must be developed for testing contemporary MOS VLSI circuits. Similar to current design methodologies, any new testing methodology should involve a multiple-level or hierarchical approach to ease the complexity burden. Different techniques can be used and may even be required at different levels. At the lowest level, an effective testing approach must consider technology and manufacturing issues.

First, these issues should influence the formulation of a new fault model, which is the focus of this article. The physical reasons which cause faults on PCBs containing TTL SSI/MSI components and those causing faults in MOS VLSI circuit chips are quite different. For VLSI circuit testing, the fault model should be based on the physical defects caused by random process instabilities and contaminations present during the IC fabrication process. This fault model should be technology- and even layout-dependent because certain fault mechanisms may be more or less likely in different technologies and/or with different layouts.

Since faulty chips are usually not repaired, acceptance testing of IC chips during manufacturing is a pass/fail test to determine whether a chip is fault free or not. Hence the detection of more than one fault on a chip and the determination of the location of a fault are superfluous, and the testing of a chip can be terminated upon the detection of any fault. Given these observations, it appears that the testing time and cost can be reduced and the testing effectiveness can be improved if a ranked list of faults can be used, with the most likely to occur faults being tested first and the least likely to occur faults tested last.

A number of articles have been published documenting empirical observations of various nonclassical fault types and presenting clever ways of testing for these faults.[1-4] However, a systematic approach to generate and predict, prior to fabrication, both classical and nonclassical faults that are likely to occur in a given circuit does not exist.

This article presents an approach which, when given a circuit layout, will automatically generate a list of faults based on the probable physical defects. A preliminary description of this approach has been presented.[5] Here an extended and refined version of this approach is described in detail.

The probable physical defects are generated using known statistical information about defects, which can be obtained from an actual fabrication line.[6,7] The circuit-level faulty behaviors caused by these defects are extracted using a defect-to-fault translation program. These extracted faults can be ranked according to their likelihood of occurrence. The resultant ranked fault list can then be used to assess the actual effectiveness of test sets generated using the classical fault model, and to guide the generation of new and more effective test sets. An eventual goal is to help generate test sets which have very good coverage of faults that are physically likely to occur rather than faults that are based on traditional, and less realistic, models.

In this article, we present an approach called Inductive Fault Analysis (IFA). We then outline the major steps involved in generating physical defects, how these defects are translated to circuit-level faults, and how these faults are then classified and ranked to generate a ranked fault list. This approach is then applied to an example circuit, with substantial details provided to clearly illustrate the IFA approach. Some interesting observations are made based on the results obtained for this example circuit.

IFA—a systematic approach

IFA is a systematic approach to generate all the faults that are likely to occur in a specific IC using the technology and layout information. Faults in a VLSI circuit are manifestations of physical defects caused by process instabilities and contaminations during the IC fabrication process. Hence the formulation of an accurate fault model for a given circuit must involve identifying probable physical defects, simulating their effects on the circuit behavior, and grouping the faulty behaviors into a fault list.

The percentage of physical defects which cause a particular fault is used to determine the relative likelihood of occurrence of that fault. The faults can then be ranked based on their likelihood of occurrence. A large sample of physical defects may be needed to ensure the accuracy of the ranked fault list.

IFA departs from the traditional approach of making assumptions about faults at the logical level—gate input/output stuck-at-0/1, for example—by starting with particular physical defects and then using them to extract the circuit- or logical-level fault model without making any assumptions at the higher levels. Essentially, a higher-level fault model is formulated based on conclusions drawn from examining particular defects at the lower level; hence the word "inductive." Furthermore, the resultant fault model is not a subjective generalization based on empirically observed faults which may be peculiar to a particular technology and/or a particular fabrication line.

The IFA approach as presented here is intended for the analysis of IC macros, or subcircuits, containing up to several thousand devices. A larger circuit can be easily partitioned into smaller pieces and analyzed separately. The resultant fault lists can be subsequently linked and merged. This analysis technique is based on the physical structure of a circuit and concerns the connectivity of various conducting, semiconducting and insulating regions. Hence, it is quite general and can be applied to the analysis of many types of ICs. For example, this approach can be used to characterize a standard-cell library by generating a specific fault list for each library macro.

Physical defects. Physical defects can be loosely divided into two groups: those that affect multiple ICs across a relatively large (global) area of the wafer and those that affect a relatively small (local) area of an IC. Examples of global defects include cracks or scratches in the material, photolithographic mask misalignments, line dislocations, and major fabrication process control errors. These defects usually have global and prominent effects on the circuit behavior and can be easily detected early in the manufacturing process. Furthermore, in a finely tuned and mature fabrication line, major process control errors, and hence global defects, can be easily detected and minimized. For the above reasons, localized *spot* or *point defects* are the primary targets for fabrication testing.

Point defects can be classified into three categories: silicon substrate inhomogeneities, local surface contaminations, and photolithography-related point defects.[8] The origin of defects from each of these categories involves distinct, usually complicated and frequently uncontrollable processes. Despite the lack of basic knowledge, some experimental results are available[6,8] and are used in this work.

Complete and accurate physical modeling of point defects inherent in the fabrication process is difficult. However, it is believed that the behavior of the most important point defects can be accurately characterized using a statistical approach based on data obtained from actual experiments. This characterization consists of the density of defects per unit area and the probability density function of the defect sizes.[6,7]

Levels of abstraction. To develop a fault modeling approach which makes use of process-related information, physical mechanisms must be viewed at different levels of abstraction. For example, a point defect caused by a pinhole in the SiO_2 can be viewed as an open region in the SiO_2 layer, or a contact between two conducting layers, or a short between two wires at the circuit level, or possibly a stuck-at-1 fault at

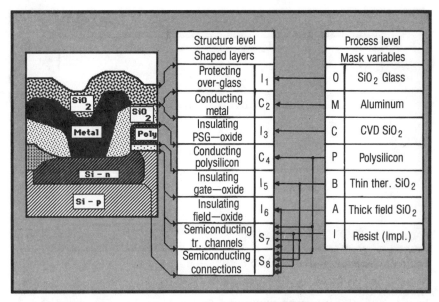

Figure 1. Shaped layers and mask variables for an NMOS technology.

the logical level. Four levels of abstraction are identified and used in this work: (1) process level, (2) structure level, (3) circuit level, and (4) logical level.

A *layer* in an IC is a slice of solid-state surface formed by chemical or thermal treatments. Each layer can be conducting, semiconducting, or insulating. A *technology* can be defined as a sequence of process steps which creates a set of layers on the surface of the substrate. In this sequence of process steps, each layer can be "shaped" by a mask (or a combination of a few masks) to produce regions of different physical properties. For example, a conducting layer can contain insulating regions, that is, regions with the conducting material removed. Similarly, an insulating layer can be shaped to contain conducting regions, or windows. These regions become vertical conducting paths between two conducting layers adjacent to the insulating layer.

Of primary concern at the process level are the masks used for a particular technology. In analyzing each point defect, typically only a small localized region or spot is examined. When considering only a particular spot, each mask can be characterized by a binary *mask variable*. The mask variable is assigned the 0 or the 1 value depending on whether the mask is transparent or opaque in that spot.

At the structure level, the physical stacking of the shaped layers produced by a technology is of interest. At this level, the physical adjacency and topological relationships between various regions of various layers are of primary importance. At the structure level, a mask variable can represent the presence or absence of a certain material in a particular layer. The stacking of n-shaped layers at a particular spot, or a "vertical core sample" of an IC structure, can be characterized by a binary n-tuple representing the values of the n mask variables responsible for producing the stacking at that spot.

This binary n-tuple is called the *mask vector* at that spot, and indicates the presence and absence of certain material at each of the shaped layers. Figure 1 uses the cross-section of an NMOS transistor to illustrate the eight shaped layers formed by the seven mask variables. The correspondence between the shaped layers and the mask variables is not necessarily one-to-one. The reason being that one mask can be used to affect the shaping of more than one layer and a shaped layer may require more than one mask for shaping. This is illustrated by the directed edges between the shaped layers and the mask variables in Figure 1.

The circuit level deals with the physics of devices resulting from the local combination of IC structure

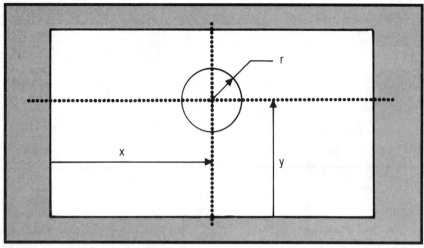

Figure 2. Generation of a random defect.

layers, and the interconnection of these devices. This interconnection can be represented by a circuit schematic. At this level the parameters of interest are voltages and currents. At the logical level, the behavior of the circuit is modeled as a logical function and represented by a logic schematic consisting of interconnected logic gates.

The IFA scenario. Essentially, the IFA procedure first generates defects at the process level by changing the value of one of the mask variables at a localized spot. This is followed by interpreting the impact of this change at the structure level and translating this impact to the circuit or logical level of abstraction. Finally, the circuit-level faults are grouped and ranked. The three major steps of the procedure are:

(1) Defect generation and analysis: Given an IC layout, a list of point defects is generated using statistical information obtained from the fabrication process or from published literature.[6,9] The defects are screened for size and location significance. A second screening is performed to identify the electrically significant defects; insignificant defects are discarded.

(2) Defect-to-fault translation: Each of the significant defects is then analyzed and the circuit-level faulty behavior caused by the defect is extracted. The extracted faulty behaviors constitute the primitive fault list. The effects of the faults in the primitive

fault list are then interpreted to produce the circuit-level fault list.

(3) Fault classification and ranking: The circuit faults are grouped and classified into circuit fault types. The relative likelihood of occurrence of each fault in the list can then be estimated to produce a ranked fault list.

Hence, given a layout of an IC, using IFA, a fault model and a ranking of the faults can be automatically generated which take into account the technology, layout, and process characteristics.

Defect generation and analysis

At each of the levels of abstraction, defects can be understood in different ways. Each point defect is generated at the process level and involves the changing of the value of a mask variable in the mask vector of a particular spot. At the structure level, a point defect can be defined as any entity or local feature in a structure layer which is not defined in the nominal artwork, and is a result of differences between the nominal artwork description and the actual artwork in the silicon (the actual stacking of shaped layers, for example).

Statistical defect generation. As stated earlier, point defects can be accurately characterized using a statistical approach based on data obtained from actual experiments.[6] This char-

acterization consists of two attributes, namely the density of defects per unit area and the probability density function of the defect sizes.

The first step of the IFA procedure involves the generation of defects. Only single defects are considered. Defects are generated randomly using the statistical characterization of defects. Present implementation of the random defect generator assumes that defects distribute themselves uniformly over an IC. The shape of the defects can be assumed to be round or square. Defects involving each mask variable are generated, placed, interpreted and translated independently. This allows different defect statistics to be used in dealing with defects involving different mask variables and in different layers.

A point defect in a layer is interpreted as a small region of extra or missing material which corresponds to changing a mask variable from 0 to 1 or from 1 to 0. For example, if the polysilicon layer is being considered, then a point defect can indicate either a spot of extra polysilicon or a spot of missing polysilicon. Hence, a technology with n mask variables will have $2n$ defect types, consisting of extra and missing material of each mask variable. The number of defects generated for each type can be varied based on available statistics. In the current implementation of the defect generator, the same number of defects is generated for each of the $2n$ defect types.

Any available probability density function, whether theoretical or empirical, of defect radii can be used. Hence the defect generator can be customized for a particular fabrication line if the defect statistics for that line are available. Each time the procedure is called, it will return three randomly generated numbers: x and y, the coordinates of the center of the defect, and r, the radius of the defect. These three numbers are generated using the appropriate probability density functions, as illustrated in Figure 2.

Size and location significance. In extracting the effects of a physical defect from the structure level to the circuit level, a procedure is needed to first determine whether a given defect will have any effect at the higher level. For example, an opaque spot in the window of the implant mask used to create a depletion mode transistor on an NMOS chip is a defect at the processing level, but it may or may not have any effect on the circuit level. This depends on the location of the defect and its size.

Figure 3a illustrates a small point defect in the implant window of a depletion mode MOS transistor which will not have any significant electrical effect at the circuit level because of its size and location. On the other hand, this is not true for the point defect of Figure 3b. Hence, the filtering out of defects that are too small to produce any significant effect at the higher level is appropriate. Different threshold values can be used for filtering out undersized defects in different layers.

In addition to size, the location of a defect is also important in determining its significance at a higher level. Figure 4 illustrates how a missing element of a polysilicon path may or may not have any significant effect at the circuit level. Figures 4b and 4c depict spots of missing polysilicon in the gate of the MOS transistor which have no real significant effect on the circuit-level behavior. However, the missing polysilicon defect of Figure 4d will have a significant effect.

There are other examples involving the issue of location significance. Many defects can be shown not to affect the operation of the circuit by simply examining the location of the defect in the layer of interest. For instance, a defect which simulates a dust particle on a photolithographic mask may fall on an opaque region of the mask. This would not change the image transferred to the photoresist so the structure of the IC and certainly the circuit behavior would be unchanged. Hence a defect which simulates a dust particle must obscure some transparent region of the mask. Therefore, other than the filtering out of the undersized defects, many defects can be disregarded because they produce

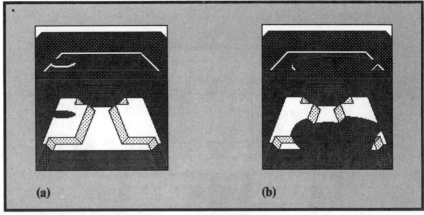

Figure 3. Implant mask defects: (a) has no significant electrical effect; (b) has significant electrical effect.

no significant effect at the structure level.

Electrical significance. A significant defect at the structure level may or may not be significant, in the electrical sense, at the circuit level. The regions that are adjacent to the defect must be considered. For example, a speck of dust on the oxide mask creating a pinhole in the oxide layer is an apparent defect at the structure level, but it has no effect at the circuit level if there are no conducting regions above the pinhole to create an electrical short.

Our methodology to determine whether a given structure-level defect

will have any electrical significance can be illustrated using a polysilicon-gate n-channel MOS technology. The cross-section of an enhancement mode transistor fabricated in this technology, and the associated shaped layers and mask variables have already been depicted in Figure 1. At the structure level, eight shaped layers are defined. Four of them are insulating layers, two are conducting layers and two are semiconducting layers.

Note that in this typical polysilicon-gate n-channel MOS technology, the eight structure layers are created using seven mask variables, as shown in Figure 1. These seven mask variables

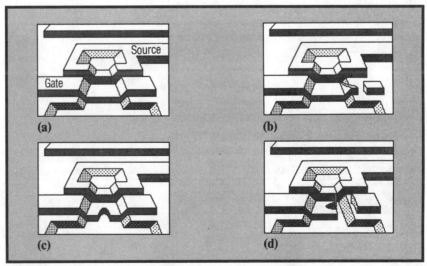

Figure 4. (a) Defect-free poly path; (b) insignificant missing poly; (c) insignificant missing poly; (d) significant missing poly.

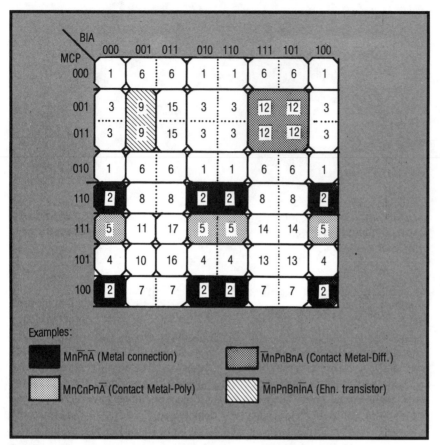

Examples:

■ MnP̄nĀ (Metal connection)   ▨ M̄nPnBnA (Contact Metal-Diff.)

▨ MnCnP̄nĀ (Contact Metal-Poly)   ▨ M̄nPnBnĪnA (Ehn. transistor)

Figure 5. Electrically equivalent classes for an NMOS technology.

are: over-glass (O), metal (M), contact (C), polysilicon (P), buried contact (B), implant (I), and diffusion or active region (A). The relationship between the shaped layers and the mask variables can be represented using Boolean functions. Each shaped layer can be represented as a Boolean func-

tion of the mask variables. Details of this representation have been presented elsewhere.[5]

In considering the local electrical behavior, the stacking of the shaped layers at that localized spot is important. In other words, the mask vector of a localized spot on the IC can be

used to determine the local electrical behavior. Disregarding the over-glass mask variable, which has no impact on the electrical behavior, there are six mask variables of interest, namely M, C, P, B, I, and A. Given these six binary variables, there are 2^6, or 64 possible combinations. Hence, there are 64 different ways of stacking the shaped layers (or 64 different stackings of shaped layers). However, the 64 different stackings do not all produce different electrical behaviors. There are fewer than 64 distinct electrical behaviors which can result.

Two different stackings, or mask vectors, are considered electrically equivalent if they imply the same electrical devices connected in the same manner. All the electrically equivalent classes can be found by examining the electrical meaning of each of the 64 stackings. It has been found that the polysilicon-gate n-channel MOS technology considered here has exactly 17 different electrically equivalent classes.

The 64 stackings resulting from the 64 combinations of the six mask variables can be represented using a six-variable Karnaugh map. Each minterm or entry in the K-map, representing one of the 64 combinations, is assigned to one of the equivalence classes. The 17 electrically equivalent classes are illustrated in Figure 5, using the K-map representation. In this K-map, the 64 minterms are partitioned into 17 distinct groups or equivalence classes. For example, class 9, consisting of the two minterms or mask vectors $<MCPBIA> = \{<001001>$ and $<011001>\}$, actually represents the possible stackings of an enhancement mode transistor.

The introduction of a defect at the structure level essentially changes the stacking of a local spot from one mask vector to another mask vector. If the resultant mask vector belongs to the same equivalence class as the original mask vector, then the defect has no electrical effect on the circuit behavior. Only those defects which cause the crossing of the equivalence class boundaries need to be further considered. If a point defect is large enough to affect an area covering multiple

```
                    Statistical          Random-
                    data from    ───▶    defect
                    fabrication          generator
                                            │
                                            ▼ <x,y,r>
                                         Size and
                                         location
                                         significance
                                            │
                                            ▼
    K-map of                             Electrical          Significant
    elec. equiv.  ─────────────────▶    significance  ───▶   defects      ───▶
    classes
```

Figure 6. The defect generation and screening procedure.

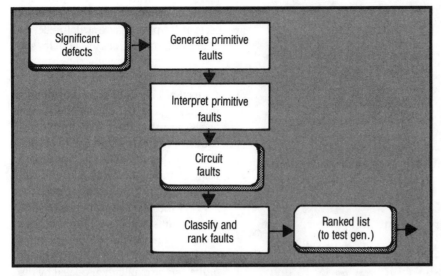

Figure 7. Fault extraction and classification procedure.

mask vectors, then all of the affected mask vectors must be considered.

Similar K-maps characterizing electrically equivalent classes for other MOS technologies can be obtained using the same approach. We have developed such K-maps for a complex silicon-gate CMOS technology.[10] For this technology, 10 mask variables are needed, resulting in a total of 2^{10} possible mask vectors. We found, however, that these 2^{10} combinations can be grouped into only 35 electrically equivalent classes. It is evident that the determination of electrical significance can be performed using these K-maps in conjunction with a table look-up approach.

Figure 6 summarizes this defect generation and screening procedure. The output from this major step is a list of defects, called *significant defects*, which can produce significant electrical effects at the circuit level. The list of significant defects becomes the input to the software program implementing the next major step, namely defect-to-fault translation, or fault extraction.

Fault extraction, classification and ranking

The circuit-level faulty behaviors caused by significant defects are extracted using a fault extractor. The function of the fault extractor resembles that of a standard circuit extrac-

tor. A circuit extractor uses the layout description of a circuit and extracts or produces the circuit net list, which is essentially the circuit diagram. A fault extractor, on the other hand, may make use of both the layout description and the original (fault-free) circuit diagram. It extracts the faulty circuit diagram from the modified layout, which incorporates the defect. In the present implementation of our fault extractor, a special circuit representation that contains sufficient topological information, extracted from the layout, is used.

In the process of translating a defect or extracting a fault, all the equipotential regions adjacent to the defect are considered. It is possible that, due to the nature of the adjacent regions, a defect may not produce any faulty circuit behavior. For example, a defect consisting of an extra spot of metal which is totally isolated (that is, all adjacent regions are nonconducting) will not cause any faulty behavior. Different fault extraction algorithms are used for defects involving different mask variables. Figure 7 outlines the fault extraction and classification procedure.

Primitive fault types. Because ICs are designed with purpose, the various layers are meaningfully shaped and stacked. Hence, given a single point defect in a particular layer, only a limited number of possible fault types can

result. This number is determined by the number of ways the topological adjacency relationships between nearby regions can be changed by the introduction of a physical defect. These changes, or manifestations of defects, are called *primitive fault types.* For a given technology, all possible primitive fault types can be systematically identified using the K-map of the electrically equivalent classes. This can be done independently for each defect type.

For example, the comprehensive list of primitive fault types for the polysilicon-gate n-channel MOS technology is shown in the box on the next page. This list is generated using the K-map of Figure 5 and considers only single point defects, that is, changing of only one mask variable's value. This technology has six mask variables, M, C, P, B, I, A. Hence, there are 12 defect types and the primitive faults caused by them are listed according to defect types. Only dc characteristics of circuit devices are of interest here. Currently, defects affecting ac performance are not considered. However, they certainly constitute an interesting topic for future work.

In examining the primitive fault types, we see that typically a defect affects either the connectivity between active devices, the devices themselves, or both. Hence, primitive fault types can be loosely grouped into the following four categories: (1) shorts between two or more equipotential regions, (2) breaks which result in the separation of a single equipotential region into two or more regions, (3) introduction of new (that is, unspecified in the good circuit description) devices to the circuit, and (4) changes in the behavior of existing devices in the circuit.

Circuit fault types. In the fault extraction procedure, defects are first translated to primitive faults and then primitive faults are interpreted, in the electrical sense, to produce the circuit faults. Circuit faults are described in terms of electrical circuit and, possibly, logic circuit properties; whereas, descriptions of primitive faults can involve both structure-level and circuit-

Taxonomy of primitive faults

Metal (M)

Extra metal (+M)
- A. Layers need to be considered: metal
- B. Fault types: shorts between metal lines

Missing metal (−M)
- A. Layers need to be considered: metal, PSG oxide, poly, diffusion
- B. Fault types: breaks between:
    1. metal—metal
    2. metal—diffusion
    3. metal—poly
    3. metal—diffusion—poly

Contact (C)

Extra contact (+C)
- A. Layers need to be considered: metal, poly, diffusion
- B. Fault types: shorts between:
    1. metal—poly
    2. metal—diffusion
    3. metal—diffusion—poly

Missing contact (−C)
- A. Layers need to be considered: metal, poly, diffusion
- B. Fault types: breaks between:
    1. metal—metal (multiple metal layers)
    2. metal—poly
    3. metal—diffusion
    4. poly—diffusion

Polysilicon (P)

Extra polysilicon (+P)
- A. Layers need to be considered: poly, diffusion, PSG oxide, gate oxide
- B. Fault types:
    1. Shorts between:
        a. poly—poly
        b. poly—metal (through PSG window)
        c. poly—metal—diffusion (through PSG window)
        d. poly—diffusion (through gate window)
    2. Breaks between:
        a. metal—diffusion (through PSG window)
        b. diffusion—diffusion (poly over diffusion)
    3. Creation of new transistor (poly over diffusion)
    4. Simultaneous break between metal-diffusion and creation of new transistor (through PSG contact)
    5. Change of transistor W/L ratio

Missing Polysilicon (−P)
- A. Layers need to be considered: poly, diffusion, PSG oxide, transistor channel, gate oxide

(Continued on next page)

---

level information. Hence, primitive faults function as a bridge between defects at the process and structure levels and faults at the circuit and logical levels.

By carefully examining the primitive faults listed in the box and interpreting their effects at the circuit and logical levels, an informal and useful classification of circuit faults can be produced. Keeping the classification simple and using commonly recognized terms, five types of circuit faults can be identified:

(1) Line stuck-at faults (LSA): These faults consist of one or more lines, or circuit nodes, permanently stuck at the logical 0 or 1 state. These faults can be explicitly modeled by the classical single and multiple line stuck-at fault models.

(2) Transistor stuck-at faults (TSA): These faults consist of one or more transistors stuck at the ON (transistor always conducting) or the OFF (transistor always nonconducting) state. A transistor is stuck at ON if its source and drain are explicitly shorted together. On the other hand, the conducting path between the source and drain of a stuck-at-OFF transistor is explicitly broken. Hence a fault involving the gate terminal of a transistor being stuck at logical 0/1 would be considered a line stuck-at fault and not a transistor stuck-at fault.

(3) Floating line faults (FLO): These faults consist of one or more floating (disconnected) lines or circuit nodes due to a physical break. These faults are not considered line stuck-at faults here although they may be viewed as line stuck-at faults. A floating line fault can manifest itself as a line stuck-at-0 or stuck-at-1, or with indeterminate value.

(4) Bridging faults (BRI): These faults consist of two or more lines, or circuit nodes, shorted together. These faults are typically caused by an extra spot of conducting material or a missing spot of insulating material. Most of these faults cannot be modeled with a line or transistor stuck-at fault model.

(5) Miscellaneous faults (MIS): This is a category for all other faults not

covered by the above four types. These faults include the creation of parasitic active devices, including transistors, faults involving power and ground lines, and other faults exhibiting unusual faulty behaviors.

In the IFA scenario, the single defect assumption is used. A single defect is generated, analyzed, and translated at a time. Faults caused by simultaneous multiple defects are not likely and therefore are not considered. However, a single defect can impact multiple layers and can produce multiple circuit-level faults. Hence, the fault list produced by the IFA procedure can include both single and multiple faults. It is possible that a defect producing a very unusual fault may not be automatically extractable by the present implementation of the fault extractor, in which case the defect is logged and manual extraction is required.

Ranking of circuit faults. After the primitive faults are interpreted to produce the circuit faults, the circuit faults are then grouped and ranked. Each circuit fault can be caused by one or more defects. The number of defects which cause a particular circuit fault is indicative of the likelihood of that fault. For instance, a fault that is the manifestation of a large number of defects in the defect sample space is statistically much more likely to occur than a fault that is caused by only a few of the defects in the same sample space.

Hence, circuit faults can be ranked according to their relative likelihood of occurrence. The ranking can be done in a variety of ways. All the faults can be ranked together or separately according to fault types. A large number of defects must be processed in order to ensure a high level of confidence on the ranking of faults.

An example circuit

The IFA procedure is demonstrated in this section using an example NMOS circuit. The example circuit is a modified full-adder cell used in the de-

---

(Continued from previous page)

  B. Fault types:
    1. Breaks between:
      a. poly—poly
      b. poly—diffusion (gate oxide or PSG oxide)
      c. poly—metal (PSG oxide)
    2. Shorts between:
      a. metal-poly—diffusion (PSG oxide)
      b. diffusion—diffusion (source to drain)
      c. diffusion—metal (PSG oxide)
    3. Simultaneous break between metal—poly and short between metal—diffusion
    4. Change of transistor W/L ratio

Buried contact (B)

Extra buried contact (+ B)
  A. Layers need to be considered: gate oxide, diffusion, poly, transistor channel
  B. Fault types:
    1. Shorts between diffusion—poly
    2. Creation of junction

Missing buried contact (− B)
  A. Layers need to be considered: gate oxide, diffusion, poly
  B. Fault types:
    1. Breaks between diffusion—poly
    2. Creation of junction

Implant (I)

Extra implant (+ I)
  A. Layers need to be considered: transistor channel, implant
  B. Fault types: transistor always conducting (ON)

Missing implant (− I)
  A. Layers need to be considered: transistor channel, implant
  B. Fault types: transistor always nonconducting (OFF)

Diffusion (A)

Extra diffusion (+ A)
  A. Layers need to be considered: diffusion, poly, gate oxide
  B. Fault types:
    1. Diffusion shorts
    2. Shorts between diffusion—poly (gate oxide contact)
    3. Creation of new transistor (poly)

Missing diffusion (− A)
  A. Layers need to considered: diffusion, poly, PSG oxide, gate oxide, transistor channel
  B. Fault types:
    1. Diffusion breaks
    2. Breaks between diffusion—metal (through PSG contact)
    3. Breaks between diffusion—poly (through gate contact)
    4. Missing transistor channel

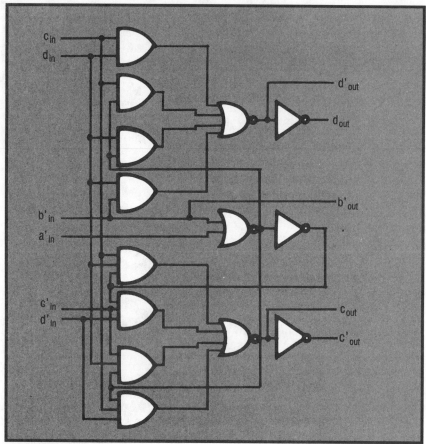

Figure 8. Logic diagram of the example circuit.

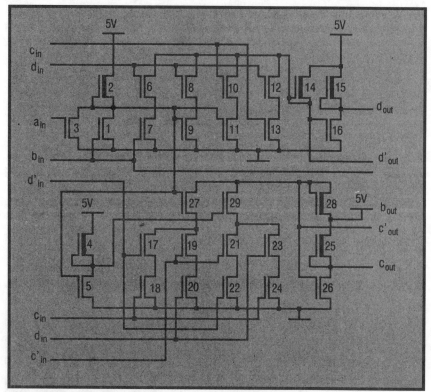

Figure 9. Circuit diagram of the example circuit.

sign of an easily testable array multiplier.[11] This cell has four inputs and three outputs. Both the complemented and the uncomplemented versions of some of the inputs and outputs are available. The logic diagram and the circuit diagram of the cell are shown in Figure 8 and Figure 9, respectively. The circuit contains 29 transistors. The layout of this cell is 198 μm x 112 μm in size and is illustrated in Figure 10. Minimum line widths and channel lengths are 4 μm which is equivalent to 2 μm per λ using the Mead and Conway[12] terminology.

Defect generation and analysis. The x and y coordinates of the center of each defect are generated by a random number generator. A uniform distribution over the entire layout is assumed. The radius of the defect is generated by another random number generator. A radius probability density function,[7] which has a good fit with reported data on point defect sizes,[6] is used in this example. Fluctuations in the differences between the dimensions of the photolithographic mask features and the dimensions of the shaped regions on the chip are caused by process lateral effects, such as overetching and lateral dopant diffusions. These fluctuations follow a normal distribution and are added to the radius generated using the radius probability density function. Different mean and variance values can be used for different defect types. For this example, the means and variances presented by Maly[7] are used.

Fault extraction. Twelve types of point defects are considered:

(1) +M : extra metal,
(2) −M : missing metal,
(3) +C : extra contact,
(4) −C : missing contact,
(5) +P : extra polysilicon,
(6) −P : missing polysilicon,
(7) +B : extra buried contact,
(8) −B : missing buried contact,
(9) +I : extra implant,
(10) −I : missing implant,
(11) +A : extra diffusion, and
(12) −A : missing diffusion.

IEEE DESIGN & TEST

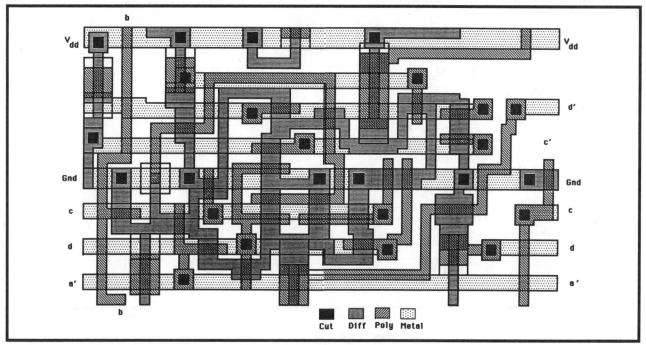

Figure 10. Layout of the example circuit.

Four hundred defects are generated for each of the 12 defect types, for a total of 4800 defects processed. Approximately 65 percent, or 3118 defects, are removed by the size, location and electrical significance screening process. The remaining 1682 defects are interpreted and translated. Many of these defects only degrade the ac performance of the circuit without changing the dc characteristics of the circuit.

Hence, of the original 4800 defects, only 476—approximately 10 percent— actually produce significant faulty behaviors at the circuit level. Table 1 summarizes the results from this defect-to-fault translation, or fault-extraction, procedure. The table summarizes the number of defects of each type which caused each of the circuit fault types or their subcategories. A comprehensive list of all the actual circuit faults extracted from the 476 defects has been documented.[10] Table 2 contains a partial list, containing only the single line stuck-at-faults.

Observations. Looking at the results of Table 1, some interesting observations can be made. Of course, supportive data from more examples are needed before these observations can be considered definitive conclusions.

Certain defect types tend to produce more circuit faults than others. For example, none of the missing buried contact ($-B$) defects and very few missing implant ($-I$) defects produced circuit-level faults. It seems that extra contact cut ($+C$) type of defects produce the most faults and defects associated with the contact cut (C), polysilicon (P), and the metal (M) mask variables are responsible for most of the circuit faults.

It is clear that multiple faults can result from single defects. There are 24 multiple line stuck-at (LSA) faults and 10 multiple transistor stuck-at (TSA) faults. The faults in the "others" subcategory of the miscellaneous (MIS) type (11 in number) are multiple faults involving multiple fault types. Other unusual faults can also result from single defects. The "power line" subcategory of the miscellaneous type involves breaks in the power and ground lines. These faults will produce catastrophic effects and can be easily detected. The two faults in the "new transistor" subcategory of the miscellaneous type actually created new transistors in the circuit, which altered the logical behavior of the circuit.

Circuit layout topology has impact on the circuit fault list. For example the two faults *cin* and *cin'* stuck-at logical 0 occurred 13 and 14 times, respectively. Looking at the layout, the observed high frequency of these two faults is due to the fact that the *cin* and *cin'* metal lines run parallel to the V_{ss} line for over half the length of the cell. On the other hand, the results show that the faults *cin* and *cin'* stuck-at logical 1 never occurred, which also concurs with the circuit layout. Many bridging faults are observed. These faults are certainly dependent on layout topology. It is clear that certain faults are very likely, and others are not, due to the layout topology.

It is also interesting to compare the number of defects causing each fault type. Table 3 presents the percentages of faults of each type. It has been verified, using statistical techniques, that these percentages are statistically significant. Only 28 percent of the faults, the line stuck-at faults, can be explicitly modeled by the classical line stuck-at fault model. This 28 percent includes both single and multiple line stuck-at faults. Less than 23 percent of the faults are actual single line stuck-at

Table 1.
Number of defects causing each fault type.

	Fault types	+M	−M	+C	−C	+P	−P	+B	−B	+I	−I	+A	−A	Total
1	One LSA	25	-	15	2	5	5	25	-	11	6	3	11	108
	Multiple LSA		-	6	1	-	-	17	-	-	-	-	-	24
2	One TSA-on	-	-	1	-	-	10	-	-	27	-	11	-	49
	One TSA-off	-	-	-	4	-	-	-	-	-	-	-	7	11
	Multiple TSA	-	1	2	-	-	-	-	-	-	-	3	4	10
3	Float lines	-	44	-	7	1	46	-	-	-	-	1	2	101
4	Bridging	10	-	77	-	30	-	27	-	-	-	-	-	144
5	Power line	-	16	-	-	-	-	-	-	-	-	-	-	16
	New Tran.	-	-	-	-	-	-	-	-	-	-	2	-	2
	Others	-	-	2	-	2	6	-	-	-	-	1	-	11
	Total	35	61	103	14	38	67	69	0	38	6	21	24	476

Defect types

Table 2.
Extracted single line stuck-at faults.

Defect types

Faults	+M	−M	+C	−C	+P	−P	+B	−B	+I	−I	+A	−A	Total
a s-a-0							1						1
b s-a-0							2						2
c_{in} s-a-0	4		4		4		2						14
c_{out} s-a-0	1	1		1									3
$\overline{c_{in}}$ s-a-0	10		1									2	13
$\overline{c_{out}}$ s-a-0						1			5				6
d_{in} s-a-0		5				2							7
d_{out} s-a-0										1		2	3
$\overline{d_{out}}$ s-a-0		3											3
b s-a-1	7												7
d_{out} s-a-1							2				1		3
$\overline{c_{out}}$ s-a-1												2	2
c_{out} s-a-0, c_{out} s-a-1										2		2	4
c_{out} s-a-1, c_{out} s-a-0						5							5
$\overline{d_{out}}$ s-a-0, d_{out} s-a-1						1			2				3
$\overline{d_{out}}$ s-a-1, d_{out} s-a-0						4							4
(a+b) s-a-0			1						2	1			4
$\overline{a+b}$ s-a-0		2				1	2		2	2	2	2	13
ab s-a-1	3					2							5
$\overline{ab}$ s-a-1						1	3				1		5
$\overline{d_{out}}$ s-a-1							1						1
Total	25	0	15	2	5	5	25	0	11	6	3	11	108

**Table 3.
Comparison of fault types.**

Fault types	Number of defects	Percentage of faults
1. Line stuck-at faults (LSA)	132	28%
2. Transistor stuck-at faults (TSA)	70	15%
3. Floating line faults (FLO)	101	21%
4. Bridging faults (BRI)	144	30%
5. Miscellaneous faults (MIS)	29	6%
Total	476	100%

faults. Most of the transistor stuck-at faults can be implicitly modeled by the classical line stuck-at fault model. This can also be said of the floating line faults, although some floating lines may not stay in one logical state.

Including the line stuck-at (28 percent), the transistor stuck-at (15 percent) and the floating line (21 percent) faults, at best, the classical fault model can only account for 64 percent of the faults. It should be noted, however, that this only illustrates the weakness of the classical fault model and not necessarily the weakness of test sets generated using such fault models.

There has been much attention paid in published literature to CMOS transistor stuck-at-OFF (or sometimes referred to as stuck-at-OPEN) faults. Our results seem to indicate that these faults only constitute a small percentage of the faults (less than three percent, in our example). Although the example circuit is an NMOS circuit, there are not many reasons for a CMOS circuit to be dramatically different.

The most prominent fault type is the bridging faults (30 percent). Hence, it seems that much more attention should be paid to bridging faults. Similar to transistor stuck-at-OFF faults, many of the observed bridging faults induced by extra

polysilicon can lead to sequential behavior. In general, these faults are difficult to test. However, it does appear that these faults are highly layout-dependent. Hence, it may be possible and worthwhile to modify the circuit layout so as to minimize the likelihood of these, and perhaps other difficult to test faults. This will certainly broaden the meaning of "design for testability" of VLSI circuits.

Finally, a number of researchers[3,4] have developed test generation algorithms for detecting circuit shorts in the n-doped silicon layer that cannot be modeled as a transistor stuck-at fault. An example of such a fault would be a short between the drains of transistors 11 and 13 in Figure 9. In the analysis of the example circuit, no such faults are produced. On the other hand, transistor source-to-drain shorts and opens, (that is, transistor stuck-at-ON and -OFF faults) do occur with reasonable frequency. Hence, test generation algorithms presented[3,13] for this type of fault can be useful.

A fault extracting/predicting methodology for MOS ICs, called Inductive Fault Analysis, and its implementation details have been presented. Using IFA software tools, when given

the layout of an IC, a fault model and a ranked fault list can be automatically generated which take into account the technology, layout, and process characteristics.

The IFA procedure involves three major steps: (1) generation of physical defects based on statistical data from the fabrication process, and analysis of generated defects for their size, location and electrical significance; (2) extraction of faulty device behaviors, called primitive faults, caused by the physical defects, and interpretation of primitive faults to produce a list of circuit-level faults; and (3) classification of fault types and ranking of faults according to their likelihood of occurrence. The ranked fault list can then be used to evaluate existing test sets and to help generate more effective test patterns.

An example NMOS circuit has been analyzed using the IFA procedure. Based on the results from this example, a number of interesting observations are made. First, many fault types, including nonclassical faults, are very likely to occur and at best only 64 percent of the faults can be modeled by the classical line stuck-at fault model. Multiple faults and unusual faults such as creation of new transistors can occur.

Furthermore, not all faults are equally likely. Contrary to their popularity in published literature, transistor stuck-at-OPEN faults accounted for less than three percent of the faults. On the other hand, many bridging faults (30 percent) were observed. It appears that faults involving interconnections are more numerous than faults involving devices. It also seems that layout topology has profound impact on the likelihood of certain faults and fault types. Probability of certain very difficult to test faults can be reduced by changing the layout. Hence, design for testability involving modifying the circuit layout appears to be an appropriate area for future research.

A set of software tools to fully automate the IFA procedure for CMOS ICs has been developed and is currently being debugged. Our next step is to analyze many actual circuits from industrial companies. Many enlightening results concerning fault model accuracy and test set effectiveness can be expected. A logical follow-up effort is to develop automatic test pattern generation programs[14] which make use of the ranked fault list produced by the IFA procedure. 🔲

Acknowledgments

This work was supported in part by the Semiconductor Research Corporation (SRC) under contract No. SRC-83-01-022, and in part by the Harris Corporation and the General Motors Research Laboratories. We appreciate the constructive comments on this work from a number of industrial companies including Harris, General Electric, GTE, ITT, and Texas Instruments. This work has also benefited from other ongoing research at CMU.[15]

References

1. J. Galiay, Y. Crouzet, and M. Vergniault, "Physical Versus Logical Fault Models in MOS LSI Circuits: Impact on Their Testability," *IEEE Trans. Computers,* Vol. C-29, No. 6, June 1980, pp. 527-531.

2. R.L. Wadsack, "Fault Modeling and Logic Simulation of CMOS and MOS Integrated Circuits," *Bell Systems Technical J.,* May-June 1978, pp. 1449-1474.

3. K. Chiang and Z.G. Vranesic, "Test Generation for MOS Complex Gate Networks," *Proc. 12th Int'l Symp. Fault-Tolerant Computing,* Santa Monica, Calif., June 1982, pp. 149-157.

4. P. Lamoureux and V.K. Agarwal, "Non-Stuck-At Fault Detection in NMOS Circuits by Region Analysis," *Proc. Int'l Test Conf.,* Philadelphia, Penn., Oct. 1983, pp. 129-137.

5. W. Maly, F.J. Ferguson, and J.P. Shen, "Systematic Characterization of Physical Defects for Fault Analysis of MOS IC Cells," *Proc. Int'l Test Conf.,* Philadelphia, Penn., Oct. 1984, pp. 390-399.

6. C.H. Stapper, "Modeling of Integrated Circuit Defect Sensitivities," *IBM J. Research and Development,* Vol. 27, No. 6, November 1983, pp. 549-557.

7. W. Maly, "Modeling of Lithography Related Yield Losses for CAD of VLSI Circuits," *IEEE Trans. Computer-Aided Design,* Vol. OE-10, No. 3, July 1985, pp. 166-177.

8. K.W. Ravi, *Imperfections and Impurities in Semiconductor Silicon,* John Wiley & Sons, New York, N.Y., 1981.

9. T.E. Mangir, "Sources of Failures and Yield Improvement for VLSI and Restructurable Interconnects for RVLSI and WSI: Part I—Sources of Failures and Yield Improvements for VLSI," *Proc. of IEEE,* June 1984, pp. 690-708.

10. J.P. Shen, W. Maly, and F.J. Ferguson, "Inductive Fault Analysis of NMOS and CMOS Integrated Circuits," ECE Department, CMU, SRC-CAD Center Research Report No. CMUCAD-85-51, Aug. 1985.

11. J.P. Shen and F.J. Ferguson, "The Design of Easily Testable VLSI Array Multipliers," *IEEE Trans. Computers,* Vol. C-33, No. 6, June 1984, pp. 554-560.

12. C. Mead and L. Conway, *Introduction to VLSI Systems,* Addison-Wesley, Reading, Mass., 1980.

13. Y.M. El-Ziq and S.Y.H. Su, "Fault Diagnosis of MOS Combinational Networks," *IEEE Trans. Computers,* Vol. C-31, No. 2, Feb. 1982, pp. 129-139.

14. S.H. Robinson and J.P. Shen, "Towards a Switch-Level Test Pattern Generation Program," *Proc. Int'l Conf. Computer-Aided Design,* Santa Clara, Calif., Nov. 1985.

15. H. Walker and S.W. Director, "VLASIC: A Yield Simulator for Integrated Circuits," *Int'l Conf. Computer-Aided Design,* Santa Clara, Calif., Nov. 1985.

John Paul Shen is an assistant professor of electrical and computer engineering at Carnegie-Mellon University. His research interests include computer-aided design and test of VLSI circuits and systems and parallel algorithms and architectures for real-time, mission-oriented systems. He has consulted for the IBM Federal Systems Division and General Electric Microelectronics Center.

He received a BS from the University of Michigan in 1973, and an MS and PhD from the University of Southern California in 1975 and 1981, respectively, all in electrical engineering. He was with the Hughes Aircraft Company from 1973 to 1975 and the TRW Systems Group in 1977. He is a member of IEEE, ACM, Tau Beta Pi, Eta Kappa Nu, and Sigma Xi, and a recent recipient of a NSF Presidential Young Investigator Award.

Wojciech Maly is a visiting associate professor of electrical and computer engineering at Carnegie-Mellon University. His research interests are in computer-aided design, testing, and manufacturing of integrated circuits. He has consulted for the General Motors Research Laboratories.

He received an MSc in electronic engineering from the Technical University of Warsaw in 1970, and a PhD from the Institute of Applied Cybernetics of the Polish Academy of Sciences in 1975. In 1973 he joined the Technical University of Warsaw, where he was appointed an assistant professor in 1975. From 1979 to 1981, he was a visiting assistant professor in electrical engineering at Carnegie-Mellon University, and rejoined the department in 1983 after returning to the Technical University of Warsaw for two years. He is a member of IEEE.

F. Joel Ferguson is a doctoral candidate in the department of electrical and computer engineering at Carnegie-Mellon University. His current research interests include the determination of accurate fault models for specific technologies, switch-level test generation and design for testability.

He received a BS in engineering from the University of North Carolina at Charlotte in 1978 and an MS in electrical and computer engineering from the Carnegie-Mellon University in 1982. He is a member of IEEE and Tau Beta Pi.

The authors' address is the Department of Electrical and Computer Engineering, Carnegie-Mellon University, SRC-CMU Research Center for CAD, Pittsburgh, PA 15213; (412) 578-3601.

Chapter III: Test Generation

The goal of test generation is to obtain test vectors of high quality at an affordable cost. The term *fault coverage* which is commonly used to denote test quality, is the fraction of the modeled faults detected by the test vectors. The test costs may be broken down into two categories associated with the processes of test generation and test application, respectively. The former is a one-time cost measured by the computational effort (computer run time) required to generate the vectors. The latter is a recurrent cost in the production or the field environments and refers to the time it takes to apply the vectors to the circuit under test. This time may be assumed to be directly proportional to the number of tests.

For a given fault in a circuit, a test is a set of input stimuli that make the fault effect observable at a primary output. As we shall see later, the test may be just a single binary vector or a sequence of such vectors. A perfect test generator must be able to find a test for each modeled fault in a circuit. Automatic test generation (ATG) methods may come close to achieving this ideal for single stuck-type faults, but their performance does not degrade gracefully with circuit size. Furthermore, their use requires substantial investment in hardware and software. Methods that are not fully automated are often used by designers and test engineers for generation of *functional* test vectors.

Functional tests are used for verifying the correctness of a design. They are developed manually (often interactively) by a designer based on an understanding of the functions implemented in a circuit. Even though functional tests may be derived without consideration of the structure of a circuit, they are still able to detect a good, but often inadequate, fraction of the faults arising from fabrication defects on a chip. In practice, additional test vectors from an automatic or manual test generation process supplement the functional tests to raise the fault coverage to a desired value.

A test engineer may also resort to functional test generation because a detailed circuit description is not available from the manufacturer, the tools for ATG are not at hand, or simply to understand the device operation better. Even for small to medium size circuits the use of editing tools adapted to this purpose can help remove a lot of the tedium associated with manipulating binary vectors. For larger circuits, these may be supplemented with an emulator allowing description of the device structure and behavior at a higher level. By using such an emulator the test engineer can create and edit test vectors for a wide range of very large scale integration (VLSI) circuits [Best84].

In the remainder of this chapter, we discuss automatic methods of test generation. Among these, exhaustive and random test generation have low computation costs but are not universally applicable. Other methods have traditionally been applied at the gate level, though, in recent years, several proposals have appeared for test generation at the transistor-switch level. The concept of path sensitization is common to both; hence, we illustrate it first before describing the algorithms themselves. Symbolic test generation is also possible by using the algebraic Boolean difference [Sell68] method but it is not practical for large circuits.

1: Systematic Approaches to Test Generation

Since VLSI circuits are characterized by their enormous complexity, low-cost methods such as exhaustive testing and random test generation are promising candidates for this application. Other methods, commonly known as *algorithmic,* have higher complexity but are effective for combinational circuits. The method chosen for test generation may vary based on considerations of desired quality and cost of tests.

1.1: Exhaustive Test Generation

In special situations, high quality may be obtainable at a very low cost. For example, if the number of primary inputs is small, application of all possible input vectors will ensure 100 percent fault coverage. Such vectors are easily generated by software or hardware, and may be applied quickly at the electronic speed. Exhaustive techniques can be extended to more complex circuits by a partitioning of the logic into smaller subcircuits Unfortunately, the logic partitioning problem is intractable, and hence, can not be fully automated. In other words, the total cost of exhaustive test generation does not reduce but shifts toward partitioning the logic. Subcircuits may be tested exhaustively in the built-in test environment where hardware test generators in the form of shift registers with feedback (*linear feedback shift registers* or LFSR) are included on the chip. In this environment, it would be impractical to store the response of the fault-free circuit to the very large number of test vectors (for comparison with the actual response of the circuit under test) so the response stream is compressed into a compact *signature* before comparison with the reference signature (see Figure 3.1). The circuits for test vector and signature generation, shown in the figure, are further described in [Will83].

1.2: Random Test Generation

The random method is another inexpensive way to generate tests. Like the exhaustive method, this depends only on the number of circuit inputs but is otherwise quite independent of the circuit topology.

By definition, in the random method, tests are generated through a random process. Once the tests have been generated, there is nothing random about them. Some knowledge of the operation of the circuit under test can be useful particularly for sequential circuits. The method, if used properly, can provide good results at a very low cost. Figure 3.2 gives a somewhat generalized flow of a random test generator. After the process is defined, an automatic or interactive program can be written to produce vectors. A fault simulator is generally useful for effective test generation [Schu75]. We will give a few illustrative examples.

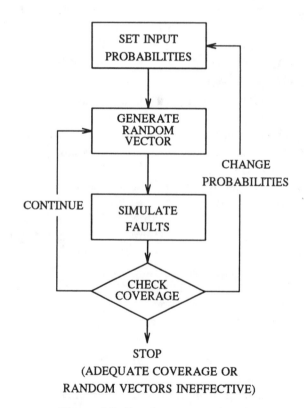

Figure 3.2: Random test generation.

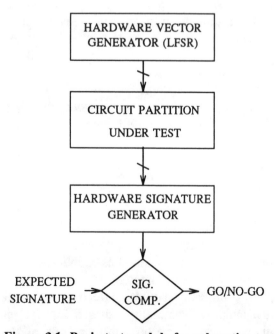

Figure 3.1: Basic test module for exhaustive test.

Consider the four-bit arithmetic logic unit (ALU) (Texas Instruments Type SN74181), which has 14 inputs. A random test generator for this circuit follows:

```
Begin  Do i = 1,1000
        Vector[1,14] = random(0.5)
        Simulate faults
        If [any fault detected]
                Remove detected faults from list
                Store Vector as a test
                Stop If [fault list empty]
        End If
End
```

This procedure can be implemented in any programming language. The function "random(0.5)" produces 1s and 0s with equal probability (i.e., 0.5) for each bit in the 14-bit vector. Notice that the procedure requires the use of a fault simulator. Also, it rejects any vector that does not enhance the fault coverage. In actual runs, this program produced from 30 to 35 test vectors after generating approximately 200 random vectors. The tests covered all detectable faults in the ALU [Agra78]. Experience with random test generation for scan type designs is described in [Will77].

Of course, random test generation is not always so effective. For combinational circuits, it has been found that the number of levels of logic and gate fanins determine its success [Agra78]. For circuits with deep logic and high fanins, augmenting the random method with a deterministic method like the D-algorithm is an effective strategy [Agra72]. Alternatively, circuit modifications to improve the fault coverage of random vectors has been suggested [Eich83].

Random test generation programs for sequential circuits require greater care. In general, the following points should be considered:

- Clock signals should not be random. They should be set according to functional specifications.

- Control signals, such as "reset," should become active with low probability to allow valid outputs from the circuit.

- Other data input signals can change randomly but must follow specified restrictions. For example, certain data signals may not change on a certain edge of clock signal to avoid race conditions.

- A vector should not be rejected just because it does not enhance the cumulative fault coverage; it may be helpful in establishing a new circuit state.

As an experiment, the authors followed the above guidelines to write a test generation program for a 16-bit multiplier (having a pipeline register). It produced a test sequence of 2,000 vectors with 98 percent fault coverage. Another 1.5 percent of the faults were redundant (i.e., not detectable by any test).

As another example, a test generator for a microprocessor could randomly pick an instruction and generate a random data pattern. By repeating this sequence a specified number of times it will produce a test program that, when assembled, will test the microprocessor by randomly exercising its logic.

The basic attractiveness of random test generation lies in its simplicity and inexpensiveness. However, the produced sequences could be very long. Several approaches have been suggested for improving the efficiency of random test generation [Agra76, Agra81, Park76, Lisa87].

2: Path Sensitization Algorithms

The combinational logic network shown in Figure 3.3 has four inputs and one output. Suppose we want to find a test for the fault "line g $s-a-0$." Any such test must apply a 1 to line g so as to *excite* the fault; that is, it must produce a normal signal at the fault site, which is different from that placed by the fault. Since g is an internal line not directly controllable from the primary inputs, appropriate input values must be found to set it to 1; in this case any input vector with $A=B=1$ will do.

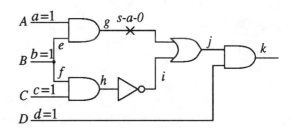

Figure 3.3: Test generation for fault g stuck-at-0.

Next, the effect of the fault must be propagated from the fault site to the output while maintaining fault-excitation. This is achieved in stages by first moving the effect to line j (by applying the non-forcing 0 on line i) and then to the output line k (by applying the non-forcing 1 on line d). However, a 0 on line i must be *justified* in terms of an input vector, which is at the same time consistent with the already set line values. Going back from i towards inputs, a 0 on i requires a 1 on line h, which, in turn, forces lines f and c to 1. Consistency is easily verified. Thus the vector shown in the figure is a test for the fault g $s-a-0$ and is unique since no choices were available during either the forward propagation of fault effect or the justification of line values set during forward propagation.

Similar considerations apply also to test generation for sequential circuits, but the presence of feedback paths complicates the process. The clocked D-latch circuit of Figure 3.4 will be used as an illustration. This circuit has two inputs, D and CK and two (normally complementary) outputs Q and $\overline{Q}$.

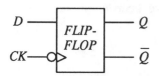

(a) Schematic of D-flip-flop.

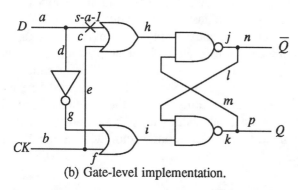

(b) Gate-level implementation.

Figure 3.4: Sequential circuit test generation example.

The circuit will latch the data value on the D input during the enabling period when the clock input CK is zero. In normal operation, it is assumed that input D does not change during this period. To latch a new data value, one must go through the following sequence: Apply the new value on the D input while CK is high, lower the clock, and raise it high again, that is, apply a zero-pulse on the CK input after the data are stable.

Consider how a test for the fault line c stuck-at-1 could be generated. As in the previous example, D

must be set to 0 to excite the fault. Then $CK=0$ will ensure that its effect is propagated to line h. However, further propagation of the effect to the output $\overline{Q}$ requires that the latch be already set to 1 (since m is required to be 1). This means that the whole sequence discussed up to this point must be preceded by a latch initialization sequence. The complete test sequence is shown in Table 3.1.

Fault	Time Step	CK	D	Q	$\overline{Q}$
		Table 3.1: Test Sequence for D-Flip Flop * indicates output strobe			

Fault	Time Step	CK	D	Q	$\overline{Q}$
	1	1	1	X	X
c	2	0	1	1	0
stuck	3	1	1	1	0
at	4	1	0	1	0
1	5	0	0	0/1	1/0
	6	1	0	0/1*	1/0*
	1	1	1	X	X
b	2	0	1	1/X	0/X
stuck	3	1	1	1/X*	0/X*
at	4	1	0	1/X	0/X
1	5	0	0	0/X	1/X
	6	1	0	0/X*	1/X*

In contrast with combinational logic, sequential circuits often require multiple input vectors applied in a predefined sequence to detect a fault. As in the above example, the test sequence can often be broken into an initialization phase during which the latch(es) in the circuit are set to desired states. This is followed by the second phase in which the fault is excited and its effect propagated to an observable output. Certain faults involving clock lines, though, may not be detectable by a fixed initialization as our next example will show.

In Figure 3.4, assume line b is stuck-at-1. This fault will effectively isolate the latch from the data input, which means the latch will forever stay in the state it assumed initially when the power was turned on. This could be either one or zero so the only way to detect this fault is to try to set the latch successively to both states and observe for the fault effect in one or the other state. Note that there is no *a priori* way of telling in which of the two states in which the fault will be detected.

2.1: Gate-Level Test Generation

The previous examples illustrate a whole class of test generation algorithms based on *path sensitization*. Consider the fault line *c* stuck-at-1 in the NAND network of Figure 3.5. Since this is an input line, the fault can be directly excited by setting input *c* to 0. Three input vectors are shown in the figure with *c*=0. In each case, the paths through which the fault effect is propagated are shown by arrows. These lines are always in a path starting from the fault site since the effect can only propagate stage by stage from the input of a gate to its output. Each such path along which the effect propagates is called a *sensitized path*. As seen in the examples before, for a fault to be detected a test vector must sensitize one or more paths from the fault site to a circuit output. For the first vector shown, the effect propagates along just one sensitized path to the output. For the second, there are two sensitized paths to the output, while for the third vector there are none. Path-sensitization algorithms would be much simpler if it could be assumed that every fault can be detected by single-path sensitization, because the number of paths that must be considered for multiple path sensitization grows exponentially with the circuit size. Unfortunately, examples exist [Schn67] to show that multiple path sensitization is *essential* to detect certain faults. A *complete* test generation algorithm (claiming to produce a test whenever one exists) must, therefore, be prepared to explore path sensitization of arbitrary multiplicity. This requirement illustrates in an intuitive way the theoretical intractability (in the worst case) of any test generation process.

While the algorithmic test generation methods based on path sensitization vary substantially in details, they all share some fundamental operations. We will consider those for combinational circuits and illustrate them on the circuit shown in Figure 3.3. It will be assumed that initially all signals in the circuit have unknown values.

Fault Excitation: This involves establishing a signal value at the fault site opposite of that produced by the fault. The subcircuit feeding the line at fault site must be examined for signal values consistent with fault excitation. As an example, in Figure 3.3, the fault *g s−a−0* is excited by setting line *g* to 1,

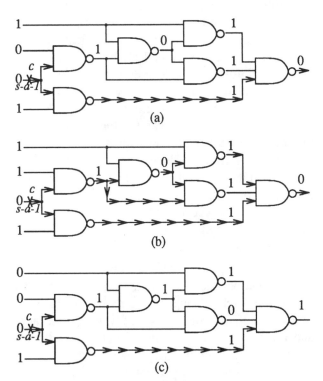

Figure 3.5: Path sensitization for *s-a-1* fault on line *c*.

which requires inputs *A* and *B* to be 1.

Fault-effect Propagation: The objective of this operation is to move the fault effect closer to a primary output. An active sensitized path is selected for extension from the input of the gate at which it currently terminates to its output. If no such path exists, the algorithm must backtrack to an earlier point of execution where a choice existed. Otherwise, path extension is attempted by changing one or more of the undefined inputs (off the sensitized path) of the gate to known values. For example, to propagate the effect of the fault *g s−a−0* in Figure 3.3 to line *j* it is necessary to set line *i* to 0.

Line-value Justification: A test generation algorithm may need to specify internal line values that must be produced by defining one or more primary input values, which must be done in such a way as to be consistent with the already defined values in the circuit. In our example, line *i* was set to 0 but not justified during the last step. In the first step of justification line h is set to 1. Since *h* is an internal line, the 1-value on it must also be justified. This causes input *C* to be set to 1 (note that input *B* was already set to 1 during the fault excitation step).

Line-value Implication: All of the preceding operations are carried out in incremental steps and typically involve specifying one or more line values. The effect of such specification may ripple through in the forward direction by implication. For instance, a logic 1 specified at the input of an OR gate would force the gate output to 1. Considering the example in Figure 3.3, we needed to set inputs A and B to 1 in the fault excitation step. Since B fans out to another gate, namely the AND with h as the output, we could have initiated a line-value implication step immediately after setting B to 1. As a result, the value at h would have been evaluated but would not have changed (from the unknown value) because of the unknown value on input C at that point.

All but the last operation in the above may involve making choices. A complete algorithm must remember the deferred choices which could be pursued if backtracking occurs owing to the detection of an inconsistency in line values. Variations and finer details involved in different test generation algorithms have to do with the heuristics used for making a choice or for selecting a deferred choice. In some algorithms, decisions are guided by approximate measures of line controllabilities and observabilities derived either in a preprocessing step or dynamically. In others, fault simulation steps may interweave steps of test generation with the results of fault simulation providing the necessary guidance.

2.2: Switch-Level Test Generation

Consider a CMOS NOR gate implementation shown in Figure 3.6a. A switch-level model of the circuit can be constructed by assuming the transistors to be perfect switches. In the model, a p-type (n-type) transistor can be represented by an inverter (a buffer). The transmission between two points separated by a series (parallel) connection of two transistors can be represented by an AND (OR) gate. In addition, a new type of block is used to represent the connection between the p-type and n-type networks. Called a "B-block" [Jain85, Redd84], its function can be described by the table shown in Figure 3.6b. When the transmission through the p-type network is 0 (open circuit) and that through the n-type network is 1 (closed circuit) the output is connected to V_{SS} and, hence, is zero. Similarly, for the opposite situation, the output is one since it is connected to V_{DD}. When both the circuits are closed, we assume the output to be zero

("zero dominance"). When both of them are open, the table has the entry M indicating a "memory" state; in this case, the output *floats* meaning that it will retain its previous value.

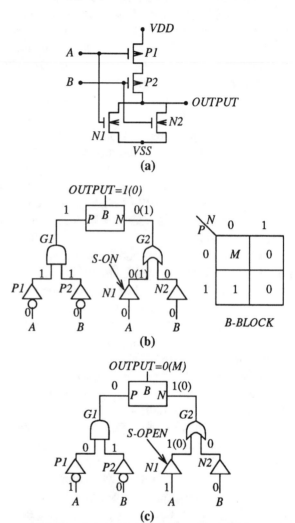

Figure 3.6: Switch-level test generation.

A commonly used fault model at the switch level adds to the usual stuck faults a new class of "technology-dependent" faults related to the transistors. A faulty transistor could be either "stuck open" or "stuck on" (see Chapter II). We will consider two examples of test generation for faults from this class. In the first example, assume transistor $N1$ is stuck on. As before, the fault must be "excited" before it can be detected; in this case, input A must be zero to set the transistor to the opposite (open) state in the fault-free circuit. From here on, the procedure becomes quite similar to path-sensitization discussed earlier, and the results are shown in Figure 3.6b. Note that the values within parentheses correspond to the faulty circuit, while those outside are for the fault-free case. Also, note that since the transmissions through the p-type and n-type networks are complementary in CMOS circuits, the normal (fault-free) values on the two inputs to the B-block will be opposite of each other. The output of the block is determined by referring to the table. In this case, the input $(A, B) = (0, 0)$ is the unique test for the stuck-on fault.

A more interesting situation occurs when transistor $N1$ is stuck open, which is our second example of test generation (see Figure 3.6c). To excite this fault, we apply 1 to input A and to propagate it through gate $G2$ we must set B to 0. This forces the normal values to the P and N inputs of the B-block as 0 and 1, respectively, so the normal output is 0. Under the fault, only input N complements, which means both the inputs of the B-block are zero. The output M means that it could be either zero or one depending on the previous value. Thus, to detect the fault, we should have initialized the previous output to one. The complete test is, therefore, a "two-vector" test: The first vector (0, 0) properly initializes the output; then the second vector (1, 0) produces differentiated outputs for the normal and faulty cases. Here is an instance of a combinational circuit exhibiting sequential behavior under a stuck-open fault. The reader will find further details of switch-level test generation in the recent literature [Agra84, Redd85].

3: Test Algorithms for Combinational Circuits

A significant theoretical study by Ibarra and Sahni [Ibar75] shows that test generation for combinational circuits belongs to the class of problems called NP-complete, strongly suggesting that no test-generation algorithm with a polynomial time complexity is likely to exist. The non-polynomial (exponential) time complexity here refers to the *worst-case* effort of test generation in a circuit. Test generation algorithms used in practice appear to be able to achieve slower *average* time growth by using heuristic search techniques. Goel [Goel80] argues that the time for complete test generation must grow at least as the square of the number of gates in the circuit. He also analyzes empirical data on fault coverage by random test vectors and shows that an exponential model fits the data quite well. Typically, the fault coverage rises very rapidly with the number of random test vectors but saturates in the 65-85 percent range.

Most well-known test generation algorithms make use of the path sensitization idea in one form or another. Of these, the oldest and undoubtedly the best known is the D-algorithm described in [Roth67]. A class of circuits for which the D-algorithm performs particularly poorly are those containing exclusive-or trees. The degradation in performance arises due to excessive amount of backtracking. This observation motivated Goel [Goel81] to devise a new test generation algorithm called *path oriented decision making (PODEM)*. He used a branch and bound technique. PODEM implementations are known to run an order of magnitude faster than the D-algorithm on most circuits.

Fujiwara and Shimono [Fuji83] describe techniques to further accelerate a path-sensitization algorithm like PODEM. Their algorithm, called FAN, does extensive analysis of the circuit connectivity in a preprocessing step to minimize backtracking. Another recent algorithm CONT [Taka87] minimizes backtracks by a different approach. If the target fault is found to be undetectable by the current input vector, CONT tries to switch the target to another undetected fault. Candidate faults for target switching are identified by interleaving fault simulation steps with incremental test generation steps. FAN and CONT can provide a reduction factor of 2 - 5 in computing time over PODEM.

A generalization of the D-algorithm, called the *subscripted D-algorithm* [Benm83] also reports significant improvements in test generation time for the same benchmark circuits [Ladj87]. Unlike the D-algorithm, which works with a *subscripted D-algorithm* single target fault in each step, the subscripted D-algorithm attempts to find tests for all faults associated with a gate in one step. Its performance data are not extensive at the time of writing but appears to be comparable to FAN and CONT. Some other speedup techniques may be found in [Abra86, Rosa85].

CONT differs from other methods in one significant way. It uses fault simulation. Use of simulation for forward implications was also suggested by Kjelkerud and Thessen [Kjel79]. More recently, a new simulation based approach has been proposed by Cheng and Agrawal [Chen87]. In this method, a new form of simulation, called the *threshold-value simulation*, is used. The advantage of this simulation is that it provides signal controllabilities in addition to the logical values. The additional information is used to compute a *cost function* for the given input vector and a target fault. The vector is modified to reduce the cost. A directed search for a test vector is conducted by successive cost reduction.

A mathematically elegant approach to test generation, called the Boolean-difference method, captures the basic concepts of path sensitization in algebraic terms. Practically, it is applicable to only small examples but the interested reader will find that the original paper by Sellers, Hsiao, and Bearnson [Sell68] is fundamental to a good understanding of any path-sensitization algorithm.

Combinational circuit test generation for transistor circuits offers two possibilities. Either the transistor model can be transformed to a logic model or the operations in path sensitization (*D*-drive, justification, etc.) can be defined for switch networks. The first approach is described in Chapter II [Redd84], and the second approach is discussed in a paper by Reddy *et al.* [Redd85]. In another system for scan circuits, Leet *et al.* [Leet84] store transfer characteristics of faulty and fault-free MOS gates in a tabular form to execute a D-algorithm like procedure.

Functional testing of combinational logic has received some attention. A majority of this work applies to programmable logic arrays (PLAs). An example is a test generator named PLATYPUS [Wei86]. Using the functional description of a PLA, it can generate tests for all stuck-type and crosspoint faults (see Chapter II). Its efficiency far exceeds that of a gate-level test generator working with an equivalent logic description.

4: Test Algorithms for Sequential Circuits

Test generation for sequential circuits remains to be a challenge in spite of a history of attempts dating back to the late 1960s. Earliest algorithms represented sequential circuits as iterative combinational circuits to which the combinational test generation algorithms could be extended [Kubo68, Putz71, Muth76]. An algorithm that formalizes the method used in the previous latch example has been programmed into a commercial product called LASAR as described by Thomas [Thom71]. Recent programs for sequential test generation have been

reported by Mallela and Wu [Mall85] and Marlett [Marl86]. Simulation based sequential circuit test generation was used in the SOFTG program at IBM [Snet77]. While some progress is evident in these attempts, an effective solution for circuits with more than a few hundred gates, large sequential depths (e.g. embedded counters and shift registers), and asynchronous elements is still not available.

The test generation algorithms discussed thus far need to know the detailed *structural description* of a circuit in terms of gates or switches. Functional test generation methods, on the other hand, use abstract fault models derivable from the *behavioral description* of a circuit. Functional tests have traditionally been generated for memory circuits [Abad83]. Thatte and Abraham [That80] pioneered the functional approach to microprocessor testing. Another recent development is a test generation program called HITEST, which employs a knowledge-based approach [Bend84] for complex stored-state circuits.

VLSI designers make extensive use of a functional hierarchy to partition their designs and thereby cope with the ever-increasing circuit complexity. Logic elements (e.g., gates) in a hierarchical design can be viewed as being a part of successively more complex functional blocks. As a rule, test generation algorithms have ignored the hierarchical circuit description and worked entirely at the gate level. This means that they are not able to exploit the interconnection and functional information at the higher levels of the hierarchy. Several efforts are underway to remove this shortcoming [Bhat85, Kris87].

For sequential circuits that are synchronous, it is possible to test signal path delays by tests generated from consideration of combinational logic. Delay tests verify timing performance and are known to have a high stuck fault coverage. They may be a good alternative for testing high-performance circuits. Work on delay tests has been reported only recently [Smit85, Lin87].

5: Conclusion

There are efficient computer-aided design (CAD) tools available for generation tests for combinational logic. These tools, however, can be used only if scan design, as will be discussed in Chapter VI, is employed. For general sequential circuits, today's

CAD tools are not very effective in handling the VLSI complexity. For the future, techniques based on expert systems may hold promise.

6: Selected Reading

The first complete algorithm for combinational test generation was given by Roth *et al.* [Roth67] and led to numerous implementations. A description of this classic algorithm, known as the D-algorithm, can be found in standard text books (e.g., [Fuji85]).

We have included four papers on test algorithms for combinational circuits. The first paper by Goel [Goel81] describes the PODEM algorithm. Many recent CAD programs use PODEM in the original or modified form. The second paper by Fujiwara and Shimono [Fuji83] describes their fan-out (FAN) heuristic to accelerate a test generator. Combinational logic on VLSI chips is often implemented as PLAs. The next paper by Bose and Abraham [Bose82] gives a very clear account of PLA fault models and their testing. Actual testing of PLAs is done in one of two ways. For PLAs that are embedded in random logic, logic modeling of PLA as described in Chapter II is quite popular. For stand alone PLAs, however, very efficient functional test generators are possible. The final paper on combinational test generation, by Reddy *et al.* [Redd85], deals with transistor-level algorithms.

Next, there are two papers on sequential circuit test generation. The paper by Muth [Muth76] describes a nine-value logic algorithm that works with time-frame expansion of circuit. The second paper describes a test generator called SOFTG [Snet77].

Memory testing is becoming important for logic designers because many VLSI chips are designed with embedded memory blocks. Our selection is a survey paper by Abadir and Reghbati [Abad83]. For functional testing, we have selected a paper by Thatte and Abraham [That80] describing their approach to microprocessor testing.

Finally, those interested in learning about tools for formatting and editing tests will find a very readable description in [Best84].

Our heavy emphasis on combinational circuits in reprints is for the following reasons: (a) test generation for large combinational circuits is algorithmically feasible, (b) efficient programs can be developed to generate tests for sequential circuits designed with the scan method as described in Chapter VI, (c) many test generation algorithms for sequential circuits are extensions of known algorithms for combinational circuits, and (d) an understanding of these algorithms can help a designer even in manual test generation.

7: References

[Abad83] M. S. Abadir and H. K. Reghbati, "Functional Testing of Semiconductor Random Access Memories," *ACM Computing Surveys*, Vol. 15, pp. 175-198, September 1983, **see reprint in this chapter.**

[Abra86] M. Abramovici, J. J. Kulikowski, P. R. Menon, and D. T. Miller, "SMART and FAST: Test Generation for VLSI Scan-Design Circuits," *IEEE Design & Test of Computers*, Vol. 3, pp. 43-54, Aug., 1986, Also *Proc. Int. Test Conf.*, Philadelphia, PA, Nov., 1985, pp. 45-56.

[Agra76] P. Agrawal and V. D. Agrawal, "On Monte Carlo Testing of Logic Tree Networks," *IEEE Trans. Computers*, Vol. C-15, pp. 664-667, June 1976.

[Agra84] P. Agrawal, "Test Generation at Switch Level," *Int. Conf. Computer-Aided Design (ICCAD-84)*, Santa Clara, CA, pp. 128-130, Nov. 1984.

[Agra72] V. D. Agrawal and P. Agrawal, "An Automatic Test Generation System for Illiac IV Logic Boards," *IEEE Trans. Computers*, Vol. C-21, pp. 1015-1017, September 1972.

[Agra78] V. D. Agrawal, "When to Use Random Testing," *IEEE Trans. Computers*, Vol. C-27, pp. 1054-1055, Nov. 1978, Also see comments by P. B. Schneck and the author's reply in *IEEE Trans. Comp.*, Vol. C-28, pp. 580-581, August 1979.

[Agra81] V. D. Agrawal, "An Information Theoretic Approach to Digital Fault Testing," *IEEE Transaction on Computers*, Vol. C-30, pp. 582-587, August 1981.

[Bend84] M. J. Bending, "Hitest: A Knowledge-Based Test Generation System," *IEEE Design & Test of Computers*, Vol. 1, pp. 83-92, May 1984.

[Benm83] C. Benmehrez and J. F. McDonald, "The Subscripted D-Algorithm – ATPG With Multiple Independent Control Paths," *ATPG Workshop Proceedings*, pp. 71-80, 1983.

[Best84] W. E. Den Beste, "Using a Software Emulator to Generate and Edit VLSI Test Patterns," *Electronics Test*, pp. 42-52, March 1984, **see reprint in this chapter.**

[Bhat85] D. Bhattacharya and J. P. Hayes, "High-Level Test Generation Using Bus Faults," *Fault-Tolerant Comp. Symp. (FTCS-15) Digest of Papers*, pp. 65-70, June 1985.

[Bose82] P. Bose and J. A. Abraham, "Test Generation for Programmable Logic Arrays," *Proc. ACM/ IEEE Design Automation Conf.*, Las Vegas, Nevada, pp. 574-580, June 1982, **see reprint in this chapter.**

[Chen87] K. T. Cheng and V. D. Agrawal, "A Simulation-Based Directed-Search Method for Test Generation," *Proc. Int. Conf. Comp. Des. (ICCD-87)*, Rye Brook, NY, pp. 48-51, October 1987.

[Eich83] E. B. Eichelberger and E. Lindbloom, "Random-Pattern Coverage Enhancement and Diagnosis for LSSD Logic Self-Test," *IBM J. Res. Develop.*, Vol. 27, pp. 265-272, May 1983.

[Fuji83] H. Fujiwara and T. Shimono, "On the acceleration of test generation algorithms," *IEEE Trans. Comp.*, Vol. C-32, pp. 1137-1144, Dec. 1983, **see reprint in this chapter.**

[Fuji85] H. Fujiwara, *Logic Testing and Design for Testability*, MIT Press, Cambridge, MA, 1985.

[Goel80] P. Goel, "Test Generation Costs Analysis and Projections," *Proc. 17th Design Automation Conference*, Minneapolis, MN, pp. 77-84, June 1980.

[Goel81] P. Goel, "An Implicit Enumeration Algorithm to Generate Tests for Combinational Logic Circuits," *IEEE Trans. Computers*, Vol. C-30, pp. 215-222, March 1981, **see reprint in this chapter.**

[Ibar75] O. H. Ibarra and S. K. Sahni, "Polynomially Complete Fault Detection Problems," *IEEE Trans. Comp.*, Vol. C-24, pp. 242-249, March 1975.

[Jain85] S. K. Jain and V. D. Agrawal, "Modeling and Test Generation Algorithms for MOS Circuits," *IEEE Trans. Computers*, Vol. C-34, pp. 426-433, May 1985, Also see, Correction, in *IEEE Trans. Computers*, Vol. C-34, p. 680, July 1985.

[Kjel79] E. Kjelkerud and O. Thessen, "Generation of Hazard Free Tests using the D-Algorithm in a Timing-Accurate System for Logic and Deductive Fault Simulation," *Proc. 16th Des. Auto. Conf.*, San Diego, CA, pp. 180-184, June 1979.

[Kris87] B. Krishnamurthy, "Hierarchical Test Generation: Can AI Help?," *Proc. Int. Test Conf.*,

Washington, DC, pp. 694-700, September 1987.

[Kubo68] H. Kubo, "A Procedure for Generating Test Sequences to Detect Sequential Circuit Failures," *NEC Res. & Dev.*(12), pp. 69-78, October 1968.

[Ladj87] M. Ladjadj and J. F. McDonald, "Benchmark Runs of the Subscripted D-Algorithm with Observation Path Mergers on the Brglez-Fujiwara Circuits," *Proc. 24th Des. Auto. Conf.*, Miami Beach, FL, pp. 509-515, June 1987.

[Leet84] D. Leet, P. Shearon, and R. France, "A CMOS LSSD Test Generation System," *IBM J. Res. Dev.*, Vol. 28, pp. 625-635, September 1984.

[Lin87] C. J. Lin and S. M. Reddy, "On Delay Fault Testing in Logic Circuits," *IEEE Trans. CAD*, Vol. CAD-6, pp. 694-703, September 1987, Also *Proc. Int. Conf. CAD (ICCAD-86)*, November 1986, pp. 148-151.

[Lisa87] R. Lisanke, F. Brglez, A deGeus, and D. Gregory, "Testability-Driven Random Pattern Generation," *IEEE Trans. CAD*, Vol. CAD-6, pp. 1082-1087, November 1987, Also *Proc. Int. Conf. CAD (ICCAD-86)*, Santa Clara, CA, Nov., 1986, pp. 144-147.

[Mall85] S. Mallela and S. Wu, "A Sequential Circuit Test Generation System," *Proc. Int. Test Conf.*, Philadelphia, PA, pp. 57-61, November 1985.

[Marl86] R. Marlett, "An Effective Test Generation System for Sequential Circuits," *23rd Des. Aut. Conf.*, Las Vegas, Nevada, pp. 250-256, June 1986.

[Muth76] P. Muth, "A Nine-Valued Circuit Model for Test Generation," *IEEE Trans. Computers*, Vol. C-25, pp. 630-636, June 1976, **see reprint in this chapter.**

[Park76] K. P. Parker, "Adaptive Random Test Generation," *J. Des. Auto. and Fault-Tolerant Computing*, Vol. 1, pp. 62-83, October 1976.

[Putz71] G. R. Putzolu and J. P. Roth, "A Heuristic Algorithm for the Testing of Asynchronous Circuits," *IEEE Trans. Computers*, Vol. C-20, pp. 639-647, June 1971.

[Redd85] M. K. Reddy, S. M. Reddy, and P. Agrawal, "Transistor Level Test Generation for MOS Circuits," *Proc. 22nd Des. Auto. Conf.*, Las Vegas, Nevada, pp. 825-828, June 1985, **see reprint in this chapter.**

[Redd84] S. M. Reddy, V. D. Agrawal, and S. K. Jain, "A Gate Level Model for CMOS Combinational Logic Circuits with Application to Fault Detection," *Proc. 21st Des. Auto. Conf.*, Albuquerque, NM, pp. 504-509, June 1984, **see reprint in Chapter II.**

[Rosa85] B. C. Rosales and P. Goel, "Results from Application of a Commercial ATG System to Large-Scale Combinational Circuits," *Proc. Int. Symp. Circ. Syst. (ISCAS-85)*, Kyoto, Japan, pp. 667-670, June 1985.

[Roth67] J. P. Roth, W. G. Bouricius, and P. R. Schneider, "Programmed Algorithms to Compute Tests and to Detect and Distinguish Between Failures in Logic Circuits," *IEEE Trans. Electronic Computers*, Vol. EC-16, pp. 567-580, October 1967.

[Schn67] P. R. Schneider, "On the Necessity to Examine D-Chains in Diagnostic Test Generation," *IBM J. Res. and Dev.*, Vol. 11, p. 114, January 1967.

[Schu75] D. M. Schuler, E. G. Ulrich, T. E. Baker, and S. P. Bryant, "Random Test Generation Using Concurrent Logic Simulation," *Proc. 12th Des. Auto. Conf.*, pp. 261-267, 1975.

[Sell68] F. F. Sellers, M. Y. Hsiao, and L. W. Bearnson, "Analyzing Errors with Boolean Difference," *IEEE Trans. Computers*, Vol. C-17, pp. 676-683, July 1968.

[Smit85] G. L. Smith, "Model for Delay Faults Based upon Paths," *Proc. Int. Test Conf.*, Philadelphia, PA, pp. 342-349, November 1985.

[Snet77] T. J. Snethen, "Simulator-Oriented Fault Test Generator," *Proc. 14th Des. Auto. Conf.*, pp. 88-93, 1977, **see reprint in this chapter**.

[Taka87] Y. Takamatsu and K. Kinoshita, "CONT: A Concurrent Test Generation Algorithm," *Fault-Tolerant Computing Symp. (FTCS-17) Digest of Papers*, Pittsburgh, PA, pp. 22-27, July 1987.

[That80] S. M. Thatte and J. A. Abraham, "Test Generation for Microprocessors," *IEEE Trans. Computers*, Vol. C-29, pp. 429-441, June 1980, **see reprint in this chapter**.

[Thom71] J. J. Thomas, "Automated Diagnostic Test Program for Digital Networks," *Computer Design*, pp. 63-67, August 1971.

[Wei86] R. S. Wei and A. Sangiovanni-Vincentelli, "PLATYPUS: A PLA Test Pattern Generation Tool," *IEEE Trans. on CAD*, Vol. CAD-5, pp. 633-644, October 1986.

[Will77] T. W. Williams and E. B. Eichelberger, "Random Patterns With a Structured Sequential Logic Design," *Semicond. Test Symp.*, pp. 19-27, October 1977.

[Will83] T. W. Williams and K. P. Parker, "Design for Testability − A Survey," *Proc. IEEE*, Vol. 71, pp. 98-112, Jan. 1983, **see reprint in Chapter VI**.

Reprinted from *IEEE Transactions on Computers*, Volume C-30, Number 3, March 1981, pages 215-222. Copyright © 1981 by The Institute of Electrical and Electronics Engineers, Inc. All rights reserved.

An Implicit Enumeration Algorithm to Generate Tests for Combinational Logic Circuits

PRABHAKAR GOEL

Abstract—The D-algorithm (DALG) is shown to be ineffective for the class of combinational logic circuits that is used to implement error correction and translation (ECAT) functions. PODEM (path-oriented decision making) is a new test generation algorithm for combinational logic circuits. PODEM uses an implicit enumeration approach analogous to that used for solving 0–1 integer programming problems. It is shown that PODEM is very efficient for ECAT circuits and is significantly more efficient than DALG over the general spectrum of combinational logic circuits. A distinctive feature of PODEM is its simplicity when compared to the D-algorithm. PODEM is a complete algorithm in that it will generate a test if one exists. Heuristics are used to achieve an efficient implicit search of the space of all possible primary input patterns until either a test is found or the space is exhausted.

Index Terms—Combinational logic, D-algorithm, decision tree, error correction, implicit enumeration, stuck faults, test generation, untestable fault.

INTRODUCTION

TEST generation for combinational circuits has traditionally been considered a solved problem [1]. However, evaluation studies conducted by us have shown that the D-algorithm (DALG) [2] is extremely inefficient in generating tests for combinational logic circuits that implement error correction and translation (ECAT) type functions. For practical purposes, a logic circuit is characterized as being ECAT type if portions of it are constituted by XOR (EXCLUSIVE-OR) gates with reconvergent fan-out. The increasing emphasis on reliability of computer systems resulted in increased usage of ECAT circuits and existing test generation tools proved to be inadequate for them. An implicit enumeration [3] algorithm (PODEM—path oriented decision making) was developed shortly thereafter and experiments demonstrate that PODEM is an effective test generator for ECAT circuits. Subsequent studies, which are reported in this paper, show that the PODEM algorithm is significantly faster than DALG over the general class of combinational logic circuits. For LSI logic circuits there is an increasing trend towards designing for testability using the level sensitive scan design approach [9] or equivalent approaches [10]. Level sensitive scan design reduces the test generation problem for sequential logic circuits to one for combinational logic circuits. Advances in the state of the art for combinational logic test generation have therefore assumed increased significance.

Manuscript received November 23, 1979; revised October 6, 1980.

The author is with IBM General Technology Division, Poughkeepsie, NY 12601.

The unique characteristics of ECAT circuits that caused DALG to perform poorly are discussed in this paper. The PODEM test generation algorithm for combinational circuits is described. Analogies are drawn between PODEM and the implicit enumeration algorithms used in integer programming. Quantitative data is provided to demonstrate the performance advantage of PODEM over DALG. As is true for DALG, PODEM is a complete algorithm in that it will generate a test for a stuck fault if a test exists.

DEFINITIONS

Common terminology pertaining to test generation for logic circuits is readily introduced with an example. Fig. 1 shows a combinational logic circuit and a test for the single stuck fault that causes net h to permanently assume a 0 state. A *stuck-at-1 (s-a-1) fault* on a signal net causes that net to permanently assume the 1 state. A *stuck-at-0 (s-a-0) fault* causes a permanent 0 on the faulted net. The five-valued logic [2] (0, 1, X, D, $\overline{D}$) of Table I is used to describe the behavior of a circuit with failures. The *value D* designates a logic value 1 for a net in the good circuit or good machine and a 0 for the same net in the failing machine, $\overline{D}$ is the complement of D, and X designates a DON'T CARE value. A behavior difference between the good circuit and the failing circuit propagates along a *sensitized path*. In Fig. 1 the signal path h, j is referred to as a sensitized path. Externally controllable nets are referred to as *primary inputs* and are abbreviated to PI's. Externally observable nets are referred to as *primary outputs* and are abbreviated to PO's. Each stuck fault is associated with either an input net or the output net of a unique gate which is referred to as the *gate under test* and abbreviated to G.U.T. A *test* is generated when a sensitized path is built from the output of the gate under test to some PO. In Fig. 1 assignment of the values, $X, X, 1, 1, 0$ to the PI nets a, b, c, d, e, respectively, along with a measurement on the PO net j constitutes a test for the fault h s-a-0. The gate driving net h is the gate under test for the fault h s-a-0.

THE ECAT PROBLEM

The first ECAT type circuit encountered was an implementation of a single error correcting/double error detecting scheme over a set of 64 data bits and 8 parity bits. Error detection schemes involve the use of EXCLUSIVE-OR (XOR) trees to determine parities over various combinations of data/parity bits. The resulting parity signals are further combined to

78

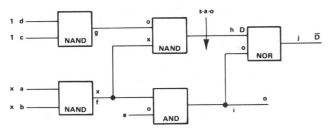

Fig. 1. Example to illustrate test generator terminology.

TABLE I
FIVE-VALUED LOGIC SYSTEM USED IN TEST GENERATION

B= NOT.A		C=A.AND.B					
A	B	A\B	0	1	x	D	$\bar{D}$
0	1	0	0	0	0	0	0
1	0	1	0	1	x	D	$\bar{D}$
x	x	x	0	x	x	x	x
D	$\bar{D}$	D	0	D	x	D	0
$\bar{D}$	D	$\bar{D}$	0	$\bar{D}$	x	0	$\bar{D}$

XOR = EXCLUSIVE OR GATE
$\overline{\text{XOR}}$ = EQUIVALENCE GATE

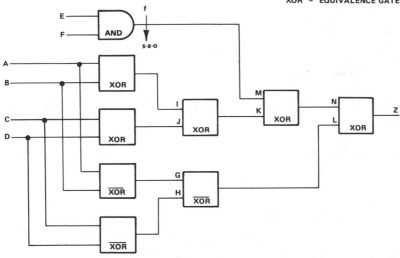

Fig. 2. ECAT type circuit exhibiting fanout and reconvergence involving XOR trees. Depicted fault illustrates DALG's inefficiency for such circuits.

generate signals that indicate error or help correct error bits. Basically, the ECAT circuit could be viewed as being made up of some number of XOR trees with reconvergence of the generated parity signals. A circuit with the basic ECAT characteristics is referred to as an "ECAT type circuit" or an "ECAT circuit." The circuit in Fig. 2 is an ECAT circuit.

DALG is typically used with the primitive gate (AND, OR, NAND, NOR) representation of a logic circuit. However, for ease of explanation DALG's techniques are extended to the XOR and equivalence gates. In generating a test, DALG creates a decision structure in which there is more than one choice available at each decision node. Through an implicit enumeration process, all alternatives at each decision node are capable of being examined. For the fault f in Fig. 2, DALG may typically go through the following steps.

1) The test for f requires a logic 1 on M for the good machine. Setting E and F each to 1 results in a D at M.

2) Generating a sensitized path from the net M to the primary output Z, using recursive intersection of D-cubes, may result in the ordered assignments $K = 1$ and $L = 1$ represented in Fig. 3. Alternative assignments $K = 0$ and $L = 0$ are still available for consideration should the present assignments prove futile.

3) DALG justifies each internal net assignment on a levelized basis (see Fig. 3). Since the functions P and $\bar{P}$ realized at nets K and L, respectively, are complementary, no justification is possible for the concurrent assignments $K = 1$, $L = 1$. However, in establishing the absence of the justification, DALG must enumerate 2^3 primary input values (2^n if $2n$ were the number of external inputs to the XOR tree) before it can

correct the bad decision made on L, that is, change the assignment on L from 1 to 0. Looked at differently, DALG made two conflicting assignments $K = 1$ and $L = 1$ (on internal nets) and to detect the conflict DALG is forced to enumerate half of all possible values on primary inputs A–D. The requirement of having all external inputs known to make the output known is peculiar to XOR (or equivalence) trees.

Next consider what would happen for parity trees with up to 72 external inputs (as in the original ECAT circuit). For some faults the number of primary input values that must be enumerated can be of the order of 2^{36}. With the above phenomenon repeating itself for most faults in ECAT circuits, it is seen that even if DALG were implemented on the fastest computers, it would have unacceptable performance in run time and therefore in test coverage.

An experimental study conducted by us demonstrated that DALG was ineffective for ECAT type circuits. When permitted to give up on faults after a large number of remade decisions, DALG was able to generate tests for only six out of 7000 faults in 2 h of CPU time with an IBM 360/85 computer and DALG had still not completed.

TEST GENERATION VIEWED AS A FINITE SPACE SEARCH PROBLEM

The test generation problem can be formulated as a search of the n-dimensional 0–1 state space of primary input patterns of an n-input combinational logic circuit. Consider the combinational circuit of Fig. 4. In Fig. 4 g is an internal net and

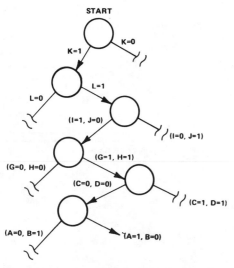

Fig. 3. DALG decision tree—DALG needs a large number of remade decisions resulting in a high test generation cost.

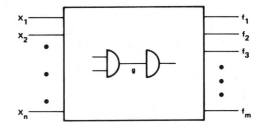

Fig. 4. Combinational circuit used in formulating test generation as an *n*-dimensional 0–1 state space search problem.

the objective is to generate a test for the stuck fault g s-a-0. The state on g can be expressed as a Boolean function of the primary inputs, $X_1, X_2, \cdots, X_n$. Similarly, each primary output $(f_j, j = 1, 2, \cdots, m)$ can be expressed as a Boolean function of the state on net g as well as the primary inputs $X_1, X_2, \cdots, X_n$. Let

$$g = G(X_1, X_2, \cdots, X_n)$$

and

$$f_j = F_j(g, X_1, X_2, \cdots, X_n)$$

$$\text{where } 1 \leq j \leq m \text{ and } X_i = 0 \text{ or } 1 \text{ for } 1 \leq i \leq n.$$

The problem of test generation for g s-a-0 can be stated [4] as one of solving the following set of Boolean equations:

$$G(X_1, X_2, \cdots, X_n) = 1$$

$$F_j(1, X_1, X_2, \cdots, X_n) \oplus F_j(0, X_1, X_2, \cdots, X_n) = 1$$

for at least one j, $1 \leq j \leq m$ and $X_i = 0$ or 1 for $1 \leq i \leq n$.

The set of equations for g s-a-1 are the same as above except that G is set equal to 0. Hence, test generation can be viewed as a search of an *n*-dimensional 0–1 space defined by the variables X_i ($1 \leq i \leq n$) for points that satisfy the above set of equations. More generally, the search will result in finding a k-dimensional subspace ($k \leq n$) such that all points in the subspace will satisfy the above set of equations.

The integer programming problem and various problems in the field of artifical intelligence have been approached using state space search methods [5] and the branch and bound technique [6]. Implicit enumeration refers to a subset of the branch and bound algorithms designed specifically for search of a *n*-dimensional 0–1 state space.

PODEM TEST GENERATION ALGORITHM

The PODEM (path oriented decision making) test generation algorithm is an implicit enumeration algorithm in which all possible primary input patterns are implicitly, but exhaustively, examined as tests for a given fault. The examination

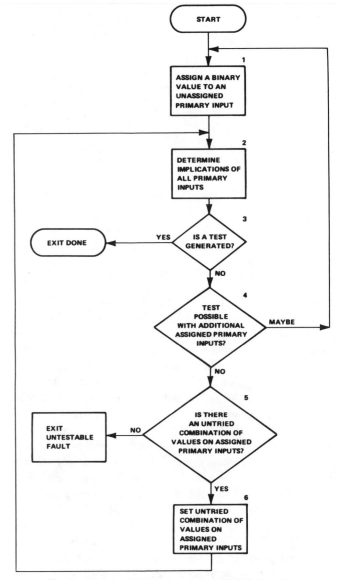

Fig. 5. High-level description of the PODEM algorithm.

of PI patterns is terminated as soon as a test is found. If it is determined that no PI pattern can be a test, the fault is *untestable* by definition.

Boolean equations were used in the preceding section for conceptual purposes. Unlike the Boolean difference approach [4], the PODEM algorithm does not involve manipulation of Boolean equations. Instead, the combinational logic schematic is used in a manner similar to that in the D-algorithm. The flowchart of Fig. 5 provides a high-level description of the PODEM algorithm. The implicit enumeration process used in PODEM results in the decision tree structure illustrated by

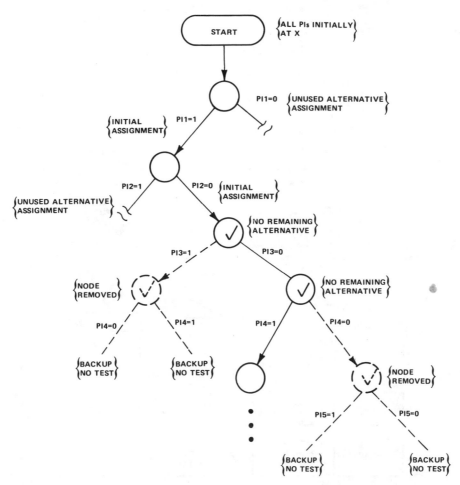

Fig. 6.   Decision tree illustrating the "branch and bound" process in the PODEM algorithm.

Fig. 6. In Figs. 5 and 6 all PI's are initially at X, that is, they are unassigned. An initial assignment ("branch"–in the context of branch and bound algorithms) of either 0 or 1 on a PI is recorded as an unflagged node in the decision tree. Implications of present PI assignments (box 2) use the five-valued logic of Table I and the process is identical to the forward IMPLY process in the D-algorithm. The decision tree is an ordered list of nodes with: 1) each node identifying a current assignment of either a 0 or 1 to one PI, and 2) the ordering reflects the relative sequence in which the current assignments were made. A node is flagged (indicated by a check mark inside the node in Fig. 6) if the initial assignment has been rejected and the alternative is being tried. When both assignment choices at a node are rejected, then the associated node is removed and the predecessor node's current assignment is also rejected. The last PI assignment made is rejected if it can be determined (box 4 of Fig. 5) that no test can be generated with the assignments made on the assigned PI's, regardless of values that may be assigned to the as yet unassigned PI's. The rejection of a PI assignment results in a "bounding" of the decision tree, in the context of branch and bound algorithms, since it avoids the enumeration of the subsequent assignments to the as yet unassigned PI's. The two simple propositions listed below are evaluated to carry out the process of box 4 in Fig. 5.

Proposition 1: The signal net (for the given stuck fault) has the same logic level as the stuck level.

Proposition 2: There is no signal path from an internal signal net to a primary output such that the internal signal net is at a D or $\overline{D}$ value and all other nets on the signal path are at X.

If Proposition 1 is true, then it is obvious that assignment of known values to unassigned PI's cannot result in a test. If Proposition 2 is true, then there exists no signal path along which the D or $\overline{D}$ can propagate to a circuit output. Hence, only if both Propositions 1 and 2 are false, then in box 4 it is concluded that a test is possible with the present PI assignment even though further enumeration may show that it is not.

Fig. 7 is a more detailed description of the basic PODEM algorithm and provides the steps used to carry out the "bounding" of the decision tree—see boxes 5 through 9. The decision tree being an ordered list of nodes can be implemented as a LIFO stack. An initial PI assignment (box 2) results in pushing the associated unflagged node onto the stack. The "bounding" of the decision tree is done by popping the stack until an unflagged node is on the top of the stack. The alternative assignment is made on the PI associated with the unflagged node and the node is modified to be flagged (box 8). All nodes popped out of the stack are in effect removed from

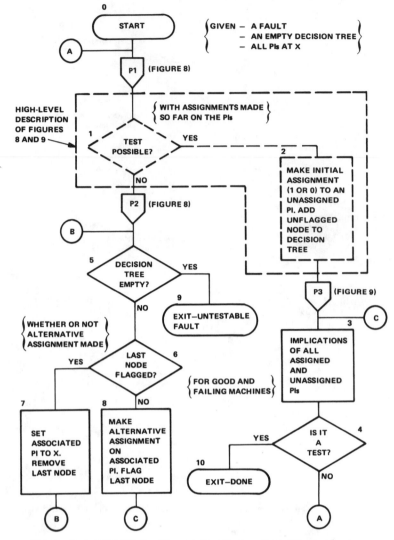

Fig. 7. Basic PODEM algorithm detailing the bounding of the decision tree.

the decision tree and their associated PI's are set to X (box 7). A new combination of values on the PI's is obtained by the bounding process and is evaluated (boxes 3 and 4) for constituting a test. The entire process is iteratively continued until a test is found (box 10) or it is determined that a test is possible with additional PI assignments (box 2) or the decision tree becomes empty (box 9). Note that bounding of the decision tree results in rejection of only those combinations of values on the PI's that cannot be a test for the given stuck fault. Therefore, if the decision tree becomes empty the given fault must be untestable. It is thus shown that PODEM is a complete test generation algorithm in that a test will be found if one exists.

In the flowchart of Fig. 7 it would be most desirable to have the least number of remade decisions (reversals of initial PI assignments) before either a test is found or a fault is determined to be untestable. Practical considerations dictate that when a preset number of decisions are remade, the fault being worked on is given up and a new fault is selected for test generation. Poor initial PI assignments can cause a large number

of remade decisions before a test is found. However, the process of determining initial assignments should not be so expensive as to outweigh the benefits of good initial assignments.

In PODEM heuristics are used to select the next PI to be assigned as well as the initial logic level to be assigned (box 2 of Fig. 7). Branch and bound algorithms also use heuristics for the analogous process of "choosing the partitioning variable and branching" [7].

CHOOSING A PRIMARY INPUT AND LOGIC LEVEL FOR INITIAL ASSIGNMENT

A two-step process is used to choose a PI and logic level for initial assignment.

Step 1: Determine an initial objective—the objective should be to bring the test generator closer to its goal of propagating a D or $\overline{D}$ to a primary output.

Step 2: Given the initial objective, choose a PI and a logic level such that the chosen logic level assigned to the chosen PI has a good likelihood of helping towards meeting the initial objective.

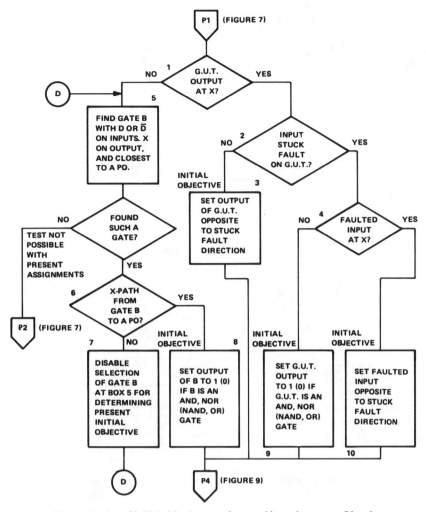

Fig. 8.   Determination of initial objective—used as a guide to choose next PI assignment.

Initial objectives are determined through the procedure flowcharted in Fig. 8. An objective is defined by: 1) a logic level 0 or 1 that is referred to as the *objective logic level,* and 2) an *objective net* which is the net at which the objective logic level is desired. If the failing gate or gate under test (G.U.T.) does not have a D or $\overline{D}$ on its output (that is, is not setup), the initial objective is directed towards promoting setup for that gate. Once the gate under test has been setup, the initial objective is aimed at propagating a D or $\overline{D}$ one level of logic closer to a PO than before. In box 5 of Fig. 8 the shortest distance from a gate to a PO is used as a crude measure of the difficulty of creating a sensitized path between the gate and the PO. More sophisticated measures are certainly available although the cost of determining them may exceed the added benefits obtained. In boxes 8 and 9 the statement of the objective is intended only to establish the requirement for sensitizing logic levels on those inputs of gate B which are presently at X.

The flowchart of Fig. 9 describes a procedure, referred to as *backtrace,* to obtain an initial PI assignment given an initial objective. Boxes 4 and 5 of Fig. 9 require relative measures of controllability for the inputs of the logic gate Q. The rationale for choosing the "easiest to control" input or the "hardest to control" input of Q is apparent from the following:

1) In box 5 the current objective level is such that it can be

obtained by setting any one input of gate Q to a *controlling state* (e.g., 0 for an AND/NAND gate or 1 for an OR/NOR gate). The intent is to choose that input which can be most easily set.

2) In box 4 the current objective level can only be obtained by setting each input of gate Q to a *noncontrolling state* (e.g., 1 for an AND/NAND gate or 0 for an OR/NOR gate). The intent is to choose that input which is hardest to set, since an early determination of the inability to set the chosen input will prevent fruitless time spent in attempting to set the remaining inputs of Q.

The backtrace procedure causes a path to be traced from the objective net backwards to a primary input. Since the initial PI assignment corresponds to making a decision at a node of the decision tree, the algorithm has been named path-oriented decision making (PODEM) test pattern generator.

The controllability measures for the inputs of Q influence only the efficiency of determining a valid PI assignment that satisfies the chosen initial objective. Hence, heuristic measures for controllability are adequate. Methods for determining heuristic controllability measures are available in published literature [8]. The backtrace process in PODEM is much more simplified than (though similar to) the corresponding *consistency operation* [2] carried out in other test generators.

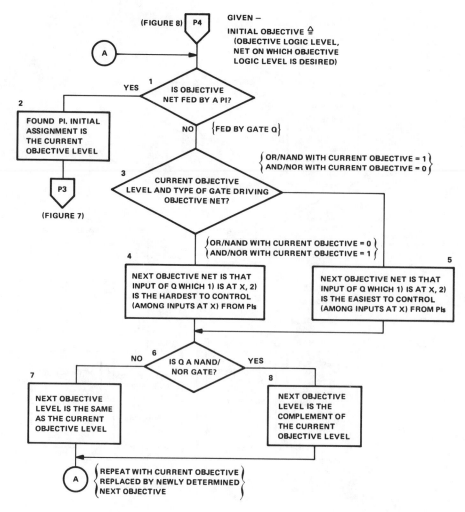

Fig. 9. Backtrace—determine initial PI assignment given an initial objective.

PERFORMANCE COMPARISON

A practical version of DALG was compared with an implementation of PODEM. It showed that PODEM achieved 100 percent test coverage on each of the four ECAT type circuits used. Since DALG and PODEM are complete algorithms, given enough time, both will generate tests for each testable fault. The results cited indicate that DALG will require impractical amounts of time to attain 100 percent test coverage for ECAT structures. While the results demonstrate that PODEM performs very effectively for ECAT structures, there is no proof that such performance is guaranteed for all ECAT structures. The test coverage on non-ECAT type circuits was generally the same for PODEM and DALG. However, the execution speed of PODEM was strikingly faster than that of DALG. Table II shows the test coverages and a normalized comparison of the execution speeds of PODEM and DALG as derived from the evaluation study. To obtain the data of Table II, both PODEM and DALG were first executed to generate tests for the stuck faults in each case. The tests were minimized by an automatic procedure that compacted the tests using a static compaction procedure [11]. The compacted tests were then fault simulated to obtain the test coverage. The test coverage of 31.2 percent obtained by DALG on case 3 should not be interpreted as indicating the percentage of faults for

TABLE II
COMPARISON OF PODEM AND DALG

TEST CASE	TYPE	# OF BLOCKS	NORMALIZED RUN TIME		TEST COVERAGE %	
			PODEM	DALG	PODEM	DALG
1	ECAT	828	1	34.5	100.0	99.7
2	ECAT	935	1	12.8	100.0	93.1
3	ECAT	2,002	1	Not meaningful*	100.0	31.2
4	ECAT	948	1	5.7	100.0	95.7
5	-	951	1	2.2	99.5	99.5
6	-	1,249	1	3.5	98.2	98.2
7	-	1,172	1	2.6	98.5	98.5
8	ALU	1,095	1	15.3	96.5	96.2
9	MUX	1,082	1	3.2	96.6	96.6
10	-	915	1	3.9	96.3	96.3
11	ALU	919	1	1.7	99.7	99.8
12	DECODER	1,018	1	3.8	99.1	99.1
13	PLA	538	1	2.5	94.5	94.5
14	PLA	682	2.6	1	89.4	89.4
15	PLA	1,566	1	3.1	97.4	97.4

* Test coverage from DALG was much lower making a run time comparison lose its significance.

which DALG actually generated tests. Actually, DALG generated tests for 14 faults only and the remainder of the tested faults were tested "accidentally."

SUMMARY AND CONCLUSIONS

An explanation has been developed for the poor performance of the D-algorithm in generating tests for stuck faults in the ECAT class of combinational logic circuits. The PODEM algorithm is described in detail and it has been demonstrated that PODEM solves the test generation problem faced by the D-algorithm. Study results are quoted to demonstrate that PODEM is significantly faster than the D-algorithm for the general class of combinational logic circuits. The similarities of the PODEM algorithm with other implicit enumeration algorithms, a subset of branch and bound algorithms, have been identified. The problem of test generation has been formulated as one involving the search of an n-dimensional 0–1 state space constrained by a set of Boolean equations and hence, amenable to an implicit enumeration approach. The description of PODEM uses a combinational logic schematic for test generation; however, it is evident that the technique used in PODEM is applicable for solving a set of generalized Boolean equations.

REFERENCES

[1] S. G. Chappell, "Automatic test generation for asynchronous digital circuits," *Bell Syst. Tech. J.,* vol. 53, pp. 1477–1503, Oct. 1974.
[2] J. P. Roth, "Diagnosis of automata failures: A calculus & a method," *IBM J. Res. Develop.,* vol. 10, pp. 278–291, July 1966.
[3] E. Balas, "An additive algorithm for solving linear programs with zero-one variables," *Oper. Res.,* vol. 13, pp. 517–546, 1965.
[4] F. F. Sellers, M. Y. Hsiao, and L. W. Bearnson, "Analyzing errors with the Boolean difference," *IEEE Trans. Comput.,* vol. C-17, pp. 676–683, July 1968.
[5] N. J. Nilsson, *Problem-Solving Methods in Artificial Intelligence.* New York: McGraw-Hill, 1971, ch. 3.
[6] E. W. Lawler and D. E. Wood, "Branch-and-bound methods—A survey," *Oper. Res.,* vol. 14, pp. 669–719, 1966.
[7] R. Garfinkel and G. L. Nemhauser, *Integer Programming.* New York: Wiley, 1972, ch. 4, pp. 4–24.
[8] T. J. Snethen, "Simulator oriented fault test generator," in *Proc. 14th Des. Automat. Conf.,* June 1977, pp. 88–93.
[9] E. B. Eichelberger and T. W. Williams, "A logic design structure for LSI testability," in *Proc. 14th Des. Automat. Conf.,* June 1977, pp. 462–468.
[10] A. Yamada *et al.,* "Automatic system level test generation and fault location for large digital systems," in *Proc. 15th Des. Automat. Conf.,* June 1978, pp. 347–352.
[11] P. Goel and B. C. Rosales, "Test generation and dynamic compaction of tests," in *Proc. 1979 Annu. Test Conf.,* Cherry Hill, NJ.

Prabhakar Goel was born in Meerut, India, on January 16, 1949. He received the B. Tech. degree in electrical engineering from the Indian Institute of Technology, Kanpur, India, in 1970 and the M.S. and Ph.D. degrees in electrical engineering from Carnegie-Mellon University, Pittsburgh, PA, in 1971 and 1974, respectively.

Currently, he is a Development Engineer with the IBM Corporation and manages a group responsible for developing design automation tools for test generation and design verification. He has received two invention awards, an outstanding innovation award, and a corporate award for his work at IBM.

On the Acceleration of Test Generation Algorithms

HIDEO FUJIWARA, SENIOR MEMBER, IEEE, AND TAKESHI SHIMONO, STUDENT MEMBER, IEEE

Abstract—In order to accelerate an algorithm for test generation, it is necessary to reduce the number of backtracks in the algorithm and to shorten the process time between backtracks. In this paper, we consider several techniques to accelerate test generation and present a new test generation algorithm called FAN (fan-out-oriented test generation algorithm). It is shown that the FAN algorithm is faster and more efficient than the PODEM algorithm reported by Goel. We also present an automatic test generation system composed of the FAN algorithm and the concurrent fault simulation. Experimental results on large combinational circuits of up to 3000 gates demonstrate that the system performs test generation very fast and effectively.

Index Terms—Combinational logic circuits, *D*-algorithm, decision tree, multiple backtrace, PODEM algorithm, sensitization, stuck faults, test generation.

I. INTRODUCTION

WITH the progress of LSI/VLSI technology, the problem of fault detection for logic circuits is becoming more and more difficult. As the logic circuits under test get larger, generating tests is becoming harder. Recent work has established that the problem of test generation, even for monotone circuits, is NP-complete [1]. Hence, it appears that the computation is, for the worst case, exponential with the size of the circuit. One approach to overcome this is to take several techniques known as design for testability. The techniques using shift registers such as LSSD [2], Scan Path [3], etc., allow the test generation problem to be completely reduced to one of generating tests for combinational circuits. Hence, for these LSSD-type circuits, it is sufficient to develop a fast and efficient test generation algorithm only for combinational circuits.

Many test generation algorithms have been proposed over the years [4]–[8], [11]. The most widely used is the *D*-algorithm reported by Roth [5]. However, it has been pointed out that the *D*-algorithm is extremely inefficient in generating tests for combinational circuits that implement error correction and translation functions. To improve this point, a new test generation algorithm called PODEM was recently developed by Goel [8]. Goel showed that the PODEM algorithm is significantly faster than the *D*-algorithm by presenting experimental results. Indeed, the PODEM algorithm has succeeded in re-

ducing the number of occurrences of backtracks in comparison to the *D*-algorithm. However, there still remain many possibilities of reducing the number of backtracks in the algorithm.

In order to accelerate an algorithm for test generation, it is necessary to reduce the number of occurrences of backtracks in the algorithm and to shorten the processing time between backtracks. In this paper we consider several techniques to accelerate test generation, and we present a new algorithm for generating tests called FAN (fan-out-oriented test generation algorithm). FAN is a complete algorithm in that it will generate a test if one exists. Experimental results on large combinational circuits of up to 3000 gates demonstrate that the FAN algorithm is faster and more efficient than the PODEM algorithm over these circuits. We also present an automatic test generation system composed of the FAN algorithm and the concurrent fault simulation [9] which performs test generation very fast and effectively over the above large combinational circuits.

II. ACCELERATION OF ALGORITHM

Now we assume that the readers are familiar with the *D*-algorithm and the PODEM algorithm, and so we shall use some terminologies such as *D*-frontier, *D*-drive, implication, line justification, backtrace, etc., without definitions (see [5] and [8] for definitions). In this paper, we shall consider multiinput and multioutput combinational circuits composed of AND, OR, NAND, NOR, and NOT gates. The type of fault model assumed here is the standard stuck fault, i.e., all faults can be modeled by lines which are stuck at logical 0 (s-a-0) or stuck at logical 1 (s-a-1). A fault consisting of a single stuck line is called a single fault. We shall focus our attention only on detecting single stuck faults.

In this section, aiming at the acceleration of test generation, we shall point out some defects of the PODEM algorithm and consider several effective techniques to eliminate these disadvantages.

In generating a test, the algorithm creates a decision tree in which there is more than one choice available at each decision node. The initial choice is arbitrary, but it may be necessary during the execution of the algorithm to return and try another possible choice. This is called a backtrack. In order to accelerate the algorithm, it is necessary to

1) reduce the number of backtracks, and
2) shorten the process time between backtracks.

Manuscript received September 27, 1982; revised June 1, 1983.

H. Fujiwara is with the Department of Electronic Engineering, Osaka University, Osaka 565, Japan.

T. Shimono was with the Department of Electronic Engineering, Osaka University, Osaka, Japan. He is now with the NEC Corporation, Tokyo 108, Japan.

Reprinted from *IEEE Transactions on Computers*, Volume C-32, Number 12, December 1983, pages 1137-1144. Copyright © 1983 by The Institute of Electrical and Electronics Engineers, Inc. All rights reserved.

The reduction of the number of backtracks is particularly important.

Heuristics should be used to achieve an efficient search. The PODEM algorithm adopted heuristics in the backtrace operation as follows.

• If the current objective level is such that it can be obtained by setting any one input of the current gate to a controlling state, e.g., 0 for an AND/NAND gate or 1 for an OR/NOR gate, then choose that input which can be most easily set.

• If the current objective level can only be obtained by setting all inputs of the current gate to a noncontrolling state, e.g., 1 for an AND/NAND gate or 0 for an OR/NOR gate, then choose that input which is hardest to set, since an early determination of the inability to set the chosen input will prevent fruitless time spent in attempting to set the remaining inputs of the gate.

In this heuristic, we can use controllability measures. In the PODEM algorithm as well as the D-algorithm, the D-frontier usually consists of many gates, and a choice of which gate to D-drive through next must be made. To decide this choice, PODEM adopted heuristics using a very simple observability measure as follows.

• As a D-frontier to D-drive, choose a gate closest to a primary output.

In this heuristic, we can use other observability measures. Methods for determining controllability/observability measures are available in the published literature, such as [10].

In order to reduce the number of backtracks, it is important to find the nonexistence of the solution as soon as possible. In the "branch and bound" algorithm, when we find that there exists no solution below the current node in the decision tree, we should backtrack immediately to avoid the subsequent unnecessary search. The PODEM algorithm seems to lack the careful consideration in this point.

• In each step of the algorithm, determine as many signal values as possible which can be *uniquely* implied.

To do this, we take the implication operation which completely traces such signal determination both forwards and backwards through the circuit. The idea of this complete implication is inherent in the D-algorithm, and hence represents an improvement only with respect to PODEM. Moreover, we can take other techniques as follows.

• Assign a faulty signal value D or $\overline{D}$ which is uniquely determined or implied by the fault under consideration (see Fig. 1).

Note that we specify only the values that are uniquely determined. As an example, for a three-input AND gate in Fig. 1(a) and the fault E s-a-0, we assign the value D to the output E and 1's to all inputs of the AND gate since these values are uniquely implied by the fault E s-a-0. However, for the fault E s-a-1, we assign only the value $\overline{D}$ to the output E. All the input values of the AND gate are left unspecified, i.e., X, since those values are not determined uniquely from E s-a-1 [see Fig. 1(c)].

As an example, consider the circuit of Fig. 2. For the fault L s-a-1, we assign the value $\overline{D}$ to the line L and 1's to the inputs J, K, and E. Then after the implication operation, we have a test pattern for the fault without backtracks, as shown in Fig.

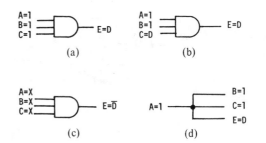

Fig. 1. Assignment of fault signals. (a) E s-a-0. (b) C s-a-0. (c) E s-a-1. (d) E s-a-1.

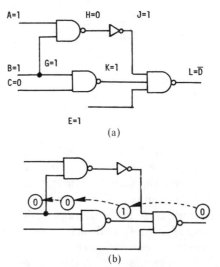

Fig. 2. Effect of fault signal assignment. (a) Fault signal assignment and implication. (b) PODEM.

2(a). On the other hand, in PODEM, the initial objective (L, 0) is determined to set up the faulty signal $\overline{D}$ to the line L, and then the backtrace procedure starts. As shown in Fig. 2(b), the backtrace procedure causes a path to be traced from the initial objective line L backwards to a primary input B. The assignment $B = 0$ implies that $L = 1$. This contradicts the initial objective, and setting L to $\overline{D}$ fails and a backtrack occurs. As seen in this example, the assignment of Fig. 2(a) is a condition necessary for a test of the fault L s-a-1. By assigning the values which are uniquely determined, we can avoid the unnecessary choice.

Consider the circuit of Fig. 3(a). Suppose that the D-frontier is {$G2$}. When the D-frontier consists of a single gate, we often have specific paths such that every path from the site of the D-frontier to a primary output always goes through those paths. In this example, every path from the gate $G2$ to a primary output passes through the paths F-H and K-M. In order to propagate the value D or $\overline{D}$ to a primary output, we have to propagate the fault signal along both F-H and K-M. Therefore, if there exists a test in this point, paths F-H and K-M should be sensitized. Then we have the assignment $C = 1$, $G = 1$, $J = 1$, and $L = 1$ to sensitize them. This partial sensitization which is uniquely determined is called a *unique sensitization*. In Fig. 3(a), after the implication of this assignment, we have $A = 1$, $B = 0$, $F = \overline{D}$, and $H = D$ without backtracks. On the other hand, PODEM sets the initial objective (F, 0) to propagate the fault signal to the line F and performs the

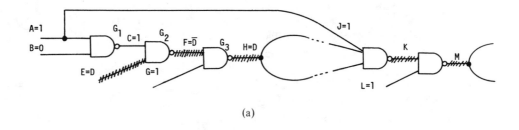

(a)

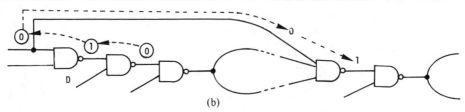

(b)

Fig. 3.   Effect of unique sensitization. (a) Unique sensitization and
implication. (b) PODEM.

backtrace procedure. If the backtrace performs along the path as shown in Fig. 7(b), we have to assign 0 to A, and we have $J = 0$ and $K = 1$ by the implication. Although no inconsistency appears at this point, an inconsistency or the disappearance of the D-frontier will occur in the future when the faulty signal propagates from H to K. To find such an inconsistency, the PODEM algorithm uses a lookahead technique called the X-path check, i.e., it checks whether there is any path from a gate in the D-frontier to a primary output such that all the lines along the path are at X. However, in our example, the back-tracking from $A = 0$ to $A = 1$ is unavoidable in PODEM.

• When the D-frontier consists of a single gate, apply a *unique sensitization.*

As seen in the above examples, in order to reduce the number of backtracks, it is very effective to find as many values as possible which are uniquely determined in each step of the algorithm. This is because the assignment of the uniquely determined values could decrease the number of possible selection.

The execution of the techniques mentioned above may result in specifying the output of a gate G, but leaving the inputs of G unspecified. This type of output line is called an *unjustified line.* It is necessary to specify input values so as to produce the specified output values. In PODEM, since all the values are first assigned only to the primary inputs and only the forward implication is performed, unjustified lines never appear. However, if we take the techniques mentioned above, the un-justified lines may appear, and thus in this case, some initial objectives will be produced simultaneously so as to justify them. This will be managed by introducing a multiple back-trace procedure which is an extention of the backtrace procedure of Goel [8].

Early detection of an inconsistency is very effective to de-crease the number of backtracks. We shall continue to consider some techniques to find an inconsistency at an early stage.

When a signal line L is reachable from some fan-out point, that is, there exists a path from some fan-out point to L, we say that L is *bound.* A signal line which is not bound is said to be

free. When a free line L is adjacent to some bound line, we say that L is a *head* line. As an example, consider the circuit of Fig. 4(a). In the circuit, $A, B, C, E, F, G, H,$ and J are all free lines, and $K, L,$ and M are bound lines. Among the free lines, J and H are head lines of the circuit since J and H are adjacent to the bound lines L and M, respectively.

The backtrace procedure in PODEM traces a single path backwards to a primary input. However, it suffices to stop the backtrace at a head line for the following reasons. The sub-circuit composed of only free lines and the corresponding gates is a fan-out-free circuit since it contains no fan-out point. For fan-out-free circuits, line justification can be performed without backtracks. Hence, we can find the values on the pri-mary inputs which justify all the values on the head lines without backtracks. It is sufficient, or even efficient, to let the line justification for head lines wait to the last stage of test generation.

• Stop the backtrace at a *head line,* and postpone the line justification for the head line to the last.

To illustrate this, consider the circuit shown in Fig. 4(a). Suppose that we want to set $J = 0$ and do not know at the current stage that there exists no test under the condition $J = 0$. In PODEM, the initial objective is set to $(J, 0)$, and the backtrace may result in the assignment $A = 1$. Since the value of J is still not determined, PODEM again starts the backtrace procedure, and we get the assignment $B = 0$. $A = 1$ and $B = 0$ imply that $J = 0$. Here, by hypothesis, there exists no test under $J = 0$, and thus an inconsistency occurs for the current assignment, and PODEM must backtrack to change the as-signment on B, as shown in Fig. 4(b). In this case, if we stop the backtrace to the head line J, we can decrease the number of backtracks, as shown in Fig. 4(c).

Performing a unique sensitization, we need to identify paths which would be uniquely sensitized. Also, we need to identify all the head lines in the circuit. These must be identified, and that topological information should be stored in some manner before the test generation starts. According to our experi-mental results, the computing time of the preprocess can be

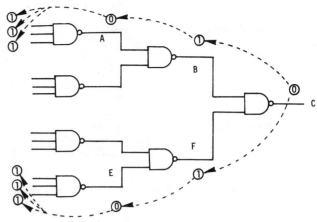

Fig. 5.   Backtrace.

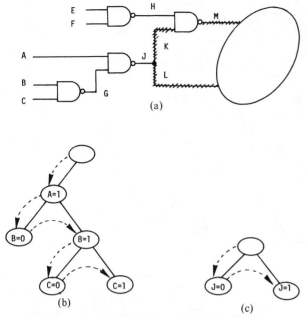

Fig. 4.   Effect of head lines. (a) Illustrative circuit. (b) PODEM. (c) Backtracking at head lines.

as small as *negligible* compared to the total computing time for test generation.

• *Multiple backtrace*, that is, concurrent tracing more than one path, is more efficient than the backtrace along a single path.

Consider the circuit of Fig. 5. For the objective of setting $C = 0$, PODEM repeats the backtrace three times along the same path C-B-A, and also along the same path C-F-E before the value 0 is specified on C by the implication. Thus, we can see that the backtrace along a single path is inefficient and wastes time, which may be avoided. From this point of view, we could guess that the multiple backtrace along plural paths is more efficient than the single backtrace. The modes of procedure which implement multiple backtrace are various. In the following, we shall introduce a procedure for multiple backtrace.

In the backtrace of PODEM, an objective is defined by an objective logic level 0 or 1 and an objective line which is the line at which the objective logic level is desired. An objective which will be used in the multiple backtrace is defined by a triple:

$$(s, n_0(s), n_1(s))$$

where s is an objective line, $n_0(s)$ is the number of times the objective logic level 0 is required at s, and $n_1(s)$ is the number of times the objective logic level 1 is required at s.

The computation of $n_0(s)$ and $n_1(s)$ will be described later. The multiple backtrace starts with more than one initial objective, that is, *a set of initial objectives*. Beginning with the set of initial objectives, a set of objectives which appear in the midst of the procedure is called *a set of current objectives*. A set of objectives which will be obtained at head lines is called *a set of head objectives*. A set of objectives on fan-out points is called *a set of fan-out-point objectives*.

An initial objective required to set 0 to a line s is

$$(s, n_0(s), n_1(s)) = (s, 1, 0)$$

and an initial objective required to set 1 to s is

$$(s, n_0(s), n_1(s)) = (s, 0, 1).$$

Working breadth-first from these initial objectives backwards to head lines, we determine next objectives from the current objectives successively as follows.

1) AND gate [see Fig. 6(a)].

Let X be an input which is the easiest to control setting 0. Then

$$n_0(X) = n_0(Y), \quad n_1(X) = n_1(Y)$$

and for other inputs X_i,

$$n_0(X_i) = 0, \quad n_1(X_i) = n_1(Y)$$

where Y is the output of the AND gate.

2) OR gate [see Fig. 6(b)].

Let X be an input which is the easiest to control setting 1. Then

$$n_0(X) = n_0(Y), \quad n_1(X) = n_1(Y)$$

and for other inputs X_i,

$$n_0(X_i) = n_0(Y), \quad n_1(X_i) = 0.$$

3) NAND gate.

Let X be an input which is the easiest to control setting 0. Then

$$n_0(X) = n_1(Y), \quad n_1(X) = n_0(Y)$$

and for other inputs X_i,

$$n_o(X_i) = 0, \quad n_1(X_i) = n_0(Y).$$

4) NOR gate.

Let X be an input which is the easiest to control setting 1. Then

$$n_0(X) = n_1(Y), \quad n_1(X) = n_0(Y)$$

and for other inputs X_i,

$$n_0(X_i) = n_1(Y), \quad n_1(X_1) = 0.$$

5) NOT gate [see Fig. 6(c)].

$$n_0(X) = n_1(Y), \quad n_1(X) = n_0(Y).$$

6) Fan-out point [see Fig. 6(d)].

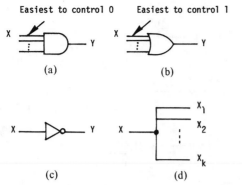

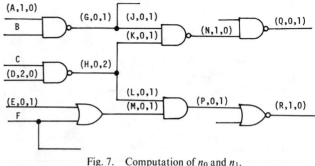

Fig. 7.   Computation of n_0 and n_1.

Fig. 6.   Gates and fan-out point. (a) AND. (b) OR. (c) NOT. (d) Fan-out point.

$$n_0(X) = \sum_{i=1}^{k} n_0(X_i), \quad n_1(X) = \sum_{i=1}^{k} n_1(X_i).$$

Fig. 7 shows an example to illustrate the computation of $n_0(s)$ and $n_1(s)$. The initial objectives are $(Q,0,1)$ and $(R,1,0)$, i.e., Q and R are first required to set 1 and 0, respectively. At the fan-out point H, $n_1(H)$ is obtained by summing $n_1(K)$ and $n_1(L)$, and the corresponding fan-out point objective becomes $(H,0,2)$.

The flowchart of Fig. 8 describes the multiple backtrace procedure. Each objective arriving at a fan-out point stops its backtracing while there exist other current objectives. After the set of current objectives becomes empty, a fan-out point objective closest to a primary output is taken out, if one exists. If the fan-out point objective satisfies the following condition, the objective becomes the final objective in the backtrace process, and the procedure ends at the exit (D) in Fig. 8. The condition is that the fan-out point p is not reachable from the fault line and both $n_0(p)$ and $n_1(p)$ are nonzero. In this case, we assign a value [0 if $n_0(P) \geq n_1(p)$ or 1 if $n_0(p) < n_1(p)$] to the fan-out point and perform the implications. The first part of the condition is necessary to guarantee that the value assigned is binary, that is, neither D nor $\overline{D}$.

In PODEM, the assignment of a binary value is allowed only to the primary inputs. In our algorithm, FAN, we allow to assign a value to fan-out points as well as head lines, and hence the backtracking could occur only at fan-out points and head lines, and not at primary inputs. The reason why we assign a value to a fan-out point p is that there might exist a great possibility of an inconsistency when the objective in backtracing has an inconsistent requirement such that both $n_0(p)$ and $n_1(p)$ are nonzero. So as to avoid the fruitless computation, we assign a binary value to the fan-out point as soon as the objective involves a contradictory requirement. This leads to the early detection of inconsistency which would decrease the number of backtracks.

• In the multiple backtrace, if an objective at a fan-out point p has a contradictory requirement, that is , both $n_0(p)$ and $n_1(p)$ are nonzero, stop the backtrace so as to assign a binary value to the fan-out point.

When an objective at a fan-out point p has no contradiction, that is, either $n_0(p)$ or $n_1(p)$ is zero, the backtrace would be continued from the fan-out point. If all the objectives arrive

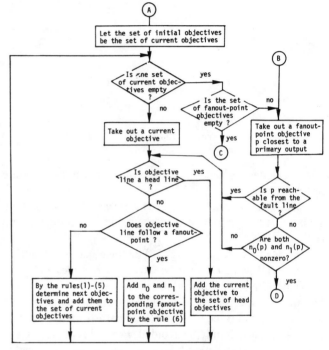

Fig. 8.   Flowchart of multiple backtrace.

at head lines, that is, both sets of current objectives and fan-out point objectives are empty, then the multiple backtrace procedure terminates at the exit (C) in Fig. 8. After this, taking out a head line one by one from the set of head objectives, we assign the corresponding value to the head line and perform the implication. For details, see the flowchart of the FAN algorithm in Fig. 9.

III. DESCRIPTION OF THE FAN ALGORITHM

The FAN (fan-out-oriented) test generation algorithm is similar to PODEM based on the implicit enumeration process. However, the FAN algorithm is characterized by putting emphasis on the following points.

1) FAN pays special attention to fan-out points in circuits.

2) FAN is a branch-and-bound algorithm which adopts many techniques presented in the preceding section so as to detect an inconsistency as early as possible.

As mentioned in the preceding section, those techniques would be very useful to decrease the number of backtracks, and thus FAN could be faster and more efficient than PODEM.

90

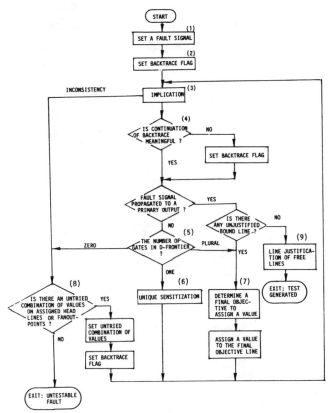

Fig. 9. Flowchart of FAN algorithm.

The flowchart of the FAN algorithm is given in Fig. 9. Each box in the flowchart will be explained in the following.

1) Assignment of Fault Signal: In box 1, a fault signal D or $\overline{D}$ is assigned in the manner shown in Fig. 1.

2) Backtrace Flag: The multiple backtrace procedure of Fig. 8 has two entries: one entry is (A) where the multiple backtrace starts from a set of initial objectives, and the other entry is (B) where the multiple backtrace starts with a fan-out-point objective to continue the last multiple backtrace which terminated at a fan-out point. The backtrace flag is used to distinguish the above two modes.

3) Implication: We determine as many signal values as possible which can be uniquely implied. To do this, we take the implication operation which completely traces such signal determination both forwards and backwards through the circuit. In PODEM, since all the values are assigned only to the primary inputs and only the forward implication is performed, unjustified lines never appear. However, in FAN, since both forward and backward implications are performed, the unjustified lines might appear. Therefore, so as to justify those lines, the multiple backtrace is necessary, not only to propagate the fault signal (D or $\overline{D}$), but also to justify the unjustified lines.

4) Continuation Check for Multiple Backtrace: In box 4, we check whether or not it is meaningful to continue the backtrace. We consider that it is not meaningful to continue the backtrace if the last objective was to propagate D or $\overline{D}$ and the D-frontier has changed or if the last objective was to justify unjustified lines and all the unjustified lines have been justified. When it is not meaningful to continue, the backtrace flag is

set so as to start the multiple backtrace with new initial objectives.

5) Checking D-Frontier: PODEM uses a lookahead technique called an X-path check, i.e., it checks whether there is any path from a gate in the D-frontier to a primary output such that all lines along the path are at X. In FAN, the same technique is adopted to eliminate a meaningless D-frontier. FAN counts only those gates in the D-frontier which have an X-path.

6) Unique Sensitization: The unique sensitization is performed in the manner mentioned in the previous section (see Fig. 3). Although the unique sensitization might leave some lines unjustified, those lines will be justified by the multiple backtrace.

7) Determination of a Final Objective: The detailed flowchart of box 6 is described in Fig. 10. By using the multiple backtrace procedure, we determine a final objective, that is, we choose a value and a line such that the chosen value assigned to the chosen line has a good likelihood of helping towards meeting the initial objectives.

8) Backtracking: The decision tree is identical to that of PODEM, that is, an ordered list of nodes, with each node identifying a current assignment of either 0 or 1 to one head line or one fan-out point, and the ordering reflects the relative sequence in which the current assignments were made. A node is flagged if the initial assignment has been rejected and the alternative is being tried. When both assignment choices at a node are rejected, then the associated node is removed and the predecessor node's current assignment is also rejected. The backtracking done by PODEM does not require saving and restoring of status because, at each point, the status could be revived only by forward implications of all primary inputs. The same backtracking can be done in FAN, which does not require saving and restoring of status, by implications of all associated head lines and fan-out points. However, to avoid the unnecessary repetition of implications, FAN allows the process of saving and restoring of status to some extent.

9) Line Justification of Free Lines: We can find values on the primary inputs which justify all the values on the head lines without backtracks. This can be done by an operation identical to the consistency operation of the D-algorithm.

IV. Experimental Results

We have implemented three programs, SPS (single path sensitization), PODEM, and FAN test generation algorithms, in Fortran on an NEAC System ACOS-1000. The SPS is a test generation algorithm which is restricted to sensitize only single paths, and thus it is simpler than the D-algorithm. These programs were applied to a number of combinational circuits shown in Table I. The number of gates in these circuits ranged from 718 to 2982. The results are shown in Tables II and III. To obtain the data of Tables II and III, three programs were executed to generate a test for each stuck fault.

The number of times a backtrack occurs during the generation of each test pattern was calculated by the programs, and the average number of backtracks is shown in Table II. Since PODEM and FAN are complete algorithms, given enough time, both will generate tests for each testable fault. However,

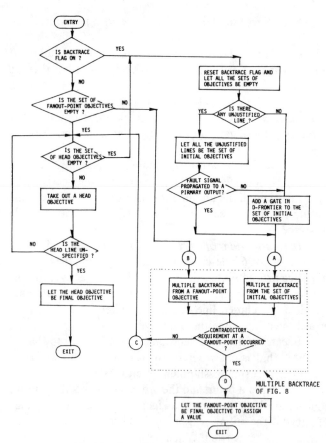

Fig. 10. Determination of final objective.

TABLE I
CHARACTERISTIC OF CIRCUITS

Circuit		Number of Gates	Number of Lines	Number of Inputs	Number of Outputs	Number of Fanout-Points	Number of Faults
#1	Error Correcting Circuit	718	1925	33	25	381	1871
#2	Arithmetic Logic Unit	1003	2782	233	140	454	2748
#3	ALU	1456	3572	50	22	579	3428
#4	ALU and Selector	2002	5429	178	123	806	5350
#5	ALU	2982	7618	207	108	1300	7550

TABLE II
NORMALIZED COMPUTING TIME AND AVERAGE NUMBER OF BACKTRACKS

Circuit	Normalized Computing Time			Average Number of Backtracks		
	SPS	PODEM	FAN	SPS	PODEM	FAN
#1	5.2	1.3	1	31.2	4.9	1.2
#2	4.5	3.6	1	51.7	42.3	15.2
#3	14.5	5.6	1	189.7	61.9	0.6
#4	3.1	1.9	1	1.5	5.0	0.2
#5	3.4	4.8	1	38.1	53.0	23.2

TABLE III
TEST COVERAGE

Circuit	% Tested Faults			% Aborted Faults			% Untestable Faults		
	SPS	PODEM	FAN	SPS	PODEM	FAN	SPS	PODEM	FAN
#1	99.04	99.20	99.52	0.48	0.48	0.11	-	0.32	0.37
#2	91.15	94.25	95.49	4.70	3.49	1.38	-	2.26	3.13
#3	66.25	92.53	96.00	16.25	5.05	0	-	2.42	4.00
#4	98.77	98.75	98.90	0.07	0.26	0	-	0.99	1.10
#5	94.73	94.38	96.81	3.54	4.79	2.17	-	0.82	1.02

TABLE IV
FAN COMBINED WITH CONCURRENT SIMULATOR

Circuit	Computing Time (seconds)			% Tested Faults	% Aborted Faults	# of Test Patterns
	FAN	Concurrent Simulator	Total			
#1	3.8	4.6	8.4	99.52	0.11	151
#2	34.6	3.7	38.3	95.74	1.13	159
#3	7.4	9.5	16.9	96.00	0	215
#4	4.0	10.5	14.5	98.90	0	195
#5	76.5	18.9	95.4	98.20	0.78	283

IV. Computing times on an ACOS-1000 (15 millions of instructions per second) were reasonable, and a high-speed test generation system has been implemented, as seen from Table IV.

V. CONCLUSIONS

The PODEM reported by Goel succeeded in improving the poor performance of the *D*-algorithm for error-correction and translation-type circuits. However, we have shown that there still remain many possibilities of reducing the number of backtracks in the algorithm. The FAN algorithm presented in this paper adopts many techniques to reduce the number of backtracks. Experimental results on large combinational circuits of up to 3000 gates show that the FAN algorithm is faster and more efficient than the PODEM algorithm in computing time, the number of backtracks, and test coverage. An automatic test generation system composed of the FAN test generator and the concurrent fault simulator has also been implemented. The results on large circuits show that computing

being limited in computing time, we gave up continuing test generation for the faults for which the number of backtracks exceeds 1000. Such faults are called *aborted faults* in Table III. The results shown in Tables II and III demonstrate that, although PODEM is faster than SPS, FAN is more efficient and faster than both PODEM and SPS. The average number of backtracks in FAN is extremely small compared to PODEM and SPS.

We have also implemented an automatic test generation system composed of FAN and the concurrent fault simulator [9] in such a way that the fault simulator is used after each test pattern is generated to find what other faults are detected by the tests. Note that the test pattern is completed by replacing the unspecified inputs by 0's and 1's. These faults are deleted from the fault list. The results of this system are shown in Table time on an ACOS-1000 were reasonable, and the system achieved a high-speed test generation. Recently, a new method has been presented by Savir and Roth [11] which leads to the elimination of fault simulation. Considering that a nontrivial amount of time is spent on the fault simulation, their method could be incorporated in FAN to yield a more powerful test generator.

ACKNOWLEDGMENT

We would like to express our thanks to Prof. H. Ozaki and Prof. K. Kinoshita for their support and encouragement of this work.

REFERENCES

[1] H. Fujiwara and S. Toida, "The complexity of fault detection: An approach to design for testability," in *Proc. 12th Int. Symp. Fault Tolerant Comput.*, June 1982, pp. 101–108.
[2] E. B. Eichelberger and T. W. Williams, "A logic design structure for LSI testing," in *Proc. 14th Design Automation Conf.*, June 1977, pp. 462–468.
[3] S. Funatsu, N. Wakatsuki, and T. Arima, "Test generation systems in Japan," in *Proc. 12th Design Automation Conf.*, June 1975, pp. 114–122.
[4] F. F. Sellers, M. Y. Hsiao, and L. W. Bearnson, "Analyzing errors with the Boolean difference," *IEEE Trans. Comput.*, vol. C-17, pp. 676–683, July 1968.
[5] J. P. Roth, "Diagnosis of automata failures: A calculus and a method," *IBM J. Res. Develop.*, vol. 10, pp. 278–291, July 1966.
[6] C. W. Cha, W. E. Donath, and F. Ozguner, "9-V algorithm for test pattern generation of combinational digital circuits," *IEEE Trans. Comput.*, vol. C-27, pp. 193–200, Mar. 1978.
[7] K. Kinoshita, Y. Takamatsu, and M. Shibata, "Test generation for combinational circuits by structure description functions," in *Proc. 10th Int. Symp. Fault Tolerant Comput.*, Oct. 1980, pp. 152–154.
[8] P. Goel, "An implicit enumeration algorithm to generate tests for combinational logic circuits," *IEEE Trans. Comput.*, vol. C-30, pp. 215–222, Mar. 1981.
[9] E. G. Ulrich and T. Baker, "The concurrent simulation of nearly identical digital networks," in *Proc. 10th Design Automation Workshop*, June 1973, pp. 145–150.
[10] L. H. Goldstein, "Controllability/observability analysis of digital circuits," *IEEE Trans. Circuits Syst.*, vol. CAS-26, pp. 685–693, Sept. 1979.
[11] J. Savir and J. P. Roth, "Testing for, and distinguishing between failures," in *Proc. 12th Int. Symp. Fault Tolerant Comput.*, June 1982, pp. 165–172.

Hideo Fujiwara (S'70–M'74–SM'83) was born in Nara, Japan, on February 9, 1946. He received the B.S., M.S., and Ph.D. degrees in electronic engineering from Osaka University, Osaka, Japan, in 1969, 1971, and 1974, respectively.

Since 1974 he has been with the Department of Electronic Engineering, Faculty of Engineering, Osaka University. In 1981 he was a Visiting Research Assistant Professor at the University of Waterloo, Waterloo, Ont., Canada. His research interests include switching theory, design for testability, test generation, fault diagnosis, and fault-tolerant systems.

Dr. Fujiwara is a member of the Institute of Electronics and Communication Engineers of Japan and the Information Processing Society of Japan. He was a member of the Technical Program Committee of the 1982 International Symposium on Fault Tolerant Computing, and received the IECE Young Engineer Award in 1977.

Takeshi Shimono (S'81) was born on November 25, 1958. He received the B.S. and M.S. degrees in electronic engineering from Osaka University, Osaka, Japan, in 1981 and 1983, respectively.

He is now with the NEC Corporation, Tokyo, Japan. His research interests include design for testability, test generation, and fault simulation.

Mr. Shimono is a member of the Institute of Electronics and Communication Engineers of Japan.

TEST GENERATION FOR PROGRAMMABLE LOGIC ARRAYS[†]

Pradip Bose and Jacob A. Abraham

Coordinated Science Laboratory
Urbana, IL 61801

ABSTRACT

The problem of fault detection and test generation for programmable logic arrays (PLAs) is investigated. The effect of actual physical failures is viewed in terms of the logical changes of the product terms (growth, shrinkage, appearance and disappearance) constituting the PLA. Methods to generate a minimal single fault detection test set (T_s) from the product term specification of the PLA, are presented. It is shown that such a test set can be derived using a set of simple, easily implementable algorithms. Methods to augment Ts in order to obtain a multiple fault detection test set (T_M) are also presented.

1. INTRODUCTION

With the phenomenal proliferation of LSI and VLSI technology, programmable logic arrays (PLAs) have been receiving increasing recognition as powerful, cost-effective modules in large-scale logic design. Structural regularity, coupled with smaller design and verification time, is the main reason behind this popularity.

Understandably, there has been a growing interest in the development of test generation procedures for PLAs [1-4]. In [1] and [2], classical stuck-fault test generation algorithms were applied after modeling the PLA as a functionally equivalent random logic network. The computational inefficiencies implied by this approach have been discussed in [3]. The fault analysis and test generation procedures described in [3], on the other hand, are based on the detailed bit pattern or personality of the PLA. This approach requires repeated fault simulation (to determine the fault coverage) during the test generation process. In [4], the effect of faults is analyzed at a higher level; however, the test generation method involves path sensitization and fault simulation, with attendant backtrack procedures. In both [3] and [4], heuristics to reduce the size of the test set are suggested; minimality is not guaranteed.

[†]This work was supported by the Joint Services Electronics program, under contract N-00014-79-C-0424.

In this paper, we present our approach to the problem of testing PLAs. The effect of actual physical failures is viewed in terms of the changes (growth, shrinkage, appearance and disappearance [4,6]) in the product term configurations on the Karnaugh Map. Systematic methods to select test vectors for detecting these changes are discussed. A specific set of algorithms to derive a single fault detection test set (T_S) is presented. A procedure to derive a multiple fault detection test set (T_M), by suitably augmenting a T_S, is also described.

2. PHYSICAL AND LOGICAL FAULT MODELING

In this section, we shall briefly discuss how physical failures can be modeled at a higher, logical level. The test generation algorithms to be presented in section 3, are based on this logical fault model.

Physical Failures: The Contact Fault Model

Figure 1 shows a simple schematic diagram of a PLA implementing two 4-variable switching functions: $f_1 = x_1x_2 + x_2x_3 + x_3x_4$ and $f_2 = x_1x_2 + x_2x_3 + \bar{x}_2x_3\bar{x}_4$. The PLA has a total of forty contacts (junctions, or crossings between rows and columns). A general single-input decoder PLA with n variables (hence, 2n input columns), m product terms (hence, m rows), and p functions (hence, p output columns), will be referred to as a (n,m,p)-PLA. This general PLA organization has m(2n+p) contacts. Following Agarwal [4], we shall classify the contacts of a PLA into 1-contacts and 0-contacts, defined as follows.

Definitions

For a given row and an output column in a fault free PLA, the junction will be called a 1-contact (0-contact) if the link between the row and the column is intact (not intact).

For a given row and an input column in a fault free PLA, the junction will be called a 0-contact (1-contact) if the link between the two is intact (not intact).

(In Figure 1, the intact links are indicated by heavily dotted junctions).

Contact faults are defined as follows:

A single 0-contact (1-contact) fault is said to exist in a PLA if due to some failure, a 0-contact (1-contact) of the fault free PLA becomes a

1-contact (0-contact) in the faulty PLA.

A 0-contact (1-contact) fault shall be referred to as a C^0-fault (C^1-fault) for convenience.

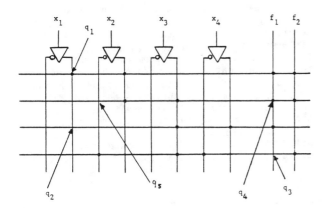

Figure 1. Schematic diagram of a PLA.

Logical Faults: The Product Term Fault Model

A single input contact fault on the ith row of an (n,m,p)-PLA causes "growth", "shrinkage" or "disappearance" of the ith product term (as viewed on the K-Map). Similarly, a single output contact fault on the ith row causes the "appearance" of a new implicant, or the "disappearance" of the ith implicant, depending on whether it is a C^0-fault or a C^1-fault, respectively. The effect of contact faults at q1, q2, q3, q4 and q5 of the PLA in Figure 1 is shown in Figure 2. To summarize the effects, (i) an input C^0-fault is the same as a growth fault; (ii) an output C^0-fault is equivalent to an appearance fault; (iii) an input C^1-fault is equivalent to either a shrinkage fault or a disappearance fault and (iv) an output C^1-fault is the same as a disappearance fault.

The growth, shrinkage, appearance and disappearance faults will be referred to as product term faults; since these are simply a logical reflection of contact faults, we shall use the two phrases interchangeably.

3. TEST GENERATION USING PRODUCT TERMS

In this section, we shall discuss ways to choose test vectors for detecting product term faults. Our objective is to select the minimum number of tests wherever possible, provided these tests can be derived algorithmically, using simple product term operations and manipulations. A specific set of algorithms to derive a minimal single fault detection test set (T_s) will be presented.

Initially, we shall restrict our attention to (n,m,1)-PLAs. This will enable us to present the basic principles behind our test generation technique in a clear and concise manner. Generaliza-

tion to the (n,m,p) case will be discussed subsequently.

We shall frequently use an n-tuple notation for the product terms of a (n,m,1)-PLA. This notation is of the form $(y_1 y_2 ... y_n)$, with $y_i \in \{0,1,x\}$. ($y_i = x$ signifies that the product term is independent of the ith input variable). Thus, a product term $x_1 x_2 \overline{x}_4$ of a 5-variable function would be represented by the 5-tuple 11x0x.

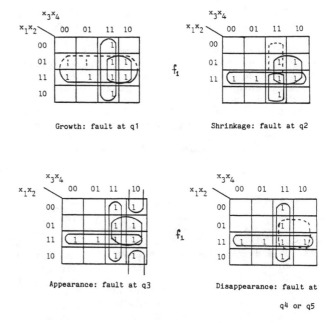

Growth: fault at q1

Shrinkage: fault at q2

Appearance: fault at q3

Disappearance: fault at q4 or q5

Figure 2. Product term faults caused by contact faults in the PLA shown in Figure 1.

The following definitions will be useful in developing the results of this section.

Definitions

A product term P_i is said to be non-isolated (with respect to a given output function), if there is at least one other product term P_j ($i \neq j$), in the functional specification, such that P_i and P_j cover one or more common minterms. Otherwise, it is said to be an isolated product term.

For a given output function, a minterm covered by a product term is said to be free if it is not covered by any other product term of the function under consideration. Otherwise, it is said to be bound.

Two minterms covered by a product term are said to be adjacent if they differ in only one bit.

Since for now we are considering (n,m,1)-PLAs only, all m product terms belong to the single output function f. So, appearance faults need not be considered. Also, disappearance faults are tested for automatically while testing for shrinkage faults. Thus, the only faults we need consider are growth and shrinkage faults.

Growth Tests

In what follows, a <u>growth term</u> stands for the set of extra minterms contributed by a growth fault. For example, the growth fault shown in Figure 2a, caused the product term x_1x_2 (11xx) to grow to x_2 (x1xx). The growth term in this case is $\bar{x}_1x_2$ (01xx). Note that for a given product term P, a growth term may be derived simply by complementing one of the non-x elements of P. Thus, for P = 11xx, the growth terms are 01xx and 10xx. (See Algorithm A).

Clearly, any free minterm covered by a growth term qualifies as a test vector for the corresponding growth fault. For a given set of growth faults, a set of free minterms, chosen to cover all the growth terms, is a (single) growth fault test set. If the selected minterms constitute a <u>minimal</u> cover [7] over the growth terms, then clearly we have a minimal growth test set. In order to reduce the complexity of the above covering problem, the redundant growth terms (viz. those corresponding to undetectable growth faults) may initially be eliminated. (See Step B of Procedure 1).

Shrinkage Tests

Consider the two isolated product terms $P_1 = x_3$ and $P_2 = x_1\bar{x}_2\bar{x}_3\bar{x}_4$, shown in Figure 3a. P_2 covers only one minterm, 1000; clearly, this minterm is the one and only candidate as a shrinkage test vector for P_2. P_1, on the other hand, may shrink in six different ways (or disappear), on a single input C'-fault. It can easily be verified that the number of test vectors needed to detect all six shrinkage faults, is two. In fact, the following lemma holds. (The formal proof is available in [8]).

<u>Lemma</u>: The number of shrinkage tests, n_i^1, needed for an isolated product term P_i is given by

$$n_i^1 = \begin{cases} 1 \text{ if } P_1 \text{ covers only one minterm;} \\ \\ 2 \text{ if } P_i \text{ covers two or more minterms.} \end{cases}$$

It is easy to derive a minimal shrinkage test set for an isolated product term. Thus, for the product term P_1 = xx1x (Figure 3a), an initial test vector t_1 may be obtained by setting the three x's to arbitrary binary values, say 0, 1 and 1, so that t_1 = 0011. The other test vector t_2 can then be obtained by complementing the x-values chosen for t_1. Thus, t_2 = 1110. Since there are three x's in P_1, clearly, $2^3/2$ = 4 possible (t_1, t_2) pairs qualify as minimal shrinkage test sets for P_1.

For a non-isolated product term, however, upto three test vectors may be needed to account for all the shrinkage faults (see Figure 3b). In this case, the following lemma can be proved [8].

<u>Lemma</u>: the number of shrinkage tests n_i^1 needed for a non-isolated product term P_i (assuming that $\leq \frac{1}{2}$ the minterms covered by P_i are bound), satisfies the inequality:

$$1 \leq n_i^1 \leq 3.$$

To understand how a minimal shrinkage test set for a general product term P_i can be derived systematically (see Algorithm D), consider a pair of minterms (t_1, t_2) derived in the manner suggested for the isolated product term case, but with the restriction that at least one of the minterms, (say t_1) is free. If t_2 is also free, then of course, (t_1, t_2) <u>is</u> a minimal shrinkage test set for P_1. If t_2 is not free, then it is invalid as a test vector. However, any two free minterms t_{21}, t_{22} of P_i which are <u>adjacent</u> to t_2, can be shown to to detect all the shrinkage faults which would have been detected by t_2 if it were free.

(i) p_1 = xx1x:

    4 possible shrinkage test sets: -
(0011,1110), (0010,1111), (0111,1010) and (0110,1011).

(ii) p_2 = 1000: 1 possible shrinkage test set: (1000)

Figure 3a. Isolated product terms and their shrinkage tests.

Product Term	Shrinkage Tests
P_1 = 00x1	0001
P_2 = 01x0	0100
P_3 = 11x1	1101
P_4 = 10x0	1000
P_5 = xx1x	0010,0111,1110

$$f = \bar{x}_1\bar{x}_2x_4 + \bar{x}_1x_2\bar{x}_4$$
$$+ x_1x_2x_4 + x_1\bar{x}_2\bar{x}_4$$
$$+ x_3$$

Figure 3b. Non-isolated product terms and their shrinkage tests.

Derivation of a minimal T_s for a (n,m,1)-PLA

In the light of the previous discussion, the basic steps involved in deriving a minimal T_s for a (n,m,1)-PLA from its product term specification can be listed as follows:

Procedure 1: Derivation of a minimal T_s for a (n,m,1)-PLA.

Step A: Generate the set of growth terms G from the set of input product terms P.

Step B: Remove redundant growth terms from G. (This step is optional; its purpose is to reduce the complexity of Step C).

Step C: Choose a set of free minterms, T_s^0, such that it forms a minimal cover over the set of growth terms, G. T_s^0 is then the minimal growth test set.

Step D: Generate a minimal shrinkage test set, T_s^1, by choosing a set of minterms (a maximum of three for each product term) in accordance with the method discussed earlier.

The required minimal test set is obtained as the union of the sets obtained in steps C and D, i.e. $T_s = T_s^0 \cup T_s^1$.

We present below, a set of _algorithms_ (A, B, C and D) to implement the corresponding steps of Procedure 1. The algorithms are based on simple product term manipulations and operations.

Algorithm A: Derivation of all growth terms from a given set of product terms.

Input: A set of input product terms P, of a (n,m,1)-PLA.

Output: The set of growth terms, G.

Begin

    for each product term $(y_1 y_2 \ldots y_n)$ $[y_j \in \{0,1,x\}]$

    do begin

        p := number of y_j's in $(y_1 y_2 \ldots y_n)$ which are not equal to 'x';

        for i := 1 to p **do begin**
        scan the n-tuple $(y_1 y_2 \ldots y_n)$ from left to right and complement the ith non-x y_j. All other components are left unchanged. (This new n-tuple is then the ith growth term corresponding to the original product term);

        end;
    end;
end;

The growth terms derived from the product terms of an example function are shown in Figure 4.

For the purposes of the next algorithms, we need to introduce the following definitions:

Definitions

The _intersection_ of two product terms $y = (y_1 y_2 \ldots y_n)$ and $z = (z_1 z_2 \ldots z_n)$, if it exists, is defined to be the n-tuple $w = (w_1 w_2 \ldots w_n)$, where,

$$w_i = \begin{cases} z_i & \text{if } y_i = x \ldots \text{(i)} \\ y_i & \text{if } z_i = x \ldots \text{(ii)} \\ y_i \text{ or } z_i & \text{if } y_i = z_i \ldots \text{(iii), for } 1 \le i \le n, \end{cases}$$

where $y_i, z_i, w_i \in \{0,1,x\}$. For example, the intersection of 1x0x and x1xx is 110x.

The _mask_ operation (#) is used to find the minterms covered by one term (i.e. n-tuple) that are not covered by another. If p, q are two terms, then q#p denotes the set of minterms which are covered by q, but not by p. In general, it is not possible to represent q#p by a single term. In other words, q#p in general, must be represented by a _set_ of terms. For example, if p = x110 and q = 0xxx, then one set of (disjoint) terms representing q#p is {00xx, 010x, 0111}. A simple algorithm to derive q#p is available in [8].

A term y is said to be _covered_ by a set of terms $t_1, t_2, \ldots, t_k$ if every minterm covered by y is also covered by at least one of the terms t_i, i = 1, 2, ...,k. For example, in Figure 4, growth term 1x0x is covered by the set of input product terms; in particular, it is covered by the product terms 1x00 and 1x01.

Product Terms	Growth Terms
1. 0x01	_1x01_, 0x11, 0x00
2. 01x1	_11x1_, 00x1, 01x0
3. 1x00	0x00, _1x10_, _1x01_
4. 1x01	_0x01_, _1x11_, _1x00_
5. 1x1x	0x1x, _1x0x_
6. xx10	xx00, xx11

Figure 4. Growth terms derived from input product terms. (Redundant growth terms are underlined).

Algorithm B: Removal of redundant growth terms.

Input: A set of input product terms P, and the corresponding set of growth terms, G, of a (n,m,1)-PLA.

Output: An irredundant set of growth terms, G.

    Algorithm B': Determining if a given term (i.e. n-tuple) is covered by a given set of terms.

    Input: A single term t and a set of terms S.

    Output: A boolean flag, 'redundant', indicating whether t is covered by S or not. (* redundant = true, if t is covered by T *)

```
Begin (* Alg. B' *)

    reduntant := false;

    repeat

        s := a term in S which has not yet been
        considered;

        if an intersection between t and s exists
        (let INT denote the intersection vector)
        then

            if INT = t then redundant := true

            else begin

                for each term in the set t#s, use
                Alg. B' to determine if that term is
                redundant;

                if each term in t#s is redundant
                then redundant := true

            end;

        until (all terms in S have been considered)
        or (redundant = true);

    end; (* of Alg. B' *)

Begin (* Alg. B *)

    for each growth term g ∈ G, do begin

        use Alg. B' to determine if g is covered by
        the set of input product terms P;

        if redundant then discard g from G;

        end; (* of for loop *)

end; (* of Alg. B *)
```

In Figure 4, the underlined growth terms are redundant. These would be eliminated by an application of Algorithm B.

Algorithm C: Derivation of a minimal growth test set T_s^0 from a set of growth terms, G.

Input: A set of input product terms P, and set of growth terms G, of a (n,m,1)-PLA.

Output: A minimal growth test set, T_s^0.

1. Arrange the growth terms into groups, such that each group contains growth terms which were derived from the same product term. (See list i of Figure 5).

2. For each vector in the first group, try to intersect it with a vector in the second group, starting with the first vector in each group. If an intersection succeeds, use Algorithm B' to determine if the intersection vector is covered by the set of input product terms P. If it is not covered, then enter the intersection vector as the next entry in group 1 of the next list (which is initially empty). Check marks are placed alongside the vectors intersected, and these are no longer considered in subsequent applications of step 2. After all vectors in group 1 have been tried, copy the unchecked vectors of groups 1 and 2 into the next list as part of group 1. The other groups of the previous list are copied unchanged to the next list as subsequent groups.

3. Repeat step 2 for each list, until the new list consists of just one group of vectors.

4. Choose a set of free minterms to cover the vectors in the final list.

Figure 5 illustrates the application of the above algorithm on the irredundant set of growth terms of our example function.

```
XXXX
1234

0x11✓  0011   0100   0011✓  0011  ⎫ Final
0x00✓  0100✓  0011✓  0100✓  0100  ⎬ minimal
00x1✓  0x00✓  0x1x✓  xx00✓        ⎭ growth
01x0✓  0x1x   xx00   xx11✓  (v)   test set.
0x00   xx00   xx11
0x1x   xx11          (iv)
xx00         (iii)
xx11   (ii)

(i)
```

Figure 5. Derivation of growth tests from growth terms.

Algorithm D: Derivation of the set of shrinkage tests:

Input: A set of input product terms P, of a (n,m,1)-PLA.

Output: A minimal shrinkage test test set, T_s^1.

```
Begin

    done := false; shrinkage test set := null;

    for i := 1 to m do begin

        p := 1;

        q := number of free minterms of $P_i$;

        while (p<=q) and (not done) do begin

            t_1 := pth free minterm of $P_i$;

            t_2 := compl (t_1, i);

                (* this function returns a minterm
                derived from t_1 by complementing those
                bit positions which correspond to x's
                in P_i *)
```

```
if t₂ is free then begin

        add t₁ and t₂ to the set of  shrinkage
        tests;

        done := true

        end

    else p := p + 1;

    end; (* while loop *)

  if (not done) then begin

        choose a valid (free) t₁,  such  that  the
        corresponding  t₂  has  at least one free adja-
        cent minterm within Pᵢ;

        t₂₁ := a free minterm of Pᵢ, adjacent to t₂;

        add t₂₁ to the set of shrinkage tests;

        t₂₂ := any (available) free  minterm  of  Pᵢ,
        which detects  the  only remaining shrinkage
        condition;

        if such a t₂₂ was available then add  t₂₂  to
        the set of shrinkage tests;

        end;

    end; (* of for loop *)

end; (* of Algorithm D *)
```

Figure 6 shows the shrinkage tests derived for our example $(n,m,1)$-PLA, by applying Algorithm D.

Product Terms	Shrinkage Tests
0x01	0001
01x1	0111
1x00	1000, 1100
1x01	1001, 1101
1x1x	1111, 1011
xx10	0010, 0110

Figure 6. Shrinkage tests derived from product terms

Generalization to (n,m,p) case:

Clearly, appearance faults must now be considered, in addition to the shrinkage and growth faults. Consider a product term P_i (ith row), which belongs to the function f_j (jth output column) but does not belong to f_k (kth output column). Now, under an output C^0-fault at the junction of the ith row and kth output column, the product term P_i causes an appearance fault as far as the function f_k is concerned. Clearly, any minterm which is covered by P_i, and is free with respect to f_k, qualifies as a test vector for the appearance fault in question. Such a test vector can be derived during the generation of shrinkage tests for P_i.

The steps to generate a T_s for a (n,m,p)-PLA may be stated as follows:

Procedure 2: Derivation of a T_s for a (n,m,p)-PLA.

Steps A, B, C: as in Procedure 1.

Step D: For each product term, generate a minimal shrinkage and appearance test set. (The shrinkage tests are generated using the same basic principles as before; however, now these test sets must be chosen to cover as many appearance faults as possible. Any remaining appearance faults must be covered by additional test vectors).

General algorithms for the (n,m,p) case are reported in [8].

Size of a minimal test set

The following theorem expresses the upper and lower bounds on the size of a minimal T_s for the general (n,m,p)-PLA. The proof is available in [8].

Theorem: For a general (n,m,p)-PLA, the total number of growth, shrinkage and appearance tests constituting a minimal T_s, is bounded in the following manner:

$$m+p \leq |T_s| \leq m(n+p),$$

where the P_i's are the product terms of the PLA.

Thus, for a PLA with 16 inputs, 48 product terms and 8 outputs, $|T_s| \leq 1152$.

Note:- Algorithm D is based on the lemma, which states that the upper bound on the number of shrinkage tests for Pi is 3; this is strictly valid under the absence of the No-opposite-adjacent (NOA) condition [8]. If at least 1/2 the minterms of Pi are free, absence of the NOA condition is guaranteed.

<u>Complexity of the test generation algorithms</u>:

In terms of the number of comparisons between n-tuples, the worst case complexity of the test generation algorithms has been shown in [8] to be $O(m^2 n)$, where m = number of input product terms, and n = number of input variables.

4. MULTIPLE CONTACT FAULT DETECTION

Even though a T_s inherently covers most of the multiple contact faults of interest (see [5]), it might be useful to have a multiple fault detection test set, T_M. In this section, we shall present a simple method for generating a T_M, by suitably augmenting a minimal T_s. Such a T_M is <u>not</u> guaranteed to be minimal.

The following definition will be useful in presenting the method.

Definition

Two product terms P_i and P_j are said to be <u>mutually touching</u> if there is at least one minterm which is covered by both P_i and P_j (i.e., if the intersection of P_i and P_j exists). Otherwise, they are said to be <u>mutually non-touching</u>.

We shall consider only (n,m,1)-PLAs, and state how Procedure 1 of section 2 must be modified, to generate a T_M. (Extension to the n,m,p case is straightforward, by treating appearance terms as additional growth terms).

<u>Procedure 3</u>: Derivation of a T_M for a (n,m,1)-PLA.

<u>Step A</u>: Generate the shrinkage test set as in Step D of Procedure 1.

<u>Step B</u>: For each pair of mutually touching input product terms, select a common minterm as a test vector.

<u>Step C</u>: Generate the set of growth terms as in Step A of Procedure 1. For each of these terms, generate a <u>shrinkage</u> test set, as if it were an isolated product term. Try to minimize the number of test vectors chosen by considering common minterms covered by the growth terms.

For lack of space we shall not discuss the rationale behind the steps of the above procedure. Detailed explanation is available in [8]. Suffice it to say that the test vectors selected in Step B are needed to detect certain multiple shrinkage faults, while those selected in Step C are required for situations involving a combination of growth and shrinkage faults. Figure 7 shows a T_M derived for a (n,m,1)-PLA according to the above procedure.

5. DISCUSSION

In this paper, we have looked into the problem of test generation for programmable logic arrays. The well known contact fault model was assumed, and a completely functional (or logical) approach was adopted. This approach allows test generation directly from the product term specification of a PLA; detailed personality bit patterns of the PLA need not be considered. The set of algorithms for deriving a minimal T_s, has been implemented by a PASCAL program, TESTPLA [8]. The program optionally derives a multiple detection fault test set, T_M.

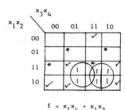

$$f = x_1 x_4 + x_1 x_3$$

✓:(Minimal) T_S = $\{1101, 1001, 1110, 1010, 0011, 1000\}$

(Minimal) T_M = $\{1101, 1001, 1110, 1010, 0011, 0101, 0110, 1111, 1000\}$

✓,*: T_M derived according to our method = $\{1101, 1001, 1110, 1010, 0011,$

$0101, 0110, 1111, 1000, 1100\}$

(one more than the minimal set).

Figure 7. Multiple contact fault detection test set (T_M) for a (n,m,1)-PLA.

REFERENCES

[1] C. W. Cha, "A testing strategy for PLAs," <u>Proc. 15th Design Auto. Conf.</u>, 1978, pp. 83-89.

[2] E. J. Muelhdorf and T. W. Williams, "Optimized stuck-fault test pattern generation for PLA macros," <u>Dig. IEEE Semiconductor Test Symp.</u>, Cherry Hill, Oct. 1977, pp. 88-101.

[3] D. L. Ostapko and S. J. Hong, "Fault analysis and test generation for programmable logic arrays," <u>IEEE Trans. Comput.</u>, vol. C-28, pp. 617-626, Sept. 1979.

[4] J. E. Smith, "Detection of faults in programmable logic arrays," <u>IEEE Trans. Comput.</u>, vol. C-28, pp. 845-853, Nov. 1979.

[5] V. K. Agarwal, "Multiple fault detection in programmable logic arrays," <u>IEEE Trans. Comput.</u>, vol. C-29, pp. 518-522, June 1980.

[6] M. Paige, "Generation of diagnostic tests using prime implicants," Coordinated Science Laboratory Report R-414, University of Illinois, May 1969.

[7] S. Muroga, <u>Logic Design and Switching Theory</u>, John Wiley, 1978.

[8] P. Bose, "Functional testing of programmable logic arrays," Coordinated Science Laboratory Report R-918, University of Illinois, 1982 (to appear).

Transistor Level Test Generation for MOS Circuits

Madhukar K. Reddy and Sudhakar M. Reddy

Department of Electrical and Computer Engineering
University of Iowa
Iowa City, Iowa 52242

Prathima Agrawal

AT&T Bell Telephone Laboratories
600 Mountain Avenue
Murray Hill, New Jersey 07974

ABSTRACT

Due to inaccuracies in gate level models of VLSI digital circuits, current practice is to use transistor level simulators to analyze VLSI digital circuits. The inaccuracies of gate level models are even more severe when faults in digital circuits are considered. For this reason, recently several researchers have proposed the use of test pattern generation from digital circuits described at the transistor level. In this paper an efficient test pattern generation procedure for digital circuits described at the transistor level is given.

1. Introduction

NMOS and CMOS technologies are two of the dominant VLSI technologies today due to their desirable properties of high circuit density, good speed and low costs [1,2]. It has been shown that classical boolean logic gate models based only on the function of a MOS circuit and classical line stuck-at fault models do not model some important failures in MOS circuits [3]. Hence, recent research efforts in test generation and simulation for MOS circuits have been directed toward transistor level logic modeling, taking transistor interconnection structure into consideration [4-13]. In this paper, we model a MOS circuit using the switch-level model of Bryant [12], and present a test generation algorithm for detection of single transistor stuck-on and single transistor stuck-open faults in MOS combinational logic circuits. The faults considered are limited to single transistor stuck-on and single transistor stuck-open faults in the interests of brevity and more complex faults will be considered in a future paper.

The test generation algorithm to be presented is based on the classical D-algorithm [14] and uses transistor groups much like the way boolean logic gates are used in the D-algorithm. Transistor groups can be explained as follows. Assume that each FET connected to a primary input (power supply (V_{DD}) and ground (V_{SS}) are also considered as primary inputs in this paper) at the source or drain terminal has its own separate primary input. Then, all the nodes and transistors that are interconnected through source and drain terminals and FET channels form a transistor group. A MOS circuit and the transistor groups in it are shown in Figure 1. Further constraints are imposed on the circuits being considered for test generation to keep the algorithm simple. These constraints are: (1) The gate terminals of all the enhancement FETs in a transistor are controlled by other transistor groups, (2) there is no feedback between transistor groups, and (3) the only type of ratioing allowed is between depletion FETs and enhancement FETs in NMOS, and depletion FETs are used only as pull-ups. Constraints

*The research reported was supported in part by Army Research Office Contract No. DAAG 2908-K-0044.

1 and 2 are imposed to avoid dividing a time frame or a transition phase (in a time frame all the primary inputs are constant, primary inputs change only in transition phases between two consecutive time frames) into many time intervals to be able to compute the steady state of the circuit in a time frame or transition phase respectively, which would be required if feedback were present. The algorithm can be easily modified to cover circuits which do not satisfy constraints 1 or 2 by allowing division of a time frame into many time intervals. Constraint 3 is imposed so that cutset and path generation needed by the test generation algorithm is simple. Note that most common MOS circuits satisfy constraint 3.

Some FET stuck-open and stuck-on faults in a MOS combinational logic circuit change the circuit into a sequential circuit and require two-pattern tests [4,7-11,13]. It has been shown that if two-pattern tests are not chosen carefully they may be invalidated (that is, fail to detect the fault they were supposed to detect) due to circuit delays [4,10,13]. Two-pattern tests that remain valid in the presence of arbitrary circuit delays were called robust two-pattern tests [13]. The test generation algorithm to be presented generates robust two-pattern tests whenever they are needed and available.

2. Switch-Level Model, Logic Values, Test Cube Representation, Cubical Intersection, and Consistency Check

Bryant's Switch Level Model: Bryant's switch-level model of a MOS logic circuit is a network consisting of a set of nodes connected by transistor *switches*. Nodes in a switch-level network are classified into two types: Primary input nodes and storage (internal) nodes. Primary input nodes provide strong signals (a signal is a pair made of logic value and the strength of the logic value) and are not affected by behavior of the network. Primary input nodes have maximum strength denoted by ω. Storage nodes have states determined by operation of the network. Each storage node is assigned a size from the set $K = \{k_1, \ldots, k_{max}\}$ to indicate its approximate capacitive size in relation to other storage nodes with which it may share charge. The elements of set K are totally ordered $k_1 < k_2 \ldots < k_{max}$. An isolated storage node retains its logic state indefinitely. A transistor is modeled as a bidirectional switch with strength from the set $R = \{r_1, \ldots, r_{max}\}$ to indicate its relative conductance when turned-on with respect to other transistors with which it may form a ratioed path in ratioed MOS logic. The elements of set R are totally ordered, $r_1 < r_2 < \cdots < r_{max}$. The strengths and sizes are totally ordered according to the relation $k_1 < k_2 < \ldots < k_{max} < r_1 < r_2 \ldots < r_{max} < \omega$. A conducting path p from node n_a to n_b supplies a signal to node n_b. The strength of the signal supplied by p is the minimum of the size of n_a and the weakest FET in the path p, and the logic value of the signal is the logic value of n_a. The logic value of node n_b is determined by the strongest signals supplied by the conducting paths to n_b. The switch-level model of the MOS circuit in Figure 1 is shown in Fig-

Reprinted from *Proceedings of the 22nd Design Automation Conference*, 1985, pages 825-828. Copyright © 1985 by The Institute of Electrical and Electronics Engineers, Inc. All rights reserved.

ure 2. For a more detailed description of the switch-level model, the reader may refer to [12].

For the MOS circuits considered in this paper, except in Section 3, all the enhancement FETs have strength r_2, all the depletion FETs have strength r_1, and all storage nodes have size k in the switch-level model.

Logic Values: We propose to use the logic values 0,1,i,d,u,and x for test generation. 0 and 1 are the normal boolean logic values, i denotes the state of an uninitialized or improperly initialized node or the state of a node having voltage between V_{DD} and V_{SS} due to improper charge sharing or comparable conductance paths between V_{DD} and V_{SS}. d represents 0 or i, u represents 1 or i, and x represents all of these logic states. States of fault-free transistors resulting from the presence of logic states from the above set at their gate terminals are given in Table 1.

One could use a smaller set {0,1,i,x} of logic values also instead of the proposed set {0,1,i,d,u,x} (note that in the smaller set x combines d,u,and x of the larger set into one single x). But, we decided in favor of the larger set of logic values as this appears to minimize the number of backtracks made in the decision space during test generation. For example, a node n_j having value u when the larger set of logic values is used would have the value x when the smaller set of logic values is used. During test generation process using the smaller set of logic values, one may specify the value of n_j to be 0 only to realize later that justification of the value 0 at n_j is not possible. Another advantage with the larger set of logic values is in finding cutsets and paths of FETs needed by the test generation algorithm.

Test Cube Representation: A test cube in the D-Algorithm has line values from the set {0,1,x,D,$\overline{D}$} [14]. In the test generation algorithm being proposed, the faulty and fault-free circuits each has its own test cube. It has been shown that robust two-pattern tests generate static hazard-free requirements to be justified; that is some nodes in the MOS circuit need to be static-0 hazard-free and/or some nodes static-1 hazard-free when a transition is made at the inputs from the initializing input to the test input of a two pattern test [10,13]. It is decided to adapt the *ternary simulation* technique [15,16] for generation of robust two-pattern tests. For circuits considered in this paper , since only faulty circuits could be sequential, the static hazard-free requirements need be satisfied only in the faulty circuits. Therefore, a node in the faulty circuit is represented in the test cube of the faulty circuit by an ordered triplet $l_1l_2l_3$ of logic values, where $l_i \epsilon$ {0,1,i,d,u,x} and l_1 is the logic value of the node in the time frame (denoted by t_1) in which initializing input is applied, l_2 is the logic value of the node in the transition phase (denoted by $t_1 \rightarrow t_2$), and l_3 is the logic value of the node in the time frame (denoted by t_2) in which the test input is applied. States of primary input nodes in the transition phase are determined according to Table 2. A node which is static-0(1) hazard-free has the value 000(111)in the test cube. A storage node which has a static-0(1) hazard has the value 0i0(1i1) in the test cube. Since the fault free circuit is combinational, a node is represented in the testcube of the fault-free circuit by a singlet l_3 of logic value where $l_3 \epsilon$ {0,1,i,d,u,x} and l_3 is the logic value of the node in the time frame t_2 in which the test input is applied. It is assumed that prior to time frame t_1 (t_2) the state of the faulty (fault-free) circuit is not known and hence the initial states of storage nodes in time frame t_1 (t_2) are assumed to be i in the faulty (fault-free) circuit.

Cubical Intersection and Consistency Check: Intersection of test cube with primitive cubes, and consistency check of implied node values with test cube are done using Table 3. Table 3 is used for faulty and fault-free circuits separately and for each time frame and transition phase separately. If an inconsistency occurs while checking for implied node values backtracking will be needed.

3. Forward Implication Procedure for General MOS Circuits

Bryant gave a method for performing forward implication in simulation environment [12] (Note that Bryant's x logic value and x transistor states are respectively i logic value and I transistor states here). When applied in test generation environment Bryant's method can correctly identify which nodes have 0 and 1 states in the current time interval but has problems in identifying which nodes have state i and which nodes have state x, due to the presence of transistors in X state when the smaller set of logic values is used (or which nodes have states i,u,d, and x when the larger set of logic values is used, due to the presence of transistors in ONI,OFFI, and X states). In this section, we present an accurate forward implication method when the larger set {0,1,i,d,u,x} of logic values is used. When the smaller set {0,1,i,x} of logic values is used, the method can be easily modified.

Gate Inputs of a Transistor Group: The nodes connected to the gate terminals of FETs in a transistor group are called *gate inputs* to the group.

Source Inputs of a Transistor Group: Primary input nodes connected to source or drain terminals of FETs in a transistor group are called *source inputs* to the group.

Inputs of a Transistor Group: Gate inputs and source inputs of a transistor group together are called *inputs* of the group.

Outputs of a Transistor Group: Storage nodes in a transistor group connected to primary outputs and gate terminals of FETs are called *outputs* of the group.

For example, in Figure 1, node A is a gate input of group 1, nodes V_{DD} and V_{SS} are source inputs of group 1, and node n_1 is the output of group 1.

Forward implication in FET level test generation algorithm being presented in this paper is the determination of logic states of storage nodes in a transistor group in a time interval for a given combination of logic states at inputs to the group and initial states of the storage nodes in the group. While performing forward implication on a transistor group, it is assumed that the states of FETs in the transistor group do not change.

The procedure IMPLY given below is used for performing forward implication on a group GP. In procedure IMPLY TS_s and $TS_{\overline{s}}$ are sets of transistor states, NS_s and $NS_{\overline{s}}$ are sets of node states, and $L_s(s_1)$ and $L_{\overline{s}}(s_1)$ are lists of nodes for s_1: $=\omega$, r_{max}, ...r_1, k_{max},...k_1. *done* is a flag associated with each node. *done* of a node is *false* initially, and after the *effect* of the node on all of its neighboring nodes is determined *done* of that node is set to *true*. To perform forward implication on group GP, procedure IMPLY is called four times:

(1) The call IMPLY(GP, TS_0, $TS_{\overline{0}}$, NS_0 , $NS_{\overline{0}}$, 0, $\overline{0}$) with $TS_0=$ {ON}, $TS_{\overline{0}}=$ {ON,ONI,OFFI,I,X}, $NS_0=$ {0}, and $NS_{\overline{0}}=$ {1,d,u,i,x} determines which nodes in the group GP have logic state 0 in the current time interval. A node n_j has logic state 0 in the current time interval if it is in a list $L_0(s_1)$, s_1: $= \omega$, r_{max},..., r_1 , k_{max},...k_1 after return from the above call of procedure IMPLY.

(2) The call IMPLY(GP, TS_1, $TS_{\overline{1}}$, NS_1,$NS_{\overline{1}}$,1, $\overline{1}$) with $TS_1=$ {ON}, $TS_{\overline{1}}=$ {ON,ONI,OFFI,I,X,}, $NS_1=$ {1}, and $NS_{\overline{1}}=$ {0,d,u,i,x} determines which nodes in the group GP have logic state 1 in the current time interval. A node n_j has logic state 1 in the current time interval if it is in a list $L_1(s_1)$,s_1:$= \omega$, r_{max} ,..., r_1, k_{max},..., k_1 after return from the above call of procedure IMPLY.

(3) Let α denote 0 or d. The call IMPLY(GP,TS_α,$TS_{\overline{\alpha}}$,NS_α,$NS_{\overline{\alpha}}$,α,$\overline{\alpha}$) with $TS_\alpha =$ {ON,ONI,X}, $TS_{\overline{\alpha}} =$ {ON,ONI,I}, $NS_\alpha =$ {0,d,x}, and $NS_{\overline{\alpha}}=$ {1,i,u} determines which nodes in the group GP have logic state 0 or could possibly be set to 0 (by properly specifying d,u,x inputs to GP and initial

states of storage nodes in GP with d,u and x initial states) in the current time interval. A node n_j has logic state 0 or could possibly be set to 0 in the current time interval if it is in a list $L_\alpha(s_1)$, $s_1 := \omega, r_{max}, \ldots r_1, k_{max}, \ldots, k_1$ after return from the above call of procedure IMPLY.

(4) Let β denote 1 or u. The call IMPLY(GP, $TS_\beta, TS_{\overline{\beta}}, NS_\beta$, $NS_{\overline{\beta}}, \beta, \overline{\beta}$) with $TS_\beta = \{ON, ONI, X\}$, $TS_{\overline{\beta}} = \{ON, ONI, I\}$, $NS_\beta = \{1, u, x\}$, and $NS_{\overline{\beta}} = \{0, d, i\}$ determines which nodes in the group GP have logic state 1 or could possibly be set to 1 (by properly specifying d,u,x inputs to GP and initial states of storage nodes in GP with d,u,x initial states) in the current time interval. A node n_j has logic state 1 or could possibly be set to 1 in the current time interval if it is in a list $L_\beta(s_1)$, $s_1 := \omega, r_{max}, \ldots r_1, k_{max}, \ldots k_1$ after return from the above call of procedure IMPLY.

Procedure IMPLY(GP, TS_a, $TS_{\overline{a}}$, NS_a, $NS_{\overline{a}}$, a, $\overline{a}$)

1. Initialize lists $L_a(\omega), L_a(r_{max}), \ldots L_a(r_1)$, $L_a(k_{max}), \ldots, L_a(k_1)$ and $L_{\overline{a}}(\omega), L_{\overline{a}}(r_{max}), \ldots L_{\overline{a}}(r_1), L_{\overline{a}}(k_{max}), \ldots, L_{\overline{a}}(k_1)$ to null.

2. Place all the nodes in GP with strength s_1 and states (current states for primary input nodes and initial states for storage nodes) in the set $NS_{\overline{a}}(NS_a)$ in the list $L_{\overline{a}}(s_1)(L_a(s_1))$, $s_1 = \omega, k_{max}, \ldots k_1$. Note that for primary input nodes the placement is final and for storage nodes the placement is tentative. For every node, initialize *done* to *false*.

3. For $s_1 = \omega$, $r_{max}, \ldots r_1$, $k_{max}, \ldots k_1$, do

while there is a node n_j in $L_{\overline{a}}(s_1)$ such that *done* of n_j is *false* do

Begin

    done of $n_j := $ true;

    For every transistor T which has n_j as its source (drain) node and with state in $TS_{\overline{a}}$ do

        If the drain (source) node n_l of T is in a list $L_{\overline{a}}(s_2)$ and $s_2 <$ minimum of (s_1, strength of T) or is in a list $L_a(s_2)$ and $s_2 \leq$ minimum of (s_1, strength of T) then delete n_l from that list and add n_l to $L_{\overline{a}}(s_1)$.

end

While there is a node n_j in $L_a(s_1)$ such that *done* of n_j is *false* do

Begin

    done of $n_j := $ true;

    For every transistor T which has n_j as its source (drain) node and with state in TS_a do

        If the drain (source) node n_l of T is in a list $L_{\overline{a}}(s_2)$ or $L_a(s_2)$ and $s_2 <$ minimum of (s_1, strength of T) then delete n_l from that list and add n_l to $L_a(s_1)$.

end.

After all the four calls to procedure IMPLY are returned, the implied logic state of a node n_j in group GP in the current time interval is determined by the Table 4. Explanation of the theory behind the forward implication method and the correctness of the method is beyond the scope of this paper and will be presented in a future paper. It can also be proved that the forward implication method is accurate (neither pessimistic nor optimistic) in dealing with transistors in ONI,OFFI,I, and X states (or transistors in I and X states if the smaller set of logic values $\{0,1,i,x\}$ is used). By carefully choosing the data structures associated with nodes, transistors, and the lists in the procedure IMPLY, one call of the procedure can be completed in O($|s| + |T|$) time, where $|s|$ is the total number of node sizes and transistor strengths and $|T|$ is the number of transistors in a group GP. Details of data structures are not given here due to lack of space. When an input or an initial state of a storage node in a group gets specified, actually it is not necessary to consider the whole group for forward implication. The effect of a specification will be confined to a subregion (called *vicinity* in [12]) in the group which is separated from the rest of the

group by OFF transistors and in which the specification occurred. Therefore, the efficiency of the forward implication method can be improved by considering only *vicinities* of groups. This is how the forward implication method will be implemented.

It is interesting to compare the performance of forward implication method presented here and Bryant's method [12] in simulation environment. In simulation environment only 0,1,i logic values and OFF,ON,I transistor states are present, and to determine the effect of a change in an input of a vicinity only two calls to procedure IMPLY need be made; one for determining which nodes are 0 and which nodes are 1 in the current time interval. If a node is not 0 or 1 then it is i. In Bryant's method, a procedure SOLVE is called three times to determine the effect of a change in an input of a vicinity. Time and space complexities of procedures IMPLY and SOLVE are about the same and it may be advantageous to use procedure IMPLY as it is called only two times.

4. Justification of Logic Values and Hazard Free Requirements, and D-cube Generation and Propagation:

In this section, we will briefly discuss generation of primitive D-cubes of faults, propagation of D-cubes, justification of logic values in a time frame, and justification of hazard-free requirements. Detailed procedures to perform these operations are not given due to lack of space. The test generation algorithm uses transistor groups as logic blocks and performs these operations on a transistor group using paths and cutsets [17,18] of transistors in the group.

Justification of Logic Values:

Next we will consider justification of logic values in time frames t_1 and t_2. Note that logic values in time frame t_1 have to be justified only in the faulty circuit as the fault-free circuit is considered only in time frame t_2 since it is combinational. Assume a logic value of 0(1) is to be justified at an output node n_j of a transistor group GP_a in time frame t_2. In the fault-free circuit, a logic value of 0(1) can be justified at n_j only by having a conducting path through ON transistors to n_j from a primary input node at 0(1) in GP_a in t_2 and by making sure (using cutsets of OFF transistors in t_2) that no conducting paths to n_j through only enhancement transistors are possible from primary input nodes at 1(0) or x in t_2 in GP_a, since the fault-free circuit is combinational. In the faulty circuit, it may be possible to justify a logic value of 0(1) at n_j as just described and/or by initializing n_j to 0(1) in time frame t_1 and by *maintaining* that initialization at n_j through the transition phase $t_1 \rightarrow t_2$ and in t_2 (called robust initialization in this paper). Logic values in the faulty circuit in time frame t_1 are to be justified the same way as the logic values in t_2 in the fault-free circuit are justified as we are assuming that the state of the circuit prior to t_1 is not known.

Justification of Hazard Free Requirements:

The only hazard free requirements generated for the class of circuits considered in this paper are static hazard free requirements in the faulty circuit.

A static-0 (static-1) hazard free requirement at an output node n_j of a transistor group GP_a can be justified in two ways:

(a) By having a constantly conducting path p of ON transistors (that is all the FETs in p are constantly ON) to n_j in t_1, in $t_1 \rightarrow t_2$ and in t_2 from a source input of GP_a at 000(111) and by ensuring that a conducting path is through only enhancement transistors is not established even momentarily from a source input of GP_a not at 000(111). This can be easily done by considering paths and cutsets in the transition phase $t_1 \rightarrow t_2$.

(b) By justifying a logic state 0(1) in time frame t_1 at n_j and by maintaining the initialization done at n_j in t_1 through $t_1 \rightarrow t_2$ and in t_2. Maintenance of initialization at n_j requires that nodes in the group not at 000(111) and which can alter the logic value of n_j should be cut-off from n_j by using cutsets of OFF transistors in $t_1 \rightarrow t_2$. This is called robust initialization of node n_j.

Primitive D-cube of a Fault: Let GP denote the transistor group in which a fault occurred. For a transistor T_f stuck-open fault in GP, a primitive D-cube of the fault is generated at an output node n_j of GP by justifying a logic value of 0(1) at n_j in the fault-free circuit in t_2 such that all the conducting paths to n_j from source inputs to GP at 0(1) contain T_f and by justifying a logic value of 1(0) at n_j in the faulty circuit in t_2. If a 1(0) is obtained as n_j in the faulty circuit through robust initialization then hazard free requirements need be satisfied.

For an enhancement transistor T_f stuck-on fault, a primitive D-cube can be generated at an output n_j of GP only if in the fault-free circuit the logic value justified at n_j in t_2 is 1 and there are no conducting paths to n_j from source inputs of GP at 1 though only enhancement transistors. Otherwise one can only hope to generate i logic value at n_j in the faulty circuit due to conducting paths through only enhancement transistors from both V_{DD} and V_{SS} to n_j. In CMOS circuits, one can hope to detect a FET stuck-on fault by measuring steady-state power supply current in such situations.

Propagation of a D-cube: Let GP be a transistor group which has one or more FETs in ON→OFF state in fault-free→faulty network and/or one or more FETs in OFF→ON state in fault-free→faulty network. Then one or more FETs in ON→OFF state and/or one or more FETs in OFF→ON state can be used to propagate a D or $\overline{D}$ to an output node n_j of GP in a way similar to generation of a primitive D-cube for a FET stuck-open or stuck-on fault.

5. CONCLUSION

Procedures needed for a path sensitization based test generation algorithm are given in this paper. The proposed test generation algorithm uses a switch-level model of a MOS circuit and is capable of handling a wide variety of nMOS circuits in which all the NFETs are of the same conducting strength and ratio-less CMOS circuits which satisfy some constraints.

References

1. C. Mead and L. Conway, "Introduction to VLSI Systems," Addison-Wesley Publishing Company, 1980.
2. Rick D. Davies, "The Case for CMOS," IEEE Spectrum, Oct. 1982, pp. 26-32.
3. J. Galiay, Y. Crouzet and M. Vergniault, "Physical Versus Logical Fault Models in MOS LSI Circuits, Impact on their Testability," IEEE Trans. on Comp., vol. C-29, June 1980, pp. 527-531.
4. S.K. Jain and V.D. Agrawal, "Test Generation for FET Switching Networks," Proceedings of the 10th Design Automation Conference, 1983, pp 64-70.
5. S.M. Reddy et. al., "A Gate Level Model for CMOS Combinational Logic Circuits with Application to Fault Detection," Proceedings of the 21st Design Automation Conference, 1984.
6. J.P. Roth et. al., "Test Generation for FET Switching Networks," Proceedings of the 1984 International Test Conference, 1984, pp. 59-62.
7. K.W. Chiang and Z.G. Vranesic, "Test Generation for MOS Complex Gate Networks," Proceedings of the 12th International Symposium on Fault-Tolerant Computing, June 1982, pp. 149-157.
8. Y.M. El-Ziq and R.J. Cloutier, "Functional-Level Test Generation for Stuck-Open Faults in CMOS VLSI," Proceedings of the 1981 International Test Conference, Oct. 1981, pp. 536-546.
9. P. Banerjee and J.A. Abraham, "Generation Tests for Physical Failures in MOS Logic Circuits," Proc. IEEE International Test Conference, pp. 554-449, Oct. 1983.
10. Harry H. Chen et. al., "Test Generation for MOS Circuits," Proceedings of the 1984 International Test Conference, Oct. 1984, pp. 70-78.
11. P. Agrawal, "Test Generation at Switch Level," Proceedings of the IEEE International Conference on Computer Aided Design, Santa Clara, California, November 12-15, 1984.
12. R. Bryant, "A Switch-Level Model and Simulator for MOS Digital Systems," IEEE Trans. on Comp., vol. C-33, pp. 160-177, Feb. 1984.
13. S.M. Reddy, M.K. Reddy and V.D. Agrawal, "Robust Tests for Stuck-Open Faults in CMOS Combinational Logic Circuits," Proceedings of the 14th International Symposium on Fault-Tolerant Computing, Kissimmee, Florida, June 20-22, 1984, Digest of papers, pp. 44-49.
14. M.A. Breuer and A.D. Friedman, "Diagnosis and Reliable Design of Digital Systems," Computer Science Press Inc., 1976.
15. M. Yoeli and S. Rinon, "Application of Ternary Algebra to the Study of Static Hazards," Journal of the ACM, vol. 11, pp. 84-97, Jan 1964.
16. R.E. Bryant, "Race Detection in MOS Circuits by Ternary Simulation," Tech. Report 5091, Computer Science, California Institute of Technology, 1983.
17. R.C. Read and R.E. Tarjan, "Bounds on Backtrack Algorithms for Listing Cycles, Paths, and Spanning Trees," Networks, 5, 1975, pp. 237-252.
18. S.T. Sukiyama et. al., "Algorithm to Enumerate All the Cutsets in O(V + E) Time Per Cutset," Proceedings of the 1979 ISCAS, pp. 645-648.

Table 1: Transistor States:

Logic State at the Gate Terminal of A FET	Enhancement NFET	Enhancement PFET	Depletion FET
0	OFF	ON	ON
1	ON	OFF	ON
d	OFFI (OFF or I)	ONI (ON or I)	ON
u	ONI (ON or I)	OFFI (OFF or I)	ON
i	I (unknown or indeterminate)	I (unknown or indeterminate)	ON
x	X (all of the above states)	X (all of the above states)	ON

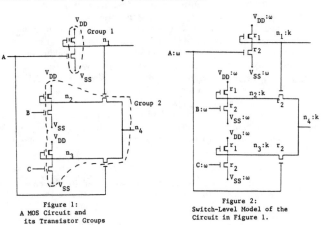

Figure 1:
A MOS Circuit and its Transistor Groups

Figure 2:
Switch-Level Model of the Circuit in Figure 1.

Primary Input Values

	in	
t_1	t_2	$t_1 + t_2$
0	0	0
0	1	i
0	x	d
1	0	i
1	1	1
1	x	u
x	0	d
x	1	u
x	x	x

Table 2: Determination of states of primary inputs during transition ($t_1 \to t_2$)

Table 3: Intersection and Consistency Check

	0	1	i	d	u	x
0	0	φ	φ	0	φ	0
1	φ	1	φ	φ	1	1
i	φ	φ	i	i	i	i
d	0	φ	i	d	i	d
u	φ	1	i	i	u	u
x	0	1	i	d	u	x

φ indicates inconsistency

Table 4: Forward Implication

node n_j is in list				implied logic state of n_j
L_0	L_1	L_α	L_β	
√	√			0
	√	√		1
		√		d
		√		u
√	√			x
				i

A Nine-Valued Circuit Model for Test Generation

PETER MUTH

Abstract—A nine-valued circuit model for test generation is introduced which takes care of multiple and repeated effects of a fault in sequential circuits. Using this model test sequences can be determined which allow multiple and repeated effects of faults on the internal state of a sequential circuit. Thus valid test sequences are derived where other known procedures, like the D-algorithm, do not find any test although one exists.

The model is defined and the test generation procedure is shown which is similar to that of the D-algorithm. Asynchronous circuits have to be transformed into synchronous or iterative combinational circuits, and tests are generated for these versions of the circuit. Validity of test sequences for asynchronous circuits has to be established by test simulation since hazards or oscillations may invalidate the test. As an example the model is applied to single and multiple faults of the "stuck at"-type in an asynchronous circuit, and a general block diagram of a program for test generation is given.

Manuscript received July 9, 1975; revised December 8, 1975.

The author was with the Institute for Information Processing, University of Karlsruhe, Karlsruhe, Germany. He is now with Brown, Boveri, and Cie AG, Mannheim, Germany.

Index Terms—Circuit testing, D-algorithm, diagnosis, many-valued model, sequential circuit, single and multiple faults, test generation.

A VERY important difference between faults in combinational and faults in sequential circuits is that in a sequential circuit one fault may have multiple and repeated effects. Known procedures of test generation for sequential circuits, like the D-algorithm in [1], do not take into account correctly repeated effects of faults on the internal state of a circuit during a test sequence. Thus, they cannot find all valid tests for a fault and sometimes do not find any test although one exists.

Here a nine-valued circuit model will be introduced which correctly takes care of repeated effects of faults. The nine values consist of the five-valued of the D-algorithm [1] and four "partly specified" values. The model is derived by viewing to a circuit in the fault-free and faulty state [2].

Reprinted from *IEEE Transactions on Computers*, Volume C-25, Number 6, June 1976, pages 630-636. Copyright © 1976 by The Institute of Electrical and Electronics Engineers, Inc. All rights reserved.

By use of the model a test sequence for every "stuck-at" fault in a *synchronous sequential* circuit having a synchronizing sequence will be found if one exists. Application to *asynchronous circuits* is restricted in such a manner that test sequences are generated for synchronized versions of the circuits and are valid with certainty only for these synchronized versions. In the real circuit a test sequence might be invalid because of oscillations or hazard faults due to the fault to be tested. Further investigation by test simulation of the faulty circuit is necessary to verify the test sequences as shown in [1].

Here application of the model to single and multiple stuck-at faults in asynchronous sequential circuits will be demonstrated. Application to combinational and to synchronous sequential circuits has been treated in [2]. The model can also be used to generate tests for faults which are not of the "stuck-at" type.

I. The Model

The nine values of the model are derived by distinguishing between a good (fault-free) and a faulty circuit. Each of the nine values n_i, $i = 1, \cdots, 9$ is defined by an ordered pair of binary values:

$$n_i = (b_g, b_f)_i \qquad i = 1, \cdots, 9,$$

where

b_g binary value in the good circuit,
b_f binary value in the faulty circuit,
$b_g, b_f \in \{0, 1, x\}$, where $x \in \{0, 1\}$ is the DON'T CARE value.

In Table I, the definition of the nine values is listed.

Values 0 and 1 are assigned to variables which have the same binary value in both the good and the faulty circuit. A variable that is surely falsified (complemented) because of a fault is assigned the value $S0$ or $S1$ (sensitive value). Values 0, 1, $S0$, and $S1$ are *fully specified*. Value U of the model is an *unspecified* value (unspecified binary values in both the good and faulty circuit). If a binary value needs to be specified only in the good circuit, we have a G-value ($G0$ or $G1$), if only in the faulty circuit, we have an F-value ($F0$ or $F1$) of the model. $G0$, $G1$, $F0$, $F1$ are called *partly specified* values.

Operations corresponding to the different types of gates can be defined for the nine-valued model, again by distinguishing between the good and the faulty case.

An example:

$$F0 \vee S0 = (x, 0) \vee (0, 1) = ([x \vee 0], [0 \vee 1]) = (x, 1) = F1.$$

In this way the nine-valued operators for AND, OR, and NOT can be defined as shown in Fig. 1. These operators and the nine values of the model form a *distributive lattice*, so that all rules which are valid for distributive lattices also hold for the model. Using these rules operators having more than two operands, and operators for other gates and for flip-flops can easily be derived. For

TABLE I
Definition of the Nine Values

n_i	$(b_g , b_f)_i$	d_j
0	(0 , 0)	0
G0	(0 , x)	
S0	(0 , 1)	$\overline{D}$
F0	(x , 0)	
U	(x , x)	x
F1	(x , 1)	
S1	(1 , 0)	D
G1	(1 , x)	
1	(1 , 1)	1

x unspecified binary value,
d_j corresponding value in D-algorithm.

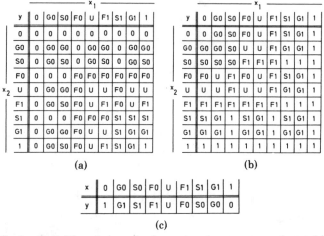

Fig. 1. Definition of nine-valued operators for AND, OR, and NOT. (a) $y = y_1 \cdot x_2$. (b) $y = x_1 \vee x_2$. (c) $y = \bar{x}$.

flip-flops, the time index has to be considered in the usual manner.

II. Test Generation by Use of the Nine-Valued Model

The test generation procedure is similar to that of the D-algorithm as proposed in [1]. If we have an asynchronous sequential circuit we first have to *transform* it into an iterative combinational circuit or to a synchronous sequential circuit. For combinational or synchronous sequential circuits, a *fault sensitizing cube* at the location of the fault is determined, and the sensitive value is driven to an output of the circuit by *fault driving cubes*. *Consistency checking* is done by "backward" *calculation* of the required values of internal variables. The test sequence generated is nine-valued and must be converted back to binary representation. Test patterns with DON'T CARE's (×) are *completed*. For asynchronous circuits validity of the generated test sequences has to be established by *test simulation*.

A. Transformation of Asynchronous Circuits

In an asynchronous circuit A, r feedback lines are selected and cut to obtain a combinational circuit C. A procedure for selecting the feedback lines to be cut is

106

described in [1], its objective is to cut feedback lines where insertion of delays will cause the least change in the logic behavior of the circuit.

Having cut the feedback lines, a *synchronous version* of the circuit is constructed by inserting delay flip-flops in these feedback lines as shown in Fig. 2(b). State variables $q_i = s_i^{-1}$ $(i = 1,\cdots,r)$ are assigned to the outputs of the flip-flops, and the input vector $\vec{X}$ is assumed to change synchronously with the clock signal of the flip-flops. A synchronous version of an asynchronous circuit can be handled like a normal synchronous circuit for test generation. (Test generation for synchronous circuits is treated in [2]).

Here the *iterative combinational version* A' of an asynchronous circuit A will be used for test generation in order to compare the algorithm to the application of the D-algorithm as shown in [1]. The iterative combinational circuit A' consists of p copies of the combinational circuit C as shown in Fig. 2(c). Each copy is fed by input variables $(\vec{X}(i))$ and has output variables $(\vec{Y}(i))$. In addition, pseudo-input variables $(\vec{Q}(i))$ enter the first copy, and pseudo-output variables $(\vec{S}(p))$ leave the last copy.

B. Fault Sensitizing Cubes

A fault sensitizing cube causes a variable to take a faulty value in consequence of a fault. It is determined with the aid of the *singular cover* of the gate (or flip-flop) output function. The singular cover consists of all prime on-cubes and all prime off-cubes of the function as shown for an OR-function in Fig. 3. (An off-cube is a cube to which the function assigns the value 0, for an on-cube, the function takes the value 1.)

To sensitize the fault "variable v stuck-at α" ($\alpha \in$ {0,1}), all prime cubes with $v = \alpha$ form the set B_f of sensitizing cubes for the faulty circuit. The set B_g of sensitizing cubes for the good circuit consists of all prime cubes with $v = \bar{\alpha}$.

In B_f the value α for variable v can be replaced by $\times$ (DON'T CARE), since the fault itself causes value α for v. After this replacement we have the set B'_f. Composition of each off-cube in B'_f with every prime on-cube in B_g, and of each on-cube from B'_f with every prime off-cube in B_g, to form a cube in the nine-valued model (Table I) results in the set of all possible sensitizing cubes. This is shown in Fig. 3 for the fault "input e_i stuck-at 0" in an OR-gate.

C. Fault Driving Cubes

For driving a fault sensitive value ($S0$ or $S1$) at an input of a logic block to one of its outputs a fault driving cube is needed. Such a cube is determined similarly to the fault sensitive cube (see Section II-B). If $v = S0$ ($v = S1$) is to be driven through a block, then B_g consists of all prime cubes with $v = 0(1)$, while B_f is made up of all the prime cubes with $v = 1(0)$. Composition of each off-cube in B_g with every on-cube in B_f, and of each on-cube in B_g with every off-cube in B_f, to form a cube in

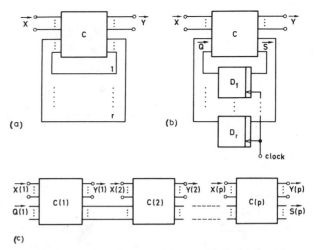

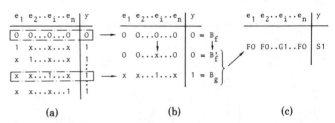

Fig. 2. Transformation of an asynchronous circuit. (a) Asynchronous circuit A. (b) Synchronous version A^S of A. (c) Iterative combinational version A' of A.

Fig. 3. Fault sensitizing cube for the fault "variable e_i stuck-at 0" in an OR-gate. (a) Singular cover of $y = e_1 \vee e_2 \vee \cdots \vee e_i \vee \cdots \vee e_n$. (b) B_f, B_g, B'_f. (c) Fault sensitizing cube.

the nine-valued model (Table I) yields all possible fault driving cubes (the procedure is similar to that of Section II-B, only the prime cubes of B_f (not of B'_f) are used here).

D. Backward Calculation

Required values for internal variables (mostly G- or F-values) are obtained by backward calculation: appropriate values are assigned to the input variables of the logic blocks that generate these internal variables. Again the singular cover is needed. If the required value is $v = 0(1)$, any prime off- (on-) cube may be used. To obtain value $v = S0(S1)$, the possible cubes are generated by composing each prime off- (on-) cube for the good circuit with every prime on- (off-) cube for the faulty circuit to a cube in the nine-valued model. All the possible cubes that guarantee a G-value (F-value) are found by composing the appropriate prime cubes for the good (faulty) circuit with the fully unspecified cube for the faulty (good) circuit to a nine-valued cube. Fig. 4 shows the backward calculation of value $G0$ for an OR-gate.

E. Consistency Checking

In circuits with reconverging fan out, backward calculation may result in two or more values being required simultaneously at a branching point. In such cases the consistency of the required values has to be checked by means of an *intersection operation* in the nine-valued model. Nine-valued intersection is defined by the intersection of the set of binary values for the good and the

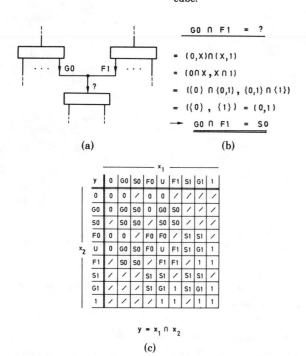

e_1 e_2··e_i··e_n	y
0 0...0...0	0
1 x...x...x	1
x 1...x...x	1
x x..1...x	1
x x..x...1	1

	e_1 e_2··e_i··e_n	y
good:	0 0...0...0	0
faulty:	x x...x...x	x

e_1 e_2··e_i··e_n	y
G0 G0..G0..G0	G0

Fig. 4. Backward calculation of value $y = G0$ at an OR-gate. (a) Singular cover. (b) Good and faulty circuit. (c) Resulting nine-valued cube.

$$G0 \cap F1 = ?$$
$$= (0,X) \cap (X,1)$$
$$= (0 \cap X, X \cap 1)$$
$$= (\{0\} \cap \{0,1\}, \{0,1\} \cap \{1\})$$
$$= (\{0\}, \{1\}) = (0,1)$$
$$\rightarrow G0 \cap F1 = S0$$

(a)   (b)

	0	G0	S0	F0	U	F1	S1	G1	1
0	0	0	/	0	0	/	/	/	/
G0	0	G0	S0	0	G0	S0	/	/	/
S0	/	S0	S0	/	S0	S0	/	/	/
F0	0	0	/	F0	F0	/	S1	S1	/
U	0	G0	S0	/	U	F1	S1	G1	1
F1	/	S0	S0	/	F1	F1	/	1	1
S1	/	/	/	S1	S1	/	S1	S1	/
G1	/	/	/	S1	G1	1	S1	G1	1
1	/	/	/	/	1	1	/	1	1

$y = x_1 \cap x_2$

(c)

Fig. 5. Consistency checking. (a) Request for two simultaneous values. (b) Checking consistency by intersection. (c) Definition of nine-valued intersection.

faulty circuit. If either of these intersections is empty, the required values are inconsistent. An example is shown in Fig. 5: for variable v, let values $v = G0$ and $v = F1$ be required at the same time. Binary intersection is nonempty in both the good and the faulty circuit. Composing the results of binary intersection, we get $G0 \cap F1 = S0$.

In this way intersection in the nine-valued model is defined for all values of the model [Fig. 5(c)]. If the required values are inconsistent, we have a contradiction. The last arbitrary choice in backward calculation has to be altered and all decisions made after this choice must be cancelled.

F. Completion of Input Patterns

Backward calculation always ends at the primary inputs of the circuit. Here values $G0$ and $F0$ are replaced by 0, $G1$ and $F1$ by 1, and U by x. Values $S0$ and $S1$ must not occur at primary inputs unless faults in these inputs are to be tested. $S0$ is replaced by 0 and $S1$ by 1. Having thus completed backward calculation, we have input patterns consisting of values $\{0,1,x\}$.

Most of these input patterns will have value x for some inputs, i.e., they are incompletely specified. For combinational and synchronous sequential circuits,

these input patterns should be completed in a manner designed to *minimize the number of input patterns* for testing all faults in the circuit. Completion is done by intersecting and merging the input patterns of all tests for faults in the circuit. For asynchronous sequential circuits, input patterns should be completed test by test in a manner designed to *minimize the number of input changes* during a test for a particular fault. Such a completion procedure is shown in [1]. It increases the probability that the test found for the synchronous version of the asynchronous circuit is also valid for the real circuit.

G. Test Simulation

Test simulation has to be performed *only for asynchronous circuits* because a generated test for a combinational or synchronous circuit always is valid. In asynchronous circuits, hazards and oscillations may invalidate the test that has been derived for the synchronous or interative combinational version of the circuit. For test simulation an Eichelberger simulator [3] or other multivalued simulators for hazard detection [4], [5] might be used to simulate application of the generated test sequence to the good and faulty circuit. Test simulation is not necessary for test sequences of length 1 [1].

Application of a test sequence to an asynchronous circuit is assumed to satisfy fundamental mode restrictions.

III. EXAMPLE

A simple asynchronous circuit A is given in Fig. 6(a). There are three inputs, a, b, and c, one output y and one loop containing gates k and h (for the sake of simplicity gates of the circuit are named after their output variables). The loop cutting procedure of [1] cuts the line from k to h.

Fig. 7 shows the iterative combinational version A' of the circuit. It consists of two copies and has a pseudo-input k_0 and a pseudo-output k_2. Inserting a delay flip-flop where the feedback line of the asynchronous circuit has been cut would yield the synchronous version of the circuit.

A. Test Generation for a Single Fault

A test sequence shall be generated for the fault "variable d stuck-at 1." The first step in test generation is to assign value $F1$ to the corresponding variables (d_1,d_2) in all (here 2) copies of the circuit, since in the faulty circuit variable d will take the binary value 1.

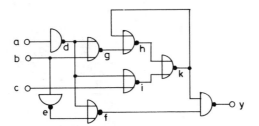

Fig. 6.   Asynchronous circuit A.

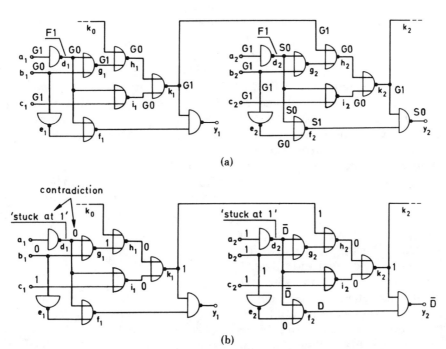

(a)

(b)

Fig. 7.   Test generation for fault "d stuck-at 1" in the iterative combinational circuit A': (a) using the nine-valued model; (b) using the D-algorithm.

Optionally we start the test generation procedure at the second copy of the circuit. The fault sensitive cube for the given fault demands value $G1$ for variable a_2 and yields value $S0$ for d_2 which is consistent with value $F1$ already assigned to d_2. Driving the fault sensitive value from d_2 to output y_2 by passing through f_2 requires values $G0$ for e_2 and $G1$ for k_2. Backward calculation of these values yields the values mapped in Fig. 7(a). It should be pointed out, that values must not be assigned to pseudo-inputs, and that pseudo-outputs have to be neglected (they must not be considered as outputs of the circuit).

All the mapped values are consistent. In particular the value $G0$ required for d_1 is consistent with the value $F1$ already assigned because of the fault. Intersection yields $F1 \cap G0 = S0$.

After replacing the nine-valued by binary values at inputs and outputs we have the test pattern $(a_1, b_1, c_1, a_2, b_2, c_2) = (1,0,1,1,1,1)$ for the iterative combinational circuit, yielding the output value $y_2 = 0$. In the asynchronous circuit this test pattern corresponds to the test sequence $(T_1, T_2) = ((1,0,1),(1,1,1))$, where $T_j = (a,b,c)_j$.

Test simulation ensures that this is a valid test sequence for the fault "d stuck-at 1." It can be shown, that this is the only test sequence of length 2 for this fault. Further investigation reveals that during application of the test sequence, the fault may influence the test twice. If the pseudo-input k_0 is at value 0,—this corresponds to value 0 of the internal state variable k in the asynchronous circuit when starting the test—the G-values of g_1, h_1, k_1, h_2 and k_2 can be replaced by S-values. Thus besides path $d_2 - f_2 - y_2$ we have a second sensitive path leading from d_1 to y_2, and this corresponds to a repeated effect of the fault in the asynchronous circuit.

Thus, the test generation procedure using the nine-valued model takes into account possible repeated effects of a fault to the circuit.

B. Comparison to D-Algorithm

Application of the D-algorithm to generate a test sequence for fault "d stuck-at 1" as shown in [1] turns out

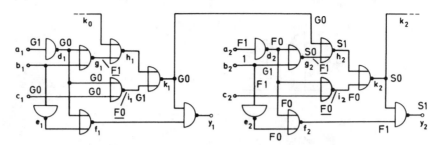

Fig. 8. Test generation for the multiple fault "i stuck-at 0," "g stuck-at 1" in the iterative combinational circuit A'.

to fail. Trying the same path as used in Section III-A ends with the contradiction, that d_1 must be 0 while d is stuck-at 1 because of the fault [Fig. 7(b)]. It can be shown that there is no way to generate a test for the iterative combinational circuit even if more than two copies of the circuit are considered. The D-algorithm does *not* take into account possible repeated effects of a fault in a circuit.

C. Test Generation for a Multiple Fault

The multiple fault to be tested shall be {"i stuck-at 0," "g stuck-at 1"} (see Fig. 8). The first step is to assign value $F0$ to variable i in both copies (i_1, i_2) and value $F1$ to variable $g(g_1, g_2)$. Next (optionally) a fault sensitive cube for fault "g stuck-at 1" is determined for the second copy. The selected cube requires value $G1$ for b_2 and results in $g_2 = S0$. For driving the sensitive value to output y_2 by passing h_2 and k_2, values $G0$ for k_1, $F0$ for i_2 and $F1$ for f_2 must be assigned. Backward calculation of value $F1$ for f_2 yields value $F0$ for d_2 and e_2, resulting in value $F1$ for a_2 and b_2. Value $F1$ for b_2 is consistent with value $G1$ which has been assigned to b_2 by the fault sensitive cube: intersection yields $F1 \cap G1 = 1$.

Value $F0$ for i_2 is guaranteed by the fault "i stuck-at 0" and is not calculated backward. Finally $G0$ has to be calculated backward, yielding $G1$ for i_1 which is consistent with value $F0$ assigned to i_1 because of the fault. Intersection yields $G1 \cap F0 = S1$. Further backward calculation results in value $G1$ for a_1 and $G0$ for c_1.

Changing to binary values at the inputs yields the test pattern $(a_1, b_1, c_1, a_2, b_2, c_2) = (1, x, 0, 1, 1, x)$ for the iterative combinational circuit. Completion of this test pattern for the asynchronous circuit in a manner to minimize the number of input changes results in the test sequence $(T_1, T_2) = ((1,1,0),(1,1,0))$. Since there is no input change the test patterns T_1 and T_2 may be composed to one input pattern $T = (1,1,0)$ which is a valid test (see Section II-F).

Again there is a possible second sensitive path for the fault. If h_1 has value 0,—this is a condition on the internal state of the asynchronous circuit at the beginning of the test—there is a sensible path from i_1 to y_2 passing k_1, h_2, and k_2, and both faults "i stuck-at 0" and "g

stuck-at 1" are sensitized and take effect on the circuit. A third sensitive path for the fault results from assigning value 0 to input variable c_2 in the completion operation: in the good circuit i_2 will take value 1 but in the faulty circuit value 0. The test derived by using the nine-valued model is valid in any case, since the partly specified values which had to be calculated backward ($G0$ for k_1 and $F0$ for i_2) allow a falsification.

Therefore the test generation procedure using the nine-valued model takes into account possible multiple and repeated effects of a multiple fault on the circuit.

V. Concluding Remarks—Advantages of the Model

Advantages of the nine-valued model are mainly due to the *higher degree of freedom* afforded by the partly specified values $G0$, $G1$, $F0$, $F1$ as compared with the values 0, 1, $\bar{D}$, and D of the D-algorithm (see Table I). For sequential circuits valid test sequences can be determined that allow *multiple and repeated effects* of a *single or multiple fault* on the circuit (repeated state falsification). In these cases use of the D-algorithm results in a contradiction, as has been shown in Section III-B. Furthermore, sensitizing any path originating at the location of the fault and directed to an output of the circuit, simultaneously takes into account all possibilities of sensitizing this path as a part of a *multiple-path-sensitization* [2]. Thus, at a fan-out point having a fan-out of N, at most N attempts have to be made at sensitizing a path (each of the N branchs at the fan-out point is selected at most once [2]). In the D-algorithm the maximum number of attempts is $2^N - 1$, since it may be necessary to try all $2^N - 1$ possible selections of one or more of the N branchs to sensitize a single or multiple path.

A test generation program for combinational circuits using the nine-valued model has been implemented on a CD 3300 [6]. This program has been run on a large number of circuits. Typical running time for a complete test generation for all "stuck-at 0" and "stuck-at 1" faults at inputs and outputs of 50–100 gates is about 10 to 30 s. Implementation of a program for sequential circuits has just been finished, too [7], a general block diagram of

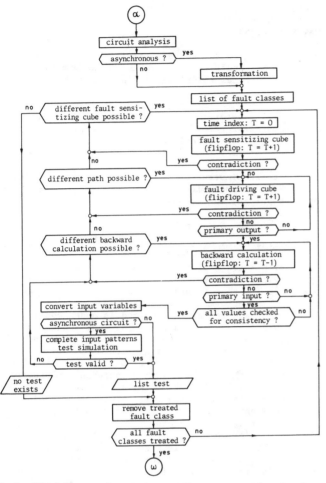

Fig. 9. Block diagram for a test generation program using the nine-valued model.

this program is shown in Fig. 9. (Here asynchronous circuits are transformed into the synchronous version rather than into the iterative combinational circuit.)

REFERENCES

[1] R. Putzolu and J. P. Roth, "A heuristic algorithm for the testing of asynchronous circuits," *IEEE Trans. Comput.*, June 1971.
[2] P. Muth, "Erstellen von Fehlererkennungs-Experimenten für Schaltnetze und Schaltwerke unter Verwendung eines neun-wertigen Schaltungsmodells," *Nachrichtentechn. Fachberichte*, Band 49, VDE-Verlag, Berlin, 1974.
[3] E. B. Eichelberger, "Hazard detection in combinational and sequential switching circuits," *IBM J. Res. Develop.*, vol. 9, pp. 90–99, Mar. 1965.
[4] G. Fantauzzi, "An algebraic model for the analysis of logical circuits," *IEEE Trans. Comput.*, June 1974.
[5] P. Muth, "Ein Verfahren zur Erkennung statischer und dynamischer Hasards in Schaltnetzen," *Elektron. Rechenanlagen*, Heft 5, 1974.
[6] M. Hennken, "Bestimmung von Testbelegungen und Testfolgen für Schaltnetze und Schaltwerke—Erstellen eines Programms," Diplomarbeit am Institut für Nachrichtenverarbeitung der Universität Karlsruhe, ID-297, 1973.
[7] H. Delong, "Bestimmen von Teiltestfolgen für Schaltwerke unter Verwendung eines neunwertigen Schaltungsmodells—Erstellen eines Programms," Diplomarbeit am Institut für Nachrichtenverarbeitung der Universität Karlsruhe, ID-318, 1975.

Peter Muth was born in Düsseldorf, Germany on May 2, 1943. He studied communication engineering at the Technical University of Karlsruhe, Karlsruhe, Germany and at Wayne State University, Detroit, MI. He received the Dipl. Ing. and Dr. Ing. degrees from the University of Karlsruhe, Karlsruhe, in 1968 and 1975, respectively.

From 1968 to 1975 he was a Research Assistant at the Institute for Information Processing at the University of Karlsruhe, where he worked on fault diagnosis of combinational and sequential circuits, design of digital circuits, and logic simulation. In 1975 he joined Brown, Boveri and Cie, Mannheim, Germany. His present activities are concerned with the test of digital circuits and with computer-aided design facilities.

SIMULATOR-ORIENTED FAULT TEST GENERATOR

Thomas J. Snethen

IBM System Products Division -- East Fishkill
Hopewell Junction, New York 12533

The problem of generating tests for sequential logic networks has become severe with large-scale integration (LSI). Since the internal gates cannot be tested by direct measurements, it is imperative that a rigorous logic test be developed to ensure quality at the chip level. The sequential complexity of many LSI chips exceeds the practical limitations of the familiar technique of modeling sequential logic for the application of combinational logic test-generation algorithms. Although other approaches, such as pseudo-random pattern generation, have been tried with some success, the pattern count may be quite large. This paper describes a method of test pattern generation that was developed with three objectives: to generate long pattern sequences systematically when needed, to model the sequential logic accurately so that any test generated would be valid, and to focus on assumed faults such as stuck 1 and stuck 0. Also discussed are the strengths and limitations of this method and some comparative results.

Introduction

Generating tests for electronic logic networks has become a critical problem with large-scale integration (LSI). The only means available for testing gates internal to an LSI chip is through logic testing, gates being inaccessible for analog or direct digital measurement. Thus, to ensure good quality, a rigorous logic test is necessary. LSI has brought another aspect of this problem to chip testing which has long plagued card and board testing - sequential, or feedback, complexity. As the complexity of the logic network increases, the complexity of the input sequences required and the cost of generating those sequences also increase.

Automated test-generation methods encompass a wide spectrum ranging from simple pseudo-random pattern generation to sophisticated algorithms.[1] The algorithmic approach generally works well if there are few memory elements, or latches, in any signal path through the network. In this case, each test typically consists of a short pattern sequence. On the other hand, random pattern generation[2,3] has considerable merit in cases where the algorithmic approach is not cost-effective. For some logic designs, however, it is also insufficient--for example, on designs that require a long sequence for initialization or readout, such as those containing shift registers and counters.

Within this spectrum lie numerous methods of test generation. Three limitations of the previous test generators motivated the development of yet another method.

1. Analytical, or algorithmic, approaches become cumbersome when long pattern sequences are required because they generally have a decision structure that allows them to exhaust all legitimate possibilities when looking for a test sequence for a given fault.

2. The logic model used by test generators is constrained by practicality to be simple. This leads to inaccuracy, especially when the signal propagation delays are important. This problem is especially relevant to the analytic approaches, because the sophistication of the test-generation algorithm can be lost in the inaccuracy of a crude model.

3. The first two limitations apply to analytic approaches. The major limitation of the random and more simple analytic test generators is that they

must be designed to stop arbitrarily or upon some statistical cutoff criteria, such as maximum number of consecutive tests which fail to increase the test coverage.

With this background, the Simulator-Oriented Fault Test Generator (SOFTG) was developed as an experimental program. The primary objective was to generate long test sequences in a deliberate manner, without arbitrary restrictions upon sequence length. The logic description available to the test generator is a gate level structure consisting of AND, OR, NAND, and NOR primitives with their interconnections and the network primary inputs and outputs identified.

Strategy

As indicated by the title, SOFTG interacts very closely with a fault simulator. (For convenience, fault simulation will be referred to as "simulation".) The only characteristics of the simulator dictated by SOFTG are (1) that it provide the logic state of each gate in the network, for the "good machine" (fault-free logic) and for all faulty models under consideration, and (2) that it save all internal logic states for one pattern so that the test generator has the option of discarding a pattern if the simulation result is not what the generator desired. It is also assumed here that the simulation includes the process of flagging faults for which tests have been found.

Before discussing the test generator operation, let us comment on the test generator-simulator interaction. First, the simulator relieves the test generator of working on a test for any fault that is detected "for free," that is flagged as detected on a pattern that was generated for another fault. This kind of interaction is well-known and is employed in test generation systems as a rule rather than an exception. It is customary to generate a complete test sequence for a fault, and then to simulate the full test sequence and flag detected faults before returning to the test generator. The close simulator interaction used by SOFTG maximizes the chances of detecting a fault for free because (a) the particular fault for which a test is being generated may be detectable by an earlier pattern than the test generator would otherwise have realized and (b) the test generator may generate a pattern that proves fruitless for detecting the target fault but detects some other faults.

Second, SOFTG effectively uses the simulator to model the behavior of the logic by incrementally generating a test sequence, one pattern at a time, and invoking the simulator before proceeding to develop the next pattern. The test generator uses the latest gate values calculated by the simulator in generating each pattern. Since a fault simulator is being used, this models the faulty behavior for each fault as well as the "good machine" behavior. Each generated pattern differs from the preceding pattern on only one input, thus avoiding races between two or more inputs.

Third, instead of looping through the fault list in a predetermined order as is done by many fault-oriented test generators, SOFTG dynamically selects the next fault to be tested. This selection is based mainly upon the existence of _test values_. A test value is the condition of a gate having opposite states in the good and faulty machines. In the popular notation of D-alg,[4] a test value is either D or D̄. Two potential advantages result from this dynamic fault selection: (1) the entire test set is somewhat minimized, since the beginning of one test can overlap the end of a previous one; (2) it may be that the test

Reprinted from _Proceedings of the 14th Design Automation Conference,_ 1977, pages 88-93. Copyright © 1977 by The Institute of Electrical and Electronics Engineers, Inc. All rights reserved.

generator, being imperfect, would have been incapable of deliberately generating and/or propagating the test value to that site within the logic.

The basic test generation strategy consists of two parts. Part 1 is an iterative process of propagating a test value for the selected fault to the network primary outputs (POs), or of first generating a test value on the faulty gate if a test value does not yet exist. Part 2 generates the sequence of input patterns to accomplish each step of Part 1 by iteratively seeking the next chronological input change. The method of finding the next input to be changed is based upon a structural analysis (backtrace). Both Parts 1 and 2 are heuristic, and examples can easily be found for which they do not work. However, as shown in the Results section, they are quite practical for testing logic where other techniques fail.

An overview of the pattern generation procedure is shown in Fig. 1. An arbitrary initial pattern of all 0's on the network primary inputs (PIs) is fault-simulated. As will be seen later, this initial pattern is not required for making the pattern generator work. It is applied only for the convenience of having all inputs at known states.

Select determines the next fault to be detected, which is called the <u>target fault</u>.

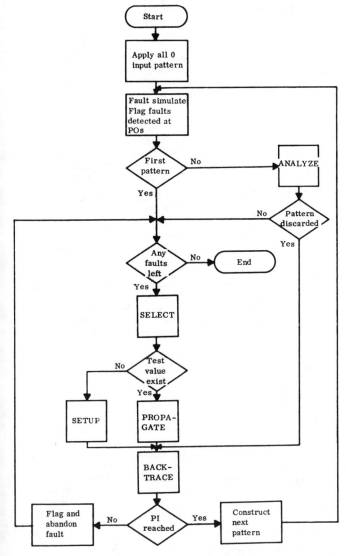

Fig. 1. Overview of SOFTG

The result of either Setup or Propagate is a starting block and value for Backtrace. This starting point is known as an <u>objective</u>. The purpose of Setup is to obtain a test value at the site of target fault. Suppose, as an example, that in a given network the target fault is the output of gate T stuck 0. Setup would define the initial objective as gate T with good machine 1 value.

If a test value presently exists, Propagate locates the test value closest in number of logic stages to network POs. Propagate then defines the initial objective so as to cause the test value to be propagated through another stage of logic toward the POs. Fig. 2a illustrates a network where a test value D (good machine 1, faulty machine 0) exists on gate T. Suppose Propagate is attempting to pass this test value through NOR gate V. Backtrace is given the objective V with faulty machine 1 value. Note that a D propagating through an inverting function becomes a D̄ (good machine 0, faulty machine 1). In this example, V is a NOR with a good machine 1 value on one of its inputs, so the good machine value of its output is already 0. This good machine 0 is flagged as an <u>assignment</u>. An assignment denotes a particular simulator gate value (in either the good or faulty machine) which exists and is to be preserved during subsequent patterns. The meaning of this will be clarified later; for the case of this example, it is obvious that to obtain the desired test value on gate V, the good machine 0 must not be lost while driving the faulty value to 1.

Backtrace begins at the initial objective defined by either Setup or Propagate and traces a single path through the appropriate (good or faulty) logic model toward the PIs. The input to be followed at each multiple-input gate is chosen so as to lead to the PI that must be changed next in the pattern sequence, which is being developed chronologically, in order to satisfy the (initial) objective.

It may happen that Backtrace, operating by the method to be described, cannot reach a PI. Then the target fault is flagged as abandoned, and a new target fault is selected. When Backtrace reaches a PI, a new pattern is formed with a new value on this PI and all other PIs unchanged. This pattern is then simulated.

The Analyze step decides whether to keep the pattern just simulated or to discard it and restore the simulator to the state resulting from the preceding pattern. This decision is based upon two factors. If the pattern caused any faults to be flagged as detected, then it is kept. If no assignments are violated, then the pattern is also kept. Conversely, if no new faults are detected and if the pattern causes some assigned gate to switch, then the pattern is discarded. This latter situation is called <u>conflict</u>. A more accurate description of conflict detection is contained in the Detailed Description section. When a conflict occurs, the pattern is discarded and Backtrace is called to find an alternate PI change. If no conflict occurs, then test generation resumes with the step of selecting a fault. Usually the same fault is repeatedly selected until flagged either detected or abandoned.

Detailed Description

Preprocessing

Before test generation is begun, a preprocessing phase calculates certain data based upon a structural analysis of the logic network.

Fan-in weights are calculated which rank each input of a multi-input gate by ease of controllability. They are used to guide the backtracing process toward the next primary input to be changed. A method of calculating the weights can be found in Ref.1.

A number called output distance is calculated for each gate. This is used to guide the test value propagation toward the POs when a selected test value exists at a gate whose fanout is greater than 1. The output distances are also used in the selection process to determine which of two or more test value gates is closest to the primary outputs. For this latter purpose, it is desirable that output distance for each gate be unique. The following method is used to calculate them. Assign output distances of 1 through k to the output gates, where k is the number of primary outputs. Then, for the gate whose output distance is 1, assign any of its unassigned input gates consecutive output distances, beginning with k+1. Repeat this step for the output distance 2 gate, and so on until all gates have been assigned an output distance. Consecutively higher output distances are used for all assignments, resulting in uniqueness, and for any pair of gates, one having a shorter possible path to a PO will have a lower output distance.

Fault Selection

The test generator maintains a flag for each fault. This flag tells if the test generator has abandoned the fault, having failed in an attempt to generate a test sequence for it. An integer is used as the flag so as to allow the test generator to reattempt a previously abandoned fault under certain promising conditions. This is done by using as the flag the output distance of the forwardmost progress of a test value for that fault. When a fault is abandoned, its flag is set according to the output distance of the gate from which propagation was being attempted. If a test value for this fault is later discovered at a closer point to the POs as indicated by the gate output distances, then a new attempt is made to test that fault. If a fault is abandoned in the Setup step, then the flag is set to a large number, specifically, 1+ the number of gates in the logic network under test.

Initially, in the process of test generation for a given logic network, the selection of a target fault is quite arbitrary. Two initial strategies have been tried: selecting a fault on a gate close to the primary inputs, and selecting one close to the primary outputs. Neither selection strategy appears clearly superior. As test values happen to appear, they are considered. In general, the fault selection step is carried out after each pattern is simulated, with the following considerations in decreasing order of priority:

1. A fault that is being attacked for the second or subsequent attempt.

2. A fault that is a candidate for a reattempt because a test value appears closer than previously to a PO.

3. A fault that has a test value closer to a PO than any other eligible (non-flagged) fault.

Backtrace

The Backtrace operation uses a stack containing objectives and assignments (Fig. 2b). Objectives are classified into three types: PI, decision, and imply. A decision objective can be satisfied by any of the inputs to the referenced gate, while an imply objective requires all inputs to be set to obtain the desired output. For example, an objective that refers to an OR gate with desired value 1 (for either good or faulty machine) is a decision objective. If an OR gate has the desired value 0, then it would become an imply objective. For a single-input gate, such as an inverter, the classification as a decision or imply objective is arbitrary.

For decision objectives, the alternative index field is used. This index determines the choice of the gate input to be followed.

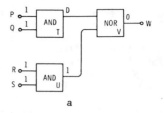

Block	Desired Value	Entry Type	Alternative Index
V	GM 0	Assignment	—
V	FM 1	Imply	—
T	FM 0	Assignment	—
U	FM 0	Decision	1
R	FM 0	PI	—

b

Fig. 2. Worklist stack format

In the example of Fig. 2, a test value (shown as D) is to be propagated through gate V. Propagate makes the first two entries, an assignment of V to a good machine 0, and an objective of V with a faulty machine 1 value.

Backtrace iteratively processes the last objective on the stack, initially gate V with a desired faulty machine value of 1. It determines that this is an imply objective and fills in the entry type. Next it inverts the desired value (because V is a NOR function) and enters FM 0 as the desired value in the third stack entry. It then decides which of V's inputs to process first. In this example the input from gate T was chosen. Observing that T already has the desired faulty machine value of 0, this entry is classified as an assignment, and the fourth stack entry is started. The next input of V to be processed is from U, which is found to have a 1 on its output. Thus, U is an objective entry and, being an AND function with the desired value of 0, is classified as a decision entry. When this classification is made, the alternative index field is set to 1 so that, the first time this entry is processed, the first choice among U's inputs will be selected. The first choice was the primary input R.

Refer now to Fig. 3. The first decision box checks whether any objectives exist on the stack. The stack could be empty when this decision is entered from Backup. (Under any other condition, an empty stack indicates a program error.) The return from this point results in abandoning the target fault.

In the decision objective processing box, i refers to the alternative index value retrieved from the stack. The precalculated fan-in weights determine the order of processing gate inputs. Inputs of a decision objective gate are processed in order of decreasing controllability; that is, the most easily controllable input is processed first. Subsequent processing of the same decision entry, where i=2, would select the second most easily controllable input, etc.

Backup is reached when no more choices remain for a decision objective or when a chosen input comes from a gate that is already an objective on the stack. Backup removes entries from the stack in last-in, first-out order until it encounters a decision entry. It then increments the alternative index for this entry by 1, and backtracing resumes.

Imply objective gate inputs are processed in order of increasing controllability. This is considered an important factor in the success of SOFTG. The basic strategy of Backtrace, as mentioned earlier, is to find the next input to be changed in

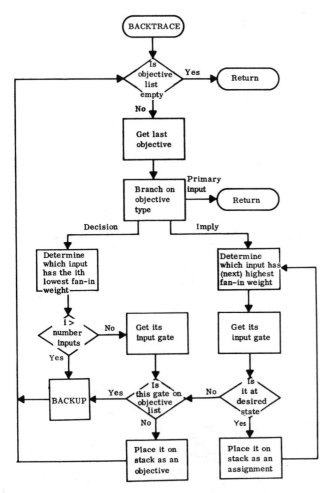

Fig. 3. Backtrace flow

chronological order. To do this, it relies upon the structural analysis performed in calculating the fan-in weights and uses this increasing controllability rule to guide the direction of the backtrace path. An intuitive argument for processing inputs in this order is based on two premises: (1) since all inputs eventually must be specified, starting with the most difficult has no disadvantage and may very likely result in a quicker realization of ultimate failure; (2) the more controllable an input is, the oftener it can be allowed to change, and hence it is good to establish the less controllable lines while freedom for manipulating the more controllable lines is still allowed.

Omitted from the Backtrace flow in Fig. 3 is any consideration of the faulty gate when the objective list pertains to the faulty machine. Such detail would considerably complicate the diagram while shedding little light on how the program works. It is mentioned here only to emphasize that the distinction is made between the good and faulty logic models and between their respective states.

Analyze

The Analyze step (in Fig. 1) will now be described. If the pattern just simulated caused any faults to be detected for the first time, the pattern is accepted. Otherwise, Analyze processes the stack entries in their chronological order of creation. It compares the gate values found there with the corresponding gate values produced by the simulator. It looks for the first occurrence of either an assignment that is no longer satisfied or an

objective that has become satisfied. If an unsatisfied assignment is found first, a conflict flag is set, the pattern is discarded, and Backup is called. If the search terminates at a satisfied objective, the remainder of the stack including this satisfied entry is erased, and the "no conflict" flag is set.

An Example

Fig. 4a is a three-stage shift register composed of edge-sensitive clocked flip-flop cells. Each cell is made up of six NOR gates connected as shown. The relative fan-in weights are indicated by the top-to-bottom order of the gate inputs. The uppermost input of a gate is considered most easily controllable; the bottom input, most difficult to control.

For the purpose of illustration, a single fault in this shift register is considered: the output of block 25 stuck 0. This fault was chosen in the middle of the register to illustrate two facets of the test generation process: (1) getting a desired value to appear at the output of a network (cells 1 and 2 in this example) and (2) propagating a test value through a network (cell 3).

In this example the following notation is used: simulator block values are shown immediately to the right of the blocks. Good machine values are shown above, and faulty machine values appear below the line which represents the block output net. Unpredictable, or X, values are left blank. The path traced by the Backtrace routine is shown as a heavy line; stack values, when shown, appear in boldface to the right of the simulator values. The only stack values shown are the objectives at the beginning and end points of the backtrace, and assignments.

For illustration purposes, the step of initializing the PIs to 0 is skipped here. The fault selection step is also skipped, because only one fault is being considered.

In Fig. 4a, the only known value in the logic is the faulty machine value of the faulty gate, 25. Since no test value exists, one must be generated by obtaining a good machine 1 on gate 25. This is the start of the backtrace, which alternately follows the lower and uppermost inputs of gates 25, 26, and 23. (These respectively represent imply, decision, and imply objectives.) Gate 24, which is a decision objective, has its "easiest" input already on the path (objective list). Hence, the next gate is 15, and the path ends at the clock PI with the desired value of good machine 1.

The clock is set to 1, and simulation is performed. The results are shown in Fig. 4b. The backtrace follows the same path as before until gate 12 is reached. Being already at the desired value, it is assigned, and the next input to gate 13 is taken, gate 14. This time the trace stops at the data input, which is set to 1, and fault simulation is again performed.

This results in the states shown in Fig. 4c. After each simulation, a check is made for the existence of a test value. None being found, the backtrace is again started at gate 25 and follows the path shown. Continuing in this fashion, Fig. 4f is finally reached.

After the simulation that results in Fig. 4f, test values are found at gates 25 and 34. According to the stated procedure for calculating output distances, 34 is closer to POs than 25. The Propagate step then chooses one of the fanouts of gate 34. Assume 33 has a lower output distance than 31. Propagate initializes the stack with an assignment of gate 33 to a faulty machine 0 and the objective of good machine 1 value on gate 33. Backtrace reaches the clock by the path shown, resulting in the simulator state of Fig. 4g. Test values now

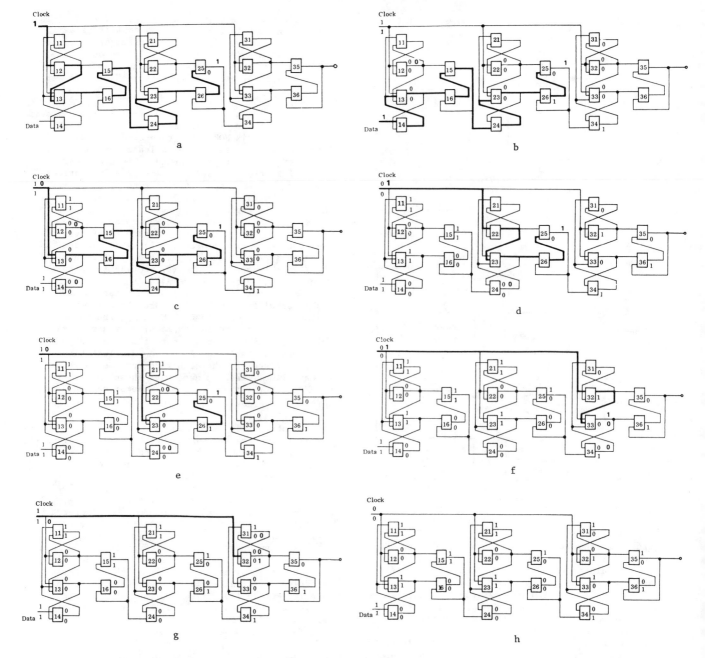

Fig. 4. Test generation example

exist on gates 25, 26, 31, and 34. Assume 31 has the lowest output distance. Propagate assigns the good machine 0 value on gate 32 and starts the back-trace with gate 32, desired faulty machine value 1. The clock is reached with desired value 0, resulting in a complete successful test as shown in Fig. 4h.

This example is not given as "proof" of the ability of the method to handle serial registers. Clearly, there is no basis for a general claim to that effect. The example is intended to clarify how the method works and to give credence to the claim that SOFTG is an effective tool for this type of network.

Results

The effectiveness of SOFTG has exceeded the original expectation. It was intended to provide some deterministic test-generation capability for logic designs that exceed the practical sequential-complexity limitation of previous analytical techniques. There is, of course, no guarantee that the program can derive a test if one exists. However, even on combinational logic networks for which practical, complete algorithms exist, SOFTG is competitive.

Table I shows comparative results for SOFTG and "X", a test generator similar in operation to D-alg.[4] All networks of Table I are combinational and contain an average of over 750 logic gates and about 200 I/O's each. The results show that the more analytical technique yielded better coverage in most cases, while SOFTG was more consistent and obtained a slightly better average test coverage. Run times shown are normalized CPU time for test generation and fault simulation. The SOFTG run times were significantly better; in only two of these ten examples was SOFTG slower, and in both cases it paid off in more complete test coverage.

TABLE I. Comparative Test Results
for SOFTG and "X"

	Percent of Stuck Faults Detected		Relative Run Time	
Network	X	SOFTG	X	SOFTG
1	99.5	98.9	63	21
2	98.2	98.0	103	39
3	98.5	98.1	85	46
4	96.2	96.2	246	74
5	96.9	96.4	108	75
6	82.8	87.0	153	193
7	94.5	93.9	51	22
8	99.8	98.9	67	30
9	99.1	98.9	74	32
10	99.7	99.9	50	78
Mean	96.5	96.6	100	61

Table II is the percent stuck fault coverage on
a sample of sequential logic networks. These averaged about 600 gates each, with an average of 80
feedback lines. The Previous Results column is the
combined coverage of two test generators, one similar
in operation to the Iterative Test Generator
described in Ref. 1 and the other a path-sensitizing
technique. SOFTG yielded generally superior and

TABLE II. Comparative Stuck-Fault Test Coverage

Network	Previous Results	SOFTG
1	92.5	95.9
2	95.1	97.3
3	93.5	95.0
4	87.9	84.0
5	43.3	96.3
6	51.8	85.7
7	77.7	92.6
8	88.6	90.5
9	95.0	90.6
10	85.6	77.9
Mean	81.1	90.6

more consistent results on this sample. Its worst
performance was 7.7% less than the previous results
on network 10, while overall it averaged 9.5% better
coverage. Comparative run times were, unfortunately,
not saved from this study. In general, run time
comparisons are less favorable for SOFTG as logic
complexity increases, while fault coverage comparisons are more favorable.

Conclusion

The original objective of providing a practical
"intelligent" automatic test generator for dense
sequential logic has been reached. This heuristic
procedure has proved quite effective on sequential
logic that operates serially. It is less effective
in operating parallel functions, and there are latch
designs it cannot properly excercise. This procedure
can be elaborated to overcome some such shortcomings.
Its success can be attributed in part to luck, and, in
this regard, it might be considered a sort of random
generator. On the other hand, the simple but
elegant backtracing and pattern evaluation
technique puts SOFTG in a rank with the most
intelligent pattern generators for sequential logic
presently available.

References

1. W. G. Bouricius, E. P. Hsieh, G. R. Putzolu,
J. P. Roth, P. R. Schneider, and C. J. Tan, "Algor-
ithms for Detection of Faults in Logic Circuits,"
IEEE Trans. Computers, vol. C-20, pp. 1258-1264,
November 1971.

2. H. D. Schnurmann, E. Lindbloom, and
R. G. Carpenter, "The Weighted Random Test-Pattern
Generator," IEEE Trans. Computers, vol. C-24, pp.
695-700, July 1975.

3. D. M. Schuler, E. G. Ulrich, T. E. Baker, and
S. P. Bryant, "Random Test Generator Using Concurrent Logic Simulation," Proc. 12th Design Automation Conference, pp. 261-267, June 1975.

4. J. P. Roth, "Diagnosis of Automata Failures:
A Calculus and a Method," IBM J. Res. Dev., vol.
10, pp. 278-291, 1966.

Functional Testing of Semiconductor Random Access Memories

Magdy S. Abadir

Department of Electrical Engineering, University of Southern California, Los Angeles, California 90007

Hassan K. Reghbati

Computing Science Department, Simon Fraser University, Burnaby, British Columbia, Canada V5A 1S6

This paper presents an overview of the problem of testing semiconductor random access
memories (RAMs). An important aspect of this test procedure is the detection of
permanent faults that cause the memory to function incorrectly. Functional-level fault
models are very useful for describing a wide variety of RAM faults. Several fault models
are discussed throughout the paper, including the stuck-at-0/1 faults, coupled-cell faults,
and single-cell pattern-sensitive faults. Test procedures for these fault models are
presented and their fault coverage and execution times are discussed. The paper is
intended for the general computer science audience and presupposes no background in the
hardware testing area.

Categories and Subject Descriptors: B.3.4 [**Memory Structures**]: Reliability, Testing,
and Fault Tolerance—*test generation*; B.7.3 [**Integrated Circuits**]: Reliability and
Testing—*test generation*

General Terms: Algorithms, Reliability

Additional Key Words and Phrases: Checking experiments, fault detection

INTRODUCTION

Recent developments in semiconductor memory technology have greatly increased the use of semiconductor random access memories (RAMs). These memories are usually large-scale-integration (LSI) devices and employ either bipolar or metal oxide semiconductor (MOS) techniques [INTEL 1975]. To detect the variety of faults that can occur within a memory chip, extensive testing of semiconductor memories is carried out by both users and manufacturers. As a result of the large number of cells involved, most of the standard fault-detection techniques [Muehldorf and Savkar 1981] are not suitable for memory testing.

A RAM chip consists mainly of a memory cells array, an address decoder, a memory address register (MAR), a memory data register (MDR), and read/write logic (sense amplifiers, write drivers, etc.). The general organization of a semiconductor RAM is given in Figure 1.

Physical faults can occur in any part of the memory chip. The causes of failure in RAMs, though not yet fully understood, are known to depend on such factors as component density, circuit layout, and method of manufacture. In this paper, we limit ourselves to the fault-detection, rather than the fault-location, problem. In this way, testing for faults that have similar effects on the functional behavior of the memory system can be simplified by testing for one of these faults.

We intend to survey the different methods for detecting functional faults in semiconductor RAMs and to compare these

CONTENTS

methods in terms of their time efficiency and fault coverage. We begin in Section 1 by describing the three most commonly used fault models for semiconductor RAMs, concentrating on the stuck-at faults model, the coupling faults model, and the pattern-sensitive faults model.

1. MEMORY FAULT MODELS

A wide variety of internal faults can occur in semiconductor memories, causing various types of failures in the memory function. Test procedures necessary to detect these faults can be classified—as in any digital circuit test—into three classes: DC parametric testing, AC parametric testing, and functional testing [Abadir and Reghbati 1983; Akers 1980; Breuer and Friedman 1976; Muehldorf and Savkar 1981].

DC parametric testing, as the name suggests, measures the DC parameters in semiconductor RAMs. It checks for unacceptable output level, high power consumption, fanout capability, noise margins, rise and fall times in electrical signals, etc. Clearly, this kind of testing depends on the implementation details of the RAM under test, and usually the DC parametric test

procedure is supplied by the manufacturer. Because DC parametric testing is so implementation dependent, we do not discuss it further in this paper.

AC parametric testing, or dynamic testing, measures AC parameters of the RAM to detect any malfunction. The parameters measured include memory access time, setup time, and hold time. Examples of malfunctions that can be detected by AC testing include [Breuer and Friedman 1976]

(1) Slow write–recovery: the memory may not produce the correct information at the specified access time when each read cycle is preceded by a write cycle.
(2) Sleeping sickness: memory loses information in less than the specified hold time.[1]

Although AC parametric test procedures are not considered in this paper, functional test procedures detect many AC malfunctions. For example, the stuck-at faults tests, when applied to the memory at the maximum possible rate, may detect slow write–recovery faults.

Functional testing is designed to detect permanent faults that cause the memory to function incorrectly.[2] Generally speaking, a

---

[1] Metal oxide semiconductor (MOS) dynamic memories store their data via the charge across a capacitor; because of leakage this charge must be refreshed at fixed intervals, or the value in the cell will be lost. The maximum period of time that data can be stored without refreshing is called the hold time.
[2] The contrast between software program testing and functional testing of digital systems is worth noting. In program testing, the main concern is achieving an acceptable assurance that the programmer has put together his primitives (i.e., language constructs) correctly. Although functional testing of digital systems is similarly concerned with whether hardware primitives have been put together correctly, it is further concerned with the integrity of the primitives themselves. Moreover, while human factors and software complexity make program testing largely an art at present, the relative simplicity of digital systems (memories, in particular) makes functional testing more methodological. The program testing work that is most analogous to functional testing is that of compiler validation [Hoyt 1977]. An area of special interest is test data selection techniques [Demillo et al. 1978].

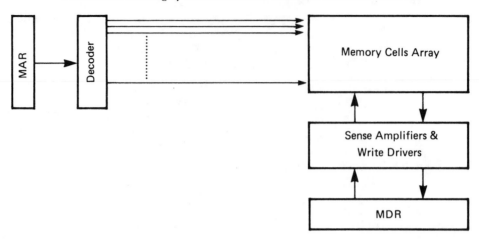

Figure 1.   A semiconductor RAM organization at the functional level of description.

read/write RAM can be defined as *functional* if it is possible to store a 0 or a 1 into every cell of the memory, to change every cell from 0 to 1 as well as from 1 to 0, and to read every cell correctly when it stores a 0 as well as when it stores a 1, regardless of the contents of the remaining cells or the previous memory access sequences.

A functional test that will cover all the possible faults is impossible from the practical point of view, since the complexity of such a test will be on the order of 2^n [Hayes 1975], where n is the number of cells in the memory (we have to check every cell for all possible states of the remaining cells). For example, assuming an access time of ~500 nanoseconds, testing a 1 Kbit RAM would take approximately 10^{293} seconds! Therefore, in order to develop any practically feasible test procedure, we should restrict ourselves to a subset of faults that are most likely to occur. This practice is known as "selecting a *fault model*."

The following three fault models for RAMs are the most widely used ones (listed according to their degree of complexity):

(1) *Stuck-at Faults Model.*   One or more logic values in the memory system cannot be changed. For example, one or more cells are "stuck at" 1 or 0. Stuck-at faults are also useful for modeling faults in other parts of the memory system (see Figure 1).

(2) *Coupling Faults Model.*   There exist two or more cells that are coupled. A pair of memory cells, i and j, are said to be coupled if a transition from x to y in one cell of the pair, say cell i, changes the state of the other cell, that is, cell j, from 0 to 1 or from 1 to 0. This, of course, does not necessarily imply that a similar transition in cell j will influence cell i in a similar manner.

(3) *Pattern-Sensitivity Faults (PSF) Model.*   The fault that alters the state of a memory cell as a result of certain patterns of zeros, ones, zero-to-one transitions, and/or one-to-zero transitions in the other cells of the memory is called a PSF. Also, the fault that causes a read or a write operation of one cell of the memory to fail owing to certain patterns of zeros and ones in the other cells of the memory is called a PSF. General pattern-sensitivity tests are infeasible in practice [Hayes 1975]. However, some restricted, and realistic, models of PSFs allow for the generation of efficient test sequences [Hayes 1980; Suk and Reddy 1980]. It should be noted that coupling faults are a special case of PSF.

There are many test procedures for RAMs. These procedures can be partitioned into three classes, according to the fault model that each procedure adopts. Procedures for testing stuck-at faults are simple and fast. Procedures for testing coupling faults are more complicated and usually require more time, but they detect all stuck-at faults, as well as all coupling faults. Procedures for testing pattern-sensitivity faults are very complicated and they only consider some restricted case of PSFs. In the rest of the paper we describe different representatives from each class of procedure, their time complexity, and their degree of fault coverage.

2. TESTING FOR STUCK-AT FAULTS

This section describes different testing algorithms intended to detect stuck-at faults in read/write semiconductor RAMs. This kind of fault is independent of the memory state and can occur in any part of the memory system. Thus we have to consider stuck-at faults in the memory data register, memory address register, address decoder, the memory cells array, and the read/write logic. Note that fault detection is our main concern, not fault location, since the whole RAM is assumed to be on one chip.

2.1 The MSCAN Test Procedure

A trivial test procedure, called Memory Scan (MSCAN), is presented to illustrate some aspects of the complexity of testing a RAM [Breuer and Friedman 1976]. A word with address i is denoted W_i. A write operation to W_i is denoted as

Write: $W_i \leftarrow \alpha$ where α is the all 0 word or the all 1 word.

Similarly, a read operation of W_i is denoted as

Read: $W_i (=\alpha)$ where the value in parenthesis is the expected value of W_i.

MSCAN Procedure

For i = 0, 1, 2, ..., n − 1 do:
  Write: $W_i \leftarrow 0$
  Read: $W_i (=0)$
  Write: $W_i \leftarrow 1$
  Read: $W_i (=1)$.

This test writes each word, first with a 0 and then with a 1, and verifies the writing with two read statements.

The above test procedure will not detect any stuck-at fault in the memory address register or in the decoder. But on the assumption that those two are fault free, the test can detect any stuck-at fault in the memory array, in the memory data register, or in the read/write logic. Of course, such a test is of little value because at the end of this procedure we can only be sure that there is at least one word in the memory that is functionally correct. (A fault could have occurred in the decoder such that the same word is always referenced.) The complexity of the MSCAN test is $4n$.

2.2 The ATS Procedure

Knaizuk and Hartmann developed a test algorithm called ATS (algorithmic test sequence) that detects any combination of stuck-at-0 or stuck-at-1 multiple faults in a RAM. In their first paper [Knaizuk and Hartmann 1977a] they introduced the ATS algorithm, showing that it detects any single stuck-at fault in a RAM. In their second paper [Knaizuk and Hartmann 1977b] they proved that the same algorithm detects all multiple stuck-at faults. A discussion of the ATS will be given in this section.

Assume that the memory contains n words, each denoted as W_i for $0 \le i \le n - 1$, and that each word is m bits long.

The memory words are grouped into three partitions, G_0, G_1, and G_2, such that

$$G_0 = \{W_i \mid i = 0 \ (\text{modulo } 3)\},$$

$$G_1 = \{W_i \mid i = 1 \ (\text{modulo } 3)\},$$

$$G_2 = \{W_i \mid i = 2 \ (\text{modulo } 3)\}.$$

The same notation for the read and write operations used in Section 2.1 is used here:

ATS Procedure

1. For all $W_i \in G_1 \cup G_2$
     Write: $W_i \leftarrow 0$ "0 denotes the all 0 word"
2. For all $W_i \in G_0$
     Write: $W_i \leftarrow 1$ "1 denotes the all 1 word"
3. For all $W_i \in G_1$
     Read: $W_i (=0)$
4. For all $W_i \in G_1$
     Write: $W_i \leftarrow 1$
5. For all $W_i \in G_2$
     Read: $W_i (=0)$
6. For all $W_i \in G_0 \cup G_1$
     Read: $W_i (=1)$
7. For all $W_i \in G_0$
     Write: $W_i \leftarrow 0$
     Read: $W_i (=0)$

Computing Surveys, Vol. 15, No. 3, September 1983

Step / Partition	1	2	3	4	5	6	7	8
G_0		Wr1				R1	Wr O, R O	
G_1	Wr O		R O	Wr 1		R 1		
G_2	Wr O				R O			Wr 1, R1

Figure 2. ATS algorithm (Wr means write and R means read).

8. For all $W_i \in G_2$
      Write: $W_i \leftarrow 1$
      Read: $W_i (=1)$
END.

The algorithm is shown in tabulated form in Figure 2.

The RAM is assumed to consist of a memory address register (MAR), an address decoder, a memory data register (MDR), and a memory cells array. The decoder is assumed to be of "noncreative" design [Klayton 1971]; that is, a single fault within the decoder does not create a new memory address to be accessed[3] without also accessing the programmed address. Stuck-at faults occurring in other physical parts of the memory can be visualized as stuck-at faults in the above subsystems. Furthermore, stuck-at faults in the MAR are indistinguishable from those in the inputs of the decoder. Thus it is enough to only consider the three remaining subsystems (i.e., decoder, MDR, and memory cells array).

To prove that the ATS detects all multiple stuck-at faults in the RAM, we first prove that it detects multiple faults in each subsystem, assuming that all other subsystems are fault free. Next, in Section 2.2.4,

[3] By accessing a memory address we mean reading from, or writing to, the memory cells associated with that address. If, owing to a fault, more than one word is accessed during a read operation, the words will be ORed or ANDed together, depending on the RAM technology.

we show how ATS detects any combination of faults in the RAM.

2.2.1 Decoder Faults

A noncreative decoder is an l-input, 2^l-output device constructed of AND and NOT gates with no reconverging paths [Klayton 1971]. An example of a 4-input, 16-ouput decoder is given in Figure 3.

We first consider the faults in the input of the decoder. Because we grouped the memory locations into three different partitions, no single stuck-at fault in the decoder input can map an address in one partition into another address in the same partition [Knaizuk and Hartmann 1977a]. The following test sequence detects any fault in the input of the decoder [Ravi 1969]:

1. Write: $W_2 \leftarrow 0$
2. For every W_i which is Hamming distance 1 apart from W_2 Write: $W_i \leftarrow 1$
3. Read: $W_2 (=0)$

The effectiveness of this test stems from the fact that any fault in the input of decoder will cause W_2 and at least one of the W_i's to access the same location. It should be clear that Steps 1, 2, 4, and 5 of ATS implement the above test sequence. Thus, any multiple stuck-at fault in the decoder input will be detected by ATS.

Since the decoder is of noncreative design, any stuck-at-0 fault in the decoder not masked by another stuck-at-1 fault will be

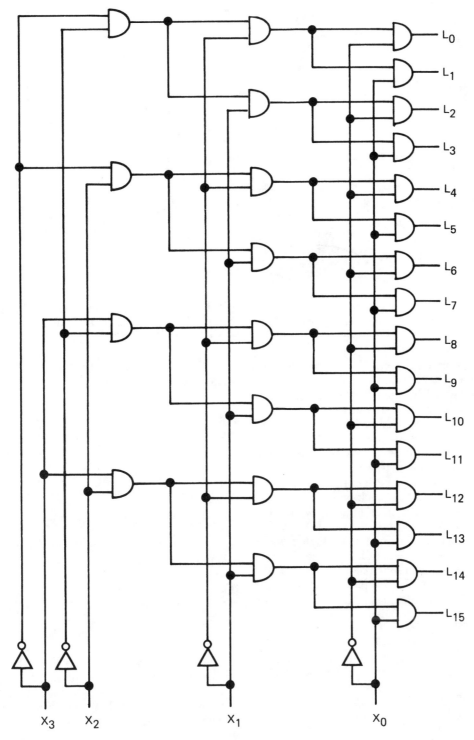

Figure 3.   A 4-bit input, 16-bit output noncreative decoder.

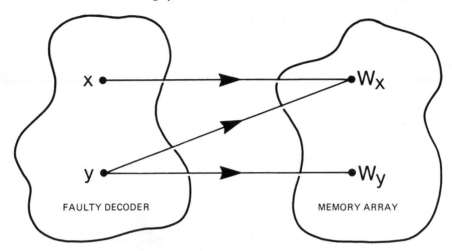

Figure 4. Faulty decoder accesses.

propagated to the output of the decoder. This will inhibit the selection of at least one word line, causing a constant reading of 0 or 1, depending on the physical implementation of the RAM. Hence the fault will be detected because ATS must read both 0 and 1 from all storage locations.

Now we will consider any combination of faults in the decoder such that any address will access some memory word. In fact these remaining faults will contain at least one stuck-at-1 fault in the decoder. As shown in Figure 4, let X be the address that will place 1 on a faulty stuck-at-1 line and also sensitize a path to a memory word W_x. Consider the address Y that is Hamming distance 1 apart from X such that it places 0 on the site of the stuck-at-1 fault. This address will also sensitize the same path to the memory word W_x. Now, since X and Y cannot be in the same partition of the memory address space, the fault will be detected by ATS. For example, suppose that X is in G_0 and Y is in either G_1 or G_2. If Y is in G_1, the fault will be detected in Step 3 of ATS owing to reading 1 instead of 0. If Y is in G_2, the fault will be detected in Step 5 owing to reading 1 instead of 0.

Thus far we have proved that ATS detects the decoder faults, assuming that all other subsystems are fault free.

2.2.2 Memory Data Register Faults

Any stuck-at fault in the MDR will prohibit reading either the all-0 word or the all-1 word. Thus ATS detects any fault in the MDR. Note also that this is true, independent of any other fault in the other subsystems.

2.2.3 Memory Array Faults

As in the above paragraph, any stuck-at fault in any bit position at any word in the memory array will prohibit reading either the all-0 word or the all-1 word from this place in the memory. Since ATS reads these two words from all storage locations, then the fault is detected.

2.2.4 Multiple Subsystems Faults

Recall that the MDR faults are detected independently, and so the only faults that remain to be considered are those affecting both the decoder and the memory array. The proof that ATS detects these faults is quite long, and hence omitted. The interested reader can refer to Knaizuk and Hartmann [1977b].

The complexity of the ATS algorithm is $4n$, since $4n$ memory accesses are needed. In fact, to detect even a single stuck-at fault in the memory array alone, we need at least $4n$ memory accesses (to read and write both 0 and 1 in all storage locations). Thus the ATS is optimal with respect to the stuck-at faults class of procedures. However, it only works if the decoder is of a noncreative design and if the RAM has a wired-OR behavior. The latter restriction is not very

Computing Surveys, Vol. 15, No. 3, September 1983

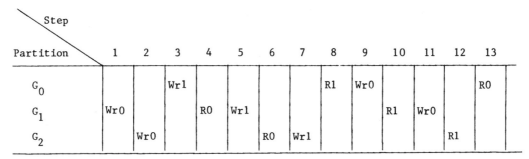

Figure 5.   The ATS+.

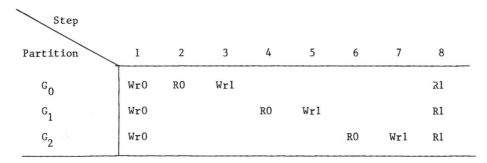

Figure 6.   First modification of ATS.

severe, and by duality it is easy to modify the ATS for RAMs with a wired-AND behavior. This is simply done by complementing all the 1's and 0's in the ATS. Nair [1979] modified the ATS by rearranging the test sequence and adding an extra $n/3$ write operations, as shown in Figure 5. The resulting test sequence covers all stuck-at faults if the wired logic behavior of the RAM is either wired-OR or wired-AND, but not a mixture of both [Nair 1979]. For convenience, we refer to this new test sequence by the name ATS+.

2.3 The MATS Procedure

Nair developed a test sequence called Modified ATS (MATS) that detects any combination of stuck-at faults in a RAM, irrespective of the design of the decoder combinational circuit [Nair 1979]. As indicated by its name, MATS is a modification of the ATS described in the previous section.

The first modification that was made to the ATS is to rearrange the test sequence as shown in Figure 6. It is easy to see that

the resulting test sequence has the same capabilities of the ATS, and at the same time has a much simpler structure. Nair [1979] also noticed that the validity of the ATS depends to a great extent on the fact that any single stuck-at fault in the input of the decoder cannot map an address in one partition into another address in the same partition. Hence the number of partitions is not important as long as the partitions satisfy the above mentioned criterion. One such number is n, the number of words in the memory; that is, each word will constitute a partition. Clearly, using n partitions will satisfy the above criterion. The resulting test sequence, called MATS, is shown in Figure 7.

The MATS has two advantages over the ATS. The most obvious one is its structure, which makes implementation a very simple task. More important, it was proved that MATS covers all stuck-at faults in RAMs, independent of the decoder design. Because the proof is similar to the ATS proof, we omit it here. The interested reader can refer to the original paper [Nair 1979].

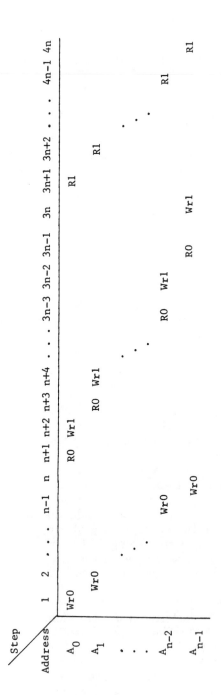

Figure 7. Modified ATS: MATS.

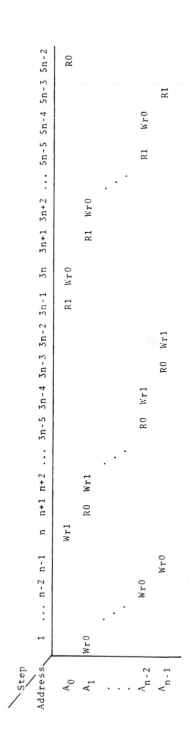

Figure 8. The MATS+.

As in the ATS, the MATS works only for RAMs with wired-OR behavior. Again, by duality a test sequence can be constructed for RAMs with wired-AND behavior. Nair also presented a test sequence—which we call MATS+—that can be used for RAMs with unknown logic behavior. The MATS+ is of complexity $5n - 2$ and is shown in Figure 8.

2.4 Comparative Study

Table 1 lists the time complexity and the fault coverage of the procedures presented in the previous sections. The fault coverage of the procedures is given in terms of the stuck-at fault model.

3. TESTING FOR COUPLING FAULTS

An important type of fault that can cause a semiconductor RAM to function incorrectly is the cell's coupling fault. Such faults can occur as a result of a short circuit or a circuit's parasitic effects such as current leakage or stray capacitances.

In this section we discuss several procedures that adopt the coupling fault model. A common feature of all these procedures is that they cover most (or all) of the stuck-at faults in the RAM while testing for coupling faults.

It is very important to note that when considering the coupling fault model (or the later PSF model), memory bits cannot be treated as being functionally independent, as they could in the stuck-at fault model. Therefore in the rest of our discussion we shall assume that the memory under test is an array of n cells (bits) rather than an array of multiple-bit words.

Various test procedures such as Column Bars, Marching 1's and 0's, and Galloping 1's and 0's (GALPAT) have been proposed and used in the industry to test for different classes of coupling faults and stuck-at faults [Breuer and Friedman 1976; Barraclough et al. 1976; Sohl 1977]. The complexity of these test procedures ranges from $O(n)$ to $O(n^2)$.

They vary in complexity mainly because they vary in the amount of fault coverage they provide. However, more powerful test procedures have been proposed in the literature with complexities $O(n \log_2 n)$, and even $O(n)$ [Thatte and Abraham 1977; Nair et al. 1978; Suk and Reddy 1981]. These procedures provide more fault coverage than the ones used commercially with comparable or faster execution times.

3.1 Commonly Used Test Procedures

In this section we discuss three representative testing procedures, used commercially, to test semiconductor RAMs for coupling and stuck-at faults.

3.1.1 Column Bars Test

Assume that the RAM contains n accessible cells and is organized as an array of two dimensions, such that the even addresses are in the even columns and the odd addresses are in the odd columns. The test procedure is given as

Step 1. Write 1's in all even addresses and 0's in all odd addresses.
Step 2. Read all the memory cells.
Step 3. Repeat Steps 1 and 2, interchanging 1's and 0's.

The procedure is designed to test for possible coupling between any two cells in adjacent columns [Breuer and Friedman 1976]. It is not very effective, though, because it only guarantees that there are two cells in the whole memory that are not coupled and that they do exist. This limitation results from the possibility that a stuck-at fault could have occurred in the memory decoder, causing all the even addresses to be mapped to one cell and all the odd addresses to be mapped to the other cell. Such a fault will not be detected by the Column Bars test. Even if we were to assume that the decoder is fault free, the Column Bars test would not detect some of the coupling faults between cells in the same column. The complexity of this procedure is $4n$, but it is of limited value because it does not cover the decoder or the MAR stuck-at faults and it also fails to cover many coupling faults in the RAM.

Table 1. Summary of Stuck-at Faults Test Procedures

	Com-plexity	Fault coverage	
		Stuck-at faults	Coupling and PSFs
MSCAN	$4n$	Covers memory array faults, but does not cover decoder or MAR faults	No
ATS	$4n$	Covers all, for RAMs with wired-OR logic behavior and noncreative decoder design	No
Complemented ATS	$4n$	Same as ATS, but for RAMs with wired-AND logic behavior	No
ATS+	$13n/3$	Covers all, for RAMs with arbitrary wired logic behavior and noncreative decoder design	No
MATS	$4n$	Covers all, for RAMs with wired-OR logic behavior and arbitrary decoder design	No
Complemented MATS	$4n$	Same as MATS, but for RAMs with wired-AND logic behavior	No
MATS+	$5n - 2$	Covers all, for RAMs with arbitrary wired logic behavior and arbitrary decoder design	No

3.1.2 Marching 1's and 0's Test

Assume that the RAM consists of n cells. The Marching 1's and 0's test procedure is given as follows:

Step 1. Write: $C_i \leftarrow 0$ for $i = 0, 1, \ldots, n - 1$
Step 2. For $i = 0, 1, \ldots, n - 1$
    Read: $C_i (=0)$ (Read cell i; the expected value is 0)
    Write: $C_i \leftarrow 1$ (Write 1 into cell i)
    Read: $C_i (=1)$
Step 3. For $i = n - 1, n - 2, \ldots, 0$
    Read: $C_i (=1)$
    Write: $C_i \leftarrow 0$
    Read: $C_i (=0)$
Step 4. Repeat Steps 1–3, interchanging 0's and 1's.

The idea behind this algorithm is that, while scanning the memory in ascending order, any direct coupling between the current cell and a higher order cell is detected when reading the second cell [Breuer and Friedman 1976]. Similarly, scanning the memory in descending order detects all the effects on lower numbered cells. Another good point about the procedure is that while scanning the memory in Step 2 (3), we leave a trail of 1's (0's) behind while we read a 0 (1). Thus in each iteration we ensure that a new cell is being read. Hence this algorithm guarantees that the n cells exist.

It is interesting to note that all the components of the MATS discussed in Section 2.3 exist in the Marching 1's and 0's test sequence. Hence the Marching 1's and 0's test covers all stuck-at faults.

A disadvantage of this test is that it does not detect some coupling faults such as the following:

(1) The coupling fault between cells i and j for $j > i$ such that a 0-to-1 (1-to-0) transition in cell i will write a value 0 (1) in cell j.
(2) Any two coupling faults that mask each other. For example, consider cells i, j, and k such that $i < j < k$. If a 0-to-1 (1-to-0) transition in cell i writes 1 (0) in cell k, and a 0-to-1 (1-to-0) transition in cell j writes 0 (1) in cell k, the fault between cells i and k is masked by the fault between cells j and k.

3.1.3 GALPAT Test

GALPAT or Galloping 1's and 0's is a very famous testing algorithm used by the industry to test RAMs. A major disadvantage of this algorithm is that its length is $O(n^2)$, which makes it impractical to use for large memories. For instance, testing a 64K RAM, with a 500-nanosecond access time, requires ~1.5 hours. The GALPAT procedure is as follows [Breuer and Friedman 1976]:

Step 1. Write: $C_i \leftarrow 0$ for $i = 0, 1, \ldots, n - 1$
Step 2. For $i = 0, 1, \ldots, n - 1$
    Write: $C_i \leftarrow 1$
    For all $j \neq i$
      Read: C_j (=0)   (test that no cell is disturbed)
      Read: C_i (=1)   (check that test bit is still correct)
    Write: $C_i \leftarrow 0$
Step 3. Repeat Steps 1 and 2, interchanging 1's and 0's.

This test verifies that every cell can be set to both 0 and 1 without causing any other cell to change its state; thus it proves that all the memory cells exist and that there is no coupling between any two cells. Also, all stuck-at faults in the decoder and in the memory array are covered by the test. The fault coverage of this procedure is better than that of the Marching 1's and 0's. For example, when this procedure is used, no two coupling faults can mask each other because we read the whole state of the memory after each write. However, there are some coupling faults that are not detected. For example, the coupling fault between any two cells i and i + 1 such that a 1-to-0 (0-to-1) transition in i causes 1 (0) to be written in cell i + 1 cannot be detected. Such faults can be detected by adding the statement "Read: C_i (=0)" before the first write statement in Step 2 of the procedure. This correction would add $2n$ to the complexity of the procedure, which is already $4n^2 + 2n$.

The GALPAT procedure is considered to be inefficient because its fault coverage does not justify its lengthy time requirement. In the next sections we will present test procedures proposed in the literature that are more efficient. These procedures provide more fault coverage than GALPAT and are less time consuming.

3.2 More Effective Procedures for the Detection of Coupling Faults

Thatte and Abraham [1977] considered a functional fault model for semiconductor

RAMs covering multiple stuck-at faults affecting the various memory subsystems, as well as coupling faults between pairs of memory cells. They also developed a procedure of complexity $O(n \log_2 n)$ to detect all the faults covered by the fault model. Nair et al. [1978] developed a more efficient testing procedure of complexity $O(n)$ to detect the same type of faults. Suk and Reddy [1981] developed a marching test procedure capable of detecting stuck-at faults and coupling faults in RAMs, given that only one of these two types of faults is present at any time. In the next two sections, the latter two procedures will be discussed.

3.2.1 Nair, Thatte, and Abraham's Testing Procedure

Nair et al. [1978] considered testing RAMs for both stuck-at faults and coupling faults. Recall from Section 1 that stuck-at faults can occur in any place in the RAM, whereas coupling faults occur only between pairs of cells in the memory cell array.

Assuming that the decoder will not change into a sequential circuit, any failure in the decoder will make it behave in one of the following ways:

(a) The decoder will not access the addressed cell. In addition, it may access nonaddressed cells.
(b) The decoder will access multiple cells including the addressed cell.

The multiple access fault can be viewed as a coupling fault in the memory cell array. Also the no access case can be viewed as a stuck-at fault in the addressed cell. Thus we do not have to consider the decoder faults since it is enough to consider the memory cell array faults. Similarly, some output lines or write driver lines may be stuck at 0 or 1. These faults can be considered as stuck-at faults in the corresponding memory cells. Also, the data input or output lines may have shorts or coupling between them. This fault can be visualized as coupling between the memory cells that correspond to the coupled data lines. Therefore, in order to test a semiconductor RAM for stuck-at and coupling faults, it is enough to concentrate on the faults in the memory cell array.

On the assumption that the memory consists of n cells, the following is a set of necessary and sufficient conditions for all faults in the memory cell array to be detected by a test sequence [Nair et al. 1978]:

Condition 1. Each cell must undergo a 0-to-1 ($\uparrow$) transition and a 1-to-0 ($\downarrow$) transition, and must be read after each transition and before undergoing any subsequent transition. If this condition is not satisfied, a cell "stuck at" 0 or 1 will not be detected.

Condition 2. For every pair of cells (i, j), cell i must be read after cell j makes a transitions and before cells i and j make any further transitions, for all the possible states of cell i (two states), and all possible transitions in cell j (two transitions). If this is not satisfied, a coupling fault between a pair of cells may not be detected.

Condition 3. For every cell triple (i, j, k), if the test makes a transition in cell j from y to $\bar{y}$ after cell i makes a transition from x to $\bar{x}$ and before cell k in state z is read, then the test must possess another sequence, where either

- cell k in state z is read after an x to $\bar{x}$ transition in cell i and before a y to $\bar{y}$ transition in cell j, or
- cell k in state $\bar{z}$ is read after a y to $\bar{y}$ transition in cell j and before an x to $\bar{x}$ transition in cell i.

If this condition is not satisfied, a coupling fault between cell j and cell k may mask the effect of another coupling fault between cell i and cell k, and prevent the fault from being detected. Note that the pair of faults, which mask the effect of each other, cannot be detected by using the Marching 1's and 0's test procedure. (See Section 3.1.2 for an example of these masking faults.)

The three conditions stated above have been shown to be necessary and sufficient for a test to detect all the faults in the memory fault model [Nair et al. 1978].

A test procedure that can detect all the faults in the fault model and satisfies all the conditions stated above is shown in Figure 9 in tabular form [Nair et al. 1978].

To prove that the above procedure detects all the faults in the fault model, it is enough to show that the procedure satisfies the above three conditions:

(1) Condition 1 is satisfied in sequences 1 and 2 of the procedure.
(2) Condition 2 is satisfied for the two cases, when $i < j$ and when $i > j$, as shown in Figure 10a.
(3) Eight cases are sufficient to demonstrate that Condition 3 is satisfied; these are shown in Figure 10b for $i < j < k$.

Hence the procedure is a complete test for the memory.

The number of operations required to perform the entire memory test is about $30n$, where n is the number of cells in the memory. The above procedure is very efficient when compared with the ones previously considered because of its high fault coverage and its low execution time.

3.2.2 Suk and Reddy's Testing Procedure

Using a fault model similar to the one considered in Section 3.2.1, Suk and Reddy [1981] developed a marching test sequence, called Test A, that is capable of detecting coupling faults and stuck-at faults in a RAM when only one type of fault is present. A marching test sequence is a sequence of marching elements, where every marching element is simply a finite sequence of operations applied to each cell of memory in either increasing order or decreasing order. The Marching 1's and 0's test is an example of this class of test sequences. Test A, shown in Figure 11, is also a marching test sequence with length = $14n$. We omit the proof of the validity of Test A, and refer the interested reader to Suk and Reddy [1981].

Suk and Reddy also modified Test A and derived another test called Test B, as shown in Figure 12. The new test sequence has a length of $16n$, and it was shown that if a RAM under test does not contain multiple access decoder faults, then Test B will detect the presence of any combination of stuck-at faults or coupling faults in the RAM [Suk and Reddy 1981].

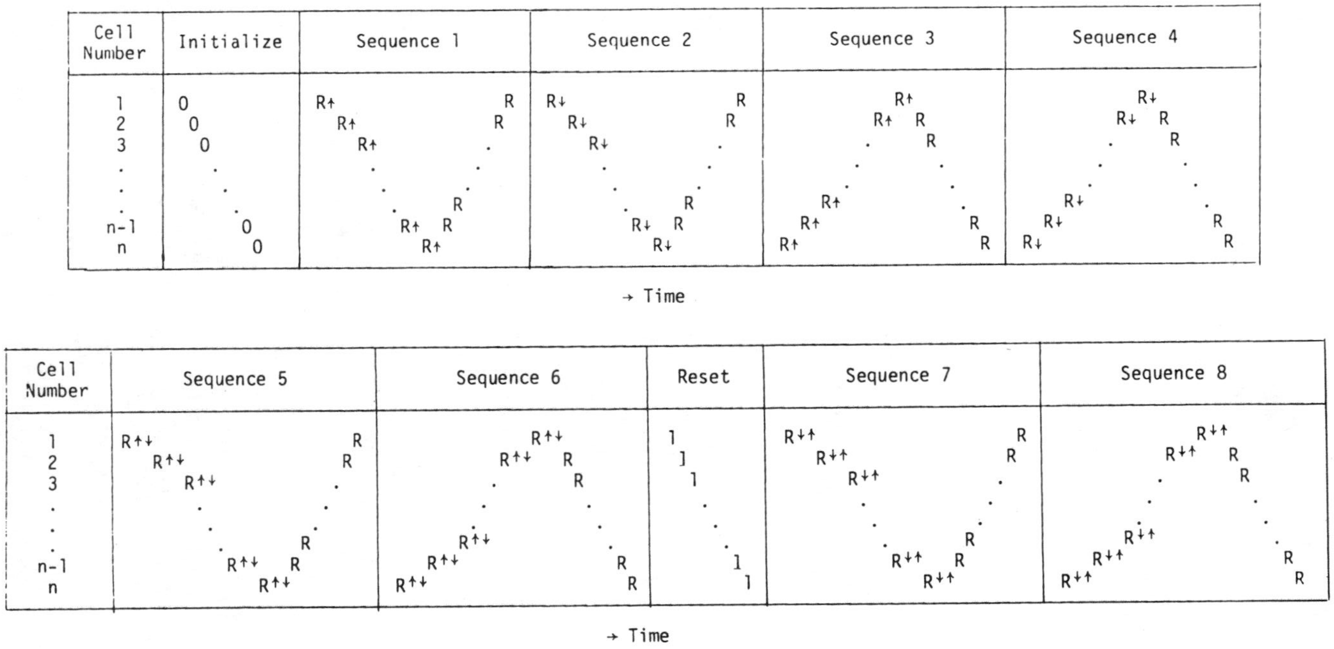

Figure 9. Nair, Thatte, and Abraham's testing procedure [Nair et al. 1978].

State of i	Transition in j	Performed in sequence
i < j		
0	0 - 1	3
1	0 - 1	1
0	1 - 0	2
1	1 - 0	4
i > j		
0	0 - 1	1
1	0 - 1	3
0	1 - 0	4
1	1 - 0	2

(a)

i	j	k	Performed in sequence	Pair of sequences satisfying condition 3
↑(↓)	↑	0	1(5)	}
↑(↓)	↑	1	7(7)	}
↓(↑)	↓	0	5(5)	}
↓(↑)	↓	1	2(7)	}
0	↑	↑(↓)	3(6)	}
1	↑	↑(↓)	8(8)	}
0	↓	↓(↑)	6(6)	}
1	↓	↓(↑)	4(8)	}

(b)

Figure 10. (a) Satisfying Condition 2. (b) Satisfying Condition 3.

131

Assume that all the memory cells
are initialized to 0.

1. For i = 1 to n do
   Read: C_i (=0)
   Write: $C_i \leftarrow 1$
   Write: $C_i \leftarrow 0$
   Write: $C_i \leftarrow 1$

2. For i = 1 to n do
   Read: C_i (=1)
   Write: $C_i \leftarrow 0$
   Write: $C_i \leftarrow 1$

3. For i = n to 1 do
   Read: C_i (=1)
   Write: $C_i \leftarrow 0$
   Write: $C_i \leftarrow 1$
   Write: $C_i \leftarrow 0$

4. For i = n to 1 do
   Read: C_i (=0)
   Write: $C_i \leftarrow 1$
   Write: $C_i \leftarrow 0$

Figure 11.   Test A.

Assume that all the memory cells
are initialized to 0.

1. For i = 1 to n do
   Read: C_i (=0)
   Write: $C_i \leftarrow 1$
   Read: C_i (=1)
   Write: $C_i \leftarrow 0$
   Read: C_i (=0)
   Write: $C_i \leftarrow 1$

2. For i = 1 to n do
   Read: C_i (=1)
   Write: $C_i \leftarrow 0$
   Write: $C_i \leftarrow 1$

3. For i = n to 1 do
   Read: C_i (=1)
   Write: $C_i \leftarrow 0$
   Write: $C_i \leftarrow 1$
   Write: $C_i \leftarrow 0$

4. For i = n to 1 do
   Read: C_i (=0)
   Write: $C_i \leftarrow 1$
   Write: $C_i \leftarrow 0$

Figure 12.   Test B.

3.3 Comparative Study

We have presented many procedures used
for testing RAMs for coupling and stuck-at
faults in the previous subsections. These
procedures are listed, and their complexities and fault coverage summarized in Table 2.

4. TESTING FOR PATTERN-SENSITIVE FAULTS

As the density of cells in memory chips
increases, pattern-sensitive faults—sometimes called "adjacent pattern interference
faults"—become the predominant fault
mode. Moreover, different classes of faults
that affect the memory cells such as shorts,
stuck-at faults, and coupling faults can be
regarded as special types of PSFs. For today's available large RAMs, testing for all
the possible PSFs is impossible from a
practical point of view. Hayes [1975] formalized pattern-sensitive testing by defining the memory as a well-defined sequential
machine with 2^n states and $3n$ inputs
(Read: C_i, Write: $C_i \leftarrow 0$, and Write: $C_i \leftarrow$
1; for i = $0, 1, \ldots, n-1$). A PSF can
change the state diagram of this sequential

machine in an arbitrary way without increasing the number of states. Hayes [1975]
developed a checking sequence for this machine of length $(3n^2 + 2n)2^n$ capable of
detecting any PSF in the memory. However, this formula results in test times that
are computationally infeasible. To deal
with this problem he introduced the concept of *neighborhood*. Thus, by assuming
that a read or a write operation on cell C_i
can only affect or be affected by the neighborhood cells, a considerable saving in the
length of the testing procedure can be
achieved.

By taking into consideration the general
features of the memory design and its operation methods it is possible to derive a
model for PSFs that are most likely to
occur. The two-dimensional organization of
the memory cell array means that only the
adjacent neighbors are likely to contribute
substantially to PSFs. The two neighborhoods defined below are most appropriate
for memories arranged as two-dimensional
cell arrays [Hayes 1980; Suk and Reddy
1980]:

Table 2.   Summary of the Coupling Faults Test Procedures

	Complexity	Fault coverage	
		Stuck-at faults	Coupling faults
Column Bar test	$4n$	Does not cover the decoder or the MAR faults	Covers coupling faults between cells in adjacent columns Does not cover faults between cells in the same column or in non-adjacent columns
Marching 1's and 0's	$14n$	All (same coverage as MATS+, see Table 1)	Does not cover all single coupling faults (its degree of fault coverage is unknown)
GALPAT	$4n^2 + 2n$	All	Covers most coupling faults
Modified GALPAT	$4n^2 + 4n$	All	All
Thatte and Abraham's test	$8n \log_2 n$	All	All
Nair, Thatte, and Abraham's test	$30n$	All	All
Suk and Reddy's Test A	$14n$	All, if coupling faults are not present	All, if stuck-at faults are not present
Suk and Reddy's Test B	$16n$	All memory array faults are covered Decoder faults are covered if coupling faults are not present	All, if decoder multiple access faults are not present

(1) the 5-cell neighborhood, consisting of a base cell and its four adjacent neighboring cells located at the top, bottom, left, and right of the base cell, and

(2) the 9-cell square neighborhood, consisting of a base cell and all 8 adjacent neighboring cells.

An illustration of the two types of neighborhoods is shown in Figure 13. Obviously, other neighborhoods can be defined, depending on the degree of fault coverage required.

In this section we will discuss mainly the work done by Hayes [1980], and by Suk and Reddy [1980]. Both tackled the problem of detecting single PSFs in two-dimensional memories by using special types of neighborhoods called *tiling neighborhoods*. In a tiling neighborhood copies of the *tile*, the neighborhood structure, can cover the whole memory in such a way that no copies overlap and no part of the memory is left uncovered except at the boundaries of the memory. Examples of such neighborhoods are the two types shown in Figure 13.

For a complete test sequence for single PSFs the following aspects must be considered:

(1) The test must apply a sequence of write operations to sensitize PSFs caused by the write operations. These can be classified into two groups:

a. PSFs caused by transition writes, that is, write operations that change the state of the memory, for example, write 1 in cell i that contains 0, and

b. PSFs caused by nontransition writes that are supposed to leave the memory state unchanged, for example, write 1 in cell i that already contains 1.

(2) The test must apply a sufficient number of reads to verify the write operations and to verify the reads themselves. The latter aspect is very important in memories with a destructive read operation. Thus a read operation of cell i may cause another cell j in the neighborhood of i to change its state when a certain PSF exists.

Assume that the memory to be tested consists of one tile, that is, a base cell and its adjacent neighboring cells. Moreover, assume that we want to test the base cell for PSFs caused by transition write operations (we will consider PSFs caused by nontransition write and read operations later). There are two classes of PSFs caused

133

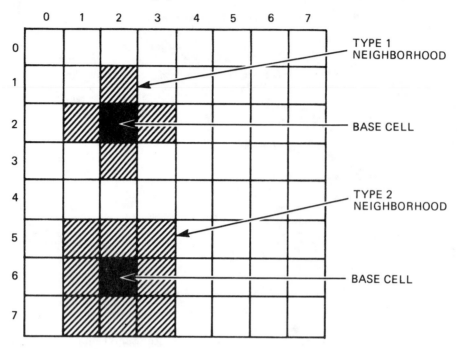

Figure 13. An illustration of two types of neighborhoods.

by transition write operations affecting the base cell of a given neighborhood:

Active Neighborhood PSF (ANPSF). The base cell change as a result of a transition write operation in one of the neighboring cells whenever a certain pattern of 0's and 1's exists in the other neighboring cells.

Passive Neighborhood PSF (PNPSF). The contents of the base cell cannot be changed from 0 to 1 and/or from 1 to 0 when a certain pattern of 0's and 1's exists in the neighboring cells.

Here *pattern of a neighborhood* (of size k) of a base cell is defined as an ordered k-tuple giving the states of the cells in the neighborhood during a memory cycle.

Two steps have to be done to test the base cell for ANPSFs and PNPSFs:

(1) Sensitize every fault using the appropriate neighborhood pattern.
(2) Read the state of the base cell after each sensitizing pattern to detect any fault.

The number of patterns needed to sensitize all ANPSFs of a neighborhood of size k is $(k - 1)2^k$ because each one of the $k - 1$ neighbors of the base cell must exercise both the ↓ and the ↑ transitions, while the other $k - 1$ cells take all the possible binary values. A pattern that sensitizes one of the ANPSFs is called an *active neighborhood pattern* (ANP). Table 3 gives all the ANPs for a neighborhood of size 5 (Suk and Reddy 1980].

Similarly, the number of patterns needed to sensitize all PNPSFs in a k-cell neighborhood is 2^k. In these patterns, the base cell will be assigned both ↑ and ↓, while the other $k - 1$ cells take all the possible binary states. These patterns are called *passive neighborhood patterns* (PNPs). Table 4 contains all the PNPs for a neighborhood of size 5.

Every ANP or PNP contains exactly one transition write operation (i.e., a ↑ or a ↓). To generate these patterns each neighborhood must be initialized to a known state and then the contents of one cell be changed at a time by a write operation. So if we define a graph G_k in which there is a node for each binary k-tuple and there is an arc between two nodes if and only if

Table 3. Active Neighborhood Patterns for a 5-Cell Neighborhood[a]

A	↑	↑	↑	↑	↑	↑	↑	↑	↓	↓	↓	↓	↓	↓	↓	↓	↑	↑	↑	↑	↑	↑	↑	↑	↓	↓	↓	↓	↓	↓	↓	↓
B	0	0	0	0	1	1	1	1	0	0	0	0	1	1	1	1	0	0	0	0	1	1	1	1	0	0	0	0	1	1	1	1
C	0	0	1	1	0	0	1	1	0	0	1	1	0	0	1	1	0	0	1	1	0	0	1	1	0	0	1	1	0	0	1	1
D	0	1	0	1	0	1	0	1	0	1	0	1	0	1	0	1	0	1	0	1	0	1	0	1	0	1	0	1	0	1	0	1
E	0	0	0	0	0	0	0	0	0	0	0	0	0	0	0	0	1	1	1	1	1	1	1	1	1	1	1	1	1	1	1	1

A	0	0	0	0	1	1	1	1	0	0	0	0	1	1	1	1	0	0	0	0	1	1	1	1	0	0	0	0	1	1	1	1
B	↑	↑	↑	↑	↑	↑	↑	↑	↓	↓	↓	↓	↓	↓	↓	↓	↑	↑	↑	↑	↑	↑	↑	↑	↓	↓	↓	↓	↓	↓	↓	↓
C	0	0	1	1	0	0	1	1	0	0	1	1	0	0	1	1	0	0	1	1	0	0	1	1	0	0	1	1	0	0	1	1
D	0	1	0	1	0	1	0	1	0	1	0	1	0	1	0	1	0	1	0	1	0	1	0	1	0	1	0	1	0	1	0	1
E	0	0	0	0	0	0	0	0	0	0	0	0	0	0	0	0	1	1	1	1	1	1	1	1	1	1	1	1	1	1	1	1

A	0	0	0	0	1	1	1	1	0	0	0	0	1	1	1	1	0	0	0	0	1	1	1	1	0	0	0	0	1	1	1	1
B	0	0	1	1	0	0	1	1	0	0	1	1	0	0	1	1	0	0	1	1	0	0	1	1	0	0	1	1	0	0	1	1
C	↑	↑	↑	↑	↑	↑	↑	↑	↓	↓	↓	↓	↓	↓	↓	↓	↑	↑	↑	↑	↑	↑	↑	↑	↓	↓	↓	↓	↓	↓	↓	↓
D	0	1	0	1	0	1	0	1	0	1	0	1	0	1	0	1	0	1	0	1	0	1	0	1	0	1	0	1	0	1	0	1
E	0	0	0	0	0	0	0	0	0	0	0	0	0	0	0	0	1	1	1	1	1	1	1	1	1	1	1	1	1	1	1	1

A	0	0	0	0	1	1	1	1	0	0	0	0	1	1	1	1	0	0	0	0	1	1	1	1	0	0	0	0	1	1	1	1
B	0	0	1	1	0	0	1	1	0	0	1	1	0	0	1	1	0	0	1	1	0	0	1	1	0	0	1	1	0	0	1	1
C	0	1	0	1	0	1	0	1	0	1	0	1	0	1	0	1	0	1	0	1	0	1	0	1	0	1	0	1	0	1	0	1
D	↑	↑	↑	↑	↑	↑	↑	↑	↓	↓	↓	↓	↓	↓	↓	↓	↑	↑	↑	↑	↑	↑	↑	↑	↓	↓	↓	↓	↓	↓	↓	↓
E	0	0	0	0	0	0	0	0	0	0	0	0	0	0	0	0	1	1	1	1	1	1	1	1	1	1	1	1	1	1	1	1

[a] Notation is as follows:

1. A = top cell; B = bottom cell; C = left cell; D = right cell; E = base cell.
2. ↑ = 0-to-1 transition; ↓ = 1-to-0 transition.
3. Each column with five entries denotes one ANP of a base cell.

Table 4. Passive Neighborhood Patterns for a 5-Cell Neighborhood[a]

Top	Bottom	Left	Right	Base	Top	Bottom	Left	Right	Base
0	0	0	0	↑	0	0	0	0	↓
0	0	0	1	↑	0	0	0	1	↓
0	0	1	0	↑	0	0	1	0	↓
0	0	1	1	↑	0	0	1	1	↓
0	1	0	0	↑	0	1	0	0	↓
0	1	0	1	↑	0	1	0	1	↓
0	1	1	0	↑	0	1	1	0	↓
0	1	1	1	↑	0	1	1	1	↓
1	0	0	0	↑	1	0	0	0	↓
1	0	0	1	↑	1	0	0	1	↓
1	0	1	0	↑	1	0	1	0	↓
1	0	1	1	↑	1	0	1	1	↓
1	1	0	0	↑	1	1	0	0	↓
1	1	0	1	↑	1	1	0	1	↓
1	1	1	0	↑	1	1	1	0	↓
1	1	1	1	↑	1	1	1	1	↓

[a] Notation is as follows:

1. ↑ = 0-to-1 transition; ↓ = 1-to-0 transition.
2. Each row with five entries denotes one PNP of a base cell.

they differ in exactly one bit, then these arcs correspond to ANPs and PNPs. Such a graph[4] for $k = 3$ is shown in Figure 14 [Suk and Reddy 1980]. For example, if we assume that the middle position in the 3-tuple corresponds to the base cell, then the arc from (101) to (001) defines the ANP (↓01).

Efficient generation of the sensitizing patterns is equivalent to finding a *Eulerian path* in the graph such that all the arcs are traversed exactly once. The length of such a Eulerian path is $k2^k$. Two different pro-

---

[4] Note that G_k is the familiar k-cube with bidirectional edges.

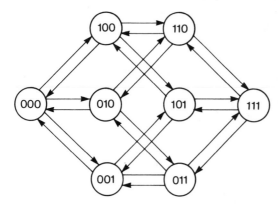

Figure 14. Eulerian graph for $k = 3$.

$$
R_3 = \begin{cases}
0 & 0 & 0 & \\
0 & 0 & 1 & W_2 \\
0 & 1 & 1 & W_1 \\
0 & 1 & 0 & \bar{W}_2 \\
1 & 1 & 0 & W_0 \\
1 & 1 & 1 & W_2 \\
1 & 0 & 1 & \bar{W}_1 \\
1 & 0 & 0 & \bar{W}_2
\end{cases}
$$

$$
T^1(R_3) = \begin{cases}
1 & 0 & 1 & W_2 \\
0 & 0 & 1 & \bar{W}_0 \\
0 & 0 & 0 & \bar{W}_2 \\
1 & 0 & 0 & W_0 \\
1 & 1 & 0 & W_1 \\
0 & 1 & 0 & \bar{W}_0 \\
0 & 1 & 1 & W_2 \\
1 & 1 & 1 & W_0
\end{cases}
$$

$$
T^2(R_3) = \begin{cases}
0 & 1 & 1 & \bar{W}_0 \\
0 & 0 & 1 & \bar{W}_1 \\
1 & 0 & 1 & W_0 \\
1 & 1 & 1 & W_1 \\
1 & 1 & 0 & \bar{W}_2 \\
1 & 0 & 0 & \bar{W}_1 \\
0 & 0 & 0 & \bar{W}_0 \\
0 & 1 & 0 & W_1
\end{cases}
$$

$$
S_0 = \quad 0 \quad 0 \quad 0 \quad \bar{W}_1
$$

Figure 15. Generation of the Eulerian Path for G_3 and the corresponding Write sequence. (Note that W_i ($\bar{W}_i$) means write 1 (0) in cell i.)

cedures have been used [Hayes 1980; Suk and Reddy 1980] to construct the Eulerian path for G_k. The one used by Hayes [1980] is as follows:

1. Construct a reflected k-bit Gray code R_k with initial state $S_0 = 00 \cdots 0$.
2. Let $X = x_0 x_1 \cdots x_{k-1}$ denote any element of R_k. Define a transformation $T^1 : R_k \rightarrow R_k$ as follows:

$$T^1(x_0 x_1 x_2 \cdots x_{k-1}) = \bar{x}_{k-1} x_0 x_1 \cdots \bar{x}_{k-2}.$$

Let T^i denote i consecutive applications of T^1.

3. The sequence of length $k2^k + 1$, formed by concatenating R_k, $T^1(R_k)$, $T^2(R_k)$, $\ldots$, $T^{k-1}(R_k)$, and S_0, is the sequence of nodes visited by the desired Eulerian path.

Figure 15 shows the construction of the Eulerian path for G_3 according to the above procedure, as well as the optimal write sequence implied by that path.

Thus far we have constructed a write sequence that will sensitize all the PSFs caused by transition writes affecting the base cell of a neighborhood of size k. We want to apply such a write sequence to every neighborhood in the memory. Both Hayes [1980] and Suk and Reddy [1980] have used similar procedures to achieve this goal. We will use Hayes' method to illustrate the idea.

Every cell in the k-cell neighborhood will be assigned an integer number from 0 to $k - 1$. When the tiling neighborhood as-

sumption is used, it is clear that if each tile in the memory is numbered as stated above, then every k-cell neighborhood in memory will be marked with all members of $\{0, 1, 2, \ldots, k - 1\}$. For example, Figure 16 demonstrates how the 5-cell tiling neighborhood is marked by the pattern

$$
\begin{matrix}
& 0 & \\
1 & 2 & 3 \\
& 4 &
\end{matrix}
$$

Every 5-cell neighborhood in the memory is marked with the above pattern.[5]

---

[5] The problem of numbering the memory cells under this restriction is equivalent to the standard graph-coloring problem: color the nodes of the graph in such a way that no two nodes connected by an edge are colored identically. For a k-cells tiling neighborhood, k colors are needed, since all the nodes for cells in a neighborhood will be adjacent on the graph [Seth and Narayanswamy 1981].

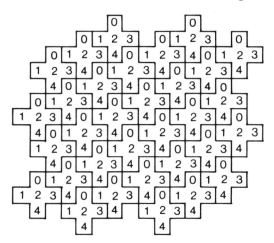

Figure 16. A tiling by the 5-cell neighborhood with a fixed pattern from (0, 1, 2, 3, 4) assigned to every tile.

Let $N_k = v_0, v_1, \ldots, v_r$, where $r = k2^k$, denote the transition write sequence obtained from the Eulerian path of a k-cell neighborhood. The next procedure shows how to construct an optimal transition write sequence N_n for a memory of size n with tiling neighborhoods of size k:

1. Generate an optimal transition write sequence $N_k = v_0, v_1, \ldots, v_r$ for a k-cell neighborhood as explained before.
2. Assign a fixed pattern of numbers from $\{0, 1, \ldots, k-1\}$ to each member of independent neighborhoods that tile the memory.
3. For each v_i in N_k that writes x into cell C, form the sequence $V_i = v_{i,0}, v_{i,1}, \ldots, v_{i,p-1}$, where $p = n/k$, in which $v_{i,j}$ writes x into any cell C' of the memory such that the number assigned to C' is equal to the number assigned to C, for $0 \leq j \leq p - 1$. Thus V_i performs the same operation as v_i on cells in the same position in each independent neighborhood.
4. N_n is formed by concatenating the sequences $V_0, V_1, \ldots, V_{r-1}$, where $r = k2^k$.

The number of the write operations in N_n is given by

$$pr = (n/k)k2^k = n2^k.$$

Thus far we have only constructed the optimal transition write operations needed to sensitize PSFs caused by transition write operations. Suk and Reddy [1980] assumed that neither read operations nor nontransition write operations cause any kind of PSFs in memories, and therefore only considered transition write faults. They derived lower bounds on the number of read and write operations capable of detecting their restricted class of PSFs. The results obtained are as follows:

(1) The minimum number of operations on each cell in a procedure that detects ANPSFs is $(k + 1) 2^{k-1} + 1$, where k is the neighborhood size.
(2) To detect all PNPSFs at least 2^k read operations and 2^k write operations per each cell of the RAM under test must be performed.

They also give several procedures to detect and locate multiple PSFs caused by transition write operations [Suk and Reddy 1980]. The complexity of these procedures is near minimal. A point worth mentioning is that, by assuming that the read operations cannot cause any fault, Suk and Reddy allowed multiple PSFs to occur in their fault model. Because they are verifying the state of the neighborhood after each write operation by using a sequence of read operations (assumed to be fault free), any number of PSFs cannot mask the effect of each other. Hence all PSFs caused by transition write operations can be detected and, furthermore, can be located.

Hayes [1980], on the other hand, considered general PSFs. He proposed a simple way to sensitize PSFs caused by nontransition write operations by applying the write operations in N_n in duplicates. Each Write: $C_i \leftarrow x$ in N_n is followed by another Write: $C_i \leftarrow x$. As Hayes points out, the minimum number of read operations required and where they should be placed in the test sequence remain open questions [Hayes 1980]. But because he assumed that the read operations can also cause faults, only single PSFs could be considered. He gave a complete test procedure, but not a minimal one, to detect single PSFs in any

Table 5.   Summary of the PSFs Test Procedures

	Complexity[a]	Restricted PSFs coverage		
		PSFs caused by read operations	PSFs caused by transition writes	PSFs caused by nontransition writes
Suk and Reddy's test procedure	$(k + 5)2^{k-1}n$	None covered	Covers multiple PFSs	None covered
Hayes' test procedure	$(3k + 2)2^k n$	Covers single PSFs	Covers single PSFs	Covers single PSFs

[a] k, the neighborhood size; n, the number of cells in the memory.

RAM with size n by using k-cell neighborhoods. The procedure is as follows:

1. Using the techniques discussed before, construct the optimal transition write sequence N_n.
2. Follow each transition write by a nontransition write.
3. Follow each write operation to cell i by a sequence R_i of k reads that read cell i and every cell in its neighborhood.
4. Follow one application of R_i by another copy of R_i when the neighborhood of cell i is in state S_j for all i and S_j.

The length of this procedure is $(3k + 2)2^k n$, which is $O(n)$, meaning that the procedure can be implemented for large memories. For example, by using the 5-cell neighborhood such a test procedure will take ~16 seconds for a 64K RAM with a 500-nanosecond access time.

Hayes [1980] tried to minimize the number of read operations in the proposed procedure for a 2-cell memory, and he empirically derived a test sequence of 36 operations (the length before minimization was 64). However, because of the trivial size of the memory considered, this problem is still an open area for more research.

From the discussion in this section, it should be clear that as more complex fault models are considered, the test procedures needed to detect these faults also become very complex.

Table 5 summarizes the main attributes of the test procedures considered in this section. Note that because stuck-at faults and coupling faults can be visualized as special cases of PSFs, many of these faults are covered by the PSF test procedures.

5. CONCLUDING REMARKS

In this paper we have addressed the problem of testing semiconductor random access memories, which form a large percentage of today's LSI products. An important aspect of testing semiconductor RAMs is the detection of permanent faults that cause the memory to function incorrectly. Functional-level fault models are very useful for describing a wide variety of faults. Several models have been discussed, including the single and multiple stuck-at fault model, the coupling fault model, and the pattern-sensitive fault (PSF) model.

Various procedures exist for memory testing. However, because the faults detected by these procedures form overlapping subsets of the set of all possible faults, a comparison of these procedures' efficiency is extremely difficult.

Many functional testing schemes have been proposed and used in the industry. Most of them tend to be ad hoc procedures and lack well-defined fault models. A detailed description of a sample of those test procedures has been given.

We have presented a survey of various RAM testing procedures proposed in the literature. Generally, these procedures are more effective than the ones used by the industry, from the viewpoints of both the time complexity and the degree of fault coverage. Two $O(n)$ procedures that detect all multiple stuck-at faults in RAMs, by Knaizuk and Hartmann [1977a, 1977b] and by Nair [1979], have been discussed in detail. Two other $O(n)$ procedures, by Nair et al. [1978] and by Suk and Reddy [1981], that address coupling faults have also been discussed in detail, demonstrating the great improvement achieved by these two procedures over the well-known GALPAT test.

The general PSF model developed by Hayes [1975] has been presented. It has been shown that it is impossible, from the practical point of view, to construct a test sequence that will detect all possible PSFs in a typical RAM. In order to keep the test length within a practical limit, some restrictions have to be imposed on the types of PSFs that can be considered. A PSF model that can only affect a restricted set of "neighborhood" cells has been presented. The efforts by both Hayes [1980] and Suk and Reddy [1980] to develop test procedures for this restricted class of PSFs have also been surveyed.

A number of tables have been presented throughout the paper to compare different test procedures in terms of their time complexity and their degree of fault coverage.

As a final note we want to stress the fact that the problem of selecting a good testing procedure for a RAM is a trade-off between the time required for applying the test and the degree of fault coverage obtained. Total test time is important because it is not economical to tie up equipment for a long period of time when testing a high-volume, inexpensive product. Test time is warranted, though, because the cost to the customer of using a defective chip could be quite high.

ACKNOWLEDGMENT

Part of this work was done when the authors were at the University of Saskatchewan.

REFERENCES

ABADIR, M. S., AND REGHBATI, H. K. 1983. LSI testing techniques. *IEEE Micro. 3*, 1 (Feb.), 34–51.

AKERS, S. B. 1980. Test generation techniques. *IEEE Computer 13*, 3 (Mar.), 9–16.

BARRACLAUGH, W., CHIANG, A. C. L., AND SOHL, W. 1976. Techniques for testing the microcomputer family. *Proc. IEEE 64*, 6 (June), 943–950.

BREUER, M. A., AND FRIEDMAN, A. D. 1976. *Diagnosis and Reliable Design of Digital Systems.* Computer Science Press, Potomac, Md.

BREUER, M. A., AND FRIEDMAN, A. D. 1980. Functional level primitives in test generation. *IEEE Trans. Comput. C-29*, 3 (Mar.), 223–235.

DEMILLO, R. A., LIPTON, R. J., AND SAYWARD, F. G.

1978. Hints on test data selection: Help for the practicing programmer. *IEEE Comput. 11*, 4 (Apr.), 34–41.

HAYES, J. P. 1975. Detection of pattern-sensitive faults in random access memories. *IEEE Trans. Comput. C-24*, 2 (Feb.), 150–157.

HAYES, J. P. 1980. Testing memories for single-cell pattern-sensitive faults. *IEEE Trans. Comput. C-29*, 3 (Mar.), 249–254.

HOYT, P. M. 1977. The Navy Fortran validation system. In *Proceedings of AFIPS National Computer Conference.* (Dallas, Tex., June 13–16), vol. 46. AFIPS Press, Reston, Va., pp. 529–537.

INTEL 1975. *Memory Design Handbook.* Intel Corp., Santa Clara, Calif.

KLAYTON, A. R. 1971. Fault analysis for computer memory systems and combinational logic networks. Ph.D. dissertation, Lehigh Univ.

KNAIZUK, J., Jr., AND HARTMANN, C. R. P. 1977a. An algorithm for testing random access memories. *IEEE Trans. Comput. C-26*, 4 (Apr.), 414–416.

KNAIZUK, J., Jr., AND HARTMANN, C. R. P. 1977b. An optimal algorithm for testing stuck-at faults in random access memories. *IEEE Trans. Comput. C-26*, 11 (Nov.), 1141–1144.

MUEHLDORF, E. I., AND SAVKAR, A. D. 1981. LSI logic testing—An overview. *IEEE Trans. Comput. 3*, 1 (Jan.), 1–17.

NAIR, R. 1979. Comments on an optimal algorithm for testing stuck-at faults in random access memories. *IEEE Trans. Comput. C-28*, 3 (Mar.), 258–261.

NAIR, R., THATTE, S. M., AND ABRAHAM, J. A. 1978. Efficient algorithms for testing semiconductor random-access memories. *IEEE Trans. Comput. C-27*, 6 (June), 572–576.

RAVI, C. V. 1969. Fault location in memory systems by program. In *Proceedings of AFIPS Spring Joint Computer Conference* (Boston, Mass., May 14–16), vol. 34. AFIPS Press, Reston, Va., pp. 393–401.

SETH, S. C., AND NARAYANSWAMY, K. 1981. A graph model for pattern-sensitive faults in random access memories. *IEEE Trans. Comput. C-30*, 12 (Dec.), 973–977.

SOHL, W. E. 1977. Selecting test patterns for 4K RAMs. *IEEE Trans. Manuf. Technol. MFT-6*, 1, 51–60.

SUK, D. S., AND REDDY, S. M. 1980. Test procedures for a class of pattern-sensitive faults in semiconductor random-access memories. *IEEE Trans. Comput. C-29*, 6 (June), 419–429.

SUK, D. S., AND REDDY, S. M. 1981. A march test for functional faults in semiconductor random access memories. *IEEE Trans. Comput. C-30*, 12 (Dec.), 982–985.

THATTE, S. M., AND ABRAHAM, J. A. 1977. Testing of semiconductor random access memories. In *Proceedings of the 7th Annual International Conference on Fault-Tolerant Computing*, pp. 81–87.

Received July 1981; final revision accepted January 1984.

Computing Surveys, Vol. 15, No. 3, September 1983

Test Generation for Microprocessors

SATISH M. THATTE, MEMBER, IEEE, AND JACOB A. ABRAHAM, MEMBER, IEEE

Abstract—The goal of this paper is to develop test generation
procedures for testing microprocessors in a user environment. Classical
fault detection methods based on the gate and flip-flop level or on the
state diagram level description of microprocessors are not suitable for
test generation. The problem is further compounded by the availability
of a large variety of microprocessors which differ widely in their organization, instruction repertoire, addressing modes, data storage,
and manipulation facilities, etc. In this paper, a general graph-theoretic
model is developed at the register transfer level. Any microprocessor
can be easily modeled using information only about its instruction set
and the functions performed. This information is readily available in
the user's manual. A fault model is developed on a functional level quite
independent of the implementation details. The effects of faults in the
fault model are investigated at the level of the graph-theoretic model.
Test generation procedures are proposed which take the microprocessor organization and the instruction set as parameters and generate
tests to detect all the faults in the fault model. The complexity of the
test sequences measured in terms of the number of instructions is given.
Our effort in generating tests for a real microprocessor and evaluating
their fault coverage is described.

Manuscript received July 13, 1979; revised February 11, 1980. This research
was supported by the Joint Services Electronics Program (U.S. Army, U.S.
Navy, and U.S. Air Force) under Contracts DAAB-07-72-C-0259, DAAG-
29-78-C-0016, and N00014-79-C-0424. Parts of this work were presented
at the COMPCON Spring '79 Conference, San Francisco, CA, February
1979, the 9th International Conference on Fault-Tolerant Computing,
Madison, WI, June 1979, and the 1979 IEEE Test Symposium, Cherry Hill,
NJ, October 1979.

S. M. Thatte was with the Coordinated Science Laboratory, University of
Illinois, Urbana, IL 61801. He is now with the Central Research Laboratories,
Texas Instruments Incorporated, Dallas, TX 75265.

J. A. Abraham is with the Coordinated Science Laboratory, University of
Illinois, Urbana, IL 61801.

Index Terms—Architecture models, complexity of tests, functional
level fault models, microprocessor architecture, test programs.

I. INTRODUCTION

THE use of microprocessors in digital systems has been rapidly expanding. This has given rise to an acute need for sound theoretical tools to develop efficient, thorough, and cost-effective test programs to detect faults in microprocessors.

Microprocessor testing practiced in industry seems to be based on ad hoc techniques such as "testing" each instruction for many operands, "exercising" various modules in the microprocessor (such as the arithmetic and logic unit (ALU), shifter, registers, indexing hardware), or running an application program [2], [5], [13]. These techniques are not based on a general model for microprocessors. Moreover, they do not consider any specific fault model. Therefore a technique followed for testing one microprocessor may be difficult to extend to other microprocessors having different architectures. It is also very difficult to know what faults can or cannot be detected using these techniques.

Classical fault detection methods are not very useful for generating tests for large scale integrated (LSI) circuits such as microprocessors which contain a very large number of gates, flip-flops, and interconnections and which therefore require an enormous amount of computation to generate complete test sets. In addition, the required gate and flip-flop level description is usually not available to microprocessor test designers working in a user environment. However, these methods were used to test and diagnose digital computers (designed with discrete components allowing many internal points to be probed) based on the knowledge of their detailed logic description [8], [11].

In view of the difficulties associated with classical fault detection, Robach and Saucier proposed a model for generating tests for control units of digital systems [9], [10]. The model considers basic control commands and control states as primitive elements rather than gates and flip-flops generating these commands and assumes that the operands required for the functional units are directly available, and the results produced by them are directly observable (possibly with some time delay). Sridhar and Hayes reported on tests for the ALU of bit-sliced microprocessors [12]. Though these approaches are steps in the right direction for testing certain digital systems where the assumptions made in the models are valid, it appears that the limited observability and controllability of internal registers and logic of microprocessors pose a very difficult problem in extending the approach to microprocessor testing.

A methodology for test generation based on a model for a restricted but "typical" microprocessor organization and instruction set was proposed in [14]. A drawback of this model is that it cannot generate tests for different microprocessor organizations and instruction sets, i.e., it fails to treat the microprocessor architecture as a parameter of test generation.

In Section II we develop a general graph-theoretic model for microprocessors at the register transfer level. This allows us to treat the microprocessor organization and the instruction set as parameters of the test generation procedures. We will illustrate how to generate the graph-theoretic model for a small example microprocessor. Functional level fault models capable of describing faulty behavior at a higher level and independent of implementation details are presented in Section III. In Section IV we will present test generation procedures to detect faults in the fault models and prove their fault coverage. The generated test sequences consist of valid machine instructions which can be assembled to produce test patterns. This may be contrasted with the classical methods which may generate bit vectors that do not correspond to any instruction. We will also discuss the complexity of the test sequences and describe our effort in generating tests for a real microprocessor.

We will not discuss testing issues related with dynamic timing problems, faulty dc parametric behavior, or manufacturing and design processes. For these aspects readers are referred to [5], [13].

We assume that an external tester monitors all the pins of the microprocessor. It also stores the test sequences generated by test generation procedures presented in this paper in its memory. The microprocessor under test executes these test sequences (which are valid machine instructions and not arbitrary bit vectors) and the tester compares observed responses with expected responses. Testing is stopped on the detection of any output different from the expected output (may or may not be in real time).

II. A GRAPH-THEORETIC MODEL FOR ARCHITECTURE

A microprocessor is modeled by a system graph (S-graph). Let $\mathcal{R} = \{R_1, R_2, R_3, \cdots\}$ denote the set of registers (including the registers used in various addressing modes, and the so-called processor status word containing various processor status bits) in the microprocessor. Each register R_i is represented by a node (labeled R_i) of the S-graph. In addition to the nodes representing registers, we incorporate two more nodes, named "IN" and "OUT" in the S-graph, representing the world external to the microprocessor, i.e., the main memory and I/O devices.

Let $\mathcal{I} = \{I_1, I_2, I_3, \cdots\}$ denote the set of instructions. The execution of instruction I_j causes data[1] flow among a set of registers, and between the main memory (or an I/O device) and registers in some sequence. The data may or may not be manipulated during the flow. We can represent the data flow during the *execution* of any instruction I_j as follows.

1) There exists a labeled directed edge from node R_p to node R_q, if data flow occurs from register R_p to register R_q (with or without manipulation) during the execution of I_j.

2) There exists a labeled directed edge from node IN to node R_j, if data flow occurs from the main memory or an I/O device to register R_j (with or without manipulation) during the execution of I_j.

3) There exists a labeled directed edge from node R_j to node OUT, if data flow occurs from register R_j to the main memory

---

[1] We use data as a generic term referring to the information as well as its address.

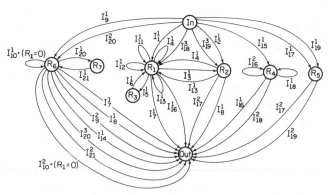

Fig. 1. *S*-graph of the example microprocessor.

TABLE I
REGISTERS OF THE EXAMPLE MICROPROCESSOR

R_1:	accumulator.
R_2:	general purpose register.
R_3:	scratch-pad register.
R_4:	stack pointer to the top of a last-in first-out (LIFO) stack in main memory.
R_5:	address buffer register to store the address of operands.
R_6:	program counter.
R_7:	subroutine register to save return addresses (allowing a single level of subroutine nesting).

(or its address register) or an I/O device (with or without manipulation) during the execution of I_j.

The exact sequence of data flow during the execution of an instruction may not be known to test designers working in a user environment because the sequence depends on the details of implementation of the microprocessor hardware. However, it is possible to deduce the precedence relation in time between the components of the data flow solely on the basis of logical data dependence. Among the set of edges representing the data flow during the execution of instruction I_j, two edges are labeled I_j^p and I_j^q, where $p < q$ and p and q are smallest such positive integers, if and only if the data flow represented by the edge labeled I_j^p must take place before that represented by the edge labeled I_j^q in order to preserve the underlying logical data dependence. Two edges are assigned the same label I_j^p, if and only if the corresponding data flows can occur simultaneously given the necessary number of resources such as buses and functional units, i.e., the required hardware parallelism exists. In the presence of some limitation on hardware resources, the data flow represented by these two edges may occur in either of the two possible sequences depending on the details of implementation. If only one edge is required to represent the data flow during the execution of instruction I_j, it is assigned a label I_j^1. It must be stated that this elaborate notation is used only for clarity in illustrating the data flow sequence and is not really necessary to generate tests to detect faults in the proposed functional fault models. However, we believe that for more elaborate fault models, enough information about sequencing of data flow exists in the *S*-graph and can be exploited. The instructions are classified as Transfer (class *T*), Manipulation (class *M*) or Branch (class *B*) as in [6], [15].

Example 1: Fig. 1 shows the *S*-graph of a hypothetical microprocessor, and a list of its registers is given in Table I. The instruction repertoire contains 21 instructions which are listed in Table II. The addressing modes used (such as immediate, direct, implied [7]) are indicated and the class (*T*, *M*, or *B*) of each instruction is given. The self loops around R_4 in Fig. 1, labeled I_{16}^1 and I_{18}^1, represent the stack pointer incrementing and decrementing functions, respectively. The edge from the node IN to R_6 (representing the program counter) labeled I_9^1 represents the transfer of the jump address from the main memory to the program counter. The R_6-OUT edge labeled I_9^2

represents the transfer of the jump address from the program counter to the address register of the main memory achieving the jump in the program sequencing. Instructions of class *B* causing only conditional changes in the program sequencing can be suitably represented by tagging instruction labels with the appropriate condition code (predicate). For example, the self loop around R_6, labeled $I_{10}^1 \cdot (R_1 = 0)$, represents the program counter incrementing function during the "Skip" instruction I_{10}, if the condition "register $R_1 = 0$" is satisfied. All the other edges in Fig. 1 are self-explanatory. □

Some registers of the microprocessor can be written (loaded with required data) or read out (i.e., its contents can be stored in the main memory or sent to an I/O device) explicitly by executing an instruction. Examples of such registers are accumulator and general-purpose registers. On the other hand, some registers can be written or read out only implicitly by executing an instruction.

Example 2: In Fig. 1, the stack pointer (R_4) can be read out only implicitly during the execution of instructions I_{16} or I_{18}. The subroutine register (R_7) in Fig. 1 can be read out only implicitly by executing the "Return from subroutine" instruction I_{21}. □

The program counter can be written only implicitly during the execution of an instruction of class *B* which alters the normal program sequencing. We assume that any register can be written (implicitly or explicitly) as well as read out (implicitly or explicitly) using a sequence of instructions of class *T* or using an instruction of class *B*. This assumption can be easily justified for current microprocessors [3].

Definition 1: The set of *source registers*, $S(I_j)$, for an instruction I_j is defined to be that set of registers which provide the operands for instruction I_j during its execution. □

Definition 2: The set of *destination registers*, $D(I_j)$, for an instruction I_j is defined to be that set of registers which are changed by instruction I_j during its execution. □

Extending this notation $S(I_1, I_2, \cdots, I_n) = S(I_1) \cup S(I_2) \cup \cdots \cup S(I_n)$. $D(I_1, I_2, \cdots, I_n)$ can be defined analogously.

Example 3: In the *S*-graph of Fig. 1, $S(I_7) = \{R_1\}$, $S(I_4) = \{R_1, R_2\}$, $S(I_2) = \{\text{IN}\}$. Similarly $D(I_7) = \{\text{OUT}\}$, $D(I_4) = D(I_{11}) = D(I_{12}) = \{R_1\}$, $D(I_{20}) = \{R_6, R_7, \text{OUT}\}$. Thus $|S(I_4)| = 2$, $|D(I_{20})| = 3$. □

TABLE II
THE INSTRUCTION REPERTOIRE OF THE EXAMPLE MICROPROCESSOR
(THE CLASS OF EACH INSTRUCTION IS ALSO INDICATED)

```
I₁  - Load register R₁ from the main memory using immediate addressing.(T)

I₂  - Load register R₂ from the main memory using immediate addressing.(T)

I₃  - Transfer the contents of register R₁ to register R₂.(T)

I₄  - Add the contents of registers R₁ and R₂ and store the results

      in register R₁.(M)

I₅  - Transfer the contents of register R₁ to register R₃.(T)

I₆  - Transfer the contents of register R₃ to register R₁.(T)

I₇  - Store register R₁ into the main memory using implied addressing.(T)

I₈  - Store register R₂ into the main memory using implied addressing.(T)

I₉  - Jump instruction.(B)

I₁₀ - Skip if the contents of register R₁ are zero.(B)

I₁₁ - Left shift register R₁ by one bit.(M)

I₁₂ - Complement (bit-wise) the contents of register R₁.(M)

I₁₃ - Logical AND the contents of registers R₁ and R₂ and store the

      result in register R₁.(M)

I₁₄ - No operation instruction.(B)

I₁₅ - Load the stack pointer (R₄) from the main memory using immediate

      addressing.(T)

I₁₆ - PUSH register R₁ on the LIFO stack maintained in the main memory.(T)

I₁₇ - Store register R₂ into the main memory using direct addressing.(T)

I₁₈ - POP the top of the LIFO stack and store it in R₁.(T)

I₁₉ - Load register R₂ from the main memory using direct addressing.(T)

I₂₀ - Jump to subroutine (return address is saved in the subroutine

      register R₇).(B)

I₂₁ - Return from subroutine.(B)
```

Definition 3: The set of directed edges denoting an instruction I_j in the S-graph is called its *edge set* and is denoted by $E(I_j)$. □

Definition 4: READ (R_i) denotes the *shortest sequence* of instructions of class T or class B that is necessary to read out register R_i (implicitly or explicitly). Similarly WRITE (R_i) denotes the *shortest sequence* of instructions of class T or class B that is necessary to write register R_i (implicitly or explicitly). □

Example 4: For the S-graph shown in Fig. 1, READ (R_1) $= \langle I_7 \rangle$, READ $(R_3) = \langle I_6, I_7 \rangle$, READ $(R_7) = \langle I_{21} \rangle$, etc. WRITE $(R_1) = \langle I_1 \rangle$, WRITE $(R_5) = \langle I_{17} \rangle$, WRITE $(R_3) = \langle I_1, I_5 \rangle$, WRITE $(R_7) = \langle I_9, I_{20} \rangle$. Thus, $|$READ $(R_3)| = 2$, $|$WRITE $(R_7)| = 2$. □

We allow $|D(I_j)| > 1$ only if instruction I_j involves data transfer between the main memory (or an I/O device) and registers of the microprocessor during its execution. Thus $|D(I_j)| = 1$ for all those instructions which do not involve data transfer between the main memory and some registers during their execution. We do not permit $|D(I_j)| > 1$ in the case of these instructions, because the results of instructions of class M or T are usually not stored in more than one register.

Definition 5: A *transfer path* is a logical path over which data flow during the execution of an instruction. The set of transfer paths associated with instruction I_j is denoted by $T(I_j)$. □

We map a physical transfer mechanism (such as a bus) used during the execution of an instruction into a logical transfer path because test designers working in a user environment may not know the details of implementation of the mechanisms used to transfer data between units, or how they are shared or time-multiplexed among different data transfers. Using the notion of transfer paths we can develop a fault model for the data transfer function (in Section III) independent of the actual implementation details of the transfer mechanisms.

Example 5: With reference to instruction I_4 in Fig. 1, $T(I_4)$ contains three transfer paths, two paths for transferring the contents of R_1 and R_2 to the ALU and one path for transferring the output of the ALU to R_1. $T(I_6)$ contains only one transfer path for transferring the contents of R_3 to R_1, while $T(I_{19})$ contains three transfer paths, one for transferring data (which is actually the address of an operand) from the main memory to R_5, one for transferring the address from R_5 to the address register of the main memory, and the third one to transfer data from the main memory to R_2. □

We now present an algorithm that assigns integer labels to

nodes and edges of the S-graph. This is the first step in developing test generation procedures.

Algorithm 1: The Labeling Algorithm

The label assigned to a node representing register R_i is denoted by $l(R_i)$, and the label assigned to the edge set $E(I_j)$ representing instruction I_j is denoted by $l(I_j)$.

Step 1: Assign a label 0 to the OUT node.

Step 2: $K \leftarrow 0$;

    WHILE a node remains unlabeled DO

    BEGIN

        Assign a label $K + 1$ to all unlabeled nodes representing registers whose contents can be transferred (implicitly or explicitly) to any registers (or I/O device or main memory) represented by a node labeled K by executing a single instruction of class T or B;

        $K \leftarrow K + 1$

    END

Step 3: Assign a label 1 to each edge in the set $E(I_j)$ where I_j is an instruction that reads out a register (implicitly or explicitly) during its execution.

Step 4: If I_j is an instruction whose edge set has not been labeled in Step 3, then assign a label $(K + 1)$ to each edge in the set $E(I_j)$, where $l(D(I_j)) = K$.   □

Example 6: The labeling algorithm will assign the following labels to the nodes and edges of the S-graph in Fig. 1.

Step 1: $l(\text{OUT}) = 0$.

Step 2: $l(R_1) = l(R_2) = l(R_4) = l(R_5) = l(R_6) = l(R_7) = 1$, $l(R_3) = 2$.

Step 3: $l(I_7) = l(I_8) = l(I_9) = l(I_{10}) = l(I_{16}) = l(I_{17}) = l(I_{18}) = l(I_{19}) = l(I_{20}) = l(I_{21}) = 1$.

Step 4: $l(I_1) = l(I_2) = l(I_3) = l(I_4) = l(I_6) = l(I_{11}) = l(I_{12}) = l(I_{13}) = l(I_{15}) = 2$, $l(I_5) = 3$.

The contents of the program counter (R_6) are read out (implicitly) on the address bus during the fetching of every instruction, hence $l(R_6) = 1$. The contents of the subroutine register (R_7) are implicitly read out on the address bus (by routing the contents through the program counter), hence $l(R_7) = 1$. Note that $l(I_1) = l(I_2) = 2$, because I_1 and I_2 both use immediate addressing (refer to Table II), so $|D(I_1)| = |D(I_2)| = 1$, and $l(D(I_1)) = l(D(I_2)) = 1$. All other labels are self-explanatory.   □

For concise description, we will use the phrase "register R_i with label K," if the node representing register R_i is labeled K. Similarly we will use the phrase "instruction I_j with label K," if the edge set $E(I_j)$ representing instruction I_j is labeled K. The phrase "Execute READ (R_i)" means execute instructions in the READ (R_i) sequence; the phrase "Execute WRITE (R_i)" can be interpreted in a similar fashion.

Lemma 1: a) If $l(R_i) = K$, $|\text{READ}(R_i)| = K$. b) If $l(I_j) = 1$, I_j reads out (implicitly or explicitly) a register with label 1.   □

Lemma 2: All instructions of class B are assigned label 1.   □

The proofs of these lemmas are not given here and can be found in [15]. Thus the labeling algorithm first assigns an integer label to each node of the S-graph. This label (which is equal to $|\text{READ}(R_i)|$) indicates the shortest "distance" of that node to the OUT node, i.e., the minimum number of instructions of class T or B that need to be executed to read out (implicitly or explicitly) the contents of the register being represented by that node. After assigning labels to the nodes of the S-graph, the labeling algorithm assigns labels to the edges representing instructions. Any instruction I_j which reads out (implicitly or explicitly) a register during its execution will have a label 1 (since OUT $\in D(I_j)$). Any other instruction I_j is labeled in Step 4. (Recall that $|D(I_j)| = 1$ in this case.)

Various test generation procedures to be presented in Section IV generate tests in such a way that the knowledge gained from the correct execution of tests used to check the decoding of registers and instructions with lower labels is utilized in generating tests to check the decoding of registers and instructions with higher labels.

III. FUNCTIONAL LEVEL FAULT MODELS

Fault models for various functions (such as instruction decoding or data transfer) present in a microprocessor are developed at a higher level independent of the details of their implementation.

Fault Model for the Register Decoding Function

Register decoding refers to the task of decoding the "address" of a register which may be stored as a specific bit pattern in the instructions involving that register or which may be generated by the control unit during the execution of the instructions. The fault model given below is able to account for the faults in the address decoders of on-chip random-access memories realizing register files [15]. It is also able to account for the faults in the multiplexers and demultiplexers responsible for choosing registers. Moreover, as shown in [15], the fault model is independent of the details of implementation.

The register decoding function can be modeled as a mapping f_D from $\mathcal{R}$ to $\mathcal{R} \cup \{\phi\}$, where ϕ denotes a null or nonexistent register. Let $f_D(R_i) \subseteq \mathcal{R} \cup \{\phi\}$ denote the set of registers which is the image of R_i under the mapping f_D. If there is no fault in the register decoding function we get $f_D(R_i) = \{R_i\}$, for every $R_i \in \mathcal{R}$. Under a fault, if $f_D(R_i) = \{\phi\}$, then whenever register R_i is to be accessed (while executing any instruction which involves R_i), no register is accessed, i.e., when R_i is to be written, its contents remain unchanged and when the contents of R_i are to be retrieved, a ONE[2] or ZERO[2] (depending on technology) are in fact retrieved. If $f_D(R_i) \neq \{\phi\}$ then whenever R_i is accessed, all the registers in the set $f_D(R_i)$ are accessed. By this we mean, whenever R_i is to be written with data d, all the registers in $f_D(R_i)$ would be written with data d, and whenever the contents of R_i are to be retrieved, the contents formed by the bit-wise OR or AND function (depending on

---

[2] ONE denotes a binary vector with each of its bits set to logic 1 and having its width equal to that of a register, i.e., ONE $= (11 \cdots 1)$; similarly ZERO stands for $(00 \cdots 0)$.

technology) over the registers of the set $f_D(R_i)$ will be retrieved. Under this fault we allow $f_D(R_i) \neq \{R_j\}$, for every $R_i \in \mathcal{R}$. Obviously if $\phi \in f_D(R_i)$ then $f_D(R_i) = \{\phi\}$ because $f_D(R_i) = \{R_j, R_k, \cdots, \phi\}$ is meaningless.

Example 7: In terms of the S-graph of Fig. 1, $\mathcal{R} = \{R_1, R_2, R_3, R_4, R_5, R_6, R_7\}$. If $f_D(R_1) = \{R_2\}$, when I_1 is executed R_2 will be written instead of R_1. Moreover, I_7 will read out R_2 instead of R_1. If $f_D(R_2) = \{R_1, R_3\}$, then I_8 will read out $R_1 * R_3$, where $*$ denotes the bit-wise OR or AND function over registers R_1 and R_3 depending on technology. Similarly when I_2 is executed, both R_1 and R_3 will be written instead of R_2. If $f_D(R_7) = \{\phi\}$, the "Jump to subroutine" instruction I_{20} will correctly execute the jump in the program sequencing, but will not save the return address in R_7. The fault will show up when the "Return from subroutine" instruction I_{21} is executed, because the program sequence will return to the main memory location whose address is ONE or ZERO depending on technology, as a ONE or a ZERO will be loaded into the program counter (R_6) instead of the contents of the subroutine register (R_7). □

We now extend the notation developed in Section II.

Definition 6: $f_D(D(I_j))$ denotes the set of registers formed by making the union of the image sets of registers in $D(I_j)$ under the mapping f_D. $f_D(S(I_j))$ can be analogously defined. Extending this notation further, $f_D(D(I_1, I_2 \cdots, I_n)) = f_D(D(I_1)) \cup \cdots \cup f_D(D(I_n))$. The set $f_D(S(I_1, I_2, \cdots, I_n))$ can be defined similarly. □

We now present a lemma describing the behavior of a microprocessor under faulty register decoding. This will then be used to prove that the test generated using procedure 1 will detect any fault in the register decoding function.

Lemma 3: Let READ $(R_i) = \langle I_{k_1}, I_{k_2}, \cdots, I_{k_m} \rangle$ and WRITE $(R_i) = \langle I_{p_1}, I_{p_2}, \cdots, I_{p_n} \rangle$.

1) When R_i is written with data d by executing the instructions in the WRITE (R_i) sequence, all registers in the set $f_D(D(\text{WRITE } (R_i))) = f_D(D(I_{p_1}, I_{p_2}, \cdots, I_{p_n}))$ are written with data d, unless (1). $f_D(D(I_{p_j})) = \{\phi\}$ for some $I_{p_j} \in$ WRITE (R_i), $1 \leq j \leq n - 1$, in which case R_i is written with either a ONE or a ZERO depending on technology, or (2). $f_D(D(I_{p_n})) = \{\phi\}$, in which case the contents of R_i remain unchanged.

2) When R_i is read out by executing the instructions in the READ (R_i) sequence, during the process of reading out R_i all registers in the set $f_D(D(I_{k_1}, I_{k_2}, \cdots, I_{k_{m-1}}))$ are written with data d and data d are read out, if R_i contains data d, unless $f_D(S(I_{k_j})) = \{\phi\}$, for some $I_{k_j} \in$ READ (R_i), in which case a ONE or a ZERO will be read out, depending on technology.

Proof: The lemma follows immediately from the faulty behavior of the register decoding function f_D. □

Example 8: With reference to the S-graph of Fig. 1, READ $(R_3) = \langle I_6, I_7 \rangle$ and WRITE $(R_3) = \langle I_1, I_5 \rangle$. When R_3 is written with data d by executing I_1 with data d, and I_5, all registers in the set $f_D(D(\text{WRITE}(R_3))) = f_D(D(I_1, I_5)) = f_D(D(I_1)) \cup f_D(D(I_5)) = f_D(R_1) \cup f_D(R_3)$ are written with data d, unless $f_D(R_1) = \{\phi\}$, in which case R_3 is written with either a ONE or a ZERO, or $f_D(R_3) = \{\phi\}$, in which case the

contents of R_3 remain unchanged. When R_3 is read out by executing I_6 and I_7, all registers in the set $f_D(R_1)$ are written with data d and data d are read out, if R_3 contains data d, unless $f_D(R_1) = \{\phi\}$ or $f_D(R_3) = \{\phi\}$, in which case either a ONE or a ZERO is read out. □

Fault Model for the Instruction Decoding and Control Function

Under a fault in the instruction decoding and control function, the faulty behavior of the microprocessor can be specified as follows. When instruction I_j is executed any one of the following can happen.

1) Instead of instruction I_j some other instruction I_k is executed. This fault is denoted by $f(I_j/I_k)$.

2) In addition to instruction I_j, some other instruction I_k is also activated. This fault is denoted by $f(I_j/I_j + I_k)$.

3) No instruction is executed. This fault is denoted by $f(I_j/\phi)$.

This fault model is strongly motivated by the fact summarized in the following theorem.

Theorem 1: If a decoder is realized without any reconvergent fanout then under a single stuck-at fault its behavior can be formulated independent of its implementation details as follows: for a given valid input to the decoder, instead of, or in addition to the expected output, some other output is activated, or no output is activated.

Proof: The proof is given in [15]. □

The assumption of no reconvergent fanout in the instruction decoding mechanism is quite reasonable as it has n inputs and as many as 2^n outputs. We would like to allow the faulty behavior stated above for each instruction of the microprocessor. However, this makes the test generation procedures extremely complicated. Therefore we impose two constraints (given below as 4 and 5) on the faulty behavior under faults in the instruction decoding and control function.

4) If either $f(I_j/I_k)$ or $f(I_j/I_j + I_k)$ is present, then instruction I_k will be correctly executed.

5) If $f(I_j/I_k), f(I_j/I_j + I_k)$ or $f(I_j/\phi)$ is present then neither $f(I_q/I_j)$ nor $f(I_q/I_q + I_j)$ can be present.

The behavior of a decoder under a single stuck-at fault does not violate these constraints [15]. Any number of instructions could be faulty, subject to the set of specifications 1) through 5). As an example, under the fault model, faults $f(I_1/I_2)$, $f(I_3/I_3 + I_2), f(I_4/I_2)$ can exist simultaneously, so can $f(I_1/I_2)$, $f(I_3/\phi), f(I_4/I_6), f(I_5/I_5 + I_6)$.

In practice, some faults in the instruction decoding and control function such as $f(I_j/I_k)$ or $f(I_j/I_j + I_k)$ may be readily detected if a different number of machine cycles are needed to execute instructions I_j and I_k, or different status signals are emitted during their execution.

Example 9: In terms of the S-graph of Fig. 1, under fault $f(I_2/\phi)$, register R_2 will not be written, i.e., its contents remain unchanged. Note that the faults in the instruction decoding and control function cannot be treated as faults in the register decoding function. For example, if I_8 is executed correctly, then $f(I_3/I_5)$ is not equivalent to $f_D(R_2) = \{R_3\}$. Under $f(I_{10}/I_{21})$, instead of the "Skip if the contents of R_1 are zero" instruction the "Return from subroutine" instruction is executed. Under $f(I_6/I_6 + I_{13})$, (RESULT1) $*$ (RESULT2) will be transferred to R_1 where RESULT1 and RESULT2 are the results produced by I_6 and I_{13}, respectively, and $*$ indicates the bit-wise logical OR or AND function (depending on technology) between RESULT1 and RESULT2. □

Fault Model for the Data Storage Function

In this section a fault model for the data storage function is presented which accounts for the faults in various registers. We allow any cell of a register to be stuck at 0 or 1, and this fault can occur with any number of cells with any number of registers.

Fault Model for the Data Transfer Function

In this section a fault model for the data transfer function is presented which accounts for faults in various transfer paths. Under a fault in the data transfer function for any instruction I_j:

1) A line in a transfer path in the set $T(I_j)$ can be stuck at 0 or 1,

2) Two lines of a transfer path in the set $T(I_j)$ can be coupled, i.e., they fail to carry different logic values. (This can happen, for example, due to metallization shorts or capacitive couplings [14].)

We allow any number of transfer paths associated with any number of instructions to be faulty in this manner. This fault model is very general and is also independent of implementation details of transfer paths. Even though physical transfer mechanisms may be shared between transfer paths in practice, by allowing each transfer path to be faulty, we are making the fault model independent of implementation details.

Fault Model for the Data Manipulation Function

The data manipulation function refers to various functional units such as the ALU, interrupt handling hardware, hardware used for incrementing (or decrementing) the stack pointer, index register or program counter, hardware used for computing the addresses of operands in various addressing modes such as indexed and relative, etc.

We do not propose any specific fault model, per se, for the data manipulation function because of the wide variety in existing designs for functional units. We will assume that complete test sets can be derived for the functional units for any given fault model. The operands necessary to execute tests for a given functional unit can be stored in the proper registers by executing instructions of class T or B only, and they do not require the use of any other functional unit. Similarly the results of these tests can be read out by using instructions of class T or B only. (Recall our discussion in Section II.) We allow any number of functional units to be faulty at one time.

Fault Model for Microprocessors

At any given time we allow the presence of any number of faults but only in one function described above. Note that we

are allowing a very general model for microprocessors (as described in Section II). In addition, if we allow multiple faults in different functions, the problem becomes extremely complex. However, since we allow each function to be faulty in a very general fashion, our assumptions are not as restrictive as the classical single stuck-at fault assumption.

IV. TEST GENERATION PROCEDURES

In this section we present procedures to generate tests for faults in the various functions presented in Section III.

Test Generation Procedure for Detecting Faults in the Register Decoding Function

The tests generated using the procedure guarantee that the register decoding function denoted by the mapping f_D is a one-to-one correspondence from $\mathcal{R}$ to $\mathcal{R}$. This procedure uses two data structures, a queue of registers and a set of registers which are named Q and A, respectively. In each iteration of the test generation procedure, set A is progressively augmented by removing the register lying in the front of the queue Q and including it in set A; now the register which was second in the queue before the augmentation of set A lies in the front of the queue, i.e., the queue is updated. The tests assure that at any given stage, registers in set A have disjoint image sets under mapping f_D. When the procedure terminates it is guaranteed that all the registers have disjoint image sets under mapping f_D, establishing that f_D is a one-to-one correspondence.

ONE and ZERO are used as operands. This choice is arbitrary. We could have used $(1010 \cdots 10)$ and its bit-wise complement $(0101 \cdots 01)$ as operands instead. The tests should be applied in the same order in which they are generated.

Procedure 1: Procedure to Generate Tests for Detecting Faults in the Register Decoding Function

Step 1: Initialize the queue Q with all the registers so that R_i lies ahead of R_j, if and only if $l(R_i) \leq l(R_j)$; Initialize the set A as empty.

Step 2: $A \leftarrow$ register at the front of Q; Update Q.

Step 3: REPEAT

a) Generate instructions to write each register R_i of set A with data ONE, and the register R_j at the front of Q (if there is one) with data ZERO. (The instructions of the corresponding WRITE (R_i) sequences and WRITE (R_j) sequence need to be generated.)

b) Generate instructions to read out each register R_i of set A, such that register R_a will be read before register $R_b(R_a, R_b \in A)$, if and only if $l(R_a) \leq l(R_b)$. (The instructions of the corresponding READ (R_i) sequences need to be generated.)

c) Generate instructions to read out the register R_j at the front of Q (if there is one). (The instructions of the READ (R_j) sequence need to be generated.)

d) $A \leftarrow A \cup \{$Register at the front of $Q\}$.

e) Update Q.

UNTIL $Q =$ empty.

Step 4: Repeat Steps 1, 2, and 3 with complementary data. □

We now illustrate one iteration of Step 3 of Procedure 1 for the S-graph of Fig. 1. It may be noticed that both data and its address need to be carefully chosen.

Example 10: At the end of the fourth iteration of Step 3, $A \leftarrow \{R_1, R_2, R_4, R_5, R_6\}$ and $Q \leftarrow \langle R_7, R_3 \rangle$. The instructions generated during the fifth iteration of Step 3 are given below.

a) I_1 with operand ONE; I_2 with operand ONE; I_{15} with operand ONE; /R_1, R_2, stack pointer (R_4) are written with data ONE/
I_{17} with the *address* of the operand equal to ONE; /R_5 is written implicitly with "data" ONE/
I_9 with jump address = LOC 2; /program counter is written implicitly with "data" = LOC 2/
LOC 2: I_{20} with jump address = LOC 3; /Note that I_{20} is the "Jump to subroutine" instruction, hence program counter (now containing LOC 2 + 1) is saved in the subroutine register (R_7), and a new jump address = LOC 3 is loaded into the program counter. Thus R_6 and R_7 are written implicitly with "data" LOC 3 and LOC 2 + 1, respectively. Choose LOC 3 different from LOC 2 + 1 and also different from ONE/

b) and c) LOC 3: I_7; /I_7 is stored in LOC 3. When I_7 is fetched, the program counter is read out implicitly on the address bus; expected output "data" = LOC 3. Thus, I_7 is the first instruction in the subroutine. I_7 explicitly reads out R_1/
I_8; I_{16}; I_{17} with the *address* of the operand equal to ONE; /R_2 is explicitly read out. R_4 and R_5 are implicitly read out/ I_{21};
/I_{21} is the "Return from subroutine" instruction. The contents of the subroutine register (R_7) are transferred to the program counter. The next instruction will be fetched from the location LOC 2 + 1, as LOC 2 + 1 is the return address for the subroutine. When this new instruction is fetched, the subroutine register will be effectively read out through the program counter/

d) $A \leftarrow \{R_1, R_2, R_4, R_5, R_6, R_7\}$
e) $Q \leftarrow \langle R_3 \rangle$ □

Theorem 2: The test sequence generated by using Procedure 1 is capable of detecting any detectable fault in the fault model for the register decoding function.

Proof: The proof is by induction. At the beginning of Step 3 a) of Procedure 1, let set $A = \{R_{i_1}, R_{i_2}, \cdots, R_{i_k}\}$. Let the induction hypothesis be $f_D(R_{i_1}) \cap f_D(R_{i_2}) \cap \cdots \cap f_D(R_{i_k}) = \{\phi\}$, and $f_D(R_{i_j}) \neq \{\phi\}$, for each $R_{i_j} \in A$. At the end of Step 3 d) of Procedure 1, i.e., when set A is augmented, let set $A = \{R_{i_1}, R_{i_2}, \cdots, R_{i_k}, R_{i_{k+1}}\}$. We will prove that $f_D(R_{i_1}) \cap f_D(R_{i_2}) \cap \cdots \cap f_D(R_{i_k}) \cap f_D(R_{i_{k+1}}) = \{\phi\}$, and $f_D(R_{i_{k+1}}) \neq \{\phi\}$.

In Step 3 a), registers of set A are written with data ONE (ZERO), and register $R_{i_{k+1}}$, which is at the front of the queue, is written with data ZERO (ONE), by executing the instructions in the corresponding WRITE sequences. If $f_D(R_{i_{k+1}}) = \{\phi\}$, the fault will be readily detected when appropriate instructions are executed to read out $R_{i_{k+1}}$ in Step 3 c), as it will fail to produce either a ONE or a ZERO following Lemma 3. (ONE or ZERO corresponds to the expected data d in terms of

Lemma 3.) Assume that for some register R_{i_l} of set A, $f_D(R_{i_l}) \cap f_D(R_{i_{k+1}}) \neq \{\phi\}$. If R_{i_l} is written after $R_{i_{k+1}}$ in Step 3 a), the fault will be detected when $R_{i_{k+1}}$ is read out in Step 3 c), since according to Lemma 3, all the registers in the set $f_D(R_{i_l})$, and hence in the set $f_D(R_{i_l}) \cap f_D(R_{i_{k+1}})$ will be written with ONE (ZERO). Since $f_D(R_{i_l}) \cap f_D(R_{i_{k+1}}) \subseteq f_D(R_{i_{k+1}})$, when $R_{i_{k+1}}$ is read out in Step 3 c), it will either produce a ONE instead of a ZERO, or a ZERO instead of a ONE. Note that since $l(R_{i_l}) \leq l(R_{i_{k+1}})$, the process of reading out of R_{i_l} will not require routing of R_{i_l} through $R_{i_{k+1}}$. Similar arguments apply when R_{i_l} is written before $R_{i_{k+1}}$ in Step 3 a). In this case the fault will be detected when R_{i_l} is read out in Step 3 b).

The basis of induction, i.e., when $A = \{R_{i_1}\}$, $f_D(R_{i_1}) \neq \{\phi\}$, and when $A = \{R_{i_1}, R_{i_2}\}$, $f_D(R_{i_1}) \cap f_D(R_{i_2}) = \{\phi\}$ can be readily proved following the same arguments used so far. Using these arguments, it is guaranteed that $\cap_{i-1}^{n} f_D(R_i) = \{\phi\}$, where $\mathcal{R} = \{R_1, R_2, \cdots, R_n\}$. Since all the registers have disjoint image sets under mapping f_D, f_D cannot be a many-to-one correspondence. Moreover, since $f_D(R_i) \neq \{\phi\}$ for each $R_i \in \mathcal{R}$, f_D cannot be a one-to-many correspondence from $\mathcal{R}$ to $\mathcal{R}$. Therefore f_D is guaranteed to be a one-to-one correspondence from $\mathcal{R}$ to $\mathcal{R}$. It follows immediately that the register decoding function (denoted by f_D) is free of any detectable fault. Note that for some registers, even if $f_D(R_i) \neq \{R_i\}$, f_D could still be a one-to-one correspondence. For example, we may have an undetectable fault $f_D(R_i) = \{R_j\}$ and $f_D(R_j) = \{R_i\}$. □

Test Generation Procedures for Detecting Faults in the Instruction Decoding and Control Function

We make an assumption about the labels of edges representing instructions. If $I_j \in$ class M then $l(I_j) \leq 2$, i.e., if $l(I_j) > 2$ then $I_j \in$ class T. Recall from Lemma 2 that all instructions of class B have label 1. Thus the destination of an instruction of class M can only be a main memory location or a register with label 1. This assumption can be easily justified for current microprocessors, since the result of an instruction of class M is usually stored in a main memory location or an accumulator or a general purpose register [3]; on the other hand, the destination register of an instruction of class T can have any label. Without this assumption the details of the test generation procedures become extremely complicated.

We now present an algorithm to determine the order of test application for detecting $f(I_j/\phi)$, $f(I_j/I_k)$, and $f(I_j/I_j + I_k)$. The order plays a very crucial role in proving the fault coverage.

Algorithm 2: The Ordering Algorithm

FOR $K \leftarrow 1$ TO $K_{\max}$ DO /$K_{\max}$ = maximum value of labels/
BEGIN
Step 1: Apply tests to detect faults $f(I_j/\phi)$, $f(I_j/I_k)$, and $f(I_j/I_j + I_k)$ where $l(I_j) = l(I_k) = K$. /k and K are not related/
Step 2: Apply tests to detect faults $f(I_j/I_j + I_k)$, where $1 \leq l(I_j) \leq K$, $l(I_k) = K + 1$, and $K < K_{\max}$.

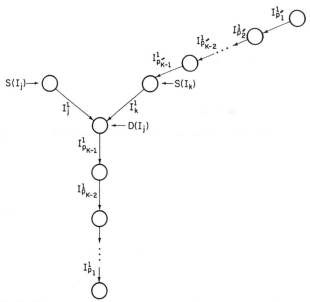

Fig. 2. The worst-case scenario for Procedure 3; $l(I_j) = l(I_k) = K \geq 3$; $l(S(I_k)) = K$.

Step 3: Apply tests to detect faults $f(I_j/I_j + I_k)$, where $K + 1 \leq l(I_j) \leq K_{max}$, $l(I_k) = K$. □

END

The details of test generation for detecting faults $f(I_j/\phi)$, $f(I_j/I_k)$, and $f(I_j/I_j + I_k)$ depend very heavily on the labels of instructions and their source and destination registers. In [15] the details are partitioned into a number of cases and the test generation procedure is given for each case. In this paper we present only those test generation procedures which are quite difficult and elaborate. We hope that these test generation procedures give the flavor of the problems.

We denote various operands for instructions by OPERAND 1, OPERAND 2, etc., and various results produced by RESULT 1, RESULT 2, etc. It is assumed that whenever any register R_i is to be read or written, instructions in the READ (R_i) or WRITE (R_i) sequence are to be executed.

Test Generation for $f(I_j/\phi)$

We consider the case when $l(I_j) = 2$. In this case $|$READ $(D(I_j))| = 1$. Let READ $(D(I_j)) = \langle I_k \rangle$. Of course, $l(I_k) = 1$. We follow the procedure below in this case.

Procedure 2

Step 1: Store OPERAND 1 in $D(I_j)$ and proper operand(s) in $S(I_j)$ such that when I_j is executed it produces RESULT 1 in $D(I_j)$ and RESULT 1 $\neq$ OPERAND 1.

Step 2: Read out $D(I_j)$. /Expected output = OPERAND 1/

Step 3: Execute I_j.

Step 4: Read out $D(I_j)$. /Expected output = RESULT 1/ □

Theorem 3: Procedure 2 detects $f(I_j/\phi)$ when $l(I_j) = 2$.

Proof: Note that $l(I_k) = 1$ where READ $(D(I_j)) = \langle I_k \rangle$. Since the tests are applied in the order specified by the ordering algorithm, the microprocessor under test executes this pro-

cedure after executing the tests required to detect $f(I_p/\phi)$, $f(I_p/I_q)$, and $f(I_p/I_p + I_q)$ where $l(I_p) = l(I_q) = 1$, and $f(I_v/I_v + I_w)$ where $l(I_v) = 1$ and $l(I_w) = 2$. Therefore, it has already been checked that the READ $(D(I_j)) = \langle I_k \rangle$ sequence can correctly read out $D(I_j)$ and its execution does not cause additional execution of any instruction with label 2; in particular the contents of $D(I_j)$ are not changed after the execution of READ $(D(I_j))$. Therefore Step 2 ensures that $D(I_j)$ stores OPERAND 1. This step is necessary because due to faults involved in the instructions used to write data in $D(I_j)$, RESULT 1 may be stored in $D(I_j)$ instead of OPERAND 1. If Step 2 is not executed, the fault $f(I_j/\phi)$ will be masked. In Step 3, I_j is executed which is expected to produce RESULT 1 in $D(I_j)$. If $f(I_j/\phi)$ is present, the contents of $D(I_j)$ will not change. Consequently when $D(I_j)$ is read out in Step 4, the fault will be detected. □

Test Generation for $f(I_j/I_k)$

We consider the case when $l(I_j) = l(I_k) = K \geq 3$, $D(I_j) = D(I_k)$, and $l(S(I_k)) = K$. This case is illustrated in Fig. 2. We follow the procedure below.

Procedure 3

Step 1: Store OPERAND 1 in $S(I_j)$ and OPERAND 2 in $S(I_k)$ such that OPERAND 1 $\neq$ OPERAND 2.

Step 2: FOR $i \leftarrow 1$ TO K DO

    BEGIN

        Execute I_j;

        Read out $D(I_j)$. /Expected output = OPERAND 1/ END

Step 3: Execute I_k.

Step 4: Read out $D(I_k)$. /Expected output = OPERAND 2/ □

We will only sketch how Procedure 3 detects $f(I_j/I_k)$ when

$l(I_j) = l(I_k) = K \geq 3$, $D(I_j) = D(I_k)$, and $l(S(I_k)) = K$. The detailed proof is beyond the scope of available space in this paper, and is given in [15]. Note that I_j, $I_k \in$ class T. In Step 2 of Procedure 3, register $D(I_j)$ is read out by executing READ $(D(I_j)) = \langle I_{p_{K-1}}, I_{p_{K-2}}, \cdots, I_{p_1} \rangle$. (Refer to Fig. 2.) Recall that $l(I_j) = l(I_k) = K$, and $l(I_{p_i}) = i$, for $1 \leq i \leq K-1$. When the microprocessor under test executes this procedure, it has already been checked that $f(I_p/\phi)$, $f(I_p/I_q)$ and $f(I_p/I_p + I_q)$ do not exist, where $1 \leq l(I_p)$, $l(I_q) \leq K-1$, and $K \geq 3$. Therefore, $D(I_j)$ can be correctly read out by executing READ $(D(I_j))$. Moreover, in particular it has been checked that no instruction in the READ $(D(I_j))$ sequence can give rise to additional execution of an instruction of class M. (Recall that according to our assumption, no instruction of class M can have a label greater than 2.)

If OPERAND 2 is really stored in $S(I_k)$ in Step 1, the fault $f(I_j/I_k)$ will be detected when $D(I_j)$ is read out during the first iteration of Step 2, since OPERAND 2 will be read out instead of OPERAND 1. On the other hand, due to the faults involved in instructions used to write data in $S(I_k)$, OPERAND 1 may have been stored in $S(I_k)$. In this situation the fault will not be detected during the first iteration of Step 2.

Note that the microprocessor has not yet executed tests to detect $f(I_p/I_p + I_q)$ where $1 \leq l(I_p) \leq K-1$, and $l(I_q) \geq K + 1$. Therefore, under such a fault, some instructions in the READ $(D(I_j))$ sequence may give rise to additional execution of instructions (of class T) with label $\geq K + 1$ which change the contents of $S(I_k)$. In the worst case the following scenario is possible.

The instruction decoding and control function has $f(I_{p_i}/I_{p_i} + I_{p_i'})$ faults for every $I_{p_i} \in$ READ $(D(I_j))$, such that $I_{p_i'} \in$ class T, $D(I_{p'_{K-1}}) = S(I_k)$, $D(I_{p'_{K-2}}) = S(I_{p'_{K-1}})$, $\cdots$, $D(I_{p'_1}) = S(I_{p'_2})$. This scenario is illustrated in Fig. 2. Thus when the loop given in Step 2 of Procedure 3 is repeated $K-1$ times, the contents of $S(I_{p_1})$ are transferred to $S(I_k)$ due to $f(I_{p_i}/I_{p_i} + I_{p_i'})$ faults. If each register $S(I_{p_i'})$, for $1 \leq i \leq K-1$, and $S(I_k)$ contains OPERAND 1 the fault will not be revealed during the first K iterations of the loop of Step 2 of Procedure 3, but the fault will be detected during Step 4 because OPERAND 1 is read out instead of OPERAND 2. This scenario explains why in the worst case it is necessary to repeat the loop of Step 2 K times. If it is repeated less than K times the fault may remain undetected depending on the initial contents of $S(I_{p_i'})$ registers. Moreover, K iterations of the loop of Step 2 are always sufficient, since $|$READ $(D(I_j))| = K-1$, and either the contents of $S(I_k)$ change during the first $K-1$ iterations of the loop of Step 2 (due to $f(I_{p_i}/I_{p_i} + I_{p_i'})$ faults) or else they remain unchanged during all the K iterations of the loop. In the earlier case the fault is detected in some iteration of the loop in Step 2, and in the latter case the fault is detected in Step 4.

Test Generation for $f(I_j/I_j + I_k)$

We consider the case when $1 \leq l(I_j) \leq K$, $l(I_k) = K+1$, $K \geq 2$. Note that $I_k \in$ class T because $l(I_k) \geq 3$. Also $l(D(I_j)) \leq K-1$ and $l(D(I_k)) = K$; hence $D(I_j) \neq D(I_k)$. We divide this case into two subcases depending on whether the value of

$l(S(I_k))$ is less than K, or is equal to K or $K+1$. Note that it cannot be greater than $K+1$ because $l(I_k) = K+1$ and I_k belongs to class T. In this paper we consider the former subcase, i.e., $l(S(I_k)) < K$. We use the following procedure.

Procedure 4

Step 1: Store OPERAND 1 in $S(I_k)$ and OPERAND 2 in $D(I_k)$, such that OPERAND 1 $\neq$ OPERAND 2.

Step 2: Read out $S(I_k)$. /Expected output = OPERAND 1/

Step 3: Execute I_j.

Step 4: Read out $D(I_k)$. /Expected output = OPERAND 2/ □

Theorem 4: Procedure 4 detects $f(I_j/I_j + I_k)$ when $1 \leq l(I_j) \leq K$, $l(I_k) = K+1$, $K \geq 2$, and $l(S(I_k)) < K$.

Proof: Since $l(S(I_k)) < K$, no instruction in the READ $(S(I_k))$ sequence can have label greater than $K-1$. Also $l(D(I_k)) = K$, hence READ $(S(I_k))$ reads out $S(I_k)$ without routing its contents through $D(I_k)$. When the microprocessor under test executes this procedure, it has already executed the tests to detect $f(I_p/\phi)$, $f(I_p/I_q)$, and $f(I_p/I_p + I_q)$ where $1 \leq l(I_p)$, $l(I_q) \leq K-1$, and $f(I_v/I_v + I_w)$ where $1 \leq l(I_v) \leq K-1$ and $l(I_w) = K$. Therefore, in Step 2 of this procedure, $S(I_k)$ is correctly read out to make sure that it stores OPERAND 1, and it continues to store OPERAND 1 after READ $(S(I_k))$ is executed. In Step 3, I_j is executed. If $f(I_j/I_j + I_k)$ is present, OPERAND 1 will be stored in $D(I_k)$ and the fault will be detected in Step 4. □

Test Generation Procedures for Detecting Faults in the Data Transfer Function and the Data Storage Function

We motivate the discussion by means of an example. Let I_{j_1}, I_{j_2}, $\cdots$, I_{j_k} be a sequence of instructions of class T such that $E(I_{j_1})$, $E(I_{j_2})$, $\cdots$, $E(I_{j_k})$ form a directed path from the IN node to the OUT node in the corresponding S-graph. Let the transfer paths in sets $T(I_{j_1})$, $T(I_{j_2})$, $\cdots$, $T(I_{j_k})$ each be w lines in width. We propose Procedure 5 to detect any fault in $T(I_{j_1})$, $T(I_{j_2})$, $\cdots$, $T(I_{j_k})$, and in registers $D(I_{j_1})$, $D(I_{j_2})$, $\cdots$, $D(I_{j_{K-1}})$. The fault models for the data storage function and data transfer function were given in Section III.

Procedure 5

I_{j_1} with data $\underbrace{111 \cdots 1}_{w \text{ width}}$; /Write $D(I_{j_1})$ with data $\underbrace{111 \cdots 1}_{w \text{ width}}$

$I_{j_2}; I_{j_3}; \cdots; I_{j_k};$ /Expected output data $= \underbrace{111 \cdots 1}_{w \text{ width}}$

Repeat the above instructions with data

$\underbrace{11 \cdots 1}_{w/2} \underbrace{00 \cdots 0}_{w/2} ; \underbrace{11 \cdots 1}_{w/4} \underbrace{00 \cdots 0}_{w/4} \underbrace{11 \cdots 1}_{w/4}$

$\underbrace{00 \cdots 0}_{w/4} ; \cdots, \underbrace{1010 \cdots 10}_{w} .$

Repeat all the instructions above with complementary data. ☐

Theorem 5: Procedure 5 detects

1) a line in any transfer path in the set $T(I_{j_1}) \cup T(I_{j_2}) \cup \cdots \cup T(I_{j_k})$ stuck at 0 or 1.

2) two or more lines in any transfer path in the set $T(I_{j_1}) \cup T(I_{j_2}) \cup \cdots \cup T(I_{j_k})$ coupled.

3) a cell of any register in the set $D(I_{j_1}) \cup \cdots \cup D(I_{j_{k-1}})$ stuck at 0 or 1.

Proof: If a fault is described by 1) or 3) above, it will be detected either after the execution of sequence $I_{j_2}, I_{j_3}, \cdots, I_{j_k}$ when the expected output data $= 111 \cdots 1$, or after the execution of the sequence when the expected output data $= 000 \cdots 0$.

Procedure 5 also detects any fault described by 2) because at some stage of the procedure, any given two lines of a transfer path are required to carry different logic values i.e., x and $\bar{x}$, $x \in \{0, 1\}$, respectively. If these two lines are coupled they will fail to carry different logic values, and the fault will be detected after the subsequent execution of the sequence $I_{j_2}, I_{j_3}, \cdots, I_{j_k}$. ☐

Definition 7: The set of tests in Procedure 5 is defined the *"transfer test set"* and the associated data being routed on the corresponding transfer paths the *"transfer test data."* ☐

Definition 8: The subgraph of the S-graph that represents instructions of class T only is called the *T-subgraph.* ☐

Let P_1 be a directed path from the IN node to the OUT node in the T-subgraph. All the instructions which are represented by edges constituting path P_1 are said to be covered by path P_1. Let $\{P_1, P_2, \cdots, P_n\}$ be a set of directed paths from the IN node to the OUT node of the T-subgraph such that this set collectively covers all the instructions of class T. It is clear from Theorem 5 that if the transfer test data are routed from the IN node to the OUT node (using the transfer test sets consisting of instructions covered by each path in set $\{P_1, P_2, \cdots P_n\}$), any fault associated with the instructions of class T in the transfer paths or in the data storage function will be detected (since the transfer test data are "routed" on every edge of the T-subgraph, every node of the graph is also visited).

We need to test the transfer paths associated with the instructions of class M. Let "$R_i \circ R_j \to R_k$" denote a typical instruction of class M which performs an operation denoted by "$\circ$" on the contents of register R_i and R_j, and stores the result in register R_k. We need to choose a set of proper operands in R_i and R_j such that when the instruction "$R_i \circ R_j \to R_k$" is executed it generates and stores data corresponding to the transfer test set in R_k. We then need to route these data from R_k to the OUT node by executing READ (R_k). Successful execution of this test ensures that the transfer path from the data manipulation logic (e.g., the ALU used in executing instruction "$R_i \circ R_j \to R_k$") to register R_k is fault free. Therefore any result generated by this instruction can be faithfully transferred to R_k. Consider instruction I_4 in the S-graph of Fig. 1. We execute Procedure 6 to test the transfer path from the ALU to R_1. (It is assumed that the microprocessor is an 8-bit processor.)

Procedure 6

I_1 with data 1111 1111;
I_2 with data 0000 0000;
I_4;
I_7;

Repeat the tests above with data (1111 0000, 0000 0000), (1100 1100, 0000 0000), (1010 1010, 0000 0000), (0000 0000 0000 0000), (0000 1111, 0000 0000), (0011 0011, 0000 0000), (0101 0101, 0000 0000). ☐

We also need to check that the transfer paths connecting R_i and R_j to the ALU in the "$R_i \circ R_j \to R_k$" instruction are fault free. This ensures that any pair of operands can be applied to the ALU in the "$R_i \circ R_j \to R_k$" instruction. For this we need to check that any line in the transfer paths from R_i and R_j to the ALU can be set to 0 or 1 independent of the logic values on any other line in these transfer paths. Consider instruction I_4 in Fig. 1. We want to test the transfer paths connecting R_1 and R_2 to the ALU. We execute Procedure 7.

Procedure 7

I_1 with data 0000 0001; /R_1 stores 0000 0001/
I_2 with data 0000 0000; /R_2 stores 0000 0000/
I_4;
I_7;   /Expected output data 0000 0001/
Repeat the four instructions with the data in I_1 (and therefore the expected output data) being 0000 0010, $\cdots$, 1000 0000.
I_1 with data 0000 0000; /R_1 stores 0000 0000/
I_2 with data 0000 0001; /R_2 stores 0000 0001/
I_4;
I_7;   /Expected output data 0000 0001/

Repeat the four instructions with the data in I_2 (and therefore the expected output data) being 0000 0010, $\cdots$, 1000 0000. Repeat the test above with the complementary data. ☐

We need to execute tests similar to those given in Procedures 6 and 7 for every instruction of class M. Finally we must test the transfer paths and registers associated with the instructions of class B. This is accomplished by choosing the set of jump or branch addresses such that they correspond to the transfer test set for jump, branch, return from subroutine, etc., instructions. For example, in order to test the transfer path associated with the jump instruction (instruction I_9) in Fig. 1 we need to execute Procedure 8. It is assumed that the width of the address bus is 16.

Procedure 8

I_9 with jump address 0000 0000 0000 0000;
I_9 with jump address 0000 0000 1111 1111;
I_9 with jump address 0000 1111 0000 1111;
I_9 with jump address 0011 0011 0011 0011;
I_9 with jump address 0101 0101 0101 0101;

Repeat the test above with the complementary set of jump addresses. ☐

Test Generation Procedure for Detecting Faults in the Data Manipulation Function

As described in Section III we assume that complete test sets are available for detecting faults (for some specified fault model) in the ALU and other functional units such as a shifter, logic used to increment the program counter, or the interrupt handling logic. The operands specified by such test sets can be provided to a functional unit using, in general, a sequence of instructions of class T. Similarly, the result produced by a functional unit can be read out using a sequence of instructions of class T.

If the logic level description of functional units is available, test sets can be generated for them using classical fault detection algorithms based on the stuck-at fault model. On the other hand, if we do not know the logic level details of the ALU, but know, for example, that it is realized using an iterative logic array we can generate test sets for it as explained in [4]. Another approach would be to generate test sets for functional testing of the ALU, shift, increment, compare logic, etc., using binary decision diagrams [1]. It might be noted that even though some faults associated with the instruction decoding and control function look like faults in the data manipulation function, and vice versa, the set of faults in one function is not a subset or a superset of the set of faults in the other function [15].

V. Complexity of Test Sequences

The complexity of test sequences (in terms of the number of instructions) as a function of n_R, the number of registers, and n_I, the number of instructions, has been derived [15]. The complexity of the test sequence for the register decoding function is found to be $\mathcal{O}(n_R^3)$.

It is very difficult to find a closed form solution for the complexity of the test sequences for the instruction decoding and control function. However, if the instruction labels do not exceed 2 (i.e., the result of any instruction is stored either in the main memory or a register with label 1) the complexity is $\mathcal{O}(n_I^2)$. For today's microprocessors, n_I ranges from 30 to 200. Therefore the test sequences for the instruction decoding and control function constitute a dominant portion of the test sequences for the microprocessor.

VI. A Case Study

We have developed the test sequences based on our test generation procedures for a real 8-bit microprocessor from the Hewlett-Packard Company [15]. In order to determine the fault coverage of the test sequences for stuck-at faults, a detailed gate and subnetwork model of the microprocessor (obtained from Hewlett-Packard) was used on the TESTAID III fault simulator. Approximately 2200 single stuck-at faults were simulated.

About 90 percent of these faults were detected by the test sequences for the register decoding, data storage, data transfer, and data manipulation functions. The length of these sequences was about 1 K instructions. About 6 percent of the faults gave rise to simultaneous execution of multiple instructions as described by the fault model for the instruction decoding and control function. The length of the sequences to detect these

faults was about 8 K instructions. Many of these faults were subtle and difficult to detect and very elaborate test sequences were required to detect them.

The remaining faults (about 4 percent) were associated with the power-up and initialization logic, or were undetectable because of redundancies in the logic, or required invalid opcodes to detect them. Thus for this particular microprocessor the fault coverage was excellent, since all single stuck-at faults which affect valid instructions during normal operation are detected.

The test generation effort was quite straightforward and we believe that it can be automated without much difficulty. The overall results of the case study were quite promising and we are convinced that our approach is a viable and effective one for generating tests for microprocessors.

VII. Concluding Remarks

A graph-theoretic model for microprocessor architecture was presented. It allows us to treat the microprocessor organization and instruction set as parameters of test generation procedures. Functional level fault models for the register decoding function, the instruction decoding and control function, and the data storage and transfer functions were presented. These models were developed independent of the details of implementation. Test generation procedures were presented to detect faults in these functions. Our approach is attractive and promising, particularly in a user environment, since all the information needed to construct the models is readily available in the typical user's manual. Future work will include research on whether any extensions to the fault models presented here are necessary (for example to include errors in control sequencing), and techniques to design microprocessors to improve their testability.

Acknowledgment

We would like to thank the Hewlett-Packard Company, Loveland Instrument Division, Loveland, CO, and especially Dr. K. Parker, for providing the TESTAID III fault simulator and the gate level description of the microprocessor.

References

[1] S. B. Akers, "Functional testing with binary decision diagrams," in *Proc. 8th Int. Conf. Fault-Tolerant Computing.* Toulouse, France: IEEE Comput. Soc., June 1978, pp. 75–82.
[2] A. C. L. Chiang and R. McCaskill, "Two new approaches simplify testing of microprocessors," *Electronics,* pp. 100–105, Jan. 22, 1976.
[3] R. H. Cushman, "Fourth annual microprocessor directory," *EDN,* vol. 22, pp. 44–83, Nov. 20, 1977.
[4] F. J. O. Dias, "Truth-table verification of an iterative logic array," *IEEE Trans. Comput.,* vol. C-25, pp. 605–613, June 1976.
[5] W. G. Fee, *Tutorial LSI testing,* 2nd ed. IEEE Comput. Soc., 1978, IEEE Catalog EHO 122-2.
[6] M. J. Flynn, "Trends and problems in computer organizations," in *1974 IFIP Proc.* Amsterdam, The Netherlands: North-Holland, 1974, pp. 3–10.
[7] H. W. Gschwind and E. J. McCluskey, *Design of Digital Computers.* New York: Springer-Verlag, 1975, pp. 355–366.
[8] E. Manning, "On computer self-diagnosis: Part I and II," *IEEE Trans. Electron. Comput.,* vol. EC-15, pp. 873–890, Dec. 1966.
[9] C. Robach and G. Saucier, "Diversified test methods for local control units," *IEEE Trans. Comput.,* vol. C-24, pp. 562–567, May 1975.
[10] ——, "Dynamic testing of control units," *IEEE Trans. Comput.,* vol. C-27, pp. 617–623, July 1978.

[11] P. Scola, "An annotated bibliography of test and diagnostics," *Honeywell Comput. J.,* vol. 6, pp. 97–102, 105–162, 1972.

[12] T. Sridhar and J. P. Hayes, "Testing bit-sliced microprocessors," in *Proc. 9th Int. Conf. Fault-Tolerant Computing.* Madison, WI: IEEE Comput. Soc., June 1979, pp. 211–218.

[13] Various papers on microprocessor testing in the *Dig. of Semiconductor Testing Symp.* Cherry Hill, NJ: IEEE Comput. Soc., Oct. 1975, 1976, 1977, 1978, 1979.

[14] S. M. Thatte and J. A. Abraham, "A methodology for functional level testing of microprocessors," in *Proc. 8th Int. Conf. Fault-Tolerant Computing.* Toulouse, France: IEEE Comput. Soc., June 1978, pp. 90–95.

[15] S. M. Thatte, "Test generation for microprocessors," Coordinated Sci. Lab., Univ. Illinois, Urbana, IL, Rep. R-842, May 1979.

Satish M. Thatte (S'76–M'80) was born in Poona, India, on April 17, 1953. He received the B.E. (Hons.) degree in electronics engineering from the Birla Institute of Technology and Science, Pilani, India, in 1975, and the M.S. and Ph.D. degrees in electrical engineering from the University of Illinois at Urbana-Champaign in 1977 and 1979, respectively.

He was a Graduate Teaching Assistant in the Department of Electrical Engineering, University of Illinois, from August 1975 to December 1975 and a Graduate Research Assistant with the Fault-Tolerant Systems and Computer Architecture group at the Coordinated Science Laboratory, University of Illinois, from January 1976 to May 1979. In May 1979 he joined the Central Research Laboratories, Texas Instruments Incorporated, Dallas, TX, where he is a Member of the Technical Staff of the VLSI systems branch. His current research interests are in computer architecture, VLSI systems, and fault tolerant computing.

Dr. Thatte is a member of the Association for Computing Machinery and is listed in the 1979 edition of *Who's Who in Technology Today.*

Jacob A. Abraham (S'71–M'74) received the B.Sc. degree in electrical engineering from the University of Kerala, Kerala, India, in 1970 and the M.S. and Ph.D. degrees from Stanford University, Stanford, CA, in 1971 and 1974, respectively.

He is an Assistant Professor in the Department of Electrical Engineering and the Coordinated Science Laboratory at the University of Illinois, Urbana, IL. His research interests include fault-tolerant computing, design automation and VLSI systems, and distributed computer systems and networks.

Dr. Abraham is a member of the Association for Computing Machinery and Sigma Xi.

Reprinted with permission from *Electronics Test,* March 1984, pages 42-52.
Copyright © 1984 by Morgan-Grampian Publishers, Inc.

Using a Software Emulator to Generate and Edit VLSI Test Patterns

An intelligent software tool, a device emulator can create and manipulate test patterns as higher-level, meaningful blocks of data, rather than as individual Ones and Zeros.

by William E. Den Beste, President
Test Systems Strategies, Inc., Beaverton, OR

The development of comprehensive testing is not keeping pace with the rising complexity of integrated-circuit (IC) devices. For this reason, test engineers face the always frustrating (sometimes overwhelming) task of generating functional test patterns for digital devices.

Test patterns — truth tables of 1s and 0s that list the stimulus pattern to be applied to the device under test (DUT) and the output patterns expected in response — are the core of IC-device test programs. When generating test patterns, such as the simple pattern in Table 1, engineers must consider three factors: the feasibility of producing error-free patterns, the thoroughness of the test and the cost.

Of the three methods (Fig 1) of generating cost-effective test patterns, each method is appropriate for a different test situation. For simple devices, manual generation offers low cost in terms of equipment and time. Automatic test generation works best for test engineers who have access to vendor databases and want to test all nodes of a device. Although the functional approach provides the test engineer with an understanding of the DUTs, to gain the most from its benefits, test engineers need new, more intelligent tools.

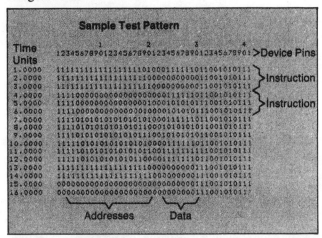

Table 1. A test pattern is a truth table that has two dimensions: one for device pins (41 in this example) and one for time flow (16 steps in this example) during the test.

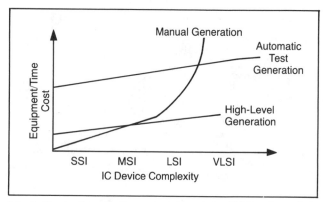

Fig 1. Depending on the complexity of the DUT and on their sources of information, test engineers can use one of these approaches to generate test patterns.

manual generation

Manually generating 1s and 0s for gate-level testing represents a thorough and sometimes cost-effective way to generate test patterns for small-scale and medium-scale integrated devices. Manual generation requires just a pencil and paper, so equipment costs are low; however, the time required, minimal for simple devices, rises quickly with device complexity. The cost becomes prohibitive with large-scale integrated (LSI) devices, and manually generating test patterns for very large-scale integrated (VLSI) devices is practically impossible.

automatic test generation

Usually adjuncts to computer-aided design systems, automatic test generators (ATGs) are too expensive to use with simple devices. And while test engineers use ATGs to advantage when handling LSI complexity, the complexity of VLSI devices (some test patterns contain more than 100,000 test vectors) is generally too great for ATGs, especially if test engineers want to understand device operations.

In real-world test environments, test engineers often reduce their tests to meaningful subsets of "testing everything." This optimizing process cuts run time and, therefore, costs. However, the massive amount of low-level information produced by ATG hinders the comprehension required to optimize test patterns.

In one situation, ATG remains useful regardless of

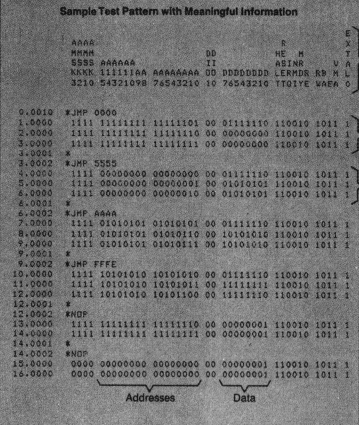

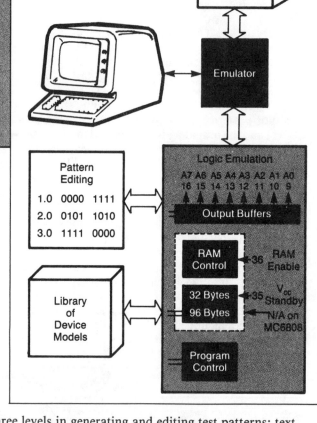

Fig 2. A third-level approach to test-pattern generation would include a pattern editor, logic emulator, pattern files and device models.

device complexity. When using stuck-at-1 and stuck-at-0 tests for all nodes, ATG can cover almost all possible faults. For gate-level testing of VLSI, ATG is a natural, cost-effective outgrowth of the device vendor's computer-aided-design database. Unfortunately, with few exceptions, only test engineers who work with the vendor company have access to the proprietary information required to identify all the device circuit nodes.

functional testing

If they lack the circuit information needed to make gate-level tests, engineers must treat a device as a black box. Yet black-box test results determine if the device performs as it should, not *why* the device fails (if it fails). Rather than gate-level testing, this kind of functional testing even appeals to those engineers who do have all the node information they need for gate-level testing, but who want to understand device operations.

Functional testing, which offers several advantages over gate-level testing (whether manual or ATG), takes the same viewpoint as that of the end user who considers the device's functions more important than the details of the circuit. Also, functional testing's high-level approach offers clarity — test engineers, not lost in 1s and 0s, can understand the way the device works and, therefore, what their test programs should do. Engineers performing functional tests now have computer-aided tools to ease the burden of creating and editing test patterns for complex devices.

three tools for functional tests

Engineers using functional tests can operate on one of three levels in generating and editing test patterns: text, 2-D, and meaningful information. Each pattern level requires a different set of tools.

For patterns treated as text, text-editing tools provide a search-and-replace capability that finds a given sequence of characters and changes it. The main limitation to this first level of operation is that test patterns use just two "characters," 1s and 0s. Changing a test condition represented by the sequence 001 in one place may inadvertently change that sequence elsewhere in the pattern (for example, where it is used in a larger sequence, such as 111001000). Another limitation of a text-editing tool is that it requires manually entering test patterns — a tedious and error-prone process. For complex devices, tedium and uncertainty decrease productivity: consider the effect of

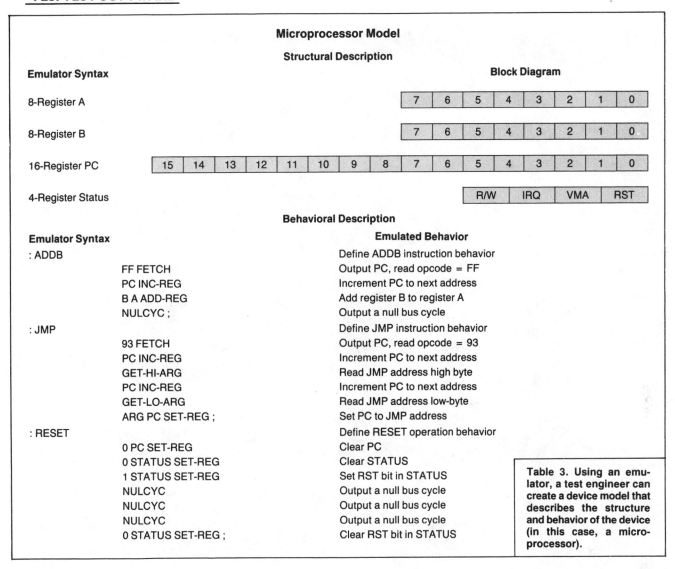

Microprocessor Model

Structural Description

Emulator Syntax		Block Diagram

8-Register A | 7 | 6 | 5 | 4 | 3 | 2 | 1 | 0 |

8-Register B | 7 | 6 | 5 | 4 | 3 | 2 | 1 | 0 |

16-Register PC | 15 | 14 | 13 | 12 | 11 | 10 | 9 | 8 | 7 | 6 | 5 | 4 | 3 | 2 | 1 | 0 |

4-Register Status | R/W | IRQ | VMA | RST |

Behavioral Description

Emulator Syntax	Emulated Behavior
: ADDB	Define ADDB instruction behavior
FF FETCH	Output PC, read opcode = FF
PC INC-REG	Increment PC to next address
B A ADD-REG	Add register B to register A
NULCYC ;	Output a null bus cycle
: JMP	Define JMP instruction behavior
93 FETCH	Output PC, read opcode = 93
PC INC-REG	Increment PC to next address
GET-HI-ARG	Read JMP address high byte
PC INC-REG	Increment PC to next address
GET-LO-ARG	Read JMP address low-byte
ARG PC SET-REG ;	Set PC to JMP address
: RESET	Define RESET operation behavior
0 PC SET-REG	Clear PC
0 STATUS SET-REG	Clear STATUS
1 STATUS SET-REG	Set RST bit in STATUS
NULCYC	Output a null bus cycle
NULCYC	Output a null bus cycle
NULCYC	Output a null bus cycle
0 STATUS SET-REG ;	Clear RST bit in STATUS

Table 3. Using an emulator, a test engineer can create a device model that describes the structure and behavior of the device (in this case, a microprocessor).

manually entering a 4K vector (test step) pattern for a 64-pin device.

Tools that manipulate patterns as 2-D matrices at least exploit the two-dimensionality of the pattern. At certain times in a test, the engineer might want to know what is happening either on all the pins (a row of 1s and 0s) or on a particular pin through all or part of the test (a column of 1s and 0s). An example of generating and editing test patterns as 2-D matrices (the second pattern level) appears in Table 1. The same pattern, but in an easier-to-use format that contains blocks of identifiable and meaningful information (e.g., the "A" columns are addresses and the "D" columns are data) is shown in Table 2. Editing follows the same lines. A 2-D tool makes it easier to change all the data in one column or row, or to rearrange the order of pins or the steps in the test.

In very complex devices, test engineers more interested in using such higher-level information as an address or an instruction will find the 2-D approach limited in that it still works only with rows and columns of 1s and 0s. More than simply a set of 1s and 0s, a device instruction contains meaningful address, data and control information (see Table 2). However, 2-D tools work only with rows and columns, not with meaningful blocks of information. The 2-D level (like the patterns-as-text level) is a tedious way to

enter the pattern in the first place, especially for very complex devices.

The third level for generating and editing test patterns allows the creation and manipulation of the test pattern as higher-level, meaningful blocks of data, rather than as individual 1s and 0s. Although the level of meaning in a gate-level device test pattern is very low, as complexity increases, the level of meaning in the test patterns also increases. Test engineers who use the functional type of patterns for LSI and more complex devices need a pattern generating and editing tool that works with meaningful data, not just with individual 1s and 0s.

better programs, less tedium

An intelligent software tool, a device emulator that creates and manipulates test patterns as meaningful information can generate functional tests of LSI and VLSI devices. Such an emulator provides a true computer-aided (rather than automatic) tool for test engineers who need to understand how their device works. When using this third-level approach to write functional tests, test engineers first focus their attention on understanding their test system and then on understanding the device. (The next major step entails designing a test program that will work for the test system and device.)

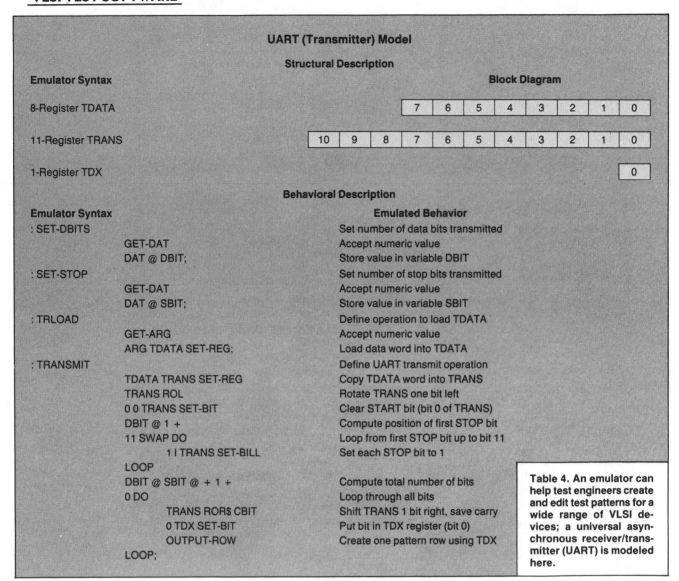

UART (Transmitter) Model

Structural Description

| Emulator Syntax | Block Diagram |

8-Register TDATA

| 7 | 6 | 5 | 4 | 3 | 2 | 1 | 0 |

11-Register TRANS

| 10 | 9 | 8 | 7 | 6 | 5 | 4 | 3 | 2 | 1 | 0 |

1-Register TDX

| 0 |

Behavioral Description

Emulator Syntax		Emulated Behavior
: SET-DBITS		Set number of data bits transmitted
	GET-DAT	Accept numeric value
	DAT @ DBIT;	Store value in variable DBIT
: SET-STOP		Set number of stop bits transmitted
	GET-DAT	Accept numeric value
	DAT @ SBIT;	Store value in variable SBIT
: TRLOAD		Define operation to load TDATA
	GET-ARG	Accept numeric value
	ARG TDATA SET-REG;	Load data word into TDATA
: TRANSMIT		Define UART transmit operation
	TDATA TRANS SET-REG	Copy TDATA word into TRANS
	TRANS ROL	Rotate TRANS one bit left
	0 0 TRANS SET-BIT	Clear START bit (bit 0 of TRANS)
	DBIT @ 1 +	Compute position of first STOP bit
	11 SWAP DO	Loop from first STOP bit up to bit 11
	1 I TRANS SET-BILL	Set each STOP bit to 1
	LOOP	
	DBIT @ SBIT @ + 1 +	Compute total number of bits
	0 DO	Loop through all bits
	TRANS ROR$ CBIT	Shift TRANS 1 bit right, save carry
	0 TDX SET-BIT	Put bit in TDX register (bit 0)
	OUTPUT-ROW	Create one pattern row using TDX
	LOOP;	

Table 4. An emulator can help test engineers create and edit test patterns for a wide range of VLSI devices; a universal asynchronous receiver/transmitter (UART) is modeled here.

The most time-consuming part of writing test programs is generating and debugging the test pattern — the core of the functional test. The time required for other tasks (such as dc parametric tests) is directly proportional to the number of pins on the device, but the number of device pins is not increasing as rapidly as internal device complexity. The time required to generate and debug test patterns is directly proportional to device complexity — and complexity is growing logarithmically. Engineering productivity and program quality (the degree of coverage of possible faults) can suffer because of the brute force effort needed to identify, type, and verify thousands of rows of 1s and 0s, with up to 80 columns (one per pin) for very complex devices.

By working with high-level elements of the pattern and allowing the software to handle the 1s and 0s, the third-level approach can reduce the tedium of conventional pattern generation and editing. Reducing tedium and working with higher-level concepts improve productivity; test engineers can handle bigger jobs more efficiently and produce higher-quality programs. Using this third-level approach, engineers can perform tests that simply were not feasible before. Because devices have been too complex to test functionally, and some test patterns are too large for

conventional approaches, test engineers have had to settle for incomplete functional testing. The emulator directly addresses the test engineer's concern with functional behavior. It approaches patterns at a high level; thus, 1s and 0s are not an issue.

pattern creation: error-free generation

To understand the features that an emulator would need (Fig 2), first consider the creation side of working with test patterns. Test engineers who take the functional viewpoint on device testing usually work with a programmer-level model of the device. At this level, a device model indicates those registers where data is stored and includes structures (similar to registers) that show what is happening on the pins. Partly a simulation language for defining register-level operations on binary data, the emulator allows the engineer to define registers by their size and other characteristics.

The device model can describe the register-level of the device and the higher-level symbols (such as instructions) that describe device behavior, and it can also allow parameters for functions. For instance, an amount that can be added to a register would be a variable parameter of the add function. An effective device model includes a structural description and a behavioral description, as in the sample models for a microprocessor (Table 3) and for a universal asynchronous receiver/transmitter (Table 4). The emulator should prove effective with any type of complex IC device.

In the structural description presented as part of Table 3, the first line of the emulator syntax defines an 8-bit register whose name is A. The second line defines register B, also an 8-bit register, and the third line defines register PC, a 16-bit register. Table 3 also describes the device behavioral model. An example of internal behavior, the first line identifies the device's ability to add register A to register B. Other lines of code describe the device's external behavior (e.g., the instruction on the device data bus that caused the add operation). This modeling approach should be general-purpose, and the emulator language should work well for a variety of device types. Each device behavioral description would include all the device instructions (if the device has an instruction set) and other behavioral actions, such as interrupt and reset.

Grey-Code Pattern Program Sequence

>MINROW = 1	(Not needed; 1 is default)
>MAXROW = 256	(Create 256 rows of pattern)
>MINCOL = 1	(Not needed; 1 is default)
>MAXCOL = 8	(Create 8 columns of input data)
>FILL WINDOW WITH GREY	(Fill window with grey-code, start with state 00000000)
>9 = NOT (1 AND 2)	(Create col. 9; nand of col. 1 and 2)
>10 = NOT (3 AND 4)	(Create col. 10; nand of col. 3 and 4)
>11 = NOT (5 AND 6)	(Create col. 11; nand of col. 5 and 6)
>12 = NOT (7 AND 8)	(Create col. 12; nand of col. 7 and 8)
>SAVE, SN7400	(Saves data as SN7400.PAT)

Table 5. With an effective emulator, a test engineer can create error-free patterns with minimal typing. This program sequence creates a 12-column, 256-row, grey-code pattern.

Pattern generation consists of three steps: analyzing device structure; exercising parts of the structure (to better understand device operation) by designing and entering instruction sequences; and verifying the operation. In the emulator's interactive mode, the test engineer can run an instruction sequence — instruction by instruction — to verify a particular internal operation. Through a window on the device model, the engineer can observe each operation and verify the cumulative result. With high-level statements, the emulator includes commands that contribute to an understanding of device operations; for instance, a status command would provide a chance to check any pin or register state.

With an understanding of how the device behaves, the engineer can create a file of the high-level test procedure. Without error and tedium, the emulator can convert the high-level test description to test-pattern 1s and 0s. The instrument provides not only pin-by-pin test-pattern information, but also input/output control and masking information that test systems need.

pattern editor: features for higher productivity

The emulator also can provide editing capabilities, useful in the following situations: when the nonpattern part of the test program changes in ways that affect the pattern (e.g., the test system may need data in a form inverted from what the device outputs); if the device changes after the engineer develops the test pattern; and if test patterns coming from other sources have to be modified for different test systems. The emulator's editing capabilities simplify these changes — saving time and reducing the frustration of translating a program from machine to machine. Four editing features would increase test-engineer productivity:

• *A window on the test pattern* might consist of a single column, one data item, or rows and columns of 1s and 0s. Within the window, the engineer can view and alter meaningful blocks of information by inverting 1s and 0s, setting to all 1s and 0s, setting to a specific pattern (a checkerboard), or performing some other operation on the windowed data. The value of window operations is twofold: a single command can change a whole section of the pattern, yet bounds are set on the changes so that the user does not inadvertently change other data.

• *Pattern data generated in such formats as binary-up-count, grey-code and checkerboard* would fill the entire window with a single command and result in substantial time savings.

• *Boolean operators and equations to calculate new pattern data from old data* are especially useful in working with less complex devices. For testing a device whose input stimulus is already defined and whose structure can be defined by boolean equations, a single command line can compute the outputs from the given inputs.

To see the power of third-level pattern-editing commands, consider the sequence shown in Table 5, which creates a test pattern for an SN7400 gate. Exercising all combinations of the eight device inputs requires 2^8 rows of pattern. With an up-counting grey-code, only one pin will change state on each pattern row. The engineer needs to create a window of eight columns, fill it with input stimulus and then use an algorithmic command to compute four more columns of expected response. The emulator allows the user to create a 12-column, 256-row, error-free pattern with little typing. The pattern-creation process would be algorithmic, automatic and straightforward.

• *Cursor-editing to insert or modify individual data elements* can specify where to start in the matrix and the direction in which changes or insertions would move.

With these four features, the third-level approach to test-pattern generation can save time, reduce boredom and improve the quality of test software for complex devices. The job of generating test patterns for VLSI is too big for manual operations, and only a small number of the engineers faced with testing VLSI will get help from ATG. A third-level approach, giving blocks of meaningful test pattern information to an informed test engineer, provides solutions to the problems of testing larger and more complex devices. ∎

Chapter IV: Test Evaluation

Simply stated, a perfect chip test must meet two criteria: reject every bad chip and pass every good one. Since the second requirement is not difficult to fulfill, in this chapter, we will focus on how well the first criterion can be met. Suppose a total of N chips passed the test and there are M bad chips among them. Then the fraction M/N, sometimes called the *reject ratio* of the tested product, is a measure of the deficiency of test according to the first criterion. Unfortunately, appealing as it may be as an indicator of test quality, accurate reject-ratio data are hard to obtain in practice. Instead, an indirect but easier-to-estimate measure is used. It is called *fault coverage* and is defined as the percentage of modeled faults detected by the test. A good (or acceptable) test may be defined as one that achieves a certain minimum percentage of fault coverage (typically, in the high 90s). Accurate evaluation of fault coverage requires the use of a fault simulator, often working with the model of the circuit at just one level (e.g., transistor) [Lo87], switch [Schu84], or logic gate [Abra86]. However, with increasing circuit densities, complete fault simulation using a low-level *non-hierarchical* circuit description is becoming very expensive and time consuming. Hierarchical [Roge85a, Roge85b] simulators are being developed in response to this need.

While fault-coverage evaluation is its main purpose, any commercial grade fault simulator will include a variety of other useful functions: detection of races and hazards, identification of hard-to-detect faults, and tester-related facilities. These are briefly described in section IV.5.

1: Methods of Fault Simulation

Given a set of faults and a set of input vectors, a fault simulator must find out which faults are detected by the input vectors. Production-quality fault simulators at the logic-gate level were available well before the advent of large scale integration (LSI) circuits. More recently, fault simulators at the transistor transistor level have been developed for more accurate modeling of faults. In all commercial simulators an effort is made to reduce computation time by simulating more than one fault in one pass for a given input vector. The simplest such technique is *parallel fault simulation* [Thom75] in which a computer word of W bits is associated with each line in the circuit. During a pass through the simulator, each bit at a particular position would be associated with the circuit which has a specific single fault (or no fault). After simulation, the bit would store the value on the line in the associated circuit. Before the beginning of a pass, a set of $(W-1)$ as-yet-unsimulated faults is chosen, where W is the word size of the computer. The remaining bit is used to simulate the fault-free circuit. Gates whose inputs/outputs are directly affected by a selected fault are flagged. When a flagged gate is simulated, the effect of the fault is injected into appropriate bits of the words representing its inputs and outputs. Each fault simulation pass starts at the primary input lines and proceeds in a breadth-first fashion towards the primary outputs. For each gate, fault simulation amounts to computing the output word as the gate's logical function of its input words. At the end of the pass, the word at each primary output can be examined to determine which of the simulated faults would be detected at that output. This is done by comparing the response of each faulty circuit against the fault-free circuit. As logical operations on computers can be carried out at the word level, $W-1$ different faults are simulated in *parallel* in each pass; hence, the name of the method. A total of F faults would be simulated in $F/(W-1)$ passes.

The ultimate, in terms of reducing the number of passes, is the *deductive fault simulator* [Arms72]. It needs just one pass for simulation independent of the number of faults simulated. The basic idea here is to associate with each line a list of just those faults sensitized to that line (that is, signals on the line for the normal and faulty circuits are different) by the simulated input vector. Simulation of a gate requires deducing the fault list at the gate output from the input fault lists. This will be illustrated for a 2-input AND gate shown in the example of Figure 4.1. The gate is assumed to be embedded in a larger circuit. The fault lists associated with the inputs a and b of the gate are as shown; these would have been computed already in previous steps of the algorithm. The signal values shown are for the fault-free circuit. Consider the effect of the fault f_1, appearing in L_a but not in L_b, on the gate output. The signal value on line a will change from 1 to 0 but that on line b will remain unchanged. Thus, the output will stay at 0, so f_1 cannot be in the fault list L_c. Indeed, no fault in L_a can occur in L_c since the output would not change under the fault. Next, consider the fault f_8, which is in L_b but not in L_a. Such a fault will change the values on lines b and c and, hence, must be included in L_c. Additionally, the fault "c stuck at 1" (or c_1) must be in the output fault list since it complements the normal value. Thus we obtain the expression for the output fault list shown in the figure.

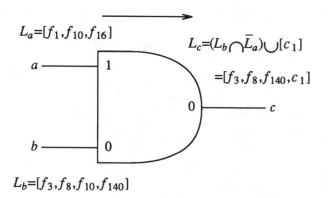

$$L_a=[f_1,f_{10},f_{16}]$$

$$L_c=(L_b\cap\bar{L}_a)\cup[c_1]$$

$$=[f_3,f_8,f_{140},c_1]$$

Figure 4.1: Fault lists in deductive simulation.

Compared with parallel fault simulation, the penalties paid for a single-pass in deductive simulation are (1) dynamically varying storage for fault lists associated with each line and (2) more complex processing of gates requiring set operations on the line fault lists.

We note that the output fault list computations are essentially dynamic: The expression for the output list is not just a function of the gate type, it also depends on the signal values on the gate inputs. Interestingly, the output fault list may change even though the gate inputs and outputs remain unchanged. This is because a line's fault list may change even when its value does not. For example, when the normal value on line a changes to 0, the value on line c is not changed, but L_c may change nevertheless. This "fault-list event" must be propagated through all the gates to which line c is an input. This undesirable characteristic of the deductive method is absent from *concurrent simulation* [Ulri74] to which we shall turn next.

The basic idea behind concurrent fault simulation is quite simple. Typically a fault changes very few signal values in a large circuit. Thus, most, if not all, of the information for simulating a fault is contained in the "good-circuit" simulation. In concurrent simulation, the good circuit is simulated in its entirety, but a faulty one is simulated only for gates whose *states* differ from their good-circuit states. For logic gates, the state is simply the combination of input and output values, however, the concurrent method is general enough to handle arbitrary elements with stored states.

As an example, consider the two-gate circuit in Figure 4.2a with the signals 1, 0, and 1 applied to the inputs a, b, and c, respectively. The figure shows the true value simulation for this vector. Also shown, attached to each gate, is a list of "faulty gates" whose states differ from their good-circuit states. These are identified by the faults marked inside. For example, when the fault "b stuck at 1" (b_1 in the figure) occurs, it changes the states of both the gates and, hence, appears on both lists. The fault "a stuck at 0" (denoted as a_0) does not cause the state of gate $G2$ to change and, hence, does not appear in $G2's$ fault list.

Next, suppose the input a was changed from 1 to 0 (Figure 4.2b). Since an input of $G1$ has changed, it must be resimulated with the new values. The resulting true values and the faulty gates are as shown in the figure. The new list for $G1$ was obtained from the original list through the following steps:

(1) The change in input a is reflected in the good as well as the faulty gates of $G1$, and the new state of each gate is determined through simulation.

(2) If there are any faulty gates with state identical

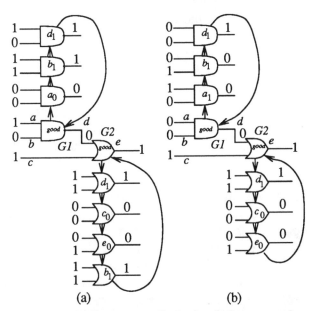

(a)	(b)

Figure 4.2: Concurrent fault simulation example.

to the good-gate state, they are deleted from the list. In the example, this causes deletion of the entry for a_0.

(3) If there are any new faulty gates whose states would be different from the good-gate state, they are added to the list. In the example, the entry for a_1 gets added because of this reason.

(4) Finally, if the output state of the good gate changed as a result of these steps, a good event is scheduled for the gates fed by the output of $G1$. Similarly, if the output state of a faulty gate changed as a result of the above steps, the corresponding faulty event is scheduled for the gates fed by the $G1$ output. In the example, no good event will be scheduled because the output in the good circuit has not changed. However, for the fault b_1 the output changes from 1 to 0, so the corresponding faulty event is scheduled at $G2$.

The faulty event at $G2$ is next processed. This involves a search for an entry for this event in the list of $G2$, changing it appropriately, and simulating the gate with the changed value. In this case, after simulation, the faulty-gate state coincides with the good-gate state; hence, the entry for b_1 is deleted from the list of $G2$. Note that the simulation did not cause a change in the output of the faulty gate so no further events need be scheduled.

The term *concurrent* is derived from the fact that

each faulty gate carries enough information for independent simulation of the associated fault. This is considerably more information than just the fault index used in deductive simulation. Thus the speed is gained in concurrent simulation at the expense of additional dynamic storage per node in the circuit. There is more to the concurrent method, however, than indicated by this simple tradeoff. The ease with which it can be adapted to any level of simulation is evident in the following sample of implementations: FMOSSIM [Schu84] at the switch level, MOTIS [Lo87] at a mixed level, and the CHIEFS hierarchical fault simulator [Roge85a]. The ability of concurrent simulation to evaluate each faulty gate independently makes it the method of choice for implementations on hardware accelerators [Blan84].

Parallel, deductive, and concurrent simulation may be used with both combinational and sequential circuits. The following methods, in contrast, apply only to combinational circuits.

Hong [Hong78] describes a clever scheme for speeding up fault simulation by partitioning the circuit in terms of its *fanout free regions* (FFRs). An FFR is defined as a maximal subcircuit which does not include an internal fanout stem. The output of an FFR is either a primary output or a fanout stem. In Hong's algorithm the simulation of faults at the outputs of FFRs is done by a traditional method in the first step. Then each FFR is processed independently and efficiently by a process linear in the size of the FFR. As a result, the detectability of each fault in the FFR is known. Hong's approach has been further refined in the critical path tracing method due to Abramovici *et al.* [Abra84] and in Fault Blaster [Brgl86], both of which sacrifice the goal of exact fault simulation.

The methods described so far perform fault simulation one vector at a time to determine the fault coverage in a given list of faults. When *grading* (evaluating the fault coverage of) a set of test vectors by any of these methods, one would start with an initial list of faults containing all the modeled faults. After simulating the first test vector against this list, the detected faults would be removed from the list before simulating the next vector. This *fault dropping* results in much faster evaluation of the cumulative fault coverage. A recently proposed fault simulation method for combinational circuits, known as *parallel vector single fault propagation*

(PPSFP), makes a departure from per-vector fault evaluation dictated by the traditional methods. It simulates 256 vectors in parallel and runs sequentially through the good and the faulty circuits to evaluate the fault coverage of these 256 vectors [Waic85].

2: A Comparison of Fault Simulation Methods

The process of fault simulation can be likened to that of shooting at a progressively diminishing target. Initially, even a randomly chosen test vector is likely to detect many undetected faults, but as their number decreases this strategy produces diminishing results. Figure 4.3 shows a typical curve of undetected faults versus number of tests. It can be partitioned into two phases where random test generation is seen to be a productive strategy for Phase I (the exponential decay part of the curve). There is a gradual transition from Phase I to an almost linear decay in Phase II.

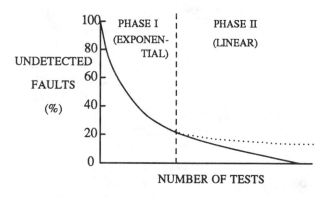

Figure 4.3: Undetected faults versus number of tests.

Empirical evidence suggests the transition point to lie somewhere between 35 and 15 percent of undetected faults. Taking such a curve as the model, it has been estimated [Goel80] that the simulation costs for a network with G gates grow proportional to G^3 and G^2 for parallel and deductive simulations, respectively. A concurrent fault simulator at the transistor level is reported to take 1527 seconds (approx. 25 minutes) of computation time for simulating a 9,478-transistor circuit on a 12-MIP computer [Lo87]. A set of 2,241 vectors were used in this simulation. According to the quadratic rise in simulation time, a 100,000-transistor circuit would require over 47 hours on the same machine! Clearly, brute-force simulation of large circuits is not a practical proposition even for the currently achievable circuit densities. One alternative is to follow the precepts of one of the testable design methods discussed in Chapter VI. Another attractive alternative is to use a statistical sampling technique as described in section 3 of this chapter.

A recent theoretical result sheds further light on the cost of fault simulation [Hare87]. By relating the fault simulation of a specific class of combinational circuits to a well-known problem in the complexity theory (the Boolean matrix multiplication problem), it essentially rules out any hope for a linear time algorithm for per-vector fault simulation. It can be easily shown from elementary considerations that the worst-case time need not grow faster than a quadratic rate in circuit size. Thus the theoretical complexity appears to be between linear and quadratic. On the said class of circuits, the paper shows that all of the standard fault simulation methods (parallel, deductive, concurrent, and critical-path-tracing) would achieve the quadratic complexity.

Another way to compare fault simulation methods is to analyze their capabilities. One such comparison was carried out by Levendel and Menon [Leve81] for the parallel, deductive, and concurrent methods. The metrics of comparison were abilities to handle multiple signal values, different levels of abstraction, and accurate timing. The concurrent method scored the highest on all three measures. The parallel method came a distant second with the deductive not too far behind it. A more recent analysis that justifies the use of hierarchical fault simulation has been reported by Rogers and Abraham [Roge86].

3: Fault Sampling

Only a fraction of faults are simulated in a sampling technique in order to estimate the fault coverage. In a method that has a direct analogy with the opinion polls, a randomly chosen sample of fixed number of faults is simulated and the fraction detected by the test set is used as an estimate for the fault coverage. The particular appeal of sampling techniques is this: The confidence range of their estimates depends essentially on the sample size and not on the population size. Also, the estimate error range narrows with higher fault coverage. For example, an estimate of 95 percent fault coverage can be accurate within 2 percent [Agra81].

Accuracy in a sampling experiment demands large sample size. A sample size of 1,000 to 2,000 faults is generally considered necessary. Simple analysis [Agra81] gives the following estimate (with 99 percent confidence) of fault coverage:

$$C = c \pm \frac{4.5\sqrt{1+Nc\,(1-c)}}{N}$$

where

c = fraction of covered faults in the sample,

and, N = number of sampled faults ($N \geq 1,000$).

As an example, consider a sample of 2,000 faults randomly picked from the fault list. After fault simulation with the given vectors if 1,900 sample faults are found detectable, then the above formula gives the range of coverage as

$$C = 0.95 \pm .022$$

Thus the fault coverage of the simulated vectors over the fault list is estimated between 92.8 and 97.2 percent.

Considering the fact that a typical very large scale integration (VLSI) circuit can have 10,000, or even 100,000, faults, simulation of just 2,000 faults will result in a significant saving of computing resources. A disadvantage is that the sampling technique does not provide a complete list of undetected faults, however, designers still find the method useful. For instance, in the above example, the sample fault simulation will give 100 undetected faults that the designer could examine to find the portions of the circuit with low detectability. On the other hand, simulation of all faults in a 100,000 fault circuit with a similar coverage would have produced a list of undetected faults with nearly 5,000 entries, a number too large to examine conveniently!

4: Statistical Fault Analysis

Another statistical technique, known as STAFAN [Jain85], completely avoids fault simulation. By using nodal activity generated during good circuit simulation, it determines controllability (the degree to which the test vectors exercise circuit nodes) and observability (the likelihood of faults propagating to the output). Taking both factors into consideration, detection probabilities of individual faults and the fault coverage can be approximated. The main overhead the analysis adds to good-circuit

simulation is the collection of nodal activity statistics. As a result, the computation time grows only linearly with the number of circuit nodes.

To understand the principle of STAFAN, consider the simple circuit of Figure 4.4. Suppose a fault-free simulation is performed, and the signal values are as shown by the bit-streams in the figure. Statistical controllabilities are determined simply by counting the 1 and 0 bits. For example, on line a there are three 1s among five bits. Therefore, the 1-controllability $C1(a)$ is 0.6. Also, the 0-controllability $C0(a)$ is 0.4. Similarly, controllabilities of all lines can be found directly from true-value (i.e., fault-free) simulation. For input lines, we also compute *sensitization* (i.e., the fraction of time the value of line is propagated to the gate output). Noticing that the value of line a propagates to the output of the AND gate when line b is 1, we get the sensitization of line a as $S(a) = 0.4$.

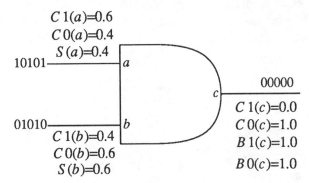

Figure 4.4: An example of statistical fault analysis.

Next, STAFAN requires computation of observabilities. One and zero observabilities of a line are the probabilities of observing a 1 or 0 value from that line at a primary output. In our example, let us assume that the output of the AND gate is a primary output. Obviously, the values of line c are then observable (i.e., $B1(c) = 1.0$ and $B0(c) = 1.0$). Analytical formulas [Jain85] allow computation of input observabilities. For example, for line a

$$B1(a) = \frac{C1(c)}{C1(a)} = 0.0$$

$$B0(a) = \frac{S(a) - C1(c)}{C0(a)} = 1.0$$

Accurate computation of observabilities will require proper consideration of signal correlations that arise due to fanouts in the circuit. The above formulas take account of correlations amongst the signals at the inputs of a gate but ignore other signal correlations. Therefore, they are approximate.

The detection of stuck-at-1 fault on line a requires controlling this line to 0 and then observing its value at primary output. Similar argument applies to the stuck-at-0 fault. The detection probabilities of both faults are found as

$$Prob\,(line\ a\ stuck-at-1) = C\,0(a){\cdot}B\,0(a) = 0.4$$

$$Prob\,(line\ a\ stuck-at-0) = C\,1(a){\cdot}B\,1(a) = 0.0$$

It can be verified that only 40 percent of the applied vectors actually detect the $s-a-1$ fault on line c and that none detected the $s-a-0$ fault. These probabilities, computed entirely from true-value simulation, provide useful information about undetected faults. Fault coverage estimate can also be obtained with an accuracy of within two or three percent (see Figure 4.5).

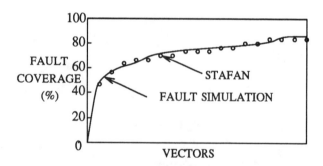

Figure 4.5: Fault coverage estimate by STAFAN.

The main advantage of STAFAN is that its space (memory) and time (CPU time) requirements are similar to true-value simulation rather than fault simulation. Both requirements for STAFAN and true-value simulation per vector are linear in circuit size.

5: Fault Simulation Tools

VLSI CAD systems normally incorporate a fault simulator. These fault simulators have three parts: (1) preprocessing, (2) fault simulation, and (3) output analysis.

A fault simulator processes the circuit connectivity description in much the same way as a true-

value simulator. Often, true-value simulation for design verification precedes fault simulation, and a compiled description of the circuit already exists. Additionally, the fault simulator makes a fault list of all stuck faults on the inputs and outputs of gates and the functional blocks. Some fault simulators provide an option to include transistor faults. The fault list is processed to collapse equivalent faults. The user can select or remove any faults from the fault list or request a random sample of given size. User inputs also include specification of the signals to be monitored (e.g., all primary outputs) and the strobe positions. Many fault simulators allow user selectable options for handling of race and oscillation faults. These faults may introduce potentially unstable states in the circuit and are often represented by the unknown value (X) in simulators. If an unknown state due to a fault propagates to a visible point, the fault can be considered as potentially detectable.

The second part of a simulator performs its main function: simulation of the circuit with selected faults by using the given vectors. It keeps the detection data (time and output of detection) for each fault and also stores the true-value response. Most simulators drop a detected fault from consideration once it is detected. Race and oscillation faults may also be dropped at user option.

Since fault simulators use a large amount of computing resources, the normal practice is to divide the vector set according to the available memory in the automatic test equipment (ATE). Each vector set (often called a *vector load*) is run through the simulator by using the list of undetected faults up to that point. At the end of a run, the simulator can store the internal states of the circuit in a checkpoint data set for use by the next vector set. However, if the ATE requires each vector set to reinitialize the circuit, the simulator checkpointing will give a coverage that is too optimistic. Also, for realistic fault detection data, the user should set the observation strobes in the same way as the ATE's strobes.

The results of the second part are fault coverage and the expected response. The latter is provided to the test program. The third part of a fault simulator analyzes the fault coverage data and displays it in an easy-to-interpret form. A popular way of presentation is the graphical form shown in Figure 4.5. The simplest way, of course, is to list the faults under the following categories: detected, undetected, race, and oscillation. These lists may be used by other programs such as automatic test generators. Displaying undetected faults on the schematic can be a great help in manual test generation. For an undetected fault, tracing the activity caused by this fault can also be useful to the designer in writing a test.

Another effective method of displaying the fault simulator result would be to display the detected faults on the chip layout. Such a display will easily isolate the portions of the chip where fault coverage needs enhancement.

6: Fault Coverage and Product Quality

Independent of whether the whole class of single line stuck faults is simulated or only a sample thereof, the obtained fault coverage is at best an imperfect measure of the test effectiveness. This must be so because a fault simulator can not evaluate the coverage of actual physical faults (shorts or opens in metal, diffusion, or polysilicon, shorts between layers, parametric irregularities, etc.). Multiple faults are also not simulated because of their very large number, even though with the small geometries used, a processing defect is quite likely to lead to multiple faults. The obtained value of fault coverage may also depend on the specific simulator used for evaluation since different simulators could employ different criteria to detect fault-induced races and oscillations. Redundant lines are not uncommon in real circuits though they may not always be identifiable because of the provable intractability of the problem. The effect of unidentified redundancies shows up in the form of unduly pessimistic fault coverage.

In spite of the above reservations, fault coverage data provided by simulators continue to be relied on as a *figure of merit* for a test. One may well ask, how is this figure of merit related to the quality of the tested chips? A quantitative answer to this question can be given based on a model of fault distribution on a chip. In one such model, it is assumed that a random number of logical faults are spawned by each physical defect on the chip. The physical defects themselves are randomly distributed over the chip and show up in clusters for a variety of processing related reasons. Thus a compound distribution is used for logical faults [Agra82, Seth84] with an appropriate clustered distribution

used for physical defects. It is possible to estimate the parameters of the compound distribution from the wafer-level test data and produce the curve shown in Figure 4.6. The vertical ordinate in the figure is *reject ratio* defined earlier. The horizontal axis represents the fault coverage for single stuck-type faults. Interestingly, it is observed that, making a transition to a finer feature size, while keeping other parameters fixed, has the effect of moving the curve to the left. This means that for denser chips actually a lower value of fault coverage would suffice for a given value of reject ratio; an encouraging result considering the disproportionately high costs involved in increasing the fault coverage in Phase II of Figure 4.3 to cover such faults.

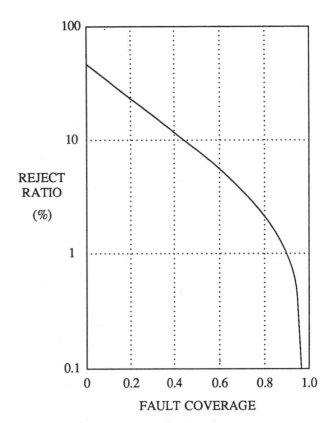

Figure 4.6: Reject ratio versus fault coverage.

In a related work by Williams and Brown [Will81] a uniformly random defect distribution model is used for logical faults. This paper employs the term *defect level* to denote what we have called the reject ratio. Although the results have been applied to both chips and boards, the uniformly random fault distribution gives pessimistic results for chips where the defects may be clustered.

7: Conclusion

While knowing the fault coverage of tests is essential, there are some difficulties in the test evaluation process. First, fault simulation used for the coverage analysis is a very complex process and requires enormous computing resources for large VLSI chips. Second, the fault coverage requirement, generally assumed to be 95 to 100 percent, may really be a function of the technology and fault models used. Further investigation is needed to solve these problems.

8: Selected Reading

In this chapter we have reprinted twelve papers. The first paper by Ulrich [Ulri69] does not deal with fault simulation but provides the basic understanding of the event-driven simulation. The next paper by Thompson and Szygenda [Thom75] describes the parallel fault simulation method. Following these are two papers [Arms72, Meno78] on the deductive method. The next three papers [Ulri74, Lo87, Schu84] deal with various aspects of concurrent fault simulation. The eighth paper by Son [Son85] describes an implementation of a recent method of fault simulation known as the parallel value list algorithm. The next paper is on the statistical method, STAFAN [Jain85]. The paper following that deals with fault sampling [Agra81]. The last two papers [Will81, Seth84] deal with product quality and fault coverage.

9: References

[Abra84] M. Abramovici, P. R. Menon, and D. T. Miller, "Critical Path Tracing: An Alternative to Fault Simulation," *IEEE Design & Test of Computers*, Vol. 1, pp. 83-93, February 1984.

[Abra86] M. Abramovici, J. J. Kulikowski, P. R. Menon, and D. T. Miller, "SMART and FAST: Test Generation for VLSI Scan-Design Circuits," *IEEE Design & Test of Computers*, Vol. 3, pp. 43-54, Aug., 1986, Also *Proc. Int. Test Conf.*, Philadelphia, PA, Nov., 1985, pp. 45-56.

[Agra81] V. D. Agrawal, "Sampling Techniques for Determining Fault Coverage in LSI Circuits," *Journal of Digital Systems*, Vol. 5, pp. 189-202, 1981, **see reprint in this chapter.**

[Agra82] V. D. Agrawal, S. C. Seth, and P. Agrawal, "Fault Coverage Requirement in Production Testing of LSI Circuits," *IEEE Journal of Solid-State Circuits*, Vol. SC-27, pp. 57-61, Feb. 1982.

[Arms72] D. B. Armstrong, "A Deductive Method for Simulating Faults in Logic Circuits," *IEEE Trans. Computers*, Vol. C-21, pp. 464-471, May 1972, **see reprint in this chapter.**

[Blan84] T. Blank, "A Survey of Hardware Accelerators Used in Computer-Aided Design," *IEEE Design & Test of Computers*, pp. 21-39, August, 1984.

[Brgl86] F. Brglez and K. Kozminski, "Fast Fault Grading of Sequential Logic," *Proc. Custom Int. Circ. Conf.*, Rochester, NY, pp. 319-324, May 1986.

[Goel80] P. Goel, "Test Generation Costs Analysis and Projections," *Proc. 17th Design Automation Conference*, Minneapolis, MN, pp. 77-84, June 1980.

[Hare87] D. Harel and B. Krishnamurthy, "Is There Hope for Linear Time Fault Simulation?," *Fault-Tolerant Computing Symp. (FTCS-17) Digest of Papers*, Pittsburgh, PA, pp. 28-33, July 1987.

[Hong78] S. J. Hong, "Fault Simulation Strategy for Combinational Logic Networks," *Fault-Tolerant Computing Symp. (FTCS-8) Digest of Papers*, pp. 96-99, June 1978.

[Jain85] S. K. Jain and V. D. Agrawal, "Statistical Fault Analysis," *IEEE Design & Test of Computers*, Vol. 2, pp. 38-44, Feb. 1985, **see reprint in this chapter.**

[Leve81] Y. H. Levendel and P. R. Menon, "Fault Simulation Methods − Extensions and Comparison," *Bell Sys. Tech. Jour.*, Vol. 60, pp. 2235-2258, November 1981.

[Lo87] C. Y. Lo, H. N. Nham, and A. K. Bose, "Algorithms for an Advanced Fault Simulation System in MOTIS," *IEEE Trans. CAD*, Vol. CAD-6, pp. 232-240, March 1987, **see reprint in this chapter.**

[Meno78] P. R. Menon and S. G. Chappell, "Deductive Fault Simulation with Functional Blocks," *IEEE Trans. Computers*, Vol. C-27, pp. 689-695, Aug. 1978, **see reprint in this chapter.**

[Roge85a] W. A. Rogers and J. A. Abraham, "CHIEFS: A Concurrent, Hierarchical and Extensible Fault Simulator," *Proc. Int. Test Conf.*, Philadelphia, PA, pp. 710-716, Nov. 1985.

[Roge85b] W. A. Rogers and J. A. Abraham, "High-Level Hierarchical Fault Simulation Techniques," *Proc. ACM Computer Science Conf.*, New Orleans, Louisiana, pp. 89-97 , March 1985.

[Roge86] W. A. Rogers and J. A. Abraham, "A Performance Model for Concurrent Hierarchical Fault Simulation," *Proc. Int. Conf. on CAD*, Santa Clara, CA, pp. 342-345, November 1986.

[Schu84] M. D. Schuster and R. E. Bryant, "Concurrent Fault Simulation of MOS Digital Circuits," *Proc. Conf. Adv. Res. in VLSI*, Cambridge, MA, pp. 129-138, January 1984, **see reprint in this chapter.**

[Seth84] S. C. Seth and V. D. Agrawal, "Characterizing the LSI Yield from Wafer Test Data," *IEEE Trans. on CAD*, Vol. CAD-3, pp. 123-126, April 1984, **see reprint in this chapter.**

[Son85] K. Son, "Fault Simulation with the Parallel Value List Algorithm," *VLSI Systems Design*, pp. 36-43, December 1985, **see reprint in this chapter.**

[Thom75] E. W. Thompson and S. A. Szygenda, "Digital Logic Simulation in a Time-Based, Table-Driven Environment, Part 2, Parallel Fault Simulation," *Computer*, Vol. 8, pp. 38-44, March 1975, **see reprint in this chapter.**

[Ulri69] E. G. Ulrich, "Exclusive Simulation of Activity in Digital Networks," *Communications of ACM*, Vol. 12, no. 2, pp. 102-110, Feb. 1969, **see reprint in this chapter.**

[Ulri74] E. G. Ulrich and T. Baker, "The Concurrent Simulation of Nearly Identical Digital Networks," *Computer*, pp. 39-44, April 1974, **see reprint in this chapter.**

[Waic85] J. A. Waicukauski, E. B. Eichelberger, D. O. Forlenza, E. Lindbloom, and T. McCarthy, "A Statistical Calculation of Fault Detection Probabilties by Fast Fault Simulation," *Proc. Int. Test Conf.*, Phidelphia, PA, pp. 779-784, Nov. 1985.

[Will81] T. W. Williams and N. C. Brown, "Defect Level as a Function of Fault Coverage," *IEEE Trans. Computers*, Vol. C-30, pp. 987-988, December 1981, **see reprint in this chapter.**

Exclusive Simulation of Activity in Digital Networks

ERNST G. ULRICH
North American Rockwell Corporation,* Anaheim, Calif.

A technique for simulating the detailed logic networks of large and active digital systems is described. Essential objectives sought are improved ease and economy in model generation, economy in execution time and space, and a facility for handling simultaneous activities. The main results obtained are a clear and useful separation of structural and behavioral model description, a reduction of manual tasks in converting Boolean logic into a structural model, the elimination of manual processes in achieving exclusive simulation of activity, an event-scheduling technique which does not deteriorate in economy as the event queue grows in length, and a simulation procedure which deals effectively with any mixture of serial and simultaneous activities. The passage of time is simulated in a precise, quantitative fashion, and systems to be simulated may be combinations of synchronous and asynchronous logic. Certain aspects of the techniques described may be used for the simulation of network structures other than digital networks.

KEY WORDS AND PHRASES: simulation, logical simulation, digital simulation, large systems simulation, network structures, scheduling, queuing, simultaneous activities, parallel events

CR CATEGORIES: 4.22, 4.29, 6.9

Introduction

In this paper work reported previously [5] is extended and simulation techniques which have been used in several computer programs for digital network simulation [7, 8] are given. The main purpose is to describe the following concepts and techniques which are compatible and have been combined to form effective simulation tools.

(1) The simulation process is based on the concept of exclusive simulation of activity. Applying this concept to digital networks constitutes a considerable advantage because, normally, only 1 percent of all elements in a typical simulated digital network are simultaneously active.

* Autonetics Division

(2) The passage of time is simulated in a precise, quantitative fashion.

(3) Element interconnections in the digital network model are represented in the form of signal-flow oriented circular lists. These lists are used as signal conductors and also serve as built-in scheduling statements to identify and schedule elements for future simulation. The return-to-source feature of the circular list permits a single-pass simulation of digital elements and thus saves considerable execution time.

(4) A "time-mapping" event-scheduling technique is used which is generally faster, although somewhat less flexible, than the "next event" list-processing technique used in SIMSCRIPT and similar simulation tools. The average scheduling time per event, achieved with time mapping, is constant instead of increasing with an increasing number of events and event types. This means that simulation economy does not deteriorate when the activity or complexity level of a simulated system is increased.

(5) The problem of simultaneous activities and events is solved here and is essentially solved during the scheduling phase. The approach used is to attach simultaneous events as side branches to the events queue instead of inserting them into the queue.

Exclusive Simulation of Activity

For the purpose of a brief introduction a digital network is sufficiently defined in terms of digital elements and their interconnections. Taking "snapshots" of a digital network under operation has led to the conclusion that the average percentage of logically active elements and interconnections is very small, and a specific value of 1 percent has been reported [1]. Analyzing a network N in terms of

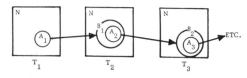

FIG. 1. Relationships between network N, source sets, and destination sets during consecutive time periods

active and idle elements for several consecutive time frames (Figure 1) will give an insight into typical network behavior and will indicate how this has suggested the general simulation approach used here and in related work.

A set of currently active elements, A_1, is, in the absence of external inputs to the network, the only source of any future network activity. Signals originating from the set A_1 are transmitted to associated destinations elements forming a destination set B_1. The set B_1, although normally larger than A_1, is again a proportionally rather small set. Many of the elements in B_1 are unaffected and do not respond with new signals, but a subset of B_1, containing only responding elements, assumes transitory importance. This subset constitutes a new set of active elements and is appropriately labeled A_2. The new set A_2, replacing the original set A_1 as a source of activity, will affect a new destination set B_2, and thus a new wave of activity is started. This process, unless externally stopped, will repeat itself in a cyclic fashion until an empty subset A_x terminates activity.

The preceding description illustrates that logical activity may be viewed as a vehicle which travels on narrowly confined but continuously shifting "paths of activity" through an otherwise idle digital network. The existence of such paths of activity suggests a simulation technique which follows these paths and avoids idle elements. Simulation techniques of this type have been developed and applied to neural networks by Reiss [3, 1960], to digital networks by Case et al. [1, 1964], and are inherent in simulation languages such as SIMSCRIPT [2].

The basic requirement for the implementation of such simulation techniques is the existence of directed connections between each source element and associated destination elements. This type of connection permits the simulation control program to identify and schedule (for individual simulation) those elements which are *potentially* affected by output signals from currently active elements. In other words, the selection process necessary for pursuing only paths of potential activity is *automatic* because idle elements receive no input signals and are consequently ignored. Another requirement for implementing the path-of-activity technique is a sufficiently precise simulation of the passage of time. A normally adequate simulation of time is achieved by considering the transition (switching) delay in digital elements and ignoring the propagation delay in conductors. (The latter may also be simulated if precise or average measures of path lengths between digital elements are provided, but this is not considered here.) The transition delay time is used to predict the points in time when stimulus signals cause response signals to be emitted from active digital elements. The predicted occurrence of response signals is recorded in the form of "future events" which are inserted into a time-ordered events queue. Thus the necessary ordering of future signal occurrences is achieved. Also, the time difference between signals or simultaneity of signals is established and can be considered, as it normally must, during subsequent simulations of individual digital elements.

Model of a Digital System

For the purpose of simulating a digital system on the detailed logic level, an adequate model to represent the system in memory can be established in three steps. First, structural models to represent digital element types, such as gates and flipflops, are specified. Second, behavior models, i.e. subroutines to simulate the normally very simple behavior of these element types, are specified. Third, a structural model of the complete digital system is specified in the form of a network consisting of nodes (elements) and interconnections.

MODEL OF AN INDIVIDUAL DIGITAL ELEMENT. Figure 2a shows a schematic diagram of a 4-input OR-element and Figure 2b is a specific version of a corresponding digital model. The model is stored in memory or table cells 01 through 06 and consists of one cell for each element input and output. Most of the information contained in the model is permanent, such as the pointers to other destinations (A_{x+1} to D_{w+1}) of the element input signals, the output signal destination E_1, input bit states 1 through 4, and

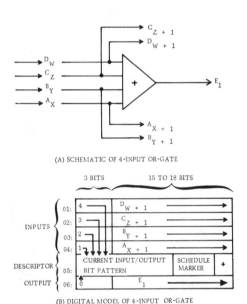

(A) SCHEMATIC OF 4-INPUT OR-GATE

(B) DIGITAL MODEL OF 4-INPUT OR-GATE

FIG. 2. Individual element model

output bit state 0. The descriptor cell of the model contains a code representing the OR operation and sufficient space for *temporary* information, such as the complete input-output bit pattern, and a schedule marker to indicate if and when an element has been scheduled. Allowing only 3 bits for the pointers to the element descriptor cell and bits located therein limits the number of element inputs to 7. However, an element may be extended by replacing the element code with a special extension marker.

BEHAVIORAL MODEL OF A DIGITAL ELEMENT. The simulation of the above OR-element may be triggered if one of the element inputs receives a signal, but only after the associated bit state in the descriptor cell has been changed. The element type code stored in this descriptor cell is then used to access the appropriate subroutine.

Specific subroutines performing behavioral simulations are not described here because they are to be defined by the user and because they consist of simple operations representing the activity of simple digital elements such as gates, flipflops, and delay circuits. The following steps are performed by all such subroutines:

1. By using the element operation, the new input signal, the states of other element inputs, the current states of element outputs, the status of the element (it may be in a scheduled or unscheduled condition), and, if necessary, "current time" together with the time of previous scheduling, an element is simulated and new output signals are calculated.

2. The new output signals and the current element output states are compared, and no further activity results if these outputs are identical.

3. In case new outputs are generated they will replace the old outputs in the element descriptor cell (Figure 2).

4. By using "current time" and the element delay time d_x, the time of element response is predicted.

If steps 3 and 4 are performed it will be necessary to schedule or cancel an event for each modified element output. The processes of events scheduling and cancellation (equivalent to scheduling or cancellation of circular lists or elements) are described later.

NETWORK MODEL OF A DIGITAL SYSTEM. Figure 3 shows the model of a small, but otherwise representative digital system.

The system is a 2-bit binary counter consisting of 2 flipflops and 2 AND-gates. Digital equations describing the system are shown in Figure 3a, a schematic representation is shown in Figure 3b, and Figure 3c is a model of the system. Each of the data blocks in Figure 3c is equivalent to one of the elements in Figure 3b. The resulting network consists of 6 circular lists, and the effective connections for 2 of these lists (signal A and $\bar{B}$) are shown in Figure 3c. The list representing signal A is again shown in Figure 3d in order to illustrate its simple circular structure. The reason for using circular lists rather than open-ended lists becomes apparent during the discussion of the scheduling process below.

Scheduling and Simulation

The concept of the *events queue* can be defined in terms of a set of (instantaneous) events which is ordered with respect to time. In a systems simulation the events queue is used to simulate the passage of time by advancing *current time* from event to event. As time is advanced, each event is processed, i.e. its effects are simulated, as soon as it becomes the *current event*.

The prevailing data structure for implementing an events queue is the list. Lists are especially useful for this purpose because (1) the advance of time can be accomplished by jumping directly from event to event rather than slowly scanning for events within a table or other structure, and (2) because a list can easily be opened at

any point to insert a newly scheduled event. However, it should be noted that the scheduling of each new event must be preceded by a scan which scans the list in either a forward or backward direction in order to find the appropriate point of insertion. In either case, the average time used for each scan is a function of the length of the events queue, and long queues will increase this unproductive use of time.

(A) BOOLEAN EQUATIONS DESCRIBING A DIGITAL SYSTEM

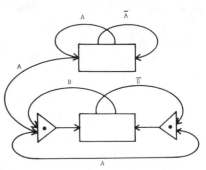

(B) SCHEMATIC REPRESENTATION OF THE DIGITAL SYSTEM

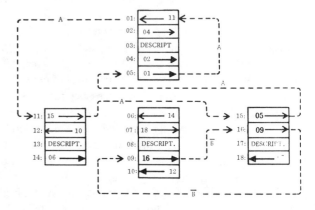

(C) MODEL OF THE DIGITAL SYSTEM

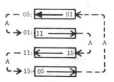

(D) CIRCULAR LIST FOR SIGNAL A

FIG. 3. Illustration of the modeling of a digital system

The events queue implementation used here is based on a requirement for the economical processing of long queues and consequently is different from the list implementation.

THE Δt-LOOP. The Δt-loop (Figure 4) is a circular table and represents time. The program, in simulating the passage of time, advances current time (t) in discrete, regular increments of size Δt. The Δt-loop contains one memory cell for each time t_x and time is advanced by moving from one cell to the next, where $t_{i+1} = t_i + \Delta t$. The size of Δt (in terms of nsec, μsec, etc.) and the length (L) of the Δt-loop must be defined by the program user. The Δt-loop scan normally advances from cell to cell without skipping, and the table location of the cell which is addressed by the scanning process is the precise numerical value of current time. Cells,

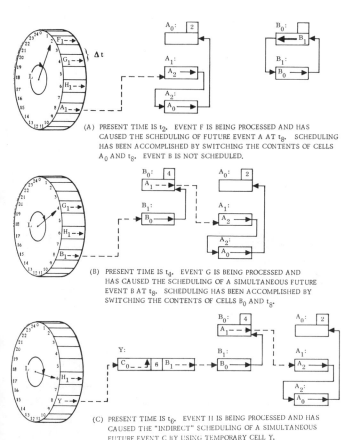

(A) PRESENT TIME IS t_2. EVENT F IS BEING PROCESSED AND HAS CAUSED THE SCHEDULING OF FUTURE EVENT A AT t_8. SCHEDULING HAS BEEN ACCOMPLISHED BY SWITCHING THE CONTENTS OF CELLS A_0 AND t_8. EVENT B IS NOT SCHEDULED.

(B) PRESENT TIME IS t_4. EVENT G IS BEING PROCESSED AND HAS CAUSED THE SCHEDULING OF A SIMULTANEOUS FUTURE EVENT B AT t_8. SCHEDULING HAS BEEN ACCOMPLISHED BY SWITCHING THE CONTENTS OF CELLS B_0 AND t_8.

(C) PRESENT TIME IS t_6. EVENT H IS BEING PROCESSED AND HAS CAUSED THE "INDIRECT" SCHEDULING OF A SIMULTANEOUS FUTURE EVENT C BY USING TEMPORARY CELL Y.

Fig. 4. Δt-loop and scheduling procedures for (a) single event, (b) simultaneous event, and (c) indirect scheduling

or time slots, in the Δt-loop are either empty or contain events. An event appearing on the Δt-loop represents the critical moment in simulated time when a signal occurs, i.e. when a specific signal is emitted from its source and is received at associated destinations. In terms of the simulation model an individual event must be associated with a specific circular list, and the event appearing on the Δt-loop takes the form of a pointer to this specific list.

The primary purpose of the Δt-loop—besides serving as a device to advance time and trigger the processing of current events—is the use of its structure in determining the time slots into which newly scheduled events must be in-

serted. The scheduling process used here is a time-to-address mapping technique which relies on the fact that the delays of digital elements are expressed as integer multiples of Δt. The detailed scheduling process is the following.

The processing of a current event, taking place while the Δt-loop scan is halted at current time or cell address t, leads to the previously described prediction of an element output signal which occurs at $t + d_x$, where d_x is the delay of the simulated element. Since d_x is a multiple of Δt, it is directly added to t (using a modulo L addition), and the result is not merely the time of the predicted signal occurrence but also the address of the time slot into which a corresponding event must be inserted.

The length of the Δt-loop is denoted by L and specifies the number of time increments (Δt's) and, simultaneously, the number of memory cells making up this table. The determination of values for Δt and L is left to the program user, and a correct choice of values depends on the delays of elements to be simulated. Basic ground rules for determining Δt, L, and delay constants for individual elements are:

1. All element delays must be of the form $D_x = d_x \Delta t$, where d_x is a positive integer and serves as a delay constant for element type x.
2. The Greatest Common Divisor (GCD) of the element delays is the optimum (largest) value for Δt.
3. The maximum element delay constant d_{max} should normally not exceed L ($d_{max} \leq L$).
4. Economy requires L to be kept as small as possible.

As an example, a small digital network may contain three types of elements with delays of 2.7, 3.9, and 9.0 nsec respectively. The GCD of these three values is 0.3 nsec, and this determines Δt. From the equation $D_x = d_x \Delta t$ the three values for d_1, d_2, and d_3 are then computed:

$$d_1 = \frac{D_1}{t} = \frac{2.7}{0.3} = 9, \quad d_2 = 13, \quad d_3 = 30.$$

Finally, $L = 30$ because $d_{max} = d_3 = 30$.

It should be noted here that another set of delays (e.g. 2.8, 3.9, and 9.0 nsec) leads to a different GCD (i.e. 0.1). Consequently, a less economical configuration ($L = 90$) would be the result. However, the equation $T = 2e + L + 1.5(e - e_d)$ (to be derived later) establishes the relationship between table length L and the total time T for scheduling and accessing e events, and shows that a threefold increase in L is not accompanied by a threefold increase in T. For an average of 25 events, the increase in T is 75 percent, and for 50 events it is only 46 percent.

SCHEDULING OF NONSIMULTANEOUS AND SIMULTANEOUS EVENTS. The part of the scheduling task establishing an exact time slot for inserting an event into the Δt-loop has already been described. The actual insertion of events into a particular slot is identical for nonsimultaneous (first) and simultaneous (second, third, etc.) events and is illustrated in Figures 4a and 4b. The insertion is simply accomplished by exchanging the contents of the first cell of the involved circular list with the contents of the established time slot.

Exchanging the contents of these cells is equivalent to "cutting" the circular list attached to the to-be-scheduled source element, and temporarily transforms this circular list into an open-ended list which becomes part of a larger, arbitrarily extendible event list (Figure 4b).

Another regular scheduling process is the setting of the schedule marker. In Figure 4, the schedule markers in circular lists A and B have been set to the values of 2 and 4, because these lists have been scheduled at t_2 and t_4.

INDIRECT SCHEDULING. Figure 4c illustrates how scheduling is carried out if two signals arrive simultaneously or almost simultaneously at the same element, and if the processing of the first signal has caused the element to be scheduled already.

Normal scheduling in response to the second signal is not possible in this case because the schedule-marker of the involved element is already occupied, and because the circular list is already used as part of an extended events list.

The example in Figure 4c shows how indirect element scheduling or cancellation is effected by obtaining a temporary storage cell y from a "supply" list serving as dynamic memory. The time of scheduling (6), a pointer to the circular list (C_0), and, if necessary, a pointer to a simultaneous event (B_1) are stored in y. Also, a pointer to cell y must be placed in cell t_8 of the Δt-loop.

TWO-PASS SIMULATION PROCEDURE. The result of the above described scheduling operations are individual events or strings of events consisting of circular lists and temporary cells (depicted in Figure 4c). The processing of these events, i.e. the simulation of the effects of signals which they represent, must occur as soon as these events become current and may be accomplished in two passes.

During the first pass all signal destinations (B_1 through A_2 in Figure 4b) are accessed, and new input signals are delivered by inverting the existing states of the critical input bits (Figure 2).

During the second pass all destination elements are simulated individually, and an element may be simulated repeatedly if it receives more than one input signal. However, only the first simulation of each element can produce a new output signal because subsequent simulations, based on an unchanged input signal pattern and an already established output, cannot generate a different output.

From the point of view of economy the two-pass simulation process is not optimal. The reason is that two complete passes must be made to account for the rare case of two or more input signals arriving simultaneously at a single element. A more economical one-pass technique which handles simultaneous signals on an exception basis is described next.

ONE-PASS SIMULATION PROCEDURE. The one-pass simulation procedure takes advantage of the fact that the percentage of individual elements receiving complementing simultaneous or almost simultaneous input signals is normally very low.

Figure 5 is a flowchart illustrating the essential steps of the one-pass procedure, and it distinguishes between normal processing and exception processing (dotted lines). The key to this procedure is the schedule marker contained in each element descriptor. This marker is "set" when the element is scheduled and "reset" after the element has emitted a response signal. The parameter stored in this

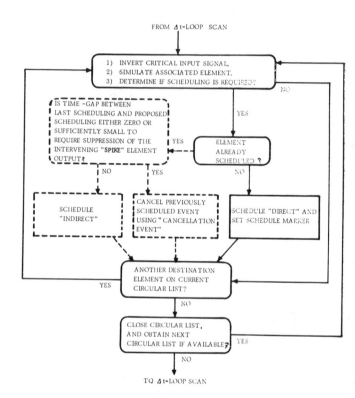

FIG. 5. Flowchart for one-pass simulation

marker is the element-scheduling time, and the contents of the marker will be checked if a second scheduling is attempted. If the current time and the marker contents are identical or very close, then it is apparent that simultaneously or closely arriving signals may cancel each other. Therefore, depending on the element characteristics, an already scheduled future event may require cancellation.

The removal of a future event is effected indirectly by placing a "cancellation event" at the beginning of the appropriate string of circular lists, rather than making an immediate "search and remove" pass through a possibly long string.

When this string is eventually processed the cancellation event will be found *before* the associated scheduled event is found and the processing pass will then be modified to check each subsequent event (circular list) before elements are simulated.

Extensions of the Time-Mapping Technique

Disadvantages associated with the time-mapping technique are (1) the fixed length of the Δt-loop and (2) its fixed time resolution.

For example, the fixed length of the Δt-loop leads to a reduction in Δt-loop scanning economy if the total number of scheduled events decreases and remains below a critical number for an extended period of time. Specifically, if remaining at about ten or less events (see Figure 6) the next-event technique should be substituted for the time-mapping technique. Automatic switching from one technique to the other can be based upon maintaining queue length as an exact, up-to-date parameter. This parameter would be checked periodically and would cause switching if a critical threshold is crossed and not recrossed within a specified period of time.

To maintain queue length as an up-to-date parameter is easily effected and will normally not increase the simula-

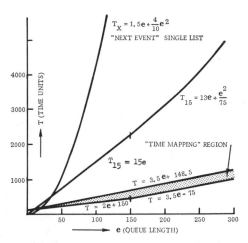

FIG. 6. Comparison between "next event" and "time-mapping" economy

tion run-time. (For example, the "TIX" instruction of the IBM 7094 could be used.) Also, in switching to a next-event technique the simpler "single list" technique would be used. This technique is more efficient for small values of e than the multiple list (SIMSCRIPT) technique (see Figure 6), and the extra time and cost in switching to and from the simpler technique is also smaller. (It should be noted that any next-event technique to be used must be equipped to handle simultaneous events.)

Another situation in which the time-mapping technique is inadequate occurs if the fixed time resolution of the Δt-loop is too coarse, i.e. when it becomes necessary to

insert events between two fixed time slots. In this case the next-event technique can provide additional resolving power by attaching next-event lists to time slots of the Δt-loop. These lists would be processed essentially like regular next-event lists. However, the "time" stored in these events could be referenced either to the beginning of the Δt-loop (cell t_0) or to the cell, t_x, to which the next-event list is attached.

Another problem related to the fixed length of the Δt-loop is the handling of elements which have a very

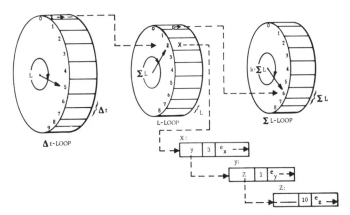

FIG. 7. Extension of the Δt-loop using additional timing loops. Events e_x, e_y, and e_z are inserted into cells t_3, t_1, and t_{10} of the Δt-loop upon completion of the currect Δt-loop scan.

long delay time. Events associated with these elements must be scheduled by extending the Δt-loop in some fashion.

A normally satisfactory solution to this problem is to extend the Δt-loop by connecting a next-event "extension" list to cell t_0. Any event not fitting into the Δt-loop would be scheduled by inserting it at its proper place into this next-event list. This list would be investigated before each scan of the Δt-loop, and all events belonging into the subsequent scan would be removed from the extension list and scheduled in the normal time-mapping manner.

Figure 7 illustrates another solution to the same problem which may be more economical for certain cases. This second solution is based on additional timing loops

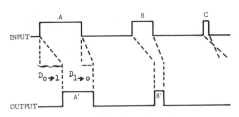

FIG. 8. Pulse narrowing (pulses A and B) and pulse suppression (pulse C) due to different delays of the same element

(here defined as L-loop and ΣL-loop) which are connected to the Δt-loop. The time step of the L-loop is L and is is equivalent to one complete scan of the Δt-loop. The advance of time is accomplished by advancing the pointer to the L-loop once before each scan of the Δt-loop. Any events found in a newly accessed cell of the L-loop (e_x, e_y, and e_z in cell 2) would then be moved to the appropriate slots of the Δt-loop. The addition of 3 timing loops of 10 cells each would increase the effective scheduling range of the Δt-loop by a factor of 1000.

Applications

ELEMENTS WITH TWO DIFFERENT DELAYS. In the preceding sections digital elements were described as having only a single fixed length delay. In reality there exist many element types with different delays for each of the two possible signal types. Figure 8 illustrates the narrowing of "true" pulses passing through an element which has two delays ($D_{0 \to 1} > D_{1 \to 0}$). The figure also shows a situation in which a very short "true" pulse is completely suppressed. The simulator described here can be used to simulate elements of this type by specifying the different delays, and by specifying the critical pulse width ($W_c = D_{0 \to 1} - D_{1 \to 0}$) for which pulse suppression must occur. The necessary condition for pulse suppression, double scheduling, is automatically detected (see Figure 5) during

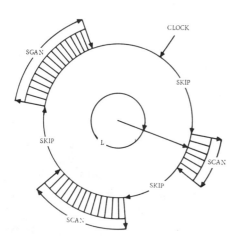

FIG. 9. Skip-and-scan processing of the Δt-loop for simulating clocked networks

the event-scheduling process, and will trigger a simple test. In this case the test will establish if the pulse occurring between these two scheduled events is "true," and if it is actually as short or shorter than the critical pulse width W_c.

RANDOM VARIATIONS OF ELEMENT DELAY. The option to vary the delay of logical elements on a random basis is also within the scope of the described technique. Requirements for the realization of this process are the

incorporation of a random number generator and the specification of a large value of L (equivalent to a rather small value of Δt). The latter requirement is necessary to make a sufficient number of time slots available into which events can be inserted. This type of random simulation is particularly suitable for asynchronous networks.

EVALUTION OF DIAGNOSTIC PROGRAMS. One of the major applications of a digital logic simulator is the testing of diagnostic programs. The testing task is normally accomplished by simulating the malfunctioning of individual logic elements and then "executing" a diagnostic program in order to establish whether or not it will detect these malfunctions. A specific technique to economize this normally quite expensive task by exploiting features of the simulation tool described here has been published and is briefly summarized here.

The diagnostic evaluation process is based on the sequential execution of individual diagnostic subroutines (tests) on the simulator. The simulator, by setting special activity markers, generates a "trace" of activity corresponding to a diagnostic subroutine. By using a backtrace technique (which is based on circular lists), the initially complex trace is then reduced in size and complexity. The digital elements remaining in the reduced trace constitute a set of "primary" potential error sources relevant to the tested subroutine. The malfunctioning of these elements and of associated "secondary" and "tertiary" error sources is simulated during the repeated reexecution of the same diagnostic subroutine. This process leads to the classification of malfunctions into detected, undetected, and catastrophic malfunctions. The effectiveness of individual diagnostic subroutines is thus established.

SIMULATION OF CLOCKED SYSTEMS. A reduction in processing time for the simulation of clocked (synchronous) networks is normally possible and is illustrated in Figure 9. The basic requirement for implementing a fast method is to equate the length of the Δt-loop with the clock period of the simulated network. The "clock" would then remain at a *fixed* position within the Δt-loop, and savings in processing time are realized by replacing the normal Δt-loop scanning process by a skip-and-scan process which takes advantage of the typical periodicity of active and idle time segments between successive clocks. Specifically, time segments during which no events can occur are skipped and time segments of potential activity are scanned in a normal manner.

Another reduction in processing time for synchronous systems is possible and is based on the fact that, normally, a clocked element must receive at least one normal input signal and a clock signal in order to generate a new output signal. This situation can be exploited as follows:

(1) The normal scheduling of clocked elements as a group is suppressed by suppressing the clock signal.

(2) Upon arrival of regular (nonclock) signals at clocked elements these elements are not simulated im-

mediately but are rescheduled to be simulated at the next clock time.

(3) At the clock time the clock inputs of all scheduled clocked elements are triggered individually and these elements are simulated.

Summary and Comparison with Special Purpose and General Purpose Simulation Tools

Almost all of the special purpose logic simulation programs known to this author belong into the category of "logic-only" simulators [4, 9, 10]. The following advantages or disadvantages with respect to the use of these special purpose tools have been established:

(1) The precise simulation of the passage of time achieved here leads to the following specific advantages:

(a) The delay of individual digital elements is simulated.

(b) The delay of individual elements or groups of elements can be varied from one simulation run to another or may be varied statistically during a run.

(c) Differences in rise-and-fall time of digital elements can be simulated by specifying different delays for zero-to-one and one-to-zero transitions.

(d) Manual preprocessing and/or extra programming to detect and handle feedback loops is unnecessary.

(e) Unrealistic "zero-delay-element" simulations are avoided, and the possibility of program-induced feedback loops is therefore eliminated.

(2) Exclusive simulation of activity based on a 1 percent activity figure and the most recent available overhead figure of approximately 12 times the normal overhead, results in run-time savings of 88 percent. Also, Selective Path Simulation leads to advantages for output and display because it is easily used for providing selective outputs.

(3) Boolean equations serve as direct data input and are automatically converted into the simulation model. However, the technique used here differs from the often used "compile" technique [4, 9, 10] which converts time-ordered Boolean equations into a sequentially executable simulation program.

(4) The manual ordering of equations, a widely-used but poor substitute for automatic-event scheduling, is eliminated.

(5) Synchronous systems, asynchronous systems, and combinations thereof are simulated with equal ease.

(6) The list storage method used here is based on partial words and requires approximately 3 memory words to store a single-level 4-input equation (Figure 2) or 6.5 memory words to store a two-level 5-input equation. This compares favorably with the compile technique requiring 5 and 7 words, respectively.

(7) The exclusive simulation of activity and the circular list storage method facilitate tracing and backtracing, i.e. techniques which are particularly useful for the simulation of diagnostic programs.

(8) A disadvantage of the simulation technique used here is the necessity for a detailed initialization of the simulation model. All elements of the model, including nonmemory elements, must be in compatible states before the simulation can be started. Special purpose simulators are superior in this respect because only a small subset of elements must be initialized.

With respect to the use of general purpose simulation tools such as SIMSCRIPT the following differences have been established:

(1) The concept of Exclusive Simulation of Activity is inherent to SIMSCRIPT and similar simulation tools but requires manual programming. The implementation used here is essentially automatic and eliminates most of the manual programming task.

(2) The model of a system is generated here while maintaining a clear distinction between behavioral and structural parts of the model. First, behavior is explicitly specified on a microlevel by coding a small self-contained simulation subroutine for each type of digital element. Second, the structural model of a system is generated automatically from input equations. This results—in contrast to the typical simulation *program* which combines behavioral and structural systems modeling—in a nonprogram of compact bit-structure.

(3) The simulation of any number of simultaneous events is possible and is an integral part of the scheduling technique used here. Also, the overhead involved in scheduling and simulating simultaneous events is minimal.

(4) For this technique, regardless of the number of signal destination points, the emission and arrival of a signal at destinations is treated as a single *scheduled* event. This reduces the number of events which must be scheduled individually by a considerable factor.

(5) The event-queuing technique described here uses fixed data storage rather than dynamic storage. This reduces the total storage requirement because the cells used for event queuing, i.e. the first and last cell of each circular list, are not added to the fixed storage to facilitate scheduling but are indispensable for the general data structure. Thus the only space exclusively reserved and used for scheduling is the fixed length Δt-loop (normally 150 words) and a small amount of dynamic storage for indirect scheduling. This technique is especially useful for simulating systems with extremely high or unpredictable activity peaks, i.e. systems which otherwise exhaust the available supply of dynamic storage.

(6) A run-time advantage of time-mapping over next-event scheduling and accessing exists for most cases and is illustrated in Figure 6. The independent variable in Figure 6 is the queue length, e. The graphs show the total time, T, which is required for scheduling e events and accessing e events and thus maintains the queue length at this value. Approximate comparative values for T were derived by at first defining the following time units

for critical activities within each technique:

Time-mapping scheduling per event	= 2. units
Time-mapping accessing per scanned Δt-loop cell	= 1. units
Time-mapping accessing per simultaneous event	= 1.5 units
Next event scheduling per scanned event	= 2. units
Next event accessing per event (includes return of temporary cell to a "supply" list, and associated bookkeeping)	= 1.5 units

For time-mapping, the total time for maintaining e-events therefore consists of three parts. These are the scheduling time, $t_1 = 2e$, to schedule e events, a fixed time, $t_2 = L$, for completing a cycle of the Δt-loop while simultaneously accessing e_d events directly attached to the Δt-loop, and finally, the accessing time, $t_3 = 1.5 \,(e - e_d)$, to access simultaneous events indirectly attached to the Δt-loop. The general equation for T is therefore:

$$T = 2e + L + 1.5(e - e_d) = 3.5e + L - 1.5e_d \quad (1)$$

Assuming a typical value for the Δt-loop length ($L = 150$) the values for T may fluctuate between an upper bound (for $e_d = 1$) and a lower bound (for $e = e_d$ and $e > L$ respectively). The equations and graphs of these upper and lower bounds are shown in Figure 6, and the shaded area between these curves is the range over which T may vary.

For next event-processing, and specifically for an efficient multilist (SIMSCRIPT) version thereof, the total time, T, for maintaining e events can be derived by at first computing the time, t, for single event processing.

$$t = \text{sched}_1 + \text{acc}_1 + \text{sched}_2 + \text{acc}_2$$

$$= p_1 \cdot \frac{e}{k} \cdot 2 + 1.5 + p_2 \cdot p_k \cdot k \cdot 2 + 1.5$$

The constants appearing in this equation are defined as follows:

k = number of event types (equal to number of individual event queues)

p_1 = percentage of individual queue to be searched before event can be scheduled

p_2 = percentage of master queue to be searched before event can be scheduled

p_k = percentage of event types on master queue

Substituting typical values for these constants leads to:

$$t = \frac{1}{10} \cdot \frac{e}{15} \cdot 2 + 1.5 + \frac{1}{2} \cdot \frac{2}{3} \cdot 15 \cdot 2 + 1.5$$

$$t = \begin{cases} 13 + \dfrac{e}{75}, & e > 150, \\[2mm] 13 + 2, & e \le 150. \end{cases}$$

Substituting the above values for t into the equation $T = te$ in order to arrive at the total time, T, for maintain

ing an event queue of e events, results in the following equations:

$$T_{15} = 13e + \frac{e^2}{75}, \qquad e > 150, \quad (2)$$

$$T_{15} = 15e, \qquad e \le 150. \quad (3)$$

The graphs of these equations are shown in Figure 6 and are based on a multilist structure of 15 individual queues ($k = 15$) and a master queue. For comparison, the equation for a single list event queue (T_x) is also shown in Figure 6.

It should be noted that the equations for time-mapping derived here are valid for any combination of serial or simultaneous events. For next-event processing, the equations derived here are only valid for nonsimultaneous events, and the total processing time will therefore increase somewhat if simultaneous events must be detected and handled.

(7) A disadvantage associated with the time-mapping technique is a lack of flexibility due to the fixed length and fixed time resolution of the Δt-loop. However, this disadvantage is not serious for the simulation of logic networks, and recourse to the above described extension techniques may only be necessary if more general systems are to be simulated.

Acknowledgments. The author thanks Richard F. Reiss of the University of Oxford and the referees for their efforts in reviewing this work.

RECEIVED MARCH, 1968; REVISED AUGUST 1968

REFERENCES

1. CASE, P. W., GRAFF, H. M., GRIFFITH, L. E., LECLERCQ, A. R., MURLEY, W. B., AND SPENCE, T. M. Solid logic design automation. *IBM J.* (Apr. 1964), 127–140.
2. MARKOWITZ, H. M., HAUSNER, B., AND KARR, H. W. Simscript—a simulation programming language. Rand Corp., Santa Monica, Calif., 1963.
3. REISS, R. F. The digital simulation of neuromuscular organisms. *Behavioral Sci. 5*, 4 (Oct. 1960), 343–358.
4. SMITH, W. E. A digital system simulator. Proc. Western Joint Comput. Conf. Vol. 11, Feb. 1957, Spartan Books, New York, pp. 31–36.
5. ULRICH, E. G. Time-sequenced logical simulation based on circuit delay and selective tracing of active network paths. Proc. ACM 20th Nat. Conf., 1965, pp. 437–448.
6. ULRICH, E. G. The evaluation of digital diagnostic programs through digital simulation. Proc. IEE Comput. Tech. Conf., England 1967, pp. 9–19.
7. WILLIAMS, L. R. SLAM II, digital network simulation program developed at TRW Systems. [Operational since 1967]
8. HARMER, D. L., AND LACY, D. L. SIMSTRAN, digital network simulation program under development at Data Systems Division, Autonetics, North American Rockwell Corp., 1968.
9. KATZ, J. M. Optimizing bit-time computer simulation. *Comm. ACM 6*, 11 (Nov. 1963), 679–685.
10. BREUER, M. A. Techniques for the simulation of computer logic. *Comm. ACM 7*, 7 (July 1964), 443–446.

Digital Logic Simulation In a Time-Based, Table-Driven Environment
Part 2. Parallel Fault Simulation

E.W. Thompson and S.A. Szygenda
The University of Texas

Reprinted from *Computer*, Volume 8, Number 3, March 1975, pages 38-49.
Copyright © 1975 by The Institute of Electrical and Electronics Engineers,
Inc. All rights reserved.

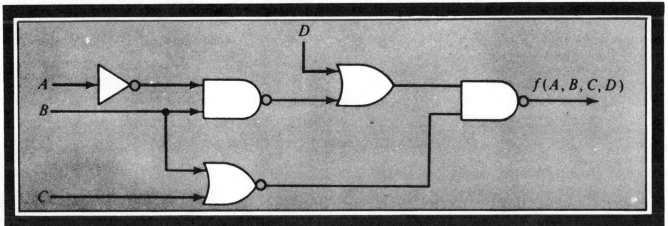

Introduction

Digital simulation is the process of modeling, by computer programs, the behavior of a digital network. Digital fault simulation is the modeling of a digital network in the presence of a physical defect. The term "fault" is used to refer to some representation of a physical defect. A simple example of this is the case where an input connection to an AND gate is broken. This would be referred to as a stuck-at-1 fault. Hence the phrase fault simulation.

In Part 1 we discussed digital logic simulation without any considerations for the presence of faults. Such simulation is frequently referred to as true value or non-fault simulation, and is primarily performed for the purpose of logic verification or design verification, depending upon the level of accuracy utilized. Although a fault simulation system can be used for logic verification and to some extent for design verification, its primary purpose is that of evaluation and verification of fault diagnostic tests. A fault diagnostic test is a sequence of input stimuli which, when applied to a digital network, will cause that network to respond with one value if a fault is present and with another distinguishably different value if a fault is not present. In conjunction with its primary purpose, a fault simulation system can be used to determine the diagnosability of a network design and to produce fault dictionaries: it is normally used as an integral part of any system utilized for the automatic generation of fault diagnostic tests.

Most fault simulation systems to date can be classified as either a parallel fault simulator or a deductive fault simulator. Parallel fault simulation is the simulation in parallel of a number of copies of the object network. These copies are normally referred to as machines. One machine represents the fault-free network and is known as the good machine, and each of the other machines represents the object network with at least one fault present. The number of machines that are simulated in parallel is normally constrained in some way by the number of bits in the host computer word. Deductive fault simulation on the other hand attempts to simulate all faults at once. This paper will be concerned only with parallel fault simulation; another paper in this issue will concern itself with deductive fault simulation.

A third classification for fault simulators might be the type wherein a single fault is simulated. In this case the object network is perturbed in some manner so that it represents the network with the presence of a single fault and then that single machine is simulated. Once the description of the object network has been perturbed, the rest of the simulation can proceed identically to non-fault simulation. In our opinion this type of fault simulation is very inefficient and completely impractical in terms of simulating a large number of faults; therefore, this type of fault simulation will not be considered. The only time it would have any merit is when a user has available a non-fault simulator and wishes to model only a very few critical faults. In this case he may wish to pay the price of inefficiency.

The rest of this paper will analyze different data structures and algorithms which can be used for parallel fault simulation. These data structures and algorithms will be weighed against different criteria which can be used to evaluate any fault simulation system. These criteria will consist of the following:

a. The accuracy with which the behavior of a faulty network can be modeled or predicted.
b. The types of faults which can be modeled and also the ease with which new fault types can be incorporated into the system.
c. The size of the object network which can be processed and the number of faults which can be efficiently simulated.
d. The ease of use of the system and the amount of flexibility and control provided to the user.

In the course of this paper a number of specific examples of data structures or algorithms will be given. These specific examples will be drawn from the digital simulation system known as CC-TEGAS3.[1,2,3,4] CC-TEGAS3 is a simulation system which embodies both non-fault simulation, for logic verification and design verification, and parallel fault simulation.

Data Structures and Algorithms

Assuming that one already has available a non-fault simulation system, or is at least familiar with the needs and requirements of a non-fault simulation system in terms of data structures and algorithms (as described in Part 1), what then are the additional needs of a fault simulation system in terms of data structures and algorithms? There are normally five major types of activity which must take place for fault simulation, which are above and beyond the normal activity which takes place for non-fault simulation. Each one of these areas of additional activity also requires appropriate data structures to support that activity. The five types of additional activity which must take place for fault simulation are described below.

1. *Fault specification.* This is the activity which determines which faults and fault types will be modeled during simulation. Normally the total set of faults to be considered is determined before any simulation takes place and is the first fault-related activity to occur. Later, certain techniques or heuristics can be used to reduce this fault set but the resulting fault set is a subset of the one that is initially specified.

2. *Fault propagation.* A fault simulation system obviously must have the ability to propagate the effects of a fault. In parallel fault simulation the effects of a number of faults must all be propagated in parallel.

3. *Fault insertion.* Fault insertion in a fault simulation system is very analogous to the process of physical fault insertion for a fabricated machine. It can also be termed a fault transformation, where the fault free network is transformed into a network which contains a physical defect or fault. This process can occur once for a given fault, before fault simulation begins, or it can occur numerous times during a fault simulation pass, for each fault that is being modeled.

4. *Fault detection.* A fault simulation system must have the ability to determine when a fault has become observable at some given point or primary output of the object network. Whether this activity takes place concur-

rently with the actual simulation or at the end of a fault simulation pass depends on other attributes of the simulator, which will be discussed later.

5. *Post processing.* The fault simulation of a given digital network can result in a large amount of data which the user must interpret and efficiently utilize. In an attempt to aid the user in this process one of the last activities which a fault simulation system performs is to organize the resulting data in a way which makes it most amenable to the user. This activity can actually take place as a stand-alone process and only the information which should be made available will be discussed in this paper.

Table 1 indicates the basic steps in fault simulation. Step 3 is where fault specification takes place. Fault insertion, propagation, and detection all occur in step 6. The order of events and how they occur can vary greatly in this step depending on the basic philosophies of the simulation. For parallel fault simulation, however, the basic concepts behind fault insertion, propagation, and detection are independent of other differences between simulators. Post processing obviously takes place in step 7.

Table 1. Basic Steps in Fault Simulation

1. Network description encoded.
2. Network description processed and internal tables created.
3. Fault set to be considered is generated and placed on a master fault file.
4. Signal values initialized to an unknown state.
5. Input stimuli specified.
6. Fault controlling options specified.
7. Simulation commences:
   a. Read specified number of faults from the master fault file and set up tables for fault simulation.
   b. Perform simulation with the above number of faults in parallel against specified stimuli.
   c. Fault detection data will either be recorded during step (b) or at the end of this fault simulation pass.
   d. If there are more faults to be simulated, reset all tables with controlling information back to their initial state and go to step (a) to begin another fault pass.
8. Post processing.

Each of the above areas of activity will now be discussed in more detail. The objective here is for the reader to become more familiar with what the needs are of each of these areas of activity and in general what are some of the techniques that can be used. Later, the appropriate areas of activity will be considered again with specific examples and in relationship to different types of simulators which achieve various levels of accuracy.

Fault Specification Obviously any digital simulation system must have some data structure for representing the object network which is being modeled. Over the years, the divergence between the data structures used in different simulation systems has drastically decreased, and at this time the data structure described in Part 1 of this tandem set of papers is very representative. For each logical element or gate in the object network there is normally a corresponding entry in a network description table of some sort. From such an entry various pieces of information can be acquired about a given logical element. Such information usually includes the logical type of an element, its propagational delay, the number of elements to which the output signal of this element fans out, which elements they are, and the name of the element. If the simulation system is capable of modeling multiple output elements, then it must also be able to determine how many output pins exist for each entry in the network description table.

As indicated earlier, the normal procedure for fault simulation is to initially specify, or in some manner generate, the total set of faults which are to be considered. The information regarding these faults is then placed on some external storage media. During actual simulation, the records describing some number of faults to be simulated in parallel can be read from the external storage media, temporary fault tables can be created, and a fault simulation pass can take place. At the end of a fault simulation pass the records describing some additional number of faults can be read in and the same process continued until all desired faults are simulated. Obviously, the information for each fault, which is stored on the external storage media (the master fault file), must be sufficient to relate it to the affected signal or input pin of an element which is described in the network description table. There must also be sufficient information to describe the type of fault which is to be modeled or inserted.

Consider the information necessary to describe a simple stuck-at fault on a signal. If there is one entry in some master network description table for every signal in the object network, then the fault record can simply contain an index number corresponding to the given signal that is to be faulted. In addition, a fault type number must be contained to indicate whether the stuck-at fault is going to be a stuck-at-1, a stuck-at-0, or a stuck-at-X (unknown) fault. This would be the absolute minimum amount of information necessary to describe a fault in relation to the internal tables which are used to describe the network.

If this were the only information which existed on the master fault file for the given fault, then at least two restrictions would exist for the use of the system. The first restriction would be that any time the network description itself was modified the master fault file would have to be created anew. This is true in that the position in the network description table may change for a given signal, due to network modifications. In this case the signal identification number on the master fault file would no longer be valid. This restriction, however, is not particularly severe for fault simulation. One reason for this is that few network modifications should be taking place at the time of fault simulation. The majority of such modifications should occur during logic or design verification and not during fault simulation. A second reason is that fault specification or fault generation normally requires only a small amount of processing time, and therefore it is not particularly expensive to recreate the master fault file if necessary.

A second and more severe restriction is that no reasonable reporting can be made from the master fault file, independent of the information in the network description table. This is true because the master fault file contains no descriptive information or alphanumeric information regarding the location of the fault, such as the signal name. It is therefore recommended that the master fault file contain all descriptive information necessary, so that an independent report can be generated utilizing only that information contained on the master fault file.

A third restriction would be that no multiple-occurring faults could be represented. This is the case wherein a user might wish to model the situation in which a number of signal faults could exist simultaneously in a network. In this case each fault description record on the master fault file must contain some type of group identification number. Hence, it can be identified as a fault which belongs to some fault group and does not exist at a single entity.

Consider an example of a stuck-at fault existing on an input pin connection of an element. The element on which the fault is to occur must be identified, and the input pin position or signal connection to that element must be identified. Again, an index into the network description table could be used as an identifier for the element on which the fault is to occur. In addition, an input pin position number might be used to identify the pin connection that is to be faulted. In other words, if the third input pin on an element were to be faulted, then a pin position of 3 could be used. However, for the same reasons as given above, additional descriptive information should be carried, so that the name of the element would be provided and also the name of the input signal connection to the faulted pin. These same fields of information could be used to represent a short between two signals. In this case, the input pin position number would actually represent the second signal of a shorted signal pair—the only difference being that the fault type number now would represent a short between signals instead of a stuck-at-1, 0, or X. Complex faults such as those causing a functional transformation on an element could also be represented by these fields of information. In this case, the input pin position number would not be utilized, nor would the name of the input signal be used. However, the element index number would represent the signal upon which a functional transformation was to take place and the fault type number would indicate the type of functional transformation.

Table 2 indicates the different fields of information contained in each fault record on the master fault file for the CC-TEGAS3 system. The length and sequence number are used together to describe multiple-occurring faults. The fault number itself is used strictly for identification purposes and some types of brief reporting. However, the identification of a fault is not dependent upon that fault number, because sufficient other descriptive information is available. It could be potentially dangerous to have the identification of a fault dependent strictly on the fault number, which was assigned at the time the original fault file was created. This is true in that if any network modification should occur and a second master fault file were created, all continuity between fault identification numbers could be lost. Therefore any previous fault reporting would not be related to succeeding reports.

One last point about the creation of a master fault file is that it is not absolutely necessary to create such a file. It would obviously be possible to incorporate fault identification for every element into the basic data structure describing the object network. In fact, that is approxi-

mately what occurs for deductive fault simulation. However, such a data structure requires more memory at simulation time and does not utilize some of the advantages of parallel fault simulation. This point will become clearer as the requirements for fault insertion are discussed in the next section.

Table 2. Fields of Information in a Master Fault File Record

Fields	Contents
1	Fault number
2	The number of faults in a multiple fault group (zero for multiple faults)
3	Sequence number, within a group, for multiple faults.
4	Internal table index of element being faulted.
5	Fault type (1=S−A−1, 2=S−A−0, 3=S−A−X). GT.100=complex)
6	Signal position (−1=signal fault, 0=complex fault, pos=pin number for an input pin fault)
7	Name of element
8	Name of signal

Fault Propagation Two critical decisions which must be made in determining the basic philosophy of any digital simulation system are the level at which network timing properties are to be modeled and the number of different states which can be used to represent the value of a signal. The consequence of such decisions and the appropriate techniques which might be used in each case for non-fault simulation were thoroughly discussed in Part 1. Once these decisions have been made, the next critical questions which must be resolved in order to produce a fault simulation system are how faults are to be inserted and how their effects will be propagated. The major decision here is whether the general technique of the deductive fault simulation will be used or whether the technique of parallel fault simulation will be utilized. As indicated earlier, this paper will concern itself only with parallel fault simulation and therefore all further discussion will be based on that technique.

The critical part of determining the algorithm for propagating a number of faults in parallel is the selection of the data structure which will be used to represent signal values. For a given signal the value for a number of different machines must be represented. We will consider several different data structures which have been used in fault simulation systems for signal values and how these data structures effect the algorithm necessary for propagating faults in parallel.

One data structure which has been used for representing three-valued signals when dealing with parallel machines is given in Figure 1a. In this case, adjacent bit pairs are used to represent the value of a signal for one machine. Normally either the right-most or the left-most bit pair is always reserved for the good machine, and other bit pairs in a word will be used to represent fault machines, which are being simulated in parallel. A bit pair of 11 is used to represent a

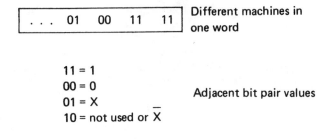

Different machines in one word

11 = 1
00 = 0
01 = X
10 = not used or $\overline{X}$

Adjacent bit pair values

(a) Adjacent bit pair structure

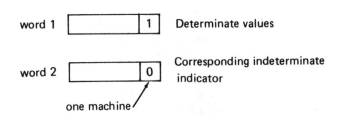

word 1   1   Determinate values

word 2   0   Corresponding indeterminate indicator

one machine

If the indeterminate flag is zero then the value is determinate, otherwise it is indeterminate.

(c) Second data structure for signals

Figure 1. Signal Value Data Structure and Propagation

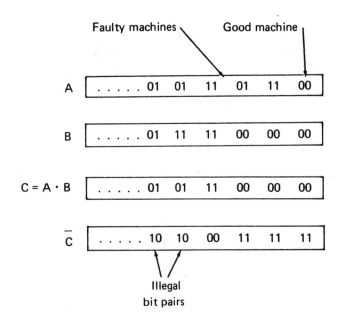

(b) Adjacent bit pair propagation

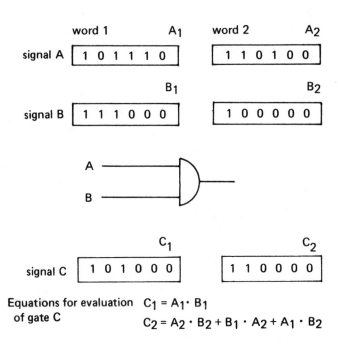

Equations for evaluation of gate C

$$C_1 = A_1 \cdot B_1$$
$$C_2 = A_2 \cdot B_2 + B_1 \cdot A_2 + A_1 \cdot B_2$$

(d) Propagation of second data structure

value of 1, 00 represents a value of 0, 01 represents an X or unknown condition, and 10 is not used or can represent $\overline{X}$.

With the data structure depicted in Figure 1a, the number of machines which can be simulated in parallel, when utilizing a single word for the storage of a signal value, is equal to the number of bits in the host machine word divided by 2. Therefore if the host computer has 32 bits in a word, then 16 machines can be simulated in parallel. Of the 16 machines one would always be used for the good machine. This data structure has the property of being fairly easy to propagate.

Figure 1b shows the results of doing a full-word Boolean AND operation between two words which contain the values for two different signals. As can be seen from the figure, all possible combinations of two values for a single machine are ANDed together and the correct results are produced. An unknown ANDed with a 0 produces a 0, whereas an unknown ANDed with a 1 produces another unknown. It should be noted that if the bit pair 10 were also allowed, then the AND of the two representations for X would result in a determinate 0, which is correct.

Difficulty arises when a signal must be complemented and $\overline{X}$ is not used. Assume that the NAND operation is to be performed, and then, after A and B are ANDed the result must be complemented, as shown in Figure 1b. In this case a known value of 0 or 1 complements into the correct opposite known value; however, the unknown value complements into the bit pair which is not allowed. Therefore, every operation in which a signal is complemented must be followed by a procedure which converts illegal bit pairs, 10, into the bit pair representing an unknown which is 01. This procedure requires approximately six instructions, and it is one of the main disadvantages of this particular data structure. The significant point with this example is that a two-input AND gate can be

evaluated for a number of machines in parallel through the use of a single Boolean operation, and that this operation exists as a single instruction in the instruction repertoire of most computers. The same is true for the logical OR operation. It is only the complement operation which, due to this particular data structure, requires additional instructions. It is this fact which provides the cornerstone upon which the technique of parallel fault simulation is built. It is also for this reason that a number of machine values for a given signal are packed into a single word. Although this data structure obviously reduces computer memory requirements for the system, its main advantage is that it allows a single Boolean instruction to process a number of machines in parallel.

Recently a number of systems have utilized a new data structure for representing data values. This data structure is a slight variation of the adjacent pair structure given in Figure 1a. In the new structure, the right-most bit of each pair is contained in the right half of the word representing a signal value. The left-hand bit in each bit pair is contained in the left half of the word. In this case, the right-most bit of the right half of the word and the right-most bit of the left half of the word, taken together, constitute a bit pair and represent the signal value for one machine. This slight variation in the data structure simplifies signal propagation or element evaluation, in the case where a signal must be complemented. For this data structure, all that is required to switch bits in a bit pair is a single circular shift instruction.

Another data structure for three valued simulation is demonstrated in Figure 1c. In this case two words are used to represent each signal, the first word containing the determinate value of the signal for each machine and the second word containing a single bit for each machine, which indicates whether that machine is in an unknown state or not. If the indeterminate flag bit in word two for a given machine is zero, the corresponding signal for that machine is in a known state; if the indeterminate flag is a one, it is in an indeterminate state, independent of the bit value in word one for that machine. With this data structure, bit pairs are again used to represent the value of a signal for one machine; however, the bits are contained in different words. The right-most bit in word one taken with the right-most bit in word two constitutes the bit pair normally used to represent the good machine value.

The equations necessary to evaluate a simple AND gate are given in Figure 1d. These equations are more complicated than those needed for the adjacent bit pair structure, but the problems involved in complementing a signal value are avoided. If signal C is to be complemented, than all that is necessary is to complement the word containing the determinate bit values for C (label C in Figure 1d).

The data structures discussed so far can be used to represent signal values for three-valued simulation. For six-valued simulation more bits would be needed to represent the signal for a machine and to evaluate Boolean equations. Six-value simulation can be accomplished using four words to represent signal values. Two words represent the future value of a signal and the other two words represent the current value of the signal. The future and current values are represented similarly to the two word combination in Figure 1c and therefore can be either 0, 1, or X. If either the future or current values of a signal are indeterminate, then the signal is indeterminate. If the future and current values are the same, the signal is in a stable state. If they are unequal, the signal is in a state of transition. The important compatibility between this data structure and the word pair structure in Figure 1c is that each bit in the words containing a signal value represents different machines; therefore, the same number of machines can be simulated in parallel with either data structure.

With any of the data structures, the number of machines simulated in parallel does not necessarily have to be constrained by the number of bits in the host computer word. Instead, a number of words or word pairs could be propagated in parallel. In this case the logic in an element routine will need to be executed once for each word being propagated in parallel. The exception to this is the case in which the host computer has either multiple word logical instructions or a high level language is used which has string manipulation capability.

A number of other data structures could be developed for signal values. These structures, however, are all judged by the same requirements. The first requirement is that the structure be such that logical instructions, such as AND and OR, operate on all bits of a word. This requirement dictates that in any given computer word, which contains at least part of a signal value, more than one machine must be represented. The second requirement is that the data structure facilitate the evaluation of logical elements, such as the primitive Boolean functions. The third requirement is simply that the data structure be as compact as possible.

Although it was not explicitly stated in the above example, the evaluation procedure for an AND gate was always in the form of a Boolean equation. Given the values for the N inputs of an N input AND gate, its output value could certainly be determined by a procedure other than Boolean equations. One procedure would be to examine each input signal until either one was found with a value of 0 or all inputs were examined. In the first case the output value would be a 0, and in the second it would be a 1 or an X depending on whether any of the inputs had a value of X. This evaluation procedure is frequently used for non-fault simulation or deductive fault simulation; however, for parallel fault simulation it is impractical. If different fault machines are packed into a computer word, then no decision about a signal value can be made on that word. This is true because some machines may have a value of zero but others may not, so no uniform decision can be made. If one insisted on using the above procedure for element evaluation, values for different machines could be placed in separate words. For I machines in parallel, I passes could be made on the N inputs, extracting the value of one machine for each input signal during each pass. One approach is extravagant in terms of storage requirements, the other is expensive in terms of processing time.

It is for the above reasons that most procedures used for evaluating logical elements and propagating parallel machines through those elements are implemented using a series of Boolean equations. No tests and branches are used. Exceptions to this can occur when large, complex logical elements such as a decoder are being modeled as a single entity. In this case, the overhead of extracting each machine individually from the input signals may be justified due to the significantly increased simplicity of evaluating the element. If one is developing a system for both fault and non-fault simulation, it may be advisable to develop element evaluation routines or procedures which would be compatible to both. This means not making any tests or branches in the non-fault routines.

Fault Insertion The Boolean equations for a number of machines in parallel are independent of how faults are inserted or what types of faults are modeled. The reason one fault machine has a different value for a given signal has no bearing on the methods used to propagate faults. Therefore, the preceding discussion was equally relevant for classical stuck-at faults, shorted signal faults, functional transformations or complex faults, and multiple-occurring faults. The procedures for inserting different types of faults, however, does vary.

At the time the actual fault simulation is about to take place, the faults to be simulated have been placed on a master fault file, the internal table describing the object network has been created, all signal values have been initialized to an unknown state with perhaps selected signal values being set by the user, and the input stimuli is available. At this point, the records describing some number of faults are read from the master fault file. Utilizing this information, internal tables needed for fault insertion are created. This is step 7a in Table 1. The significant point is that it is necessary to store information on only a small number of faults at one time. It is for this reason that storage requirements are not a constraining factor, in terms of the number of faults that a parallel fault simulator can process. However, processing time is a constraining factor and the number of gates or logical elements in the object network is constrained by storage requirements. The questions at this point are (1) what information is needed to insert faults, (2) when are they inserted, and (3) where are they inserted. These questions will be initially answered for simple stuck-at faults. The discussion of other types of faults will use the stuck-at faults as a basis.

In order to answer the question of when a fault is to be inserted, first consider the general algorithm or basic actions which take place during simulation. Table 3 depicts these basic actions and is really an expansion of step 7b in Table 1. The actual activities that take place in any given simulator will depend to a large degree on whether it is a zero delay compiled simulator, or is table driven, utilizing unit delay, nominal delay, or minimum and maximum delays. It will also depend on the type of timing analysis which is performed. However, they generally follow the steps given in Table 3. Using the actions in Table 3 as a basis, one can then determine where the additional activities of fault insertion and propagation must take place in order to accomplish fault simulation.

Table 3. General Algorithm for Digital Simulation

0. Locate next time period at which some signals are scheduled to change.
1. Take each signal which is scheduled to change at this time period and update it value.
2. IF there are any more signals which changed value at this time period but have not been processed THEN access one and call it I. ELSE stop.
3. IF all elements on the fanout of I have been processed, then go to step 2.
4. Access one of the elements on the fanout of I which has not been processed and call it J.
5. Evaluate J.
6. If J's new value is different from its old value, schedule the output signal of J to change to its new value at some time in the future.
7. Go to step 3 and continue to process elements on the fanout of signal I.

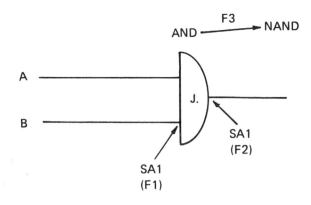

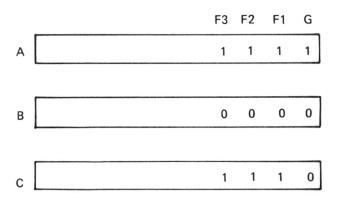

	F3	F2	F1	G
A	1	1	1	1
B	0	0	0	0
C	1	1	1	0

Figure 2. Fault Insertion Example

At step 5 in the procedure, it has been determined that at least one of the input signals to some element J has changed during the current time period, and therefore element J must be reevaluated. The process of evaluating J consists merely of accessing the value for each one of J's input signals, performing some logical function on those values (as discussed in the section on fault propagation), and producing a new value for the output of element J. If, however, a fault is to be modeled on one of the input pin connections to J, the effect of that fault must be considered at this time in order to determine the appropriate output for J when that fault is present. In other words, an input pin fault must be inserted on J before J can be evaluated. At this point it must be known which input pin of J is to be faulted (if any), what value it is to be faulted to (or stuck-at), and which fault machine is to be used to represent this fault.

Consider the example in Figure 2. Four machines are being simulated in parallel, the good machine and three faulty machines. Machine labeled F1 represents the stuck-at-1 fault on the input pin connection of signal B to element J, machine F2 represents the stuck-at-1 fault on the output pin of element J, and machine F3 is used for a functional transformation fault, which transforms element J into a NAND gate. As can be seen from the example, the value of machine F1 on signal B is currently a 0. Therefore, if the AND gate J is evaluated, then F1 would have a value of 0 and that would be incorrect for F1. The problem would be solved if, for signal B, machine F1 were forced to a 1, temporarily, while element J is being evaluated.

There are several methods by which this procedure can be carried out. The method used by CC-TEGAS3 will be

Element No.	Input pins	MASK1	MASK2

Input pin faults

(a) INFLT Table

Element No. or Signal No.	MASK1	MASK2

Output pin faults

(b) OUTFLT Table

Element No.	MASK1	Fault Type

Functional Transformation Faults

(c) FUNFLT Table

Figure 3. Tables Describing Faults to be Inserted During a Fault Simulation Pass

given first. As shown in step 7a of Table 1, fault tables which contain the information necessary to insert the faults to be simulated are set up at the beginning of a fault pass. This would be true for practically any parallel fault simulator; the difference is the structure of the tables, their exact contents, and how they are utilized. CC-TEGAS3 has three different fault tables which are set up, one for input pins stuck-at faults, one for signal stuck-at faults, and one for complex faults. These tables are given in Figure 3.

In addition to these tables, appropriate fault indicator flags are set in the circuit description table (CDT) which was described in Part 1. For any input signal connection that is to be faulted, the fan-in pointer for that signal is set negative. There are also two one-bit flags in the CDT table for every element and signal which are set if an element is to have a complex fault inserted, or if a signal is to have a stuck-at fault inserted, respectively.

For input pin faults the actual insertion is performed by a special routine through which all input signal values are accessed for element evaluations. The basic logic flow for this special routine is as follows:

1. IF the pointer to the signal to be accessed is negative THEN GO TO step 3.
2. Access the signal value and pass it to the evaluating routine. GO TO step 6.
3. Using the CDT table index of the element being evaluated and the position, on this element, of the input signal being accessed, as a key, do a linear search on the input pin fault table.
4. Using the absolute value of the signal pointer, access the signal value; call it V.

5. Using MASK1 and MASK2 from the input pin table, insert the stuck-at fault and pass the resulting signal value to the element evaluation routine.
6. Return to the element evaluation routine.

The actual Boolean equations used to insert the fault or faults on the signal value when using three valued simulation are

$$V1 = V1 \cdot \overline{MASK1} + \overline{MASK2}$$

$$V2 = V2 \cdot \overline{MASK1} + MASK2 \cdot \overline{MASK1}$$

These same equations are also used to insert the output pin faults. They are slightly expanded from what they would need to be to input just stuck-at-1 and 0 faults, but they can also insert stuck-at-X faults.

The variables in the equations will now be explained. V1 and V2 are the two-word data structure used to represent the signal value, as described previously. V1 contains the determinate bits and V2 the indeterminate bits. Masks 1 and 2 taken together determine whether a stuck-at-1, 0, or X fault is to be inserted and which bit position, or machine, will be used to represent that fault. The encoding of bit pairs, taken from corresponding bit positions of MASK1 and MASK2, is

MASK1	MASK2	
0	0	no fault
0	1	stuck-at-X
1	0	stuck-at-0
1	1	stuck-at-1

With this encoding, any number of faults up to the number being simulated could be inserted simultaneously on a signal. If the stuck-at-1, 0, and X faults are all to be inserted on some input pin or output signal, then depending on the bit position that would represent these faults, the mask values would be

$$\text{MASK1} \quad \ldots \ldots 0\ 0\ 0\ 1\ 1\ 0\ 0\ \ldots \ldots$$
$$\text{MASK2} \quad \ldots \ldots 0\ 0\ 1\ 0\ 1\ 0\ 0\ \ldots \ldots$$
$$\text{stuck-at X 0 1}$$

The masks that would be used to insert the input pin fault for the example in Figure 2 would be

$$\text{MASK1} \quad 0\ 0\ 1\ 0$$
$$\text{MASK2} \quad 0\ 0\ 1\ 0$$

After the element is evaluated, its complex fault flag is interrogated. If that flag is on, the CDT number of the element would be used as a key for a linear search in the complex or functional fault table (Figure 3c). When a match is found, the fault type number of the accessed entry is used to determine the routine that will reevaluate the element as a faulty function. MASK1 from the table entry will be used to determine the bit position in the output signal, which will be forced to take on the value from the faulty function. MASK1 will contain a 1 in that position and a 0 in all other positions. MASK1 for this example will be 1 0 0 0.

The next step is to determine if the output signal of the element is to be faulted. If so, the element number is again used as a key and a search is made on the output fault table. When a match is found, MASK1 and MASK2 are used to insert the fault or faults on the output, in the same way as was done for input pin faults. In this case, however, they are permanently inserted in the actual signal value, so that any other elements that use that signal as input will be affected.

From the above discussion it can be seen that, independent of the type of fault being inserted or modeled, a word mask was used to determine which bit position, or machine, would be used to represent a given fault. These masks, along with MASK2 type masks, are constructed along with their entry in the particular fault table, when the faults are read from the master fault file, at the beginning of a fault simulation pass. Machine one is the good machine; the rest of the machines or bit position assignments are made sequentially as the faults are read in. If a set of faults are to be modeled as if they all existed simultaneously in the object network, they are then represented by the same machine. During a single fault simulation pass the multiple-occurring faults would all be inserted, each as if it were a normal, independent single-occurring fault. The only difference is that MASK1, used to insert each of the faults, would force each to be inserted in the same bit position, and hence one machine with a number of faults is modeled. This demonstrates the real power of the proper selection of a data structure for inserting faults.

At this point we would guess that a number of readers are thinking that the procedure just discussed for inserting faults must be very expensive in terms of processing time, because of the need to do a linear search on a table each time a fault or faults is inserted on an input pin, a signal, or an element. Some alternatives will be briefly discussed, but first consider the following. On a Control Data 6600 with 60 bits per word, the maximum number of single-occurring faults that will be simulated in parallel is 59. If the majority of the elements in the object network are single-output primitive gates, then there is an average of 18 signals and 23 input pins being faulted during a fault pass, with one fault on each input pin and two on each signal. These 23 input pin faults are distributed among the same 18 elements which will contain the signal faults. The reason only one fault is usually inserted on an input pin is attributable to fault equivalences. For a large network, the number of times that one of the approximately 18 elements must be evaluated (and hence the faults inserted) is relatively small. The only exception occurs when one of the faulted elements is in a feedback loop which is forced to oscillate, due to one of the faults being inserted. Experience has shown that the number of element evaluations per second

---

The point of all this is that it is a big mistake to develop a procedure and data structure for fault insertion which slightly increases the element evaluations per second—but sacrifices flexibility, memory requirements, and ability to model different types of faults.

---

performed by a fault simulation pass is normally only one or two percent below that obtained for an equivalent level of non-fault simulation. What causes simulation time to increase, when dealing with faults, is that some of the faults being simulated in parallel can potentially increase the number of required element evaluations by an order of magnitude. This is true because a signal must be considered to have changed value, and hence cause other element evaluations (Table 3, step 6), if at least one of the machines being simulated in parallel changed value. The point of all this is that it is a big mistake to develop a procedure and data structure for fault insertion which slightly increases the element evaluations per second—but sacrifices flexibility, memory requirements, and ability to model different types of faults.

One simple modification that could be made to the fault insertion procedure, would be to associate a pointer with every fault flag. The pointer would be an address or index into the appropriate fault table. This would require allocating space for one pointer for every input pin, every element, and every signal in the network. Some simulation time would be gained at the significant increase of memory requirements.

Another method used by some systems is to have one fault flag per element. If, at the time the element is to be evaluated, the flag is set, control is turned over to a special routine which is responsible for having the element evaluated and all faults associated with the element inserted. This routine must have available the same type of information for fault insertion as discussed before. In this case, however, a single pointer is associated with an element, and it points to a collection of data which must have the capability of describing any combination of faults that would be inserted on an element.

The Effect of Basic Simulation Philosophy on Fault Processing

Most digital simulation systems are table driven and classified as being either zero delay, unit delay, assignable nominal delay, or precise delay. These classifications and their particular attributes were discussed in Part 1. The significant differences between these simulation philosophies is the level of accuracy with which they can model the behavior of a digital network. As indicated earlier, the development of fault simulation can be thought of as using some non-fault simulation system as a basis and adding fault modeling capabilities. The simulation system models selected determine the upper bound on the level of accuracy with which fault induced behavior can be modeled. The differences between these levels of accuracy have been described previously for the non-fault case. Similar differences exist for fault simulation. Each basic simulation philosophy does, however, present some unique problems and also opportunities for fault simulation. The attributes of fault simulation which are dependent upon the basic simulation philosophy used will now be discussed. Keep in mind that the data structures and algorithms discussed previously apply in general to any of the simulators in the table-driven category. It will, therefore, be mostly overall control type activity and some timing analysis problems which will be considered.

Zero Delay For a zero delay simulator the logic of the network to be simulated must be leveled and feedback loops identified and broken. No time queue is needed, since every element is evaluated in order, depending on their logic level. All level 1 elements in the first level are evaluated first, then all the level 2 elements in the second level, etc. After all the elements have been evaluated, the values of signals which were treated as break points in the feedback loops are interrogated to determine if they have changed. If any have changed value—and again this means for any machine being simulated in parallel—then all logic levels ahead of a feedback break point which changed must be evaluated again.

A fault can be declared observable and detected, on one of these signals, if its machine value, on one of those signals, is different from the good machine value. If either the good or faulty machine value is an unknown, the fault is only potentially detectable.

Initially all signal values are set to an unknown state (two-valued simulation is not even being considered), the required fault tables and flags for a fault pass are set up, and the first input vector for the primary inputs is applied. Simulation then commences and continues in the above prescribed manner until no further element evaluations are necessary. At that time, the values of each of the primary outputs or designated test points of the object network can be interrogated to determine if a fault is detected. A fault can be declared observable and detected, on one of these signals, if its machine value, on one of those signals, is different from the good machine value. If either the good or faulty machine value is an unknown, the fault is only potentially detectable.

The action that occurs next depends on which one of two possible techniques is to be used. One technique consists of applying all input vectors or test patterns against one group of faults before processing the next group. The other technique consists of applying one input vector to all groups of faults before applying the next input vector.

If the first technique is to be used, the fault flags for those faults which were detected with the first input vector would be turned off and the second vector applied. This procedure would continue until either all the faults which were being simulated in parallel were detected or all the input vectors were applied. At that point, the network would again be set to an unknown state, and the fault tables set up for the next group of faults. This is exactly the procedure that is normally followed for unit delay simulation.

For zero delay simulation, the second technique (one vector all faults) can prove to be very effective. As in the case of the first technique, after the first vector has been simulated it is determined which faults were detected. Those faults which were detected are recorded and discarded. The process of recording a detected fault is the same in either technique; the fault identification information, the number of the input vector which detected the fault, and the value of the output vector for the good machine and the faulty machine at the time of detection are placed on an external file. A reduced form would be to record the identification of the output signals on which the fault was observable, instead of the entire vector. This is usually sufficient. After this information is recorded, the state of the network for each non-detected faulty machine is saved. For anything other than zero delay simulation this would amount to saving a bit slice out of every signal value for each non-detected fault. For a large network this would require a large amount of processing time. For zero delay, however, only the values of feedback loop break points need to be saved. If the number of cuts taken to break all feedback loops is optimized, the amount of processing time required would be small. At this point the fault tables would be set up again with the next group of faults and the

---

. . .after a number of vectors have been applied to the same group of faults, only a few of the faults might be as yet undetected, and the efficiency of the simulation therefore begins to decrease. It was actually the observation of this fact which prompted the development of deductive fault simulation.

---

first vector applied again. This procedure would continue until all faults had been processed against the first input vector. Then those faults as yet undetected would be processed against the second vector. For second and succeeding vectors, the state of the feedback loop break points would have to be set for each fault that was to be simulated.

For zero delay simulation, the second technique can be much faster than the first. The reason is that after a number of vectors have been applied to the same groups of faults, only a few of the faults might be as yet undetected, and the efficiency of the simulation therefore begins to decrease. It was actually the observation of this fact which prompted the development of deductive fault simulation. With the second technique, each input vector will begin with a full set of active faults.

With regard to accuracy, zero delay simulation is very poor. The Eichelberger[5] technique, which has been described in the literature, is many times used in conjunction with zero delay simulation, so that at least if the system is incapable of predicting the correct value for a signal, it will produce an X or unknown value for this signal. The problem is that many X's are produced and as a consequence a large number of faults are not detected which could otherwise have been detected.

Unit Delay The basic technique of processing one group of faults against all input vectors before considering another group of faults was described in the section for zero delay. As stated, this is the technique used for unit delay also. Unit delay simulation is an advance over zero delay and it makes possible some different methods for dealing with timing problems. Remember that although unit delay simulation does not require a full-fledged time queue, it does operate with a queue for the next time step. That is, all elements on the fan-out of signals which changed during the current time step are placed in the next time step queue for evaluation at that time. The selective trace technique as discussed in Part 1 is obviously employed. Simulation progress can than be indicated by the number of time steps that have taken place.

Due to the weakness of the unit delay model, the oscillations encountered in simulation may not really exist in the object network, but the problem still exists with respect to processing them in the simulator.

With unit delay simulation, as with zero delay, the network is expected to stabilize between applications of input patterns. If a network does not stabilize, this means an oscillation has occurred due to some timing problem. Due to the weakness of the unit delay model, the oscillations encountered in simulation may not really exist in the object network, but the problem still exists with respect to processing them in the simulator. One procedure which has been used is to set some maximum number of time steps which should occur before the network stabilizes. This number can be based on the network topology or previous experience with non-fault simulation of the object network. Once the predetermined number of time steps have taken place, simulation is stopped. At that point one of two actions can be taken. The first is simply to apply the next input vector. The second is to examine the signal values in the next time step queue against their present values. For any machine which changed value on any of the signals examined, their next time step value would be changed to X. Simulation would then be allowed to continue for some number of additional time steps. By following this procedure, those fault machines causing oscillation would be forced to an unknown state. This is another example of a procedure that could not be followed in two-valued simulation.

Assignable Nominal and Minimum and Maximum Delays The timing properties of a network are far more closely modeled with an assignable nominal delay simulator—and

---

With nearly any fault simulation system, the user can determine how many times a fault must be detected before it can be dropped. When it is determined that a fault can be dropped, it is easy to simply turn off the fault flag that causes it to be inserted.

---

even more so when using minimum or maximum delays. In either case a full-fledged time queue is utilized. Events or signals are scheduled to occur at some appropriate time in the future. This marks a significant departure from the unit delay simulation and it allows changes on primary input signals to be scheduled to occur at given times. Because of this, the object network does not necessarily stabilize between the application of input vectors. In addition it is now possible to have clock elements which are continuously changing. These facts require that the process of fault detection, oscillation control, and timing analysis be performed differently from unit delay simulation.

In a time domain simulator such as those being discussed, signal examination for fault detection can be scheduled to occur at given time intervals. Alternatively, any time a primary output or test point signal changes value, it can be examined to determine if any of the faults being simulated are observable. If a fault is detectable, appropriate information can be recorded. In addition to the type of information discussed earlier, the time at which the detection occurred can be recorded and later used to increase diagnostic resolution.

With nearly any fault simulation system, the user can determine how many times a fault must be detected before it can be dropped. When it is determined that a fault can be dropped, it is easy to simply turn off the fault flag that causes it to be inserted. However, this does not stop all of the extra activity which may have been induced into the network because of the fault and which is currently propagating and generating new activity. A procedure was developed for CC-TEGAS3[1] to immediately stop such activity when a fault is detected, and it could be easily implemented on any unit delay or nominal delay parallel fault simulation system. This procedure consists simply of setting up a full-word mask of all zeros at the beginning of a fault pass. When a fault machine is detected, the bit position representing that fault is set to one in the mask. Then when a signal is examined to determine if it changed value (step 6 of Table 3), this mask would be used to mask out any changes in machines which have been detected. This procedure is crucial for oscillation control in a time domain simulator.

Part 1 described the timing analysis performed in CC-TEGAS3 when using nominal or minimum and maximum delays. It becomes particularly challenging to accomplish similar timing analysis when doing parallel fault simulation. How this was accomplished in CC-TEGAS3 has been described in another paper.[1]

In our opinion, the state of the art of fault simulation has progressed to the point that the development of any new zero delay, unit delay, or two-valued simulation systems should not be considered.

Conclusion

For anyone embarking upon the development of a parallel fault simulation system, the first question to be asked is what digital network model will be used as the basis of the fault simulation system. The answer to this question will determine the upper boundary on the accuracy with which faults can be modeled. In our opinion, the state of the art of fault simulation has progressed to the point that the development of any new zero delay, unit delay, or two-valued simulation systems should not be considered.

The second consideration is the data structure to be used for signal values and how element evaluation should be performed and hence faults propagated. The third question is what types of faults will be modeled and how they should be inserted. The answer to this question should be open ended. In fact, due to the rate at which technology changes occur today, flexibility in this area is a very practical concern.

Another point, which has not been discussed, is that in the selection of the basic simulation system upon which to build fault simulation, the type of elements that can be directly modeled should be seriously considered. Many simulation systems are constrained to the fact that only single-output devices can be modeled as a single entity. This constraint will also constrain the type of faults that can be modeled.

The need for accurate, flexible, and efficient fault simulation systems has steadily increased during recent years, and they are becoming a very important part of many design automation systems. Such systems require a large amount of initial programming and continued software maintenance. Because of this they are expensive to develop, and mistakes in the design phase of such systems can quickly render it useless and costly beyond all belief.

References

1. E. W. Thompson, S. A. Szygenda, N. Billawala, and R. Pierce, "Timing Analysis for Digital Fault Simulation Using Assignable Delays," *Proceedings of the 11th Design Automation Workshop*, 1974.

2. S. A. Szygenda, D. Rouse, and E. Thompson, "A Model and Implementation of a Universal Time Delay Simulator for Large Digital Nets," *Proceedings, SJCC, AFIPS*, May 1970.

3. S. A. Szygenda, "TEGAS2—Anatomy of a General-Purpose Test Generation and Simulation System for Digital Logic," *Proceedings of the 9th ACM IEEE Design Automation Workshop*, June 1972.

4. S. A. Szygenda and E. W. Thompson, "Fault Insertion Techniques and Models for Digital Logic Simulation," *Proceedings, FJBC, AFIPS*, December 1972.

5. E. B. Eichelberger, "Hazard Detection in Combinational and Sequential Switching Circuits," *IBM Journal of Research & Development*, Vol. 4, pp. 90-99, March 1965.

E. W. Thompson and S. A. Szygenda are co-authors of the first feature article. Their biographies appear on page 36.

A Deductive Method for Simulating Faults in Logic Circuits

DOUGLAS B. ARMSTRONG

Reprinted from *IEEE Transactions on Computers*, Volume C-21, Number 5,
May 1972, pages 464-471. Copyright © 1972 by The Institute of Electrical
and Electronics Engineers, Inc. All rights reserved.

Abstract—A deductive method of fault simulation is described, which
"deduces" the faults detected by a test at the same time that it simulates explicitly only the good behavior of logic circuit. For large logic
circuits (at least several thousand gates) it is expected to be faster than
"parallel" fault simulators, but uses much more computer memory than
do parallel simulators.

The simulator is table driven, employs selective trace, models the dynamic behavior of circuits reasonably well but does not perform race
analysis, and accommodates both synchronous and asynchronous circuits.
It simulates three logic states: ZERO, ONE, and DON'T KNOW.

Results for a few logic circuits are given, obtained with a version of
the simulator implemented on a Honeywell 635 computer. Versions exist
for an IBM 360/67 also, and newer versions are under development.

Index Terms—Deductive method, error symptoms, fault dictionary,
fault simulation, logic circuits, simulation, trouble location.

I. INTRODUCTION

COMPUTER simulation of faults in logic circuits is
frequently employed for the purpose of generating
fault dictionaries and for verifying the adequacy of
test sequences intended to detect and locate logic faults. Of
several fault simulation methods that have been reported in
the literature [1]–[7], the one which appears the most popular for general circuits is the "parallel" technique [1]–[4].
This technique explicitly simulates the logic behavior of the
circuit for N independent, single faults simultaneously,
where N is the number of bits in a word in the host computer
(the computer that performs the simulation). It is important
to note that only single faults are treated, both in the referenced work and in the method to be presented here. Thus,
although the parallel simulation method deals with N faults
simultaneously, it treats each as though it alone were present
in the circuit.

At least one previous method [5] does not simulate the
logic effects of each fault explicitly, but rather simulates just
the fault-free circuit's response to a sequence of binary test
vectors applied to its inputs. From the fault-free behavior it
deduces which faults would be detected by the test vectors in
question. This approach is based on sensitized path concepts
[8], that have been formalized by Roth [5] in the D Algorithm.

The deductive technique outlined in [5] is not generally
applicable to sequential circuits. A more powerful deductive
technique is described here which is valid for sequential as
well as combinational logic.[1] Specifically, the method ex-

Manuscript received May 13, 1971; revised December 15, 1971.

The author is with Bell Telephone Laboratories, Inc., Denver,
Colo. 80221.

[1] Subsequent to submitting this paper for publication it was learned
that an essentially identical technique was proposed by H. C. Godoy
and R. E. Vogelsberg. See *IBM Tech. Disc. Bull.*, vol. 13, p. 3443, Apr.
1971.

plicitly simulates the behavior of the fault-free logic only,
and simultaneously deduces, from the current "good" state
of the circuit, all faults that are detectable at any internal
terminal or circuit output terminal when in the current
state.

Because the deductive simulator computes all detectable
faults at the same time, it is necessary to perform only one
simulation run for each applied test vector. This is in contrast to the parallel method where, if M is the total number
of faults to be simulated and N faults are simulated per run,
M/N runs are needed to determine all the detectable faults
per test input. The simulation time per run for the deductive
simulator is probably much longer than the time per run for
the parallel simulator, but is expected to be less than the time
for the M/N runs which the parallel method requires to accomplish equivalent results. One reason for this potential
time reduction is that deductive simulation performs computations on each fault along only the particular paths that
are sensitized to propagate its effects. In contrast, the
parallel method performs computations along all paths for
which the effects of *any one* (or more) of the N faults in the
batch being simulated continues to propagate. The latter
method may therefore perform much unnecessary computation.

A direct comparison of run times for the two methods has
not been obtained because a parallel simulator was not
readily available. However, a few results obtained with one
version of the deductive simulator appear in Section VI.

A potential disadvantage of the deductive simulator is that
it requires considerably more memory space in the host computer than does the parallel method. Also, the amount of
memory needed is not accurately predictable prior to a run,
so dynamic memory allocation is desirable.

A brief description of the deductive technique is given
below; a more detailed account appears in later sections.
The basic logic elements that are simulated are gates and
set–reset flip-flops. More complex logic elements such as
shift registers, counters, etc., are decomposed into basic elements for simulation purposes. It will be convenient to refer
to the basic elements as nodes, because they may be thought
of as the vertices of a directed graph whose branches are the
interconnecting wires in the logic circuit. Each gate is represented by one node, each flip-flop by two nodes, one for
each of its output terminals.

The set of nodes, each of which has at least one of its inputs connected to a circuit input terminal will be called first
level nodes. The set of nodes, each of which has at least one
of its inputs connected to the output of a first-level node

(and possibly also to circuit input terminals), will be called second-level nodes, and so on.[2] The identification of nodes by level is provided automatically in the simulator, by means of a linked list structure which describes the circuit topology. At the beginning of simulation the linked list circuit description is stored in the host computer. Then the application of a test vector to the circuit's input terminals is simulated. The (good) logic states on the outputs of the first-level nodes are then computed, in response to the applied test vector.

Next, the simulator computes lists of faults, one list associated with the output terminal of each first-level node. The faults in a particular list are the ones arising within the associated node and which are detectable at the node's output terminal when in its current logic state. That is, each fault in a list, if inserted singly in the circuit, would cause complementation of the good output state of the associated node.

Next the logic states and associated fault lists for the second-level nodes are computed. In this case, and for all succeeding levels of nodes, the faults in a particular list arise from two sources. First are those arising within the associated node and which are detectable at its output when in the current logic state. Second are the faults which are associated with the node's inputs and which, for the current logic state, are permitted to propagate an erroneous logic value through the node. The faults associated with the node's inputs are those contained in the lists associated with the particular nodes in the preceding level(s) which feed the node in question.

The above computations are repeated, level by level, throughout the circuit. In this manner a fault list is generated for each node output, and is updated as necessary with every change in logic state. Each list provides a dynamic record of all the faults that are detectable at the output of the associated node at the current simulation time, during execution of a sequence of tests.

Error symptoms are obtained for each of the faults detected by a test sequence, by monitoring selected output terminals in the circuit, usually the outputs of accessible registers. An error symptom is defined to be the actual (incorrect) bit pattern existing in a monitored register due to the presence of some fault. The output of a simulation run consists of the fault lists appearing on the outputs of specified monitorable registers, at times specified in the applied test sequence. A postsimulator program generates error symptoms for these fault lists in a manner illustrated in the following example.

Suppose nodes 1, 2, 3, and 4 in Fig. 1 constitute a monitorable register, and the test sequence calls for error symptoms to be recorded for all faults that produce observable errors at the register at time t_n. Suppose the good output at time t_n is 0000, and the simulation determines the fault lists

[2] Note that the above grouping of nodes into levels is not a partition on the nodes. That is, a particular node can belong to several levels. This differs from the more usual definition of levels, which in fact generates a partition. See, for example, [9, p. 94].

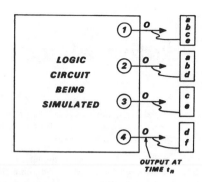

Fig. 1. Fault lists on outputs of a logic circuit.

TABLE I

Faults	Error Symptoms
a,b	1100
c,e	1010
d	0101
f	0001

to be (a,b,c,e), (a,b,d), (c,e), and (d,f) on nodes 1 through 4, respectively at t_n. This implies, for example, that faults a and b are detectable at nodes 1 and 2 but not at nodes 3 and 4 at t_n. Therefore, the error symptom produced by faults a and b is 1100. A complete table of error symptoms and associated faults for this example appear in Table I.

A fault dictionary consists of a tabulation of error symptoms and the faults, identified by their physical locations, which produce each symptom. It is evident that data such as Table I provide the necessary information for a fault dictionary.

II. Main Characteristics of the Deductive Simulator

A current implementation of the deductive simulator has the following salient characteristics.

1) It is table driven rather than compiled. That is, the description of the logic circuit to be simulated is stored in tables in the host computer. The tables are accessed by the simulation program as necessary. The simulation program is circuit independent, but a new set of tables is required for each distinct circuit to be simulated. In contrast compiled simulators [2] contain the description of the circuit implicitly in the simulation program. The latter therefore has to be recompiled for each distinct circuit.

2) It models the dynamic behavior of the simulated circuit fairly closely. Specifically it updates its computations at successive, uniform intervals of simulated time, $1T$, $2T$, $3T$ where the time interval T is chosen equal to the average gate delay. This results in accurate time modeling to the extent that all gates have the same nominal delay T, and the variation in gate delays from the nominal value in the actual circuit is small, a condition which in fact holds for many of the circuits being simulated. Through some simple changes, the simulator could be arranged to simulate a different delay for

each gate, no doubt at the expense of increased simulation time.

3) It is equally applicable to synchronous and asynchronous circuits. Critical race analyses are not performed, although some race conditions are detected at inputs to flip-flops.

4) It employs the "selective trace" procedure; that is, the output state of a logic node is computed only if one or more of its inputs have changed in the preceding time interval. This leads to economy in simulation provided the logic nodes are simulated in the order in which they occur in the normal logic flow. The desired ordering is achieved by the use of a linked list structure for the tables describing the circuit. It ensures that the first set of nodes to be simulated are those connected directly to the terminals at which a test is applied, those to be simulated next are the ones fed by the first set, and so on. In this manner the propagation of signals through successive stages of logic elements is simulated until all logic states have stabilized. If oscillating loops are present, in which case the circuit never stabilizes, the simulation can be terminated after an appropriate time interval predetermined by the user.

5) Three logic states are simulated, namely ZERO, ONE, and DON'T KNOW. The latter state is useful in cases where the complete internal state of the circuit is not known at the beginning of simulation, or the test conditions applied to the circuit are not fully specified or are only partially under the user's control.

III. ALGORITHMS FOR GENERATING FAULT LISTS

The key step in deductive simulation is the computation of fault lists from the fault-free logic behavior. We first describe the procedure for logic gates, and then for flip-flops. In the case of gates the fault lists associated with their outputs consist of two components: 1) faults located in preceding logic stages whose effects propagate to the inputs of the gate in question; and 2) faults originating within the gate and which produce the incorrect logical state at the gate's output. As an example of the procedure for computing the fault list at the output of a NOR gate, refer to Fig. 2.

Inputs A, B, C, and D to NOR gate E have associated with them the fault lists shown in the figure. They are the lists currently associated with the logic nodes which feed these inputs. Observe that several of the faults appear in more than one input list. These are faults occurring in earlier logic stages whose effects have propagated over several paths to gate E.

In order for a fault in any of the input lists to appear in E's output list, it must cause the good output of E to be complemented; in this example it must cause E to generate a ONE. By analyzing the truth table for a NOR gate, it becomes evident that the presence of a fault in preceding logic stages will be detectable at E's output if it causes all logical ONES on E's inputs to change to ZEROS, and at the same time does not cause any logical ZEROS on E's inputs to change to ONES. Because the good logical inputs in this example are $A = B = 1$, $C = D = 0$, it follows that only those faults which

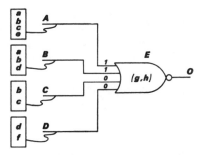

Fig. 2. Fault lists associated with a NOR gate.

appear in the lists on both A and B, and not in the lists on C or D, will cause the output to be ONE. Fault a satisfies this requirement. Fault b does not because, although it appears on both A and B, it also appears on C.

We can express the output list on E as a mathematical set function of the input lists. Let A, B, C, D, and E represent the fault *sets* associated with the similarly labeled terminals in Fig. 2, and let E_1 represent the subset of E consisting of faults external to the gate which propagate to its output via its inputs. Then E_1 is defined by the set relation

$$E_1 = AB\overline{(C + D)} \tag{1}$$

where a product denotes set intersection, a plus denotes set union, and $\overline{S}$ denotes the complement of set S. It is evident that the expression for E_1 is dependent on the good logic states appearing on the inputs, and that the output fault list must be recomputed whenever one or more input logic states, or associated input fault lists change. If the good inputs are all logical ZEROS, relation (1) is replaced by

$$E_1 = A + B + C + D \tag{2}$$

because in this case a fault in any input list or lists to the gate will produce the incorrect logical output.

Let E_2 represent the subset of E consisting of those faults internal to the gate which produce the bad output for the current good inputs. In the example, suppose g is an internal fault which causes the output to be "stuck" at a logical ZERO, while h causes the output to be "stuck" at a logical ONE: then, E_2 contains the single fault h, and E is the set (a, h).

In general, the faults constituting set E_2 are determined by referring to the truth tables that represent the behavior of the NOR gate when the various internal faults are present. Distinct physical faults internal to a gate that have the same (faulty) truth table are not distinguishable, and are treated as a single fault.

Procedures for computing fault lists for other types of logic gates are straightforward and involve the same considerations as above.

In the case of faults originating in gates on feedback loops, it is possible to have the effects of a fault propagate completely around the loop(s). In this case the fault will appear in one (or more) of the fault lists associated with inputs to the gate of origination. If the fault is one whose detectability at the output of the originating gate is dependent upon the input bit pattern applied, it will be incorrect to determine detectability in the presence of the good input pattern to the originating gate. Rather one must determine detectability in the presence of the actual input pattern generated in the presence of this fault. The actual pattern is obtained from the good pattern by complementing the states of those inputs to which the fault's effect has propagated via the feedback loops.

The generation of fault lists for flip-flops is more complicated than for gates, primarily because a flip-flop can "remember" the effects of faults which were propagated to its inputs at a previous time in the test sequence. For example, at some time in the test sequence a fault f might cause a flip-flop to be erroneously set. The erroneous setting signal might then disappear but, in the absence of a subsequent resetting signal, the flip-flop will remain set and the fault is detectable at its outputs as long as the erroneous set state persists.

To correctly account for this memory property, the new fault lists which are computed for a flip-flop's outputs at time t_i contain, in addition to faults appearing in the fault lists on its inputs at time t_i, faults from the output fault lists which were present at time t_{i-1}. To these must be added any internal flip-flop faults which are detectable on its outputs at t_i. By treating the flip-flop input and output fault lists as mathematical sets, as we did for NOR gates, we can derive expressions for the new output sets in terms of the previous output sets and the current input sets. A sample computation, for one particular flip-flop state, is now presented, for the case in which the flip-flop is realized from cross-connected NOR gates, as shown in Fig. 3.

The fault lists present at the set and reset outputs of the flip-flop at time t_1 are denoted by P_1 and Q_1, respectively. When conditions require that the flip-flop again be reevaluated, at time t_2, let S and R be the fault lists present on the set and reset inputs, respectively, at that time. It is required to evaluate new fault lists P_2 and Q_2 on the outputs.

The computation of the new lists depends on the previous logic state of the flip-flop (at time t_1) and the new logic inputs to the flip-flop (at time t_2), as well as on the associated fault lists. Therefore, the computation must be made for each combination of previous state and present inputs. We perform it for the combination shown in Fig. 3, namely the flip-flop in the "set" state at t_1 and for quiescent (i.e., nonenabling) inputs applied at t_2. In this case, the "next" state of the flip-flop is again the set state.

Treating the various fault lists as mathematical sets, we may express P_2 and Q_2 as "sum of products" functions of sets P_1, Q_1, R, and S. That is, P_2 and Q_2 may be expressed as the union of appropriate subsets of the 16 fundamental products: P_1Q_1RS, $P_1Q_1R\overline{S}$, $\cdots$, $\overline{P}_1\overline{Q}_1\overline{R}\ \overline{S}$. Each of the 16 fundamental products must be examined in turn to see if it should be present in the expression for P_2 or Q_2.

To determine whether the product P_1Q_1RS should be present in P_2 or Q_2, consider its meaning. Any fault in the product P_1Q_1RS, if actually present would, by definition, cause both outputs to be wrong at t_1 and both inputs to be wrong at t_2. That is, it would cause the flip-flop to be in the reset state at time t_1 and would cause both inputs to be ONES

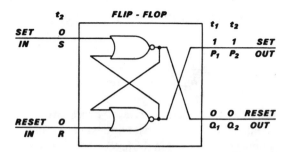

Fig. 3. Flip-flop structure and associated fault lists.

(i.e., both enabled) at time t_2. This causes both flip-flop outputs to go to ZERO at t_2, whereas the "good" flip-flop state at t_2 is "set." Therefore, this fault can be detected on the set output at t_2, but not on the reset output. Consequently, the product P_1Q_1RS is present in the expression for P_2 but is absent from the expression for Q_2.

Next, consider the second product, $P_1Q_1R\overline{S}$. Any fault in this set would cause the flip-flop to be in the reset state at time t_1 and would cause a "reset enable" to be applied to the inputs at time t_2, which would maintain the flip-flop in the reset state. Therefore, this fault would be detected on both outputs at t_2, so $P_1Q_1R\overline{S}$ will appear in the expressions for both P_2 and Q_2.

The reasoning for the remaining 14 products is in similar vein to the above, however, in some cases special considerations apply, as follows.

Case 1: Any fault in the product $P_1\overline{Q}_1\overline{R}\ \overline{S}$ would cause both outputs of the flip-flop to be ZERO at t_1, which implies that both inputs are ONE at that time. Furthermore, this fault does not affect either input at t_2, so both will be ZERO at this time independent of the presence of the fault. This means that, with the fault present, both inputs will change from ONE to ZERO in the interval (t_1, t_2), and as it is not known which input changes first, it is not known whether the flip-flop will end up in the set or reset state at t_2. This is a so-called race condition.

The conclusion is that any fault in the product $P_1\overline{Q}_1\overline{R}\ \overline{S}$ may or may not be detected by the current test, depending on which state the flip-flop goes to as a result of the race. Such faults are hereafter referred to as "star" faults. When evaluating fault lists on flip-flop outputs, the simulator includes the star faults along with the regular faults (i.e., those which are detected with certainty), but inserts a distinguishing flag in each star fault entry. A star fault which propagates to monitored outputs in any particular test generates two possible error symptoms. In one, the outputs it propagates to are in error, in the other these outputs are not in error. Both error symptoms are included in the fault dictionary.[3]

Case 2: There is no fault external to a (cross-coupled NOR) flip-flop which can cause both flip-flop outputs to be

---

[3] It is assumed that a star fault causes only one flip-flop to race in any particular test. If the fault causes N flip-flops to race, it is possible for as many as 2^N error symptoms to result. Studies of logic circuits to which the simulator is being applied indicates that in nearly all cases each star fault causes only a single flip-flop to race, thus creating only two error patterns as stated above.

one simultaneously. For the particular flip-flop state specified in Fig. 3 it is observed that such faults can appear only in the four products containing $\overline{P}_1 Q_1$. Since we are considering only faults external to the flip-flop at this stage (the internal faults will be added later), we may therefore treat these four products as DON'T CARES, and include them in expressions for P_2 and Q_2 if their inclusion permits the resulting expressions to be further simplified.

An analysis of all fundamental products for this example results in the following sum-of-products expressions for P_2 and Q_2.

$$P_2 = [P_1\overline{Q}_1\overline{R}\,\overline{S}] + [P_1 Q_1 RS + P_1 Q_1 R\overline{S} + P_1 Q_1 \overline{R}\,\overline{S}$$
$$+ P_1\overline{Q}_1 RS + P_1\overline{Q}_1 R\overline{S} + \overline{P}_1\overline{Q}_1 RS + \overline{P}_1\overline{Q}_1 R\,\overline{S}$$
$$+ (\overline{P}_1 Q_1 RS + \overline{P}_1 Q_1 R\overline{S} + \overline{P}_1 Q_1 \overline{R}\,\overline{S})]$$

$$Q_2 = [P_1\overline{Q}_1\overline{R}\,\overline{S}] + [P_1 Q_1 R\overline{S} + P_1 Q_1 \overline{R}\,\overline{S} + P_1\overline{Q}_1 R\,\overline{S}$$
$$+ \overline{P}_1\overline{Q}_1 RS + (\overline{P}_1 Q_1 \overline{R}\,\overline{S} + \overline{P}_1 Q_1 R\overline{S})]$$

where the first bracketed product represents the star faults and the products in parentheses are DON'T CARE products included to permit simplification. Performing simplification on only the products containing nonstar faults we obtain

$$P_2 = P_1\overline{Q}_1\overline{R}\,\overline{S} + R + Q_1\overline{S} \tag{3}$$

$$Q_2 = P_1\overline{Q}_1\overline{R}\,\overline{S} + R\overline{S} + Q_1\overline{S}. \tag{4}$$

Expressions (3) and (4) for P_2 and Q_2 are not complete; it is necessary to add to these lists any faults internal to the flip-flop which are detectable at t_2. For example, among the internal faults there are two, labeled A_s and A_r, which hold the flip-flop in its set state and reset state, respectively, regardless of the inputs. In this example, the fault A_r would be detectable on both the set and reset outputs at t_2 and would therefore be included in both P_2 and Q_2, whereas A_s would not be detectable at t_2 and, therefore, would not appear in either P_2 and Q_2.

In the case of faults originating in flip-flops on feedback loops, it is possible to have the effects of a fault propagate around a loop and appear on the input(s) to the flip-flop in which it originated. Similar modifications to the procedure for determining detectability of such a fault at the flip-flop's outputs apply as in the case of gates on feedback loops described earlier.

In order to perform fault computations for more complex logic devices such as shift registers, they are first decomposed into appropriately interconnected networks of gates and flip-flops. Certain devices, such as delay lines, cannot be decomposed into these basic elements. The output fault lists for delay lines are merely delayed replicas of their input lists. At present, delay lines will be assumed to contain no internal faults because they are proving to be highly reliable and because relatively few are used.

It should be noted that the rules given in this section for computing fault lists are based on the assumption that the effect of a fault may propagate over more than one path to a node's inputs. It is possible that, for the majority of nodes, each fault can propagate to at most one of its inputs. In such cases the computation of output fault lists is greatly simpli-

fied. If desired, an analysis of the circuit can be performed before simulation, to determine those nodes that satisfy this constraint. These can be flagged so that their fault lists can be computed using simplified rules, with a resulting reduction in simulation time.

Efficient implementation of the algorithms for computing fault lists based on expressions such as (1) through (4) in this section is of critical importance because the predominant percentage of simulation time is occupied in performing these computations. The basic operations involved are set intersections, set unions, and set differences. The underlying operation common to all three set operations is the matching of fault entries in two or more lists. A straightforward procedure for performing the matching operation on two lists requires a number of computational steps proportional to the product of the list lengths. The use of such a slow procedure would probably negate the potential speed advantage of the deductive simulation method. Fortunately, techniques exist for which the number of computational steps is proportional to the sum of the list lengths, and this holds true whatever the number of lists involved in the matching operation. It is of utmost importance to use these more efficient procedures in order to reduce simulation time.[4]

IV. SIMULATOR OPERATION IN MORE DETAIL

To more fully understand the operation of the deductive simulator, a particular implementation is described below. The host computer is a Honeywell 635, whose word length is 36 bits.

The main tables or lists used in this implementation are: 1) logic list; 2) current state list (CSL); 3) next state list (NSL); 4) future state list (FSL); and 5) the fault lists (LISTS).

Logic list is actually a set of three lists describing the block of logic to be simulated. One of these, called LLST, is a two-dimensional array. Each row of the array describes a logic node (e.g., a gate, half a flip-flop, an input terminal, etc.) and includes fields which specify static information such as: the node type, the node's internal faults, and pointers via the two remaining lists to those rows in the array which are its fan-in and fan-out nodes (i.e., the nodes which connect to this node's inputs and which are connected to this node's output). The only dynamic information contained in a row in LLST is the current logic state at the node's output terminal. Three logic states are permitted, namely ZERO, ONE, and DON'T KNOW.

The current state list (CSL) contains pointers to those nodes (i.e., rows in LLST) which are to be evaluated at the current simulated time. The next state list (NSL) contains pointers to those nodes which are to be evaluated at the next simulated time, which is an interval equal to the average gate delay T. The future state list (FSL) contains pointers to those nodes which are to be evaluated at times subsequent to the next simulated time, along with the time at which each

[4] The fast set operations will be described in a future paper by G. W. Smith and R. B. Walford.

node is to be evaluated. There are two types of entries in the FSL.

1) Nodes whose internal delays are greater than one gate delay, e.g., delay lines.

2) Externally applied test vectors, generated by the sequence of tests being simulated. These appear as bit patterns on circuit input terminals at specified future times.

The fault lists, one list per node, are stored in a dynamically allocated storage area called LISTS. Dynamic storage is used because of the wide variations in size which these lists undergo during a simulation run. Each fault in a fault list occupies a word, one half of the word containing the fault name, the other half containing the pointer to the next fault in the list. The pointer is zero if this fault is the last one in the list. Rapid access to any fault list in LISTS is provided by a pointer table containing one word per fault list, this word having the same index as the row index of the node it is associated with in LLST. One half of the word points to the first entry and the other half points to the last entry of the associated fault list in LISTS.

Using the above data base, a simulation run proceeds as follows. Initially the logic states of all nodes are set to DON'T KNOW in LLST except for nodes which the user elects to set to either ZERO or ONE. The simulator's control program then reads in the first test, which is usually an initializing input, and determines which registers and control flip-flops are to be set directly, along with the required setting states. Based on this analysis, control makes the following entries into the FSL: the aforementioned input logic states; their (simulated) time of application to the circuit; and pointers to the nodes in LLST into which these logic states are to be injected. (These are the zeroth-level nodes.) Control then calls the main simulation program which initializes its clock and searches FSL for entries whose assigned time matches the current clock time. The program inserts the logic states of these entries into the appropriate zeroth level nodes in LLST, and inserts into CSL the pointers to the fan-out nodes of the zeroth-level nodes. (The fan-out nodes are the first-level nodes.)

Next the main program processes all entries in CSL. For each first-level node it computes the node's output logic state as a function of the node type and its input state, and also computes its output fault list.[5] Computation of logic states is straightforward and needs no further comment. Computation of fault lists is accomplished using the algorithms in Section III. The fault lists are stored in LISTS. As each first-level node is processed, pointers to its fan-out nodes in LLST are entered in NSL if the first-level node is assigned the average gate delay T, or in FSL if the delay is greater than T.

When all first-level nodes in CSL have been processed, the simulator clock is advanced by T and NSL now becomes CSL, while the old CSL is cleared and becomes the new NSL. Thus the CSL and NSL lists interchange functions at successive intervals T. The simulation program now repeats the cycle of operations described above, commencing with a new search of FSL to find entries whose assigned time matches the updated simulator clock. Simulation ceases when there are no more entries to be processed in CSL, NSL, and FSL, or after a predetermined time, specified by the user, has elapsed.

The sequence of tests that is being simulated contains explicit instructions as to the particular nodes that are to be monitored for error symptoms, and the times at which monitoring is to occur. At these times the simulator outputs the logic states and associated fault lists for the specified nodes. These data are stored on tape for subsequent generation of error symptoms and construction of a fault dictionary if desired.

V. Miscellaneous Details

The simulation of feedback loops within the logic deserves further comment. Preanalysis of the circuit may or may not be performed to identify feedback loops. If not, the simulator will not be aware of their existence and will pursue its computations around loops repetitively until logic states stabilize. For fault-free logic it is usual for loops to settle after two traversals at most. However, in the presence of certain faults, loops will oscillate. This is manifested in the simulation by an oscillation[6] of the fault lists associated with nodes contained in such loops. In the implementation being described, the simulator continues computing oscillating lists until either the oscillations cease due to a change in inputs or until a predetermined time has elapsed.

The means for adjusting time delays in the simulated logic also needs comment. Two facilities are provided in the current version. First, during preparation of circuit descriptions for simulation, wire lengths are observed and delays are padded in multiples of T to account for propagation delays in long wires. Second, a facility has been provided, but not implemented, to permit the padding of individual gate delays, again in multiples of T, to account for significant departures of the actual measured delay along any path from the nominal value which is based on the average gate delay. Padding can be either positive or negative, subject to the constraint that no gate delay can be negative. This facility may be implemented if unacceptably large discrepancies are found to exist between measured and nominal delays.

Finally, comments are necessary concerning the treatment of DON'T KNOW logic states and the associated fault lists. DON'T KNOW states can arise from two sources.

1) It is not always possible to apply an initializing sequence which will set all memory elements to known states in the actual logic circuit at the start of a simulation. Those which cannot be initialized directly should be assigned the unknown state, in order that the simulator does not predict more complete (and possibly erroneous) error symptoms

---

[5] An option is provided which bypasses computation of fault lists if only the behavior of the fault-free logic is to be simulated.

[6] By oscillation of a fault list it is meant that the contents of the list alternate between two sets. This results from the fact that a fault causing the oscillation is detectable at any point in the loop only on alternate phases of the oscillation. Therefore, this fault entry will alternately appear in and be absent from the associated list.

than are in fact derivable by applying the same test sequence to the actual circuit.

2) Similarly, not all external inputs are under control of the applied test sequence, and those which are not must be treated as unknowns if their logic states are unknown or are changing arbitrarily during testing.

It is evident that unknown states can propagate through the circuit. For example, if one input to a NOR gate is in an unknown state and the states of the remaining inputs are ZEROS, the NOR output will be unknown. It is also evident that the fault list associated with a node whose state is unknown is not unique, because different sets of faults will be detected at that point depending on the particular state actually present.

Simulation time is increased significantly when unknown logic states are present, if an exact treatment is employed. An exact treatment essentially requires that fault lists be computed for every possible combination of determinate states in place of the unknowns. To avoid this increase in complexity, a current implementation of the deductive simulator treats unknowns by inexact methods which nevertheless are expected to produce correct results in most cases. This approach is acceptable because the majority of unknowns (namely those in category 1) above) appear only transiently. Those that persist (namely those in category 2) above) are a small minority. The rules governing treatment of unknowns for gates and flip-flops are as follows, assuming both known and unknown states are present on inputs to these logic elements.

Rule 1—Gates: If the known inputs are such that the resulting output state is unknown, then a single-entry fault list, called the "indeterminate list" is assigned to the output. If the known inputs are such that the resulting output state is known, then the output fault list is generated from the fault lists on the known inputs only, using the rules discussed in Section III. These output faults are flagged as star faults and are treated in the same manner as faults which cause races (see Section III). This is because they may or may not be detected, depending on the actual logic states present on the unknown inputs at the time the test is executed.

Rule 2—Flip-Flops: The indeterminate list is assigned to any output whose logic state is unknown. If the output state is known, the associated fault list will contain only those faults definitely known to be detected at that output in the presence of an incomplete specification of the flip-flop's previous state and/or new inputs.

It can be shown that the above rules for gates nearly always produce correct results provided no fault is present in the fault lists on both an unknown and a known input simultaneously. For persistent unknowns, studies of logic circuits currently being simulated have uncovered no cases where this condition is violated. The rule for flip-flops also is not expected to produce incorrect results, because tests can be designed so as to prevent persistent unknowns (category 2) above) from propagating to flip-flops. Therefore, normally only transient unknowns can reach flip-flops, and these will be replaced by known states before monitoring is performed, at which time correct fault lists will have been computed. To take care of the rare cases where indeterminate lists are present on flip-flop outputs when these are monitored, the simulator generates a message informing the user of this fact. The user may either redesign his tests to eliminate this situation, or, if this is not possible, he should avoid monitoring terminals that carry unknown states.

VI. Some Preliminary Results

The deductive simulator is currently implemented on two computers (Honeywell 635 and IBM 360/67) in support of ongoing development projects. The maximum size logic circuit that can be simulated at one time is determined primarily by the amount of computer core available. The amount of core required to simulate a particular circuit is not specifiable accurately in advance; it is determined primarily by the nature of the tests that are being simulated. For example, a test that detects many faults will generate large fault lists at many nodes throughout the circuit, thus using up considerable core. Because of the wide variation in sizes of fault lists from test to test, it is almost mandatory to use dynamic storage allocation for the list region in order to use core efficiently.

If the simulation of a particular circuit overflows available core, it will be necessary either to partition the circuit into smaller circuits, or retain the circuit intact and partition the associated set of faults into several blocks and repeat the simulation for each block, or design the simulator so that it uses secondary storage when core is overflowed. The last alternative is undesirable because it may increase simulation time intolerably. In the Honeywell 635 version the second alternative is invoked.

Some preliminary results obtained on the 635 are exhibited in Table II. The types of physical faults simulated in the circuits listed in the table are: open conductors within integrated circuit packages or at their terminals; and both opens and shorts between transistor terminals. These physical malfunctions are approximately equivalent, insofar as their logical effects are concerned, to the following familiar set of faults: node outputs stuck-at-one or stuck-at-zero, and opens on individual inputs to nodes.

For each circuit the table gives the number of nodes, the number of faults simulated, the number of test vectors simulated, the number of fault blocks[7] and the simulation time in hours. The number of test vectors listed is not the number needed to detect a fixed percentage of the circuit's fault population. In fact the number of faults detected varied from a few percent to nearly 90 percent. It will also be noted that the average number of faults per node in the table is approximately two. The reasons for this low ratio are: 1) there were several classes of logic elements for which faults were not simulated; and 2) a large majority of the elements for which faults were simulated correspond to nodes with at most two inputs (e.g., inverters, emitter followers, SR flip-flops and two-input NOR gates).

---

[7] For some of the larger circuits the total fault population was partitioned into several blocks and the simulation was repeated for each block. The simulation time quoted is the sum over the blocks.

TABLE II

Circuit Number	Number of Nodes	Number of Faults	Number of Test Vectors	Number of Fault Blocks	Simulation Time (hr)
1	3030	6000	1500	2	5.08
2	13 080	38 350	510	15	21.3
3	6250	13 310	48	1	0.33
4	6660	9730	1360	5	19.4
5	1940	2930	600	1	2.97
6	4820	7820	755	1	4.28
7	10 960	19 080	1310	24	42.2
8	19 480	45 450	750	15	60.9

The tabulated data apply to a simulation mode in which all faults are simulated in every test. There is a second mode, in which individual faults are eliminated from the simulation after first detection. Simulation times in the latter case average about 40 percent less than those quoted here. A third mode, which simulates only the fault-free logic, runs between 40 and 150 times faster than the first mode.

Because of the wide variation in percentage of faults detected per circuit, the quoted simulation times are not a useful measure of the simulator's performance. A more useful measure might be the simulation time per test, plotted as a function of the product [faults $\times$ nodes] for each circuit. It is found that this plot exhibits an irregular distribution of points, which indicates that simulation time is dependent upon additional parameters not appearing in Table II.

One such parameter is the fault detection power of individual tests. A powerful test will generate many long fault lists, resulting in a large computation time; a weak test will generate short lists and a corespondingly reduced computation time. Test power is determined by circuit topology, by the number of input terminals provided for test access purposes, and by the ability of the test designers to select powerful tests. The number of test access terminals per circuit ranged between 80 and 1075. Also, the tests were designed by people having varying degrees of experience, and no sophisticated tools were provided to aid them in selecting uniformly powerful tests. These factors all contributed to the variability of simulation time.

Continuing development is underway to decrease simula-tion time and memory requirements. One means of reducing running time is by "fault collapsing," that is, by replacing logically indistinguishable faults by a single fault, or by merging two faults if detection of one of them guarantees detection of the other. The latter type of collapsing results in inaccuracies in fault dictionaries, but may be tolerable in some situations. A technique similar to fault collapsing, and which avoids its potential inaccuracies, is currently under study. It sacrifices individual fault identities but permits a fault to be correctly located to one or more nodes. It is planned to report on this technique in the near future.

ACKNOWLEDGMENT

The author wishes to thank G. W. Smith and R. B. Walford who proposed the fast set operations referred to at the end of Section III, and R. G. South who implemented the Honeywell 635 version of the simulator. This version contains a very efficient algorithm for dynamic storage and retrieval of fault lists.

REFERENCES

[1] S. Seshu, "On an improved diagnosis program," *IEEE Trans. Electron. Comput.* (Short Notes), vol. EC-14, pp. 76–79, Feb. 1965.

[2] F. H. Hardie and R. J. Suhocki, "Design and use of fault simulation for Saturn computer design," Wescon Tech. Paper, vol. 10, pt. 4, pp. 1–22, 1966.

[3] I. H. Yetter, "High-speed fault simulation for the Univac 1107 computer system," in *1968 Proc. Ass. Comput. Mach. Nat. Conf.*, pp. 265–277.

[4] S. A. Szygenda, D. M. Rouse, and E. W. Thompson, "A model and implementation of a universal time delay simulator for large digital nets," in *1970 Spring Joint Comput. Conf.*, AFIPS Conf. Proc., vol. 36. Montvale, N. J.: AFIPS Press, 1970, pp. 207–216.

[5] J. P. Roth, W. G. Bouricius, and P. R. Schneider, "Programmed algorithms to compute tests to detect and distinguish between failures in logic circuits," *IEEE Trans. Electron. Comput.*, vol. EC-16, pp. 567–580, Oct. 1967.

[6] E. G. Ulrich, "The evaluation of digital diagnostic programs through digital simulation," in *Proc. IEE Comput. Tech. Conf.* (England), 1967, pp. 9–19.

[7] M. A. Breuer, "Functional partitioning and simulation of digital circuits," *IEEE Trans. Comput.*, vol. C-19, pp. 1038–1046, Nov. 1970.

[8] D. B. Armstrong, "On finding a nearly minimal set of fault detection tests for combinational logic nets," *IEEE Trans. Electron. Comput.*, vol. EC-15, pp. 66–73, Feb. 1966.

[9] H. Y. Chang, E. Manning, and G. Metze, *Fault Diagnosis of Digital Systems.* New York: Wiley, 1970.

Deductive Fault Simulation with Functional Blocks

PREMACHANDRAN R. MENON, MEMBER, IEEE, AND STEPHEN G. CHAPPELL, MEMBER, IEEE

Reprinted from *IEEE Transactions on Computers,* Volume C-27, Number 8, August 1978, pages 689-695. Copyright © 1978 by The Institute of Electrical and Electronics Engineers, Inc. All rights reserved.

Abstract—This paper presents a method of propagating the effects of faults through functional blocks using the deductive (fault list) technique. An extension of the method is shown to be effective for simulating internal faults in functional blocks. The techniques presented here have been used for implementing the functional simulation capability in the Logic Analysis for Maintenance Planning (LAMP) System at Bell Laboratories.

Index Terms—Deductive, faults, fault lists, fault propagation, functional, functional faults, simulation.

I. INTRODUCTION

DIGITAL simulation is a widely used tool in design verification and diagnosis of digital systems [1]–[3]. In fault diagnosis, digital simulation is used to determine the behavior of the digital circuit in the presence of certain faults and compare it with the normal circuit behavior. This type of simulation, called *fault simulation*, is used to determine the set of faults detected by a test sequence and also to determine the output patterns produced by these faults.

Two different techniques are commonly used for fault simulation. In *parallel simulation* [1], [4], [5], the normal (fault-free) circuit and a number of faulty circuits, each of which is usually assumed to contain a single fault, are simulated simultaneously. The number of circuits simulated simultaneously is determined by the word size of the host machine (i.e., the computer on which the simulation program is run). If a large number of faults is to be simulated, it may be necessary to partition the set of all faults into subsets which can be simulated simultaneously, and simulate each subset separately. This would require several passes through the simulation program.

In *deductive simulation* [6]–[8] faulty circuits are not explicitly simulated. Instead, only the normal circuit is simulated and the single faults that will cause any output to be incorrect are determined by a deductive technique. The computation involved in determining the set of faults that cause the output of any gate in the circuit to be incorrect (for deductive simulation) is usually more complex than that required in determining the output of a gate for the normal and faulty circuits simultaneously (for parallel simulation). However, a single pass through the deductive simulation program is sufficient to determine the effects of a large number of faults. Thus, the computation time required for simulating a large number of faults is reduced, but at the expense of memory requirements. Chang *et al.* [9] have shown experimentally that deductive simulation is more

Manuscript received January 5, 1977.
The authors are with Bell Laboratories, Naperville, IL 60540.

cost effective than parallel simulation when a large circuit is to be simulated with a large number of faults.

Most of the existing simulation programs perform fault simulation at the gate level. When the size of the circuit is too large for cost-effective gate-level simulation, it is frequently useful to simulate parts of the circuit such as memories, registers, decoders, etc., at a functional level. That is, we wish to treat such functional blocks as "black boxes" whose input/output behavior is specified (but whose actual gate level realization is unknown) and determine the effects of faults in the gate-level circuit on the complete circuit. This approach will make the simulation of larger circuits feasible since large functional blocks will usually require less host computer resources than the corresponding gate-level circuits. Functional simulation also eliminates the necessity for generating gate-level simulation models of functional blocks whose gate-level realization is not known.

Some of the existing programs which use the parallel simulation technique are capable of simulating certain types of functional blocks [4]. A deductive technique applicable to combinational functions and flip-flops has been proposed [10] but not implemented.

This paper presents a method of propagating the effects of faults through arbitrary types of functional blocks using the deductive fault simulation technique. An extension of the method is also presented for simulating faults internal to functional blocks. These techniques have been implemented in the Logic Analysis and Maintenance Planning (LAMP) System [11], [12] at Bell Laboratories.

II. GATE-LEVEL DEDUCTIVE SIMULATION

Before discussing deductive simulation of functional blocks, let us briefly review the deductive technique applied to gate-level simulation. The method was developed by Armstrong [6] and is used in the LAMP System [11], [12]. A more thorough discussion of this topic is contained in [6] and [12].

Each gate in the circuit is assumed to operate with zero delay, but the output of the gate may be delayed by an integer value. The fault-free output value of a gate at any time during simulation is called its *true value*. Associated with each gate output is a *fault list* which is the set of faults in the circuit, any *one* of which will cause the output of the gate to be incorrect (i.e., the complement of the current true value). The fault list associated with a gate output is a subset of the set of all faults being simulated. A null fault list at a gate output indicates that none of the simulated faults will cause the gate output to be complemented. A fault is detected if it is a member of the fault list associated with a monitored (i.e., observable) gate output.

The output fault list of a gate can be determined from the gate type, its input true values, input fault lists and the faults being simulated on the gate. For example, consider a 3-input NAND gate with inputs a, b, c and output d and the only faults simulated on the gate being the output stuck-at-0 and stuck-at-1 denoted by d_0 and d_1, respectively. Let the input true values be $a = 0, b = 1, c = 1$. Denoting set intersection, union, and difference by $\cap$, $\cup$, and $-$, respectively, and the fault list associated with a lead by the corresponding upper case letter, the output fault list D is given by

$$D = A - (B \cup C) \cup \{d_0\}.$$

Thus, the gate output will be incorrect, if a has the wrong value but b and c have the correct value, or if the output itself is stuck-at-0.

The fault list represented by $A - (B \cup C)$ may be considered to have *propagated* through the gate, and the fault d_0 is associated with the gate. If a circuit contains feedback, a fault associated with a gate may propagate around the feedback path to the inputs of the same gate. Such faults must be handled in a special way in order to obtain correct results. For the above example, the general equation for the output fault list, accounting for possible feedback, is

$$D = A - (B \cup C) - \{d_1\} \cup \{d_0\},$$

indicating that d_1 cannot be detected at the gate output, even if it propagates to the particular gate around a feedback path.

A 3-valued simulation will be assumed throughout this paper. The unknown value, x, may be due to uninitialized flip-flops or the result of oscillations or critical races. We shall associate a null fault list with every lead whose true value is unknown. This may result in some inaccuracy, but is a simple alternative to treating some faults as conditionally detectable (star faults) [6], [8].

III. FUNCTIONAL BLOCK DEFINITION

The functional blocks (or simply functions) which we shall consider may represent arbitrary combinational or sequential circuits. Each function may have any number (subject to some practical constraints) of inputs and outputs. Boolean variables that are internal to functions may also be used to represent internal states of sequential functions. Different delays may be associated with the outputs of a function. Although any combinational or sequential circuit can be defined in this manner, it is useful to be able to specify and simulate certain commonly used types of functions such as registers and memories, without treating each internal bit individually.

The following examples of functional block definitions are in the *Function Definition Language* (FDL) implemented in the LAMP System [13]. Key words in the language are shown in upper case. The interpretation of the function definitions in the examples should be fairly obvious.

Example 1:

```
GPF: seq;
INPUTS: a, b, c, d;
OUTPUTS: z1, z2;
BOOLEAN: y;
DEF:
    IF a & b THEN z1 = 0; z2 = 0; y = 0
        ELSE IF a & ¬b & ¬y
            THEN y = 1; z1 = c | d; z2 = 0
            ELSE z1 = 1; z2 = 1 FI FI FED
```

The first statement defines seq as a *general purpose function* (GPF). The inputs are a, b, c, and d, and the outputs are $z1$ and $z2$. y is an internal Boolean variable. The function definition begins with DEF and ends with FED. Similarly, FI's terminate IF statements. The symbols &, |, and ¬ denote logical AND, OR, and NOT, respectively. No delay has been specified in this function; outputs assume the newly computed value a unit delay (when delay is unspecified) after any input or internal Boolean variable changes. No delay is associated with Boolean variables, but the value of a Boolean variable is not updated until all the outputs have been evaluated. The Boolean variable retains its previous value for all unspecified conditions. Although the function defined above is extremely simple, it should be clear that any sequential function can be defined in this manner.

Example 2:

```
MEM: meml;
SIZE: 256, 16;
PREFIX: in, out, ad;
INPUTS: write, read, in[0-15], ad[0-15];
OUTPUTS: out[0-15];
HISTORY: 2;
DEF:
    IF write & write (−1) & ¬read & ¬read (−1)
        THEN meml⟨ad[0-7]⟩ = in[0-15];
            AT 2, out[0-15] = S0
        ELSE IF ¬write & ¬write (−1) & read & read (−1)
            THEN AT 2, out[0-15] = meml⟨ad[0-7]⟩
            ELSE AT 2, out[0-15] = out[0-15]
        FI FI FED
```

The function meml is a *memory* (MEM) with 256 16-bit words as specified by SIZE. The names in, out, and ad are declared to be prefixes, implying that two decimal digits will be concatenated with them to form names. HISTORY = 2 indicates that the present and one previous value of each input may be used in the function definition. The inputs to the function consist of the data input leads in00-in15, address leads ad00-ad07 and read and write controls, read and write. If write = 1 and read = 0 at the present time and one unit time ago, then the values of in00-in15 are written into the memory word specified by the eight address bits ad00-ad07. If the condition for writing the memory is not satisfied, it is implied the contents of the memory are unchanged. The outputs out00-out15 are specified to be 0 (denoted by $S0$, i.e., string of 0's) under this condition. The conditions for reading are also specified in essentially the same manner. A delay of two is associated with the outputs (specified by AT 2).

The above examples are intended to give a flavor of the type of functions under consideration. Another function type in FDL is the *register* (REG), which is similar to memory, except that individual bits may be accessed directly. Additional details of the language and how interconnections between functional blocks and gates are specified are given elsewhere [13].

In the following sections, we present a method of propagating faults through functions and simulating internal faults in them. We shall discuss the method in terms of functional blocks defined in FDL. However, the method is valid for arbitrary functions and is independent of the language used to specify the functions.

IV. FAULT PROPOGATION THROUGH FUNCTIONAL BLOCKS

A. General Method

Let a function be specified for all input sequences it may receive in the fault-free circuit and in the presence of any one of the simulated faults external to the function. This condition can be satisfied by specifying the function completely, i.e., for all combinations of inputs and internal states. The effect of a fault external to a function is that an incorrect input sequence may be applied to its inputs. The incorrect sequence applied to the inputs of a function can be determined from the sequence of true values and fault lists appearing at the function inputs. If the function is specified for all incorrect sequences applied to it, the incorrect output sequences can be determined without knowing how the function is realized, provided the function itself is fault-free. Thus, the input sequence and the sequence of input fault lists are sufficient for determining the output true value and fault list sequences.

Since the function outputs and output fault lists are independent of the function realization, we can use any representation of the function that is computationally convenient. We have chosen to use Boolean expressions of the internal variables and outputs for this purpose. The true values and fault lists associated with the internal variables and outputs can be computed directly from these expressions.

Let $x = (x_1, x_2, \cdots, x_m)$, $y = (y_1, y_2, \cdots, y_n)$ and $z = (z_1, z_2, \cdots, z_p)$ denote the inputs, internal variables, and outputs, respectively, of a function. In the function definition, each internal variable and output is defined by one or more assignment statements that may be expressed in the form:

$$y_i' = f_i(x, y)$$
$$z_j' = f_j(x, y, z_j),$$

where the prime denotes the next value of the variable. Note

that each output is allowed to be a function of itself so that it can retain its previous value under specified conditions. To represent the control specified by the IF-THEN-ELSE structure, we associate a variable c_j with each IF. The variable c_j will have the value 1 if the IF condition is true and 0 otherwise. Each assignment statement can be represented by a term of the form $f_i \cdot \pi c_j^*$, where c_j^* denotes c_j or $\bar{c}_j$ depending on whether the assignment is in the THEN or ELSE part of the condition represented by c_j and π represents the logical AND over all c_j^* that control the particular assignment via nesting of IF-THEN-ELSE structures. The equation for each output and internal variable is obtained by summing (logical OR) the terms corresponding to individual assignments.

The equations generated as discussed above are used for computing fault lists associated with internal variables and outputs. The equations contain only the unary operation NOT and the binary operations AND, OR, exclusive-OR and equivalence (not shown in the examples). The NOT operation does not affect the fault list associated with its operand. The fault lists, represented by upper case letters, resulting from the AND and OR operations depend on the values of the operands as given in the following tables:

Fault List Computation for AND

		a	
		0	1
b	0	$A \cap B$	$B - A$
	1	$A - B$	$A \cup B$

Fault List Computation for OR

		a	
		0	1
b	0	$A \cup B$	$A - B$
	1	$B - A$	$A \cap B$

The fault lists resulting from the exclusive-OR and equivalence operations are given by the exclusive-OR (i.e., $(A - B) \cup (B - A)$) of the fault lists associated with the operands. These fault list computations correspond to those for a circuit realizing the function using only two-input AND, OR, exclusive-OR and equivalence "gates" and inverters.

Example 3: The function of Example 1 can be represented by the following equations:

$$c_1 = ab$$
$$c_2 = ab\bar{y}$$
$$y' = 0 \cdot c_1 + 1 \cdot \bar{c}_1 \cdot c_2 + y \cdot \bar{c}_1 \cdot \bar{c}_2$$
$$= \bar{c}_1 c_2 + y\bar{c}_1 \bar{c}_2$$

$$z1' = 0 \cdot c_1 + (c + d) \cdot \bar{c}_1 \cdot c_2 + 1 \cdot \bar{c}_1 \cdot \bar{c}_2$$

$$= (c + d)\bar{c}_1 c_2 + \bar{c}_1 \bar{c}_2$$

$$z2' = 0 \cdot c_1 + 0 \cdot \bar{c}_1 \cdot c_2 + 1 \cdot \bar{c}_1 \cdot \bar{c}_2$$

$$= \bar{c}_1 \bar{c}_2.$$

In the above equations, c_1 and c_2 are variables associated with the two IF conditions and y', $z1'$, and $z2'$ denote the next values of y, $z1$, and $z2$, respectively. The term $y\bar{c}_1 \bar{c}_2$ in the equation for y' retains the previous value of y for the unspecified condition $c_1 = c_2 = 0$. To see how these equations may be used to compute output fault lists in terms of fault lists associated with inputs and internal variables, consider the case where $a = 1, b = 0, c = 0, d = 1, y = 0$. Let the fault list associated with each variable be denoted by the corresponding upper case letter. Thus, $c_1 = 0$ and using the table for the AND operation, we obtain the fault list associated with it as $C_1 = B - A$.

Similarly, $c_2 = 1$ and $C_2 = A \cup B \cup Y$, by repeated use of the same table. Note that the fault list associated with a complemented variable (for example $\bar{b}$) is the same as the fault list (B) associated with the uncomplemented variable.

The new fault list Y' associated with the internal Boolean variable y can now be computed from the fault lists C_1 and C_2 and the previous fault list Y associated with y. $y' = t_1 + t_2$ where $t_1 = \bar{c}_1 c_2$ and $t_2 = \bar{c}_1 \bar{c}_2 y$. Now, $t_1 = 1$ and $t_2 = 0$; therefore $y' = 1$,

$$T_1 = C_1 \cup C_2$$

and

$$T_2 = (C_2 \cap Y) - C_1.$$

Finally, using the table for the OR operation,

$$Y' = T_1 - T_2 = (C_1 \cup C_2) - (C_2 \cap Y - C_1).$$

Continuing in the same manner, we obtain

$$z_1' = (c + d)\bar{c}_1 c_2 + \bar{c}_1 \bar{c}_2 = t_3 + t_4$$

$$T_3 = (D - C) \cup C_1 \cup C_2$$

$$T_4 = C_2 - C_1$$

$$Z_1' = T_3 - T_4$$

$$z_2' = \bar{c}_1 \bar{c}_2$$

$$Z_2' = C_2 - C_1.$$

As mentioned earlier, the true values and fault lists of internal Boolean variables are updated only after all other computations are completed. This ensures that the same values of Boolean variables are used throughout the evaluation of a function.

Registers are evaluated by treating each internal bit of memory as an internal Boolean variable. Equations are generated for each bit of internal memory and each output bit and evaluated as in Example 3.

The method of evaluating functions discussed above may give incorrect results in some cases when one or more input values are unknown. Consider the statement:

IF a THEN $b = c$ ELSE $b = d$ FI

If the value of the variable a is unknown but $c = d$, then the output b is defined. However, if $a = x$ (unknown) the equation

$$b = ac + \bar{a}d$$

will give the correct value namely, $b = 0$ if $c = d = 0$, but the incorrect (pessimistic) value $b = x$ if $c = d = 1$. Note that this type of inaccuracy also occurs in 3-valued gate-level simulation.

B. Fault Propagation Through Memories

Fault list computation in memories is slightly more complex because address selection is implicit in the function description. Furthermore, faults on address leads will cause incorrect words in the memory to be accessed. Describing a memory in the following form enables the computation of fault lists directly from the equations.

Let n be the number of words in the memory and k the number of address leads $2^k \geq n$. Associated with each memory location (word) we define a binary variable a_i, $0 \leq i \leq n - 1$, such that $a_i = 1$ if and only if the signals on the address leads (treated as a k-bit binary number) represent the number i; otherwise, $a_i = 0$. That is, each a_i represents a decoded address, and $a_i = 1$ implies that word i of the memory is selected. A fault list A_i may now be associated with each variable a_i. The fault list A_i has the usual meaning: it is the set of faults that will cause a_i to be complemented. Thus, if $a_i = 0$, any fault in A_i will cause the location i to be accessed. If $a_j = 1$, A_j is the set of faults that will cause location j not to be accessed.

Let $c = (c_1, c_2, \cdots, c_k)$ be a binary vector denoting the signals on the address leads and let j be the integer represented by the vector c. That is, $j = 2^{k-1}c_1 + 2^{k-2}c_2 + \cdots + c_k$. For any i, the fault list A_i is computed as follows: Let $b_i = (b_{i1}, b_{i2}, \cdots, b_{ik})$ be the binary vector representing the integer i. Compute the vector $d_i = (d_{i1}, d_{i2}, \cdots, d_{ik})$, where $d_{ip} = c_p \oplus b_{ip}$, $1 \leq p \leq k$, where $\oplus$ represents modulo 2 addition (exclusive-OR).

The vector d_i will have 1's in exactly those positions where the vectors c and b_i differ. Therefore, the location i will be selected instead of the location j if and only if a fault external to the memory causes exactly those address leads corresponding to positions where $d_{ip} = 1$ to be incorrect, $1 \leq p \leq k$. The fault list A_i should contain only faults that are contained in the fault list of every address lead for which $d_{ip} = 1$ and none of the address leads for which $d_{ip} = 0$, $1 \leq p \leq k$. This can be stated mathematically as follows. Let

$$D_{1i} = \{p \mid d_{ip} = 1, 1 \leq p \leq k\}$$

$$D_{0i} = \{q \mid d_{iq} = 0, 0 \leq q \leq k\}$$

$$C_p = \text{fault list associated with } c_p$$

(i.e., the pth address lead).

If $a_i = 0$,

$$A_i = \bigcap_{p \in D_{1i}} C_p - \left(\bigcup_{q \in D_{0i}} C_q \right).$$

If $a_i = 1$,

$$A_i = \bigcup_{p=1}^{k} C_p.$$

The second equation indicates that a fault on any address lead will cause the correct location not to be accessed.

With the variables a_i and the associated fault lists defined as above, equations representing the write and read operations can be obtained. In order to write into location i, the conditions for writing must be satisfied and a_i must be 1. Similarly, the contents of location i are read out if $a_i = 1$, and the read condition is satisfied. The following example demonstrates the computation of fault lists associated with the memory of Example 2.

Example 4: Let w and r denote temporary variables, m_{ij}, $0 \le i \le 255, 0 \le j \le 15$ the variable representing the jth bit of the ith word, and m'_{ij} the next value of m_{ij}.

From Example 2, let

$$w = \text{write} \cdot \overline{\text{write} (-1)} \cdot \overline{\text{read}} \cdot \overline{\text{read} (-1)}$$

$$r = \text{read} \cdot \overline{\text{read} (-1)} \cdot \overline{\text{write}} \cdot \overline{\text{write} (-1)}.$$

Memory write:

$$m'_{ij} = w \cdot a_i \cdot \text{in}_j + \overline{(w \cdot a_i)} \cdot m_{ij},$$

where in_j is the jth data input, $0 \le i \le 255, 0 \le j \le 15$.

Memory read:

At 2, $\text{out}'_j = \sum_{i=0}^{255} \bar{w} \cdot r \cdot a_i \cdot m_{ij} + 0 \cdot w + \text{out}_j \cdot \bar{w} \cdot \bar{r}$,

$$0 \le j \le 15$$

where out_j and out'_j refer to the present and next values respectively of the jth output bit.

Using the above equations, the true value and fault list associated with every memory bit and every output may be computed as in Example 3. For writing memory, the effects of accessing incorrect locations due to address faults can be simulated by computing the fault list associated with every memory bit. Similarly, the summation over all memory words in the equation for memory read reflects the possibility of accessing incorrect locations due to faults affecting the address leads. The summation is obtained by interpreting "out[0-15] = meml⟨ad[0-7]⟩" in the function definition as

$$\text{IF } a_0 \text{ THEN out}'_j = m_{0j}$$
$$\text{ELSE IF } a_1 \text{ THEN out}'_j = m_{1j}$$
$$\cdots$$
$$\text{ELSE IF } a_{255} \text{ THEN out}'_j = m_{255,j}$$

for $0 \le j \le 15$.

If the location selected is k, then all nonnull fault lists A_i and $A_j, i \ne j, i \ne k, j \ne k$, are disjoint (i.e., no fault external to the memory can cause two incorrect locations to be accessed simultaneously). Also $A_i \subseteq A_k$. Therefore, terms containing $\bar{a}_i a_j, i \ne j$, for all i, j, will not affect the computation of the true values or fault lists of the outputs and are omitted from the equation.

The computation of the new true values and fault lists of memory bits can be simplified by making use of the fact that

if $a_i = 0$ and $A_i = \emptyset$ then m_{ij} will retain its previous value. Therefore, the new true values and fault lists need not be computed in such cases. Similarly, if $a_i = 0$ and $A_i = \emptyset$, the term $\bar{w} r a_i m_{ij}$ will have no effect on the true value or fault list associated with the output out'_j in the memory read equation. Thus, the summation need be performed only over all i such that $a_i \ne 0$ or $A_i \ne \emptyset$.

V. INTERNAL FAULTS IN FUNCTIONAL BLOCKS

The method of propagating fault lists through functional blocks can be modified to simulate internal faults which change the behavior of functions. In order to simulate these internal faults it is necessary to describe completely not only the normal behavior of the function, but also its behavior in the presence of every internal fault to be simulated. This imposes a practical limit on the number of internal faults that can be simulated. However, internal faults in functions are not restricted to the classical stuck-type faults, and therefore provide a convenient means of simulating some types of nonclassical faults. We shall first present the method in terms of a function with a single output.

Let $x = (x_1, x_2, \cdots, x_n)$ and let $g(x)$ be an expression which describes the normal behavior of the function. Let $g_1(x)$ represent the behavior of the functional block in the presence of an internal fault α_1. Now consider the function $h(x, f_1) = \bar{f}_1 g(x) + f_1 g_1(x)$. Clearly $h(x, f_1) = g(x)$ if $f_1 = 0$, and $h(x) = g_1(x)$ if $f_1 = 1$. We shall refer to f_1 as the *fault variable*.

Let us assign the true value 0 and the fault list $F_1 = \{\alpha_1\}$ to the fault variable f_1. Now, $h(x, f_1)$ describes not only the behavior of the normal function but also the behavior of the function with the single fault α_1. Since $f_1 = 0$, the true value of the function is always given by $g(x)$.

The internal fault α_1 which transforms the function $g(x)$ to $g_1(x)$ can be treated as a stuck-at-1 fault on the input f_1 of the function $h(x, f_1)$. Thus, the internal fault α_1 can be simulated by treating it as a fault on the fault variable f_1 (which behaves like an input with true value 0 and fault list $\{\alpha_1\}$) and propagating it through the function $h(x, f_1)$. The method also eliminates the need for explicitly deleting faults internal to a function from the input fault lists of the function due to feedback, as in the case of gate-level simulation. This is necessary in gate-level simulation because the faulty behavior of a gate is not explicitly defined.

The following example shows how a short circuit between two leads can be simulated as an internal fault in a function. This is intended only to demonstrate the method. It may not be an efficient method for simulating short circuit faults.

Example 5: Consider the case where the effect of a short circuit between two leads results in the logical AND of the signals on them to appear on both leads. This can be represented by a function with inputs a and b and outputs a' and b'. If f_S is the fault variable associated with the fault

$$a' = \bar{f}_S a + f_S ab$$

$$b' = \bar{f}_S b + f_S ab.$$

Let α_S denote the short-circuit fault, i.e., $F_S = \{\alpha_S\}$, and let the inputs and the input fault lists be

$$a = 0, \quad A = \{\alpha_1, \beta_0\}$$
$$b = 1, \quad B = \{\beta_0, \gamma_1\}$$

where α_1, β_0, and γ_1 are arbitrary external faults. The output true values and fault lists can be computed directly from the equations to be

$$a' = 0; \quad A' = \{\alpha_1, \beta_0\}$$
$$b' = 1; \quad B' = \{\beta_0, \gamma_1, \alpha_S\}.$$

If the input fault lists are $A = \{\alpha_1, \beta_0, \alpha_S\}$ and $B = \{\beta_0, \gamma_1\}$, then we obtain the output fault lists

$$A' = \{\alpha_1, \beta_0, \alpha_S\}$$
$$B' = \{\beta_0, \gamma_1\}$$

for the same input true values. Note that the internal fault α_S appearing in the input fault list A is treated correctly.

Another type of fault that can be simulated as an internal fault in a function is timing faults. The function realized by the gate is unaffected by the fault but the delay associated with the function is increased.

Example 6: Let a gate realize the NOR of two inputs x and y. If the normal delay through the gate is 5 and the timing fault α_t causes the delay to increase to 10, the behavior of the gate can be represented as follows:

$$z = \bar{f}_t \bar{x}(-5)\bar{y}(-5) + f_t \bar{x}(-10)\bar{y}(-10)$$

where $f_t = 0$ and the fault list F_t associated with f_t is $\{\alpha_t\}$.

The method discussed above for simulating single internal faults can also be used for simulating a number of internal faults (occurring individually). Let f_i be a fault variable representing a fault α_i, $1 \le i \le k$. If g is the normal function and g_i is the function resulting from the single internal fault α_i, the internal faults can be simulated using the equation:

$$h(x, f_i, f_2, \cdots, f_k) = f_1 g_1(x) + f_2 g_2(x) + \cdots$$
$$+ f_k g_k(x) + \bar{f}_1 \bar{f}_2 \cdots \bar{f}_k g(x).$$

Since the fault lists F_i are all disjoint and only one fault can be present in the function at any time, it is not necessary to specify the function for conditions such as $f_i \bar{f}_j$. Any internal fault α_i can be excluded from simulation by simply making $F_i = \varnothing$ (null fault list). Instead of describing each faulty function separately as discussed above, fault variables can be used within nested IF-THEN-ELSE statements, thus specifying parts of the function definition affected by each internal fault [13]. This method will, in general, result in shorter function definitions than the description of individual faulty functions.

With the approach discussed in this section, simulation of internal faults in functions is an extension of fault list propagation through functions described earlier.

VI. IMPLEMENTATION

The method discussed in Sections IV and V has been implemented in the LAMP System. Each function is described in the Function Definition Language as shown in Examples 1 and 2. Prior to simulation, function descriptions are converted from the IF-THEN-ELSE form to Boolean equations. These equations are used for computing true values and fault lists. Equations are represented in the reverse Polish (postfix) form [14] for simulation.

A last-in, first-out execution stack is used for evaluating functions. All operations performed are binary or unary Boolean operations and assignments, permitting the use of simple evaluation routines. Intermediate results obtained during evaluation, both true values and fault list pointers are left in the execution stack. This method is quite general and independent of the function being simulated. Future changes in the function types or Function Definition Language features will not necessitate changes in the evaluation programs.

Evaluation of a function is normally initiated when one or more of its inputs change. New true values and fault lists are computed for internal variables and function outputs. Internal Boolean variables are updated *after* all the outputs have been evaluated. The outputs are updated at the times specified in the function description. (This defaults to 1, i.e., the next time interval, if it is not specified.) This method guarantees that all outputs are computed based on the current values of internal variables.

Unlike internal variables, memory bits are updated as soon as their true values and fault lists are computed. This method was adopted in order to reduce the memory requirements of the program. A consequence of this method of computation is that the computed memory outputs are sensitive to the order in which the write and read operations are specified. However, this is not a serious disadvantage since the behavior of the memory function can usually be specified with sufficient accuracy by appropriate ordering of statements in the function definition.

In gate level simulation, it is sufficient to evaluate the output of a gate only if one or more of its inputs have changed (selective trace [15]). This may not be sufficient in the case of functions since they may depend on internal states and previous inputs. As in the case of gates, a function is evaluated whenever one or more of its inputs change (true value or fault list). In addition, it is reevaluated if the true value or fault list of any internal (Boolean) variable changes. If a function depends on previous values of inputs, it is scheduled for recomputation at the next instant of simulated time if the current true value and fault list of every input and all previous values and fault lists saved for that input are not equal.

The current implementation of function evaluation does not recognize critical races. Effects of simultaneous input changes will be determined by the simulator in the order in which these changes are perceived by the simulator.

VII. CONCLUSION

A method of propagating faults through functions using the deductive fault simulation technique has been presented. An extension of the method is shown to be capable of simulating arbitrary internal faults in functions. Although the need for specifying the faulty behavior of functions may restrict the number of internal faults that can be simulated practically, the capability makes the same simulator useful for widely different technologies and fault classes. A language for defining functions for simulation is presented. However, the techniques presented are independent of the language used for defining functions.

The functional simulation capabilities and algorithms described here have been implemented in the LAMP System at Bell Laboratories. They have been widely used to simulate memories, microprocessors and other large circuits. We expect that functional simulation is the vehicle which will allow us to simulate the larger and more complex circuits resulting from the new semiconductor technologies in a cost-effective manner.

ACKNOWLEDGMENT

The authors are indebted to J. F. Pellegrin, A. W. Roberts, and A. M. Schowe who developed different parts of the functional simulation feature.

REFERENCES

[1] S. Seshu, "On an improved diagnosis program," *IEEE Trans. Electron. Comput.*, vol. EC-14, pp. 76–79, Feb. 1965.

[2] F. H. Hardie and R. J. Suhocki, "Design and use of fault simulation for Saturn computer design," *IEEE Trans. Electron. Comput.*, vol. EC-16, pp. 412–429, Aug. 1967.

[3] T. T. Butler, T. G. Hallin, K. W. Johnson, and J. J. Kulzer, "LAMP: Application to switching system development," *Bell Syst. Tech. J.*, vol. 53, pp. 1535–1555, Oct. 1974.

[4] S. A. Szygenda, D. M. Rouse, and E. W. Thompson, "A model and implementation of a universal time delay simulator," in *Proc. 1970 Spring Joint Comput. Conf.*, pp. 207–216, 1970.

[5] H. Y. Chang, E. G. Manning, and G. A. Metze, *Fault Diagnosis of Digital Systems.* New York: Wiley, 1970, ch. 4.

[6] D. B. Armstrong, "A deductive method of simulating faults in logic circuits," *IEEE Trans. Comput.*, vol. C-21, pp. 464–471, May 1972.

[7] H. C. Godoy and R. E. Vogelsburg, "Single pass error effect determination (SPEED)," *IBM Tech. Disclo. Bull.*, vol. 13, pp. 3343–3344, Apr. 1971.

[8] A. D. Friedman and P. R. Menon, *Fault Detection in Digital Circuits.* Englewood Cliffs, NJ: Prentice-Hall, 1971, ch. 5.

[9] H. Y. Chang, S. G. Chappell, C. H. Elmendorf, and L. D. Schmidt, "Comparison of parallel and deductive fault simulation methods," *IEEE Trans. Comput.*, vol. C-23, pp. 1132–1138, Nov. 1974.

[10] A. Friedes, "The propagation of fault lists through combinational or sequential circuits," in *Proc. Workshop on Fault Detection and Diagnosis in Digital Circuits and Systems*, Lehigh University, pp. 12–41, Dec. 1970.

[11] H. Y. Chang, G. W. Smith, and R. B. Walford, "LAMP: System description," *Bell Syst. Tech. J.*, vol. 53, pp. 1431–1449, Oct. 1974.

[12] S. G. Chappell, C. H. Elmendorf, and L. D. Schmidt, "LAMP: Logic-circuit simulators," *Bell Syst. Tech. J.*, vol. 53, pp. 1451–1475, Oct. 1974.

[13] S. G. Chappell, P. R. Menon, J. F. Pellegrin, and A. M. Schowe, "Functional simulation in the LAMP system," in *Proc. 13th Design Automation Conf.*, pp. 42–47, June 1976.

[14] D. E. Knuth, *The Art of Computer Programming*, Vol. 1—*Fundamental Algorithms.* Reading, MA: Addison-Wesley, 1968.

[15] P. R. Menon, "A simulation program for logic circuits," Bell Lab., Naperville, IL, Internal Memo., Mar. 1965.

Premachandran R. Menon (M'70) received the B.Sc. degree from Banaras Hindu University, Banaras, India, in 1953, and the Ph.D. degree from the University of Washington, Seattle, in 1962, both in electrical engineering.

He was with the Delhi Cloth Mills, Delhi, India, from 1953 to 1957. From 1957 to 1963 he was with the Department of Electrical Engineering, University of Washington, where he became an acting Assistant Professor in 1962. He joined the Computing Techniques Research Department of Bell Laboratories, Murray Hill, NJ, in 1963, and transferred to Bell Laboratories, Naperville, IL, in 1971. His current interests are switching theory, fault diagnosis, and software verification. He is a coauthor of *Fault Detection in Digital Circuits* (Englewood Cliffs, NJ: Prentice-Hall, 1971) and *Theory and Design of Switching Circuits* (Woodland Hills, CA: Computer Science Press, 1975).

Stephen G. Chappell (M'72) received the B.E.E. degree in 1969 from Georgia Institute of Technology, Atlanta, the M.S. degree in electrical engineering in 1971, and the Ph.D. degree in computer science in 1973 from Northwestern University, Evanston, IL.

After joining Bell Laboratories, Naperville, IL, he was concerned with problems of logic-design automation, particularly logic simulation and automatic test generation. Currently, he is supervisor of a group concerned with the development and use of high level programming languages in electronic switching systems.

Dr. Chappell is a member of Eta Kappa Nu and Tau Beta Pi.

Reprinted from *Computer*, Volume 7, Number 4, April 1974, pages 39-44.

CONCURRENT SIMULATION OF NEARLY IDENTICAL DIGITAL NETWORKS

E. G. Ulrich and T. Baker
GTE Laboratories Inc.

Introduction

Test patterns for testing digital circuits are usually checked on a test verification program to determine if all or most of the possible faults will be detected. Historically, such a test verification program would be accomplished with many simulations: one for each possible fault.

Methods for a single-path simulation of all faults (or at least a substantial number of faults for larger networks) have been developed during recent years. Of the published work,[1,2,3,4,5] the earlier "deductive" method[1,2] and the "concurrent" method[5] described here are conceptually related. However, the latter method is faster, because it does not require fan-in lists, and is more accurate due to its ability to simulate the signable rise and fall transition delays.

In essence, the concurrent method consists of a single "good" network simulation and of concurrently running "bad" simulations whenever bad activity actually differs from good activity.

Some of the salient features of this technique are the following:

- The good net simulation includes the local detection of faults which have been initially injected into the network.

- These faults generate fault effects which are carried forward and cause the *divergence* of "bad gates" from good gates.

- Fault effects are either carried by good signals or by bad signals traveling within divergent bad networks.

- Diverged bad gates assume the full functional capability of good gates, i.e., they are scheduled and emit signals.

- Diverged bad gates disappear or *converge* as soon as their inputs and outputs are again in agreement with those of the associated good gate.

- The large number of events arriving due to many concurrently running bad simulations is handled by using the time-wheel[6] technique.

The efficiency of the concurrent method increases with the number of bad networks because the single good simulation assumes the burden of handling identical activity for more of these bad networks. This leads to effective simulation rates which exceed the basic simulation rate of a logic simulator by one-to-two orders of magnitude.

EH0278-2/88/0000/0204$01.00 © 1974 IEEE

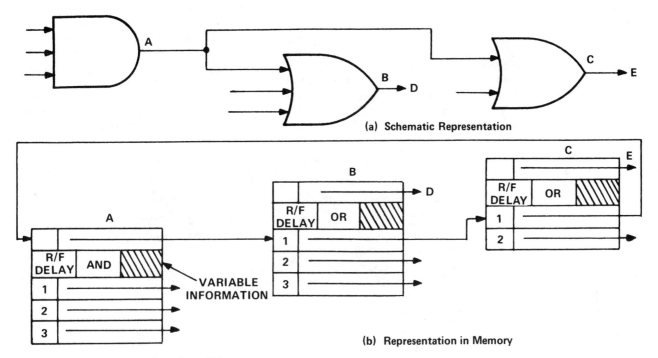

(a) Schematic Representation

(b) Representation in Memory

Figure 1. Network Modeling; Good Gates Only

A Network Model for Concurrent Simulation

The network model used here closely resembles a network model previously described[6] which was used for non-current logic simulation. Figure 1 shows an example of this network model for the case that only good gates are present in a simple network configuration. The example shows a source-gate feeding two destinations. Most of the information contained in each gate model is permanent, except for a small number of bits (9) reserved for variable information. Variable information consists of input bits, an output bit, and a bit to indicate the gate status — i.e., rest or transition.

Figure 2 shows the same network except that bad gates are temporarily attached to the permanently present good gates. These' bad gates are not due to local fault sources within gates A, B, or C, but are caused by fault sources (m and n) external to the given network. Each bad gate has a variable information field of nine bits indicating its difference from the associated good gate. Additional information contained in each bad gate is an identification number associating the bad gate with its own bad network, and simultaneously pointing back to the original fault source. In the example, m and n are the only bad networks present. The bad gate, A(n), having an output opposite to gate A, is "locally visible" and therefore responsible for the existence of B(n) and C(n). Bad gates A(m) and B(n) are "invisible" because their outputs are identical to the outputs of A and B. To facilitate fast processing, the bad gates attached to a good gate are maintained in the order of their identification numbers.

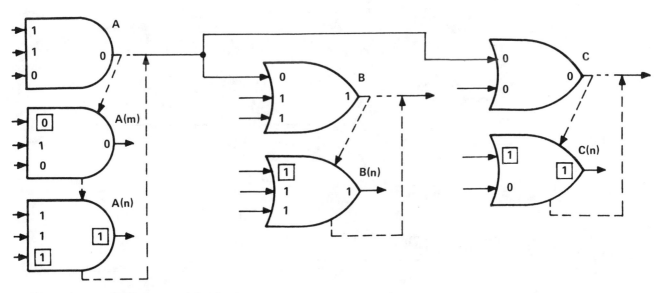

Figure 2. Network Model Containing Bad Gates

Concurrent Simulation

Figure 3 illustrates concurrent simulation for a small network involving feedback. A good signal (0→1), carrying along a single fault effect n (stuck-at-zero), enters the network at point E. In this case the good signal will cause element A to change from one to zero, but the fault effect n will cause the creation or "divergence" of bad gate A(n) from gate A. The good response signal (1→0) emerging from element A will again carry a fault effect n, indicating a stuck-at-one state. The new good signal coming from A causes element B to change and the fault effect n causes the divergence of bad gate B(n) from gate B. Again, the good response signal emerging from B will transmit fault effect n, indicating a stuck-at-zero state. Arriving at gate A, this new good signal will change only an input state, but the fault effect n rather than splitting off a second A(n) encounters the existing A(n) and will cause the second input of this gate to assume a S-A-O status.

This example illustrates concurrent simulation for the case that good network activity takes care of the propagation of fault effects. However, fault effects are also propa-

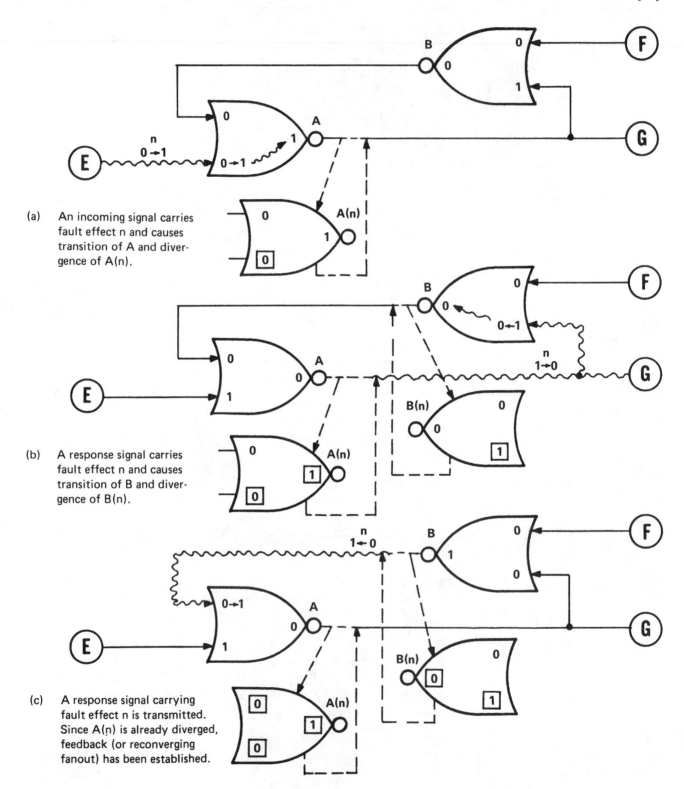

(a) An incoming signal carries fault effect n and causes transition of A and divergence of A(n).

(b) A response signal carries fault effect n and causes transition of B and divergence of B(n).

(c) A response signal carrying fault effect n is transmitted. Since A(n) is already diverged, feedback (or reconverging fanout) has been established.

Figure 3. Fault Effects Propagation Through a Feedback Loop

gated without being carried by good signals. An example of this is shown in Figure 4 where a good signal (0→1) arrives at good gate A and simultaneously at the associated bad gate A(n). The good gate, A, will not respond with an output change but the output of A(n) must be changed. This output change, although triggered by good machine activity, occurs only in machine n, and must consequently be transmitted as an independent bad signal.

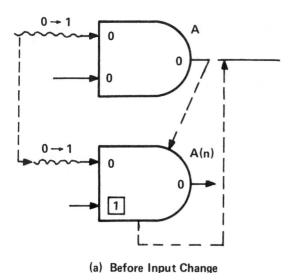

(a) Before Input Change

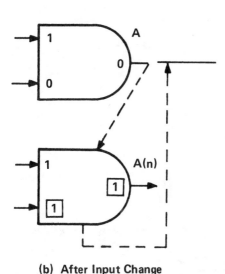

(b) After Input Change

Figure 4. A Good Signal Causes a Bad Output Response at A(n)

Treatment of Fault Sources

Associated with each gate in a digital network are the local faults originating at the gate. A good input change may make these faults visible or invisible, depending on whether the gate assumes a sensitive or insensitive input configuration. For example, the AND gate in Figure 5 is in an insensitive 0-0-1 input configuration because no single

input fault (or signal) can invert the gate output. However, complementing the second input would produce a sensitive 0-1-1 configuration, transforming an invisible stuck-at-one input fault at the first input into a visible fault.

The handling of local faults is effected here by inserting "bad origins" [see K(k) in Figure 5] into the ordered lists of bad gates. The functions of a bad origin gate are the following:

- To be simulated with the special purpose of establishing sensitivity or insensitivity.
- To substitute as an emission device for fault effects actually originating at a good gate, and simultaneously to serve as a catching device if these fault effects return via feedback paths to their point of emission.
- To serve as a fault container for *all* faults associated with a given good gate. This feature, although less natural than associating a bad origin with each fault, provides storage efficiency.

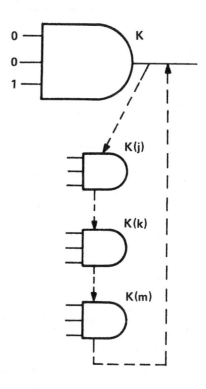

Figure 5. List of Bad Gates Containing Bad Origin K(k)

A bad origin remains within the list of bad gates as long as it contains any undetected faults, and is usually released after the last fault has been propagated to a point of detection.

Three-State Simulation and Network Initialization

An important feature of FANSSIM II is a three-state (0,1,U) simulation capability permitting six signal types (0→1, 1→0, U→0, U→1, 0→U, 1→U) to be propagated. Normal binary signals (0→1 and 1→0) are propagated and simulated at high speed, while the less frequent propagations and simulations involving the unknown state occur at a lower speed. Before network initialization, all gates, including bad

COMPUTER

origins, are in the unknown state, and the user may start his simulation by injecting zeros or ones into primary network inputs and selected internal gates. The consequences of these injected signals will quickly propagate through the network, usually causing all of the network gates to reach defined states.

Sometimes, this method of initialization and simulation produces an incompletely defined network together with oscillations which have been set up in feedback loops. To avoid this problem, the user may request that a special no-oscillations/zero delay initialization period precede his simulation. During this special initialization period, all gates, including bad origins, are simulated with zero-propagation delay and each gate may emit only a single $U \rightarrow 0$ or $U \rightarrow 1$ signal. The result of this kind of initialization is stable state networks which are still at time zero at the end of initialization. Thus, the network may be displayed after achieving stabilization in order to determine any remaining undefined gate.

Races, Oscillations, Spikes, and Hazards

Injecting faults into a good network will sometimes lead to the occurrence of races within the bad networks. This problem is solved here not via special software features but by the more flexible method of providing user options to define equivalent-gate circuits capable of race detection. As a result, user libraries frequently contain two versions of each bi-stable circuit, one with and one without race detection.

The difference between a real and a modeled bi-stable is that a race condition produces a race in the first while triggering a synchronous, but endless, oscillation in the second. The reason is that both halves of a modeled bi-stable have precisely identical delays, and thus do not provide the race-settling facility of the real circuit, which has slightly different delays. Although an oscillating bi-stable may be stopped to approximate a resolution of the race, this represents no real solution. The duration of the real race, and therefore the final state of the racing bi-stable, remain unpredictable. However, some acceptable solutions to the problem exist, and examples of this are shown in Figures 6 and 7.

A first solution involves a simulation of only two states and is based on the philosophy that a race must be detected but should continue as an endless oscillation rather than being settled arbitrarily. Figure 6 shows the model for a simple NOR-latch containing an extra "race" gate for race

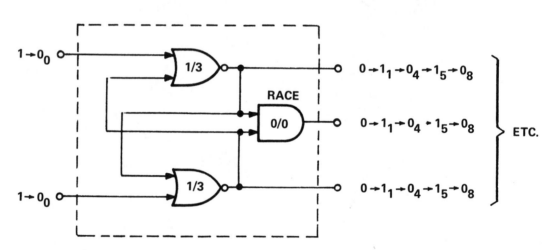

Figure 6. Example of Race Detection Using Two States

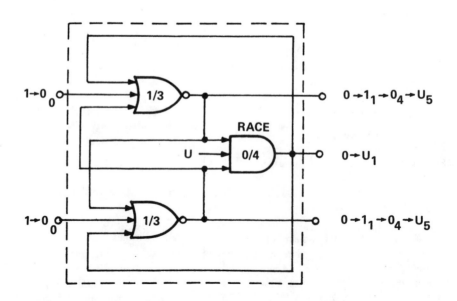

Figure 7. Example of Race Detection Using Three States

detection. The output of this gate will normally remain zero but will fluctuate with the latch outputs when a race occurs. By declaring the gate output a network output, the occurrence and timing of the race are detected and recorded even if the race causes no disturbances within the network.

Another solution to the same problem (Figure 7) uses the unknown state to settle the race. Here the race gate, having a permanent U-input, is connected to the latch gates and will force the propagation of the U-state when a race occurs.

Spikes, i.e., input states of insufficient duration to cause a gate output change, are always detected but not printed as output by the simulator. Although the action is rare, the user again has the option of defining spike-detecting versions of gates or bi-stables.

Finally, hazards as defined by Breuer[7] are not defined or detected because the unknown state (U) is not used as transition state between zero and one.

Conclusions

The major advantage of the system described is precise timing simulation in conjunction with high speed/low cost performance. An estimated effective simulation rate of a million signals/dollar exceeds the real simulation rate by a factor of 50:1, and exceeds the simulation rate of the typical contemporary logic simulator by 1000:1. Of course, this advantage exists only if a few hundred networks are simulated concurrently, and deteriorates for smaller networks having a correspondingly smaller number of faults.

A problem associated with the concurrent simulation of very large networks is a somewhat unpredictable requirement for dynamic storage. Solutions to this problem are: (1) subdivision of faults into manageable blocks[1] and the running of consecutive simulations; (2) reduction of work by eliminating equivalent faults;[5] and (3) fault sampling — i.e., the injection and simulation of a sufficiently representative sample of the total number of possible faults.

Regarding the problem of automatic fault test generation, the method of concurrent simulation offers no direct technical solution. However, the economies provided by this method are sufficient, for example, to reconsider methods such as random fault vector generation and simulation.

Acknowledgements

The authors are indebted to L. R. Williams for original contributions to the conceptual design of the concurrent simulation system. Also, technical contributions by D. Schuler, A. Margolies, and the review of drafts of this paper by S. Bryant are gratefully acknowledged.

References

1. D. B. Armstrong, "A Deductive Method for Simulating Faults in Logic Circuits," *IEEE Transactions on Computers*, May 1972.

2. A. Friedes, "The Propagation of Fault-Lists Through Combinational or Sequential Circuits," Workshop on Fault Detection, Lehigh University (December 1970).

3. R. B. Walford, "The Lamp System," Workshop on Fault Detection, Lehigh University (December 1970).

4. H. C. Godoy and R. E. Vogelsberg, "Single Pass Error Effect Determination (SPEED)," *IBM Tech. Disc. Bul.* (April 1971).

5. E. G. Ulrich, T. Baker, and L. R. Williams, "Fault-Test Analysis Techniques Based on Logic Simulation," *Proceedings Design Automation Workshop* (1972).

6. E. G. Ulrich, "Exclusive Simulation of Activity in Digital Networks," *Communications of the ACM*, February 1969.

7. M. A. Breuer, "A Note on Three-Valued Logic Simulation," *IEEE Transactions on Computers*, April 1972.

Ernst G. Ulrich is a project leader in computer-aided-design at GTE Laboratories. His primary interests are logic simulation, automatic fault test generation and verification, register transfer simulation, discrete event simulation, event processing for discrete event systems, and automatic placement.

At TRW, North American Rockwell, and Viatron Computer Systems he was responsible for the development of CAD systems for automatic placement and routing, logic simulation and automatic fault detection. Mr. Ulrich received a BS degree in mathematics from UCLA in 1959.

Thomas E. Baker is involved in the development of computer-aided-design at GTE Laboratories Inc. His effort has been primarily in the areas of logic simulation, test verification, test generation, and printed circuit board placement and layout.

He has worked for GTE Sylvania's Electronic Systems Division since 1955 in circuit, logic, and system design on various projects. These projects include the countermeasures equipment for the B-58 Hustler, the Ballistic Missile Early Warning System, MOBIDIC, ACP-1, MULTIPAC, high-speed logic circuits, all magnetic logic circuits (MADS), and logic and system design of multiprocessor systems for command/control.

Mr. Baker received his BS in physics from Union College, Schenectady, NY, in 1953 and his MS from the University of Illinois at Urbana in 1955. A member of IEEE and ACM, he has written papers on MOBIDIC, MULTIPAC, MADS, logic simulation, and test verification.

Algorithms for an Advanced Fault Simulation System in MOTIS

CHI-YUAN LO, HAO N. NHAM, AND AJOY K. BOSE, MEMBER, IEEE

Abstract—In this paper, we will present algorithms developed for an advanced fault simulation system in the MOTIS simulation environment. In particular, the algorithm to perform fault modeling and collapsing is first reviewed. Efficient algorithms to perform fault simulation are discussed in terms of fault list manipulation and primitive evaluation. The simulator realizes a speed gain factor of 787 to 2088 over serial fault simulation. Special emphasis is on an innovative fast unit delay fault simulation algorithm that achieves an additional 33–39-percent improvement in speed and 20–28-percent improvement in memory usage.

I. Introduction

FAULT SIMULATION is still, by far, the most popular method to determine the effectiveness of input vector sets that are used to separate good chips from faulty ones in a production environment. However, for today's complex circuits with thousands of faults, it is generally known that fault simulation is also a very time-consuming and expensive process. On the other hand, conventional fault simulation of MOS LSI circuits has been performed at a logic gate level. This approach suffers two problems. First, faults in the logic gate model are not always meaningful. Second, the behavior of transistor stuck-open faults is very difficult to model [12]. Therefore, it is also very important that the fault simulator provide a meaningful set of faults that is closely related to the physical defects [13] in the MOS circuits.

This motivated the development of the MOTIS fault simulator [5]. As a fault simulator, it supports circuits described at various levels, namely, transistor level, logic gate level, and functional level. It models both the classical stuck-at faults and the nonclassical transistor stuck-on, stuck-open faults. Fault simulation can be performed in either unit delay, or optionally multiple delay mode. The fault simulator was designed to simulate large circuits, with thousands of faults, in a single pass and with fast turnaround.

We begin the discussion of the algorithms by a brief review of the underlying simulator data structure. The algorithms are based on a compact *incremental* faulty gate representation and a transistor tree structure. The *incremental* faulty gate representation facilitates an efficient dynamic memory management that is practically immune to virtual memory thrashing. A fault modeling system is

Manuscript received May 27, 1985; revised October 31, 1986.
The authors are with AT&T Bell Laboratories, Murray Hill, NJ 07974.
IEEE Log Number 8612847.

based on the transistor tree structure and performs fault collapsing in almost linear time.

The attention is then directed to the main theme: fault simulation. The key to efficient fault simulation is analyzed in detail. In particular, the concept of composite event [3] is extended here to propagate only the minimum information among fault lists. The composite event concept is used to minimize the number of fault list traversals, while a novel nodal propagation list concept minimizes the fault simulation activities. In addition to fault list manipulations, efficient algorithms to perform primitive evaluation are presented. These algorithms take advantage of the functionality (enhanced *latency*) as well as the compact data structure (*incremental* evaluation). Not surprisingly, the fault simulator achieves a speed gain factor of 787 to 2088 over serial fault simulation (SFS). These numbers are very high compared to other published results. In addition, it demonstrates a superior capability to simulate a large number of faults in a single pass.

An innovative fast unit delay simulator is then derived from a simplification of the original fault simulation algorithms. The number of fault list traversals is reduced from two to one in the inner loop of fault simulation. In cases like inverters, the number of fault list traversals reduces to zero. The fast version realizes an additional speed gain of 33–39 percent, or alternatively, a factor of 1588 to 3984 over SFS. Compared to the multiple delay fault simulator, it also uses 20–28 percent less memory.

II. Basic Simulator Data Models

A circuit is represented to the simulator as interconnections of single directional gates. A gate g_i performs certain functions, and may have n inputs (I), m outputs (O), and possibly k internal states (S). The function of a gate g_i can be described by its transfer functions

$$O[1:m] = f_i(I[1:n], S[1:k])$$

$$S[1:k] = g_i(I[1:n], S[1:k]).$$

The function f_i can be simple logic functions such as NAND, NOR, or a more complex transistor structure as shown in Fig. 1. It can also be a functional memory. Bidirectional transmission gates can be grouped into larger single directional superblocks [7]. In the simulator, we differentiate two types of records, namely gate records g_i's and signal records s_j's. A gate g_i is driven by its fan-in signals $\{s_{i_1}, \cdots, s_{i_n}\}$, and is associated with its output

Reprinted from *IEEE Transactions on Computer-Aided Design*, Volume CAD-6, Number 2, March 1987, pages 232-240. Copyright © 1987 by The Institute of Electrical and Electronics Engineers, Inc. All rights reserved.

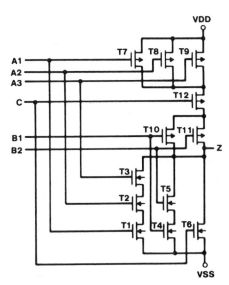

Fig. 1. A CMOS AND-OR-INVERT gate.

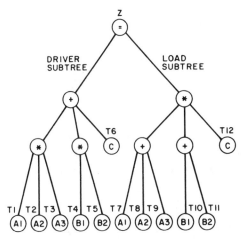

Fig. 2. The tree representation for the driver-load gate.

signals $\{s_{i_1}, \cdots, s_{i_m}\}$. Each output signal s_j, $j \in \{i_1, \cdots, i_m\}$, in turn drives its fan-out gates $\{g_{j_1}, \cdots, g_{j_l}\}$. For simplicity, signal s_i and gate g_i are labeled with the same subscript i if g_i is a single output gate.

Alternatively stated, the simulator data structure is a bipartite graph $B = \{G, S, E\}$, where G is a set of vertices representing gates g_i's, S is a set of vertices representing signals s_j's. The edge set E represents the following three relationships:

$$e_{ij}^{gs} = \text{signal } s_j \text{ is an output of gate } g_i$$

$$e_{ij}^{\text{fan-in}} = s_j \text{ is a fan-in signal of } g_i$$

$$e_{ij}^{\text{fan-out}} = g_i \text{ is a fan-out gate of } s_j.$$

A. Driver-Load Gate Representation

The most common transistor structure is a series-parallel transistor gate. An example is shown in Fig. 1. Such a transistor structure is best represented by an evaluation tree as shown in Fig. 2. The output node Z consolidates the results from both the driver and load subtrees. Each subtree can be further broken down into series ($*$) connection, parallel ($+$) connections, and unary (t) transistors. The transistors are always at the leaf nodes.

The internal data structure for such a transistor tree is an expression that consists of a driver subexpression, an output node separator, and a load subexpression. The driver(load) subexpression is basically the depth first traversal sequence of the subtree with a mixture of prefix and postfix strings. For example, the driver subexpression in Fig. 2 looks like

$$(*)_{pr}^3 A1A2A3 (*)_{pr}^2 B1B2 (t)C (+)_{po}^3.$$

The first $(*)_{pr}^3$ indicates that the operator ($*$) is in *prefix* notation and has *three* operands that are to follow. Similarly, the $(+)_{po}$ indicates that the operator ($+$) is in *postfix* notation and expects the operands to come from the top *three* entries of a working stack. It is clear that when

an expression is processed, the result of each operation is pushed back to the working stack.

As described previously [6], this transistor tree structure facilitates not only the timing and logic evaluation, but fault generation and collapsing as well.

B. Faulty Gate Data Structures

To support fault simulation, each gate g_i in the circuit is associated with a fault list $\{g_i^{f_1}, g_i^{f_2}, \cdots, g_i^{f_n}\}$, where $f_1 < f_2 < \cdots < f_n$. A faulty gate $g_i^f = \{f, \Delta I_f, \Delta O_f, \Delta S_f\}$ contains a fault number f, *incremental* input records ΔI_f, *incremental* output records ΔO_f, and *incremental* internal state records ΔS_f. These records specify the difference in status between the faulty gate g_i^f and the good gate g_i. The ΔI_f, ΔO_f, and ΔS_f all share the same format that indicates a specific pin or state *position* and the *value* that is different. For multiple delay considerations, the ΔO_f also includes some *timing* information. Note that it is possible for a ΔO_f to differ from the good circuit only in *timing* information but not in *value*.

In general, an incremental representation requires less storage than a full representation, since the differences between a faulty gate and a good gate are few. In implementation, we choose fixed-size records to represent g_i^f, ΔI_f, ΔO_f, and ΔS_f. The fixed-size record format allows for fast memory allocation. Furthermore, for a single-output gate with single-input difference and no internal state, the representation can be reduced to physically a g_i^f record by utilizing the pointer fields directly. Significant storage efficiency can be achieved since, in practice, most faulty gates are found to be of this type.

The significance of a *compact incremental* data structure is threefold. First, a very large number of faults can be simulated in a single pass. In fact, the simulator rarely goes into multiple passes for ordinary circuits having more than ten thousand faults. Second, as will become clear, an *incremental* data structure supports an *incremental* gate evaluation, which can be very efficient compared to a *full* evaluation. Finally, the incremental data structure lends itself to an efficient memory management algorithm that

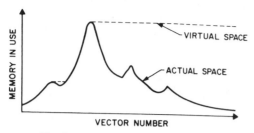

Fig. 3. Dynamic memory requirement.

is practically immune to the virtual memory thrashing problem.

C. Dynamic Memory Management

During the fault simulation process, dynamic storages are constantly allocated and deallocated for fault list processing. It is important to provide an efficient memory management scheme. By adopting the incremental representation for faulty gates, the memory management problem reduces to that of a fixed-size record allocation. The latter can easily be implemented by using a single garbage list $GB = \{R_1, \cdots, R_n\}$, where R_i is a fixed-size record that can be allocated and freed in $O(1)$ time. This simple approach, however, suffers significant performance penalties for large circuits due to virtual memory thrashing.

Fig. 3 shows the dynamic memory requirements as the simulation progresses. Initially, the circuit is in an unknown state; faults are mostly dormant. As the circuit is initialized, fault effects g_i^f's start to propagate and the memory consumption goes up. As the differences build up, faults will be detected and removed from simulation, and the memory requirements will start to decline. The dotted line in Fig. 3 shows the virtual space spanned by the relatively small memory in active use. A persistently large virtual space causes a severe page fault problem. Our experience has shown that, other than the peak periods, the average memory requirements are generally moderate. Therefore, if the memory records in use can be held physically close to each other, the page fault problem can be alleviated.

To implement such a memory management scheme, the dynamic memory space is divided into a few, say k, large partitions of equal sizes $GB_1, \cdots, GB_k$. An individual garbage list $GB_i = \{R_{i_1}, \cdots, R_{i_n}\}$ is maintained for each partition. When a record R_{ij} is freed, it is returned to the garbage list of the corresponding partition GB_i. In the allocation process, a garbage list GB_i is prioritized according to their partition number i, that is, R_{ij} will be allocated before R_{kj} only if $i > k$. The dynamic memory in use will then tend to cluster in the lower partitions as the simulation progresses.

Via direct address mapping, a free operation can be performed in $O(1)$ time. The allocation operation is normally of $O(1)$ time, and occasionally of $O(\log k)$ time when it switches between partitions. The performance of this new scheme, for one example circuit that requires 4 Mbyte of memory, is a 30-percent reduction in page fault rate on a VAX machine. Despite the additional time com-

plexity, the actual CPU time is reduced by 10 percent in this case. Obviously, the savings are more significant for larger circuits.

III. Fault Modeling

A. Basic Fault Models

A very detailed description of fault modeling and collapsing for MOS circuits has been previously presented [5]. While there are some recent works [10], [11] on more accurate MOS fault models, these simulators are fairly slow. The emphasis in this paper is on fast fault simulation algorithms. We feel that our fault model, though restricted, is practically adequate. To be brief, the classical stuck-at faults are modeled at each input and output terminal of a gate. Optionally, the nonclassical faults, transistor stuck-on and stuck-open, are modeled for each transistor inside a gate. The fault collapsing process is to group all equivalent faults into disjoint sets such that only one fault in each set needs to be simulated. The equivalence relationship can be derived from the series and parallel transistor structure, the function of the gate, and connectivity. Also, undetectable faults are discovered in the process and removed.

B. The Fault Collapsing Algorithm

Fault collapsing begins with the enumeration of all faults from each gate g_i. To illustrate, consider a driver-load gate g_i with n inputs $I_1, \cdots, I_n$, one output O_1, p transistors $t_1, \cdots, t_p$, and q operators $op_1, \cdots, op_q$, a total of $2(n + 1 + p + q)$ faults will be enumerated as shown below:

fault type	enumerated faults
input faults	$f_i^{I_1}$ s-0, $f_i^{I_1}$ s-1, $\cdots$, $f_i^{I_n}$ s-1
output faults	$f_i^{O_1}$ s-0, $f_i^{O_1}$ s-1
internal transistors	$f_i^{t_1}$ s-on, $f_i^{t_1}$ s-open, $\cdots$, $f_i^{t_p}$ s-open
internal operators	$f_i^{op_1}$ s-on, $f_i^{op_1}$ s-open, $\cdots$, $f_i^{op_q}$ s-open.

Fault equivalence is implemented by a UNION-FIND [9] algorithm. It is first performed on individual gates. For each gate, the internal fault collapsing is done by a depth first traversal of the evaluation tree, that is, a sequential execution of the expression with a stack. For example, the execution of "$(*)_{pr}^2 B1B2$" fragment in gate g_i will cause the operator stuck-open fault to be equivalent to those of its operands. That is, UNION($f_i^{(*)}$ s-open, f_i^{B1} s-open) and UNION($f_i^{(*)}$ s-open, f_i^{B2} s-open) are performed. The operator faults $f_i^{(*)}$ s-on, $f_i^{(*)}$ s-open, are saved on the stack. When "$(+)_{po}^3$" is executed, the operator stuck-on is found to be equivalent to those of the operands taken from the stack. It can be seen that transistor fault collapsing becomes a sequential execution of the tree expression with a stack. In the same process, some transistor faults can be collapsed with input pin faults. Also, undetectable faults, or unnecessary faults like the operator faults, are marked for later removal.

Following the transistor fault collapsing, the input-to-output pin fault collapsing is performed by the following functional evaluation fault collapsing rule. Finally, a global connectivity rule is applied for further collapsing. At the end, one fault is selected out of each equivalent class by a FIND operation.

Functional Evaluation Fault Collapsing Rule

let gate g_i be a driver-load transistor structure
let the function f_i represent a transfer function for g_i
let a, b be binary numbers 0 or 1
IF $f_i(x,x,\cdots,x, a,x,\cdots,x) = b$
AND the a is at the jth position
THEN
$\quad$ do UNION($f_i^{I_j}$ s-a, $f_i^{O_1}$ s-b)

Global Fault Collapsing Rule

IF signal s_i drives only gate g_j
AND s_i is the kth input of g_j
AND s_i is the mth output of g_l
THEN
$\quad$ do UNION($f_l^{O_m}$ s-0, $f_j^{I_k}$ s-0)
$\quad$ and
$\quad$ do UNION($f_l^{O_m}$ s-1, $f_j^{I_k}$ s-1)

C. Complexity Analysis

In addition to the static simulator data structures, fault collapsing requires $O(N + T + OP + I + O)$ space, where N is the total number of gates, T is the total number of transistors, OP is the total number of operators, $I(O)$ is the total number of input(output) terminals to gates. Since an average gate contains about three input, one output, and a small number of transistors, the space complexity is roughly $O(N)$.

Let TOP_{avg} denote the average number of transistors and operators per gate, I_{avg} denote the average number of inputs per gate, and EQ_{avg} denote the average number of faults per equivalence class. The total transistor fault collapsing takes $O(NTOP_{avg} \log EQ_{avg})$, the total input to output fault collapsing takes $O(NI_{avg} \log EQ_{avg})$ time. The global collapsing requires $O(N \log EQ_{avg})$ time. Since both TOP_{avg} and I_{avg} are relatively small numbers, the overall time complexity is $O(N \log EQ_{avg})$. The time complexity is very close to clear, since the average number of faults per equivalent class is also fairly small In reality, the execution time has been found to be negligible.

IV. MULTIPLE DELAY FAULT SIMULATION ALGORITHM

The idea of concurrent fault simulation was first proposed by Ulrich and Baker [1]. This approach takes advantage of the observation that each fault changes the circuit behavior only very slightly. By simulating the good circuit and all the faulty circuits (represented explicitly by the difference) at the same time, significant performance gain can be achieved as compared to the serial fault simulation method. We cite the paper by Schuler and Cleghorn [2] as the first detailed implementation of the concurrent fault simulation technique. They showed how a single good circuit event is processed by traversing the two affected fault lists. Abramovici, Breuer, and Kumar [3] extended the concurrent fault simulation concept to handle functional level primitives. The composite event was also introduced where the good and faulty events associated with the same signal are treated as a single entity. Instead of traversing fault lists for each event, the composite event approach reduces the number of fault list traversals, a desirable feature to have for the simulation of a large number of faults.

The key concept in our fault simulation algorithm is an extension of the composite event concept to propagate only minimum information. In addition, the algorithm can be easily adapted to a unique fast unit delay version.

A. Fault Effect Propagation

It is assumed that prior to fault simulation, fault origins g_i^f's are injected into a circuit. Since the circuit is initially at an unknown state, the fault origins are viewed, at this time, as having no difference from the good circuit. A fault origin record g_i^f remains on the fault list FL_i of gate g_i until the fault is detected at some network outputs. Since fault origins require special processing, they will be left out from further discussions.

The key concept in the algorithm is the composite event that consists of an even header and a list of faulty events.

The Fault Effect Propagation Problem

let CEV_i denote the composite event before processing at signal s_i
let NPL_i denote the composite event after processing at signal s_i
let FL_j denote the fault list of g_j where s_i originates (e_{ji}^{GS} exist)

The fault effect propagation problem is to find
$$NPL_i = \{ \langle s_i, G, nv \rangle \langle f_{npl_1}, vf, M \rangle, \cdots, \langle f_{npl_k}, vf, M \rangle \}$$

where $f_{npl_k} \in \{ FL_j + CEV_i \}$
given
$$CEV_i = \{ \langle s_i, G, nv \rangle \langle f_{cev_1}, vf \rangle, \cdots, \langle f_{cev_m}, vf \rangle \}$$
and
$$FL_j = \{ g_j^{fl_1}, g_j^{fl_2}, \cdots, g_j^{fl_n} \}.$$

The event header $\langle s_i, G, nv \rangle$ denotes that signal s_i is undergoing transition in either the good circuit or the fault circuits. The G flag marks that the good event is present and the new value is nv. The header is followed by a list of faulty events of the form $\langle f_{cev_j}, vf \rangle$, where f_{cev_j} identifies the fault with new value vf.

Before the effect of a composite event CEV_i is propagated to the fan-out gates, it is modified to become a nodal propagation list NPL_i. The NPL entry $\langle f_{npl}, vf, M \rangle$ is exhaustively defined for each fault in Table I based on the

TABLE I
NODAL PROPAGATION LIST

good signal	faulty signal	before->after	NPL_j	evaluation
no change	no change	same->same	none	no
		dif.->dif.	none	no
no change	change	dif.->same	M=0	yes
		same->dif.	M=0	yes
		dif.->dif.	M=0	yes
change	change	same->same	none	yes
		dif.->same	M=0	yes
		same->dif.	M=0	yes
		dif.->dif.	M=0	yes
change	no change	dif.->same	none	no
		same->dif.	M=1	no
		dif.->dif.	none	no

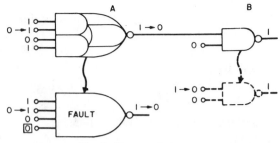

Fig. 4. Phantom faulty gate.

existence of both good and faulty events, and the difference in value between the good and faulty signals before and after the transition. Note that there are situations where an *NPL* entry is not required, as indicated by *none* under the NPL_j heading. Otherwise, an *NPL* entry is created with the fault number, the indicated *M* flag, and the newest faulty value.

The idea in the *NPL* list is that only minimum information is propagated. Simply stated, the *NPL* list is derived from the faulty events in *CEV* with two modifications. First, faulty events that are identical to the good event in value both before and after the transition are removed. Second, in the case that a stable faulty signal becomes newly visible due to a good event, it is added to the *NPL* list with the "*M*" flag set to 1.

Of particular interest is the case *same* → *same*, where the *NPL* entry is suppressed. The filtering of identical

changes is very desirable since a significant fraction of faulty events can be removed, assuming that most faulty gates only differ from the good gate very slightly. Note that in a conventional approach, these faulty events are propagated, causing unnecessary divergence, evaluation, and the subsequent convergence. An example is shown in Fig. 4, where the good circuit and the faulty circuit change simultaneously at gate A. With the *NPL* approach, only the good event is propagated, thus avoiding the creation of a *phantom* faulty gate B that is subsequently removed. The concept of minimum information in *NPL* is essential for high-speed fault simulation, since it reduces the fault simulation activities to a minimum.

B. Basic Fault Simulation Steps

With the concept of *NPL* in mind, the basic fault simulation process is simply to fetch composite events, convert them into *NPL*'s, and process the fault lists on the fan-out gates, which in turn produces new composite events for the future time points. These steps are explained more specifically below.

Basic Simulation Steps
let EV denote a list of gates to be evaluated
Step 1: advance simulation time
    time = time + 1
Step 2: output signal update
    for each current composite event CEV_i
        if(good event exist)
            update good circuit signal s_i at gate g_j
            mark good node change flag at s_i
        end if
        traverse the fault list FL_j of g_j and replace CEV_i with NPL_i
        add fan-out gates g_k of s_i to EV
    end for
Step 3: fault list evaluation
    for each gate g_i in EV with m outputs
        remove g_i from EV
        evaluate the entire fault list FL_i of g_i
        output new composite events $CEV_{O1}, CEV_{O2}, \cdots, CEV_{Om}$
    end for
Step 4: clean up
    for each NPL_i
        reset good node change flag at s_i
        release NPL_i records to the memory manager
    end for
Step 5: complete one time step
    go to step 1

1) Advance Simulation Time: At this step, the simulator time is incremented. It is assumed that external input stimuli are injected at this point by a periodic self-awakening co-process.

2) Output Signal Update: The major task at this step is to convert a composite event CEV_j into an NPL_j format by traversing the fault list FL_i. Each faulty gate g_i^f output will be updated with new value vf from the composite event entry $\langle f, vf \rangle$, and may generate NPL entry $\langle f, nf, M \rangle$ based on Table I. The fan-out gates g_k are then saved in the EV list for later fault list evaluation.

3) Fault List Evaluation: At this step, fault lists are evaluated to generate new composite events for the future simulation time. For simplicity, let's consider single-output gates without internal states and with only single-input change.

Fault List Evaluation Problem

assume g_j be a single-output gate
and there is only a single-input change at fan-in s_i

given NPL_i at s_i obtained from output signal update step
and FL_j^- at g_j
and g_j is a fan-out gate of s_i
find
   CEV_j and new FL_j^+

This fault list evaluation problem can be solved by the process depicted in Algorithm 2.

Algorithm 2: Fault List Evaluation

Step 1: good gate evaluation
   if(signal s_i changes)
      evaluate good gate g_j
      record new value at signal s_j
   end if
Step 2: fault list update
   let FL_j^+ be $\{ FL_j^- + NPL_i \}$ initially
   by diverging new g_j^f for each $f \in \{ NPL_i - FL_j^- \}$
   for each fault $f \in FL_j^+$
      perform input update at g_j^f
      if(input changes at g_j^f)
         evaluate g_j^f
         record new output value nv_f
      end if
      if(nv_f changes) schedule new $\langle f, nv_f \rangle$ entry to CEV
      remove faulty gate g_j^f from FL_j^+ if possible
   end for
Step 3: output new event
   put new composite event CEV_j to future time point

First, the good gate g_j is evaluated if there are input changes. The returned new value is saved for two purposes: one is to decide if new good event should be generated, the other is to serve as a reference for convergence. After g_j is processed, the faults in the union $\{ FL_j + NPL_i \}$ is then processed. A faulty gate g_j^f is created (diverged), if it is not previously present in FL_j^- but is in the input NPL_i. Note that since the faulty gate g_j^f is rep-

resented *incrementally*, the task of new gate creation is trivial.

The algorithm next performs an input update for g_j^f. The input update function takes two inputs: the current ΔI_f^- and the NPL_i entry $\langle f, nv, M \rangle$; it outputs a new ΔI_f^+, and a faulty gate input change flag. The input change flag is set for those cases marked *yes* under column *EVALUATION* of Table I. In other words, an input change is found if the NPL_i^f is missing and good circuit has a change or if NPL_i^f is present and M flag is 0. A faulty gate evaluation will be performed only when there are input changes. In such a case, the faulty gate is evaluated with ΔI_f^+ and ΔS_f. After the gate evaluation, a new ΔO_f^+ is created. A faulty event will be generated if a change occurs. Note that the traditional spike analysis applies in deciding whether an event should be created. Finally, if all three lists ΔI_f^+, ΔS_f^+, ΔO_f^+ in g_j^f become empty, g_j^f can be removed (converged) from the fault list FL_j.

The CEV_j is created after the fault list evaluation of FL_j. Note that for signals with different rise and fall delays, both CEV_j^{rise} and CEV_j^{fall} will be generated for different time points. These events are inserted to the appropriate future simulation time points.

If multiple input changes occur, say at s_{j1} and s_{j2}, the combined effect of these input changes has to be considered. Faults in the union $\{ FL_j^- + NPL_{j1} + NPL_{j2} \}$ will be processed. A faulty gate g_j^f is diverged if fault f is in $\{ NPL_{j1} + NPL_{j2} - FL_j^- \}$. The input change flag is set if any of the input changes. As such, the algorithm can be extended to the multiple input change situation.

4) Clean Up: This step simply resets flags and releases the NPL memory. At this time, the simulator is ready to advance to the next cycle.

It can be seen that the fault list processing can become very efficient by adopting the concept of composite event and nodal propagation list. As will become clear, the NPL concept has lead us to discover a fast unit delay fault simulation algorithm.

C. Primitive Gate Evaluation

Besides the fault list manipulation algorithms, it is equally important that gate evaluation be carried out efficiently. The approach of table lookup has been proposed for fast evaluation. However, this approach does not allow gates to have more than six inputs and is restricted to Boolean functions. Therefore, instead of a general table lookup evaluation, we take advantage of the functionality of the primitives and devise separate algorithms.

The tree expression of MOS gates facilitates efficient evaluation. Instead of actually traversing the evaluation tree, the expression is executed sequentially with a stack. Based on the operator types, many early termination schemes are possible. For example, in the execution of an (*) operator, once an operand is found to be in an OFF state, the remaining operands can be bypassed.

1) Enhanced Latency Analysis: Other than evaluating a MOS gate efficiently, it is possible to avoid gate evaluation completely. In event-driven simulators, conventional latency (or selective trace) techniques imply that gate evaluations are triggered by input signal changes. This latency technique can be enhanced by taking advantage of the fact that very often, the output states of a gate do not change in response to input changes. Under certain input and output conditions, it can be determined *a priori* that the output state will remain unchanged. In these cases, the evaluation is bypassed completely.

The enhanced latency analysis can be stated as follows:

The Enhanced Latency Rule

let g_i be a driver-load gate in CMOS,
   or in NMOS with a single pullup load
let the *opposite* of $\langle 0,1,x \rangle$ be $\langle 1,0,x \rangle$, respectively

IF an input to g_i is changing to v
AND v is the *opposite* of s_i, the output of g_i
THEN
   v has no effect on s_i

The statement can be proven by exhaustive enumeration. For example, in an NMOS gate, a current output value of 0 implies that the driver is conducting. Any input changing to 1 will only cause more driver transistors to conduct. The output value therefore remains unchanged. This rule is very simple to test and has been found to reduce the number of gate evaluations by up to 40 percent [6].

2) Incremental Evaluation: Another approach called *incremental* evaluation is developed here specifically for logic gates and some functional primitives. The incremental evaluation approach is based on the incremental representation of the faulty gates and the fact that good gate evaluation always precedes that of other faulty gates. Depending on the function of the gate, if certain information in the good gate evaluation is retained, the evaluation of the faulty gates can be simplified.

If a full good gate evaluation is defined as $O_{good} = f(I)$, then an *incremental* faulty gate evaluation is $O_f = O_{good} - \Delta f(\Delta I_f)$. Presumably, the term $\Delta f(\Delta I_f)$ is much easier to compute than $f(I_f)$. The idea can be better demonstrated by an example of a logic AND gate. In the good gate evaluation, let ONECNT(ZEROCNT) denote the number of inputs that are currently in a logic ONE (ZERO) state. The output is a logic ZERO if ZEROCNT is positive, else a logic ONE if ONECNT is equal to the number of inputs. Otherwise, the output is unknown. For the faulty gate evaluation, if the number of input differences is less than the ZEROCNT, a most likely case, then the output is a logic ZERO. Otherwise the ONECNT and ZEROCNT from the good gate are inherited as the initial local value. For each input difference, the local ONECNT and ZEROCNT are modified depending on the corresponding good circuit input value. Finally, the output is generated based on these two counts.

It should be noted that the *incremental* faulty gate evaluation significantly improves the performance if the input differences remain rare. Although this approach slows down the good gate evaluation slightly, the overall performance has been found to be improved. After all, the number of the faulty gate evaluations is much greater than that of the good gate evaluations.

The incremental evaluation concept presented here asserts the possibility that simulating a large number of faults in a single pass can be more efficient than that of multiple passes if memory permits. It also maximizes the use of an *incremental* faulty gate representation.

V. Fast Unit Delay Fault Simulation

While alternatives [8] have been proposed for fault simulation, we would like to explore the potential of a fast algorithm in a restricted unit/zero delay environment.

It is generally known that the speed of a fast unit delay simulator can be achieved by a simplified time queue structure and scheduling algorithm. While this is true for a good circuit simulator, its impact is much less for a fault simulator where the predominant CPU time is spent traversing fault lists. In this section, we will present two new algorithms, in conjunction with a simplified time queue and scheduling, that achieve 40-percent speedup over its multiple delay counter part.

A. Nodal Propagation List

In reviewing the basic fault simulation algorithm, it can be seen that fault lists are traversed in the signal update loop (step 2 of Algorithm 1) and the evaluation loop (step 3 of Algorithm 1). The idea here is to eliminate the fault list traversal at the signal update step completely.

In unit delay mode, since the spike analysis and event canceling are no longer necessary, all future events are scheduled to occur at the next time point. By looking ahead and allowing all faulty events to occur at the present moment, the *NPL*'s can be created one time step earlier. The comparison of the fast unit delay with the general algorithm is summarized in Table II.

Instead of a composite event, an *NPL* is created at the evaluation loop one time step earlier. Therefore, at the update loop in the next time point, the *NPL* list is readily available, only the good event update is performed. The need to generate NPL_i from CEV_i and FL_i^- is eliminated, thus saving one fault list traversal. The elimination of one out of two fault list traversals in the inner loop improves the efficiency significantly.

B. Fast Inverter Model

We just showed that one out of two fault list traversals can be eliminated in the fast unit delay algorithm. Furthermore, for single-input/single-output gates such as inverters or buffers, the fault list traversal can be eliminated in its entirety. Surprisingly, inverters constitute 20–30 percent of the total gate counts in typical circuits. It can be easily shown that the *NPL* at the output of an inverter is identical to its input *NPL*, except that the values are complemented. Such an observation leads to a tremendous simplification in the treatment of inverters. First, the fault lists for inverters are eliminated, saving both mem-

TABLE II
COMPARISON OF FAST UNIT DELAY VERSUS GENERAL ALGORITHM

	general	fast unit-delay
signal update step	given CEV_j and FL_j find NPL_j and new FL_j^+	given NPL_j done
fault list evaluation step	given NPL_j and FL_i^+ find new FL_i^+ and CEV_i	given NPL_j and FL_i^+ find new FL_i^+ and NPL_i

Assume s_j drives single output gate g_i.

TABLE III
SIMULATOR PERFORMANCE INFORMATION

circuit name	ckt1	ckt2	ckt3
technology	LOGIC	NMOS	CMOS
# of gates	1,111	3,440	2,906
# of faults	2,960	2,648	9,959
# of vectors	856	2,090	2,241
# of transistors	-	7,995	9,478
fault detection	96%	90%	96%
FUD good sim(Sec)	13	125	271
FUD fault sim(Sec)	61	364	1,527
speed gain factor	802	1,393	2,151
UD good sim(Sec)	21	154	437
UD fault sim(Sec)	100	541	2,522
speed gain factor	787	1,055	2,088
FUD fsim vs UD fsim	39%	33%	39%
FUD gsim vs UD gsim	38%	19%	38%
extrapolated gain factor	1,588	1,891	3,984
FUD peak memory(kb)	282	385	3,072
UD peak memory(kb)	360	532	3,825
FUD memory savings	20%	28%	20%

ory and CPU time. In the evaluation loop, the output NPL lists are simply copied from the input NPL lists with values complemented. Compared to other types of gates in the circuit, the cost of fault propagation through inverters becomes trivial. Incidentally, the simplified inverter approach is reminiscent of the earlier deductive fault simulation.

VI. PERFORMANCE

For the purpose of performance measurement, three circuits are studied in detail as shown in Table III. By setting all delay values to 1, the multiple delay simulator is used as a conventional unit delay simulator (UD), while the improved unit delay simulator is referred to as the fast unit delay simulator (FUD).

The first circuit is a bipolar circuit modeled with logic gates, and the others are MOS circuits. The circuit sizes range from 1111 to 3440 gates, which are the typical medium-size circuits. The total number of faults ranges from 2648 to 9959. Only a subset of faults was selected for the NMOS circuit, since the vectors were designed to exercise part of the circuit. For other circuits, all stuck-at faults were simulated.

The simulations were performed on an IBM 3081K machine that, for our simulator, is roughly twelve times faster than a VAX 11/780. The good circuit simulation CPU time is recorded separately for unit delay and fast unit delay simulation. The same measurements are repeated

for fault simulation. It should be noted that all fault simulations are performed in a single-pass fashion. It can be immediately seen that, compared to its unit delay counterpart, the fast unit delay fault simulator is 33–39 percent faster, while the fault-free simulation is 19–38 percent faster.

The performance of a fault simulator can be best demonstrated by the average number of faults that would lengthen the fault simulation by one unit of its base speed. The fault-free simulation time is generally used as the base speed. To calculate the average number of faults per unit of base speed, we use the first circuit as an example. The circuit contains 2960 faults, which slow down the fault simulation by 48 (61 − 13) seconds, that is 3.7 (48/13) units of its base speed. The average number of faults per unit of base speed is then 802 (2960/3.7). It can be seen that both fault simulators can realize a factor of 800–2100 faults per unit of base speed. Compared to the conventional fault simulation system with a single general-purpose multiple delay simulator, the gain factor of the fast unit delay fault simulator can be extrapolated as 1500–3900 based on the multiple delay fault free simulation time.

The unit delay fault simulator also consumes less memory compared to its multiple delay counterpart. The actual dynamic memory consumption in kilo bytes for these circuits is given at the end of Table III. The memory savings are derived mostly from the simplified inverters and partly from the elimination of faulty events. It can be seen that the unit delay simulator uses 20–28 percent less memory. In other words, for the same amount of memory, the unit delay simulator can accommodate 20–28 percent more faults in a single pass.

VII. CONCLUSIONS

In this paper, algorithms of an advanced fault simulation system have been described. The algorithms are based on a compact *incremental* faulty gate representation and a transistor tree representation. The *incremental* faulty gate representation facilitates an efficient dynamic memory management that is immune to virtual memory thrashing. A fault modeling system is based on the transistor tree data structure and performs fault collapsing in virtually linear time.

More importantly, we presented a new fault simulation algorithm that is efficient in two ways. First, the number of fault list traversals are reduced by the implementation of a composite event. In addition, the concept of nodal propagation list that propagates only minimum information results in much lower fault simulation activities. Second, primitive evaluation is improved based on the functionality; examples are the *incremental* evaluation and enhanced *latency* analysis. Not surprisingly, the simulator realizes a speed gain factor of 787–2088 over serial fault simulation. This is a very high ratio relative to other published results.

Finally, we presented a new fast unit delay algorithm that reduces the number of fault list traversals from two to one in the inner loop. In special cases such as inverters, the number of fault list traversals reduces to zero. This innovative unit delay fault simulator pushes the algorithm efficiency to an unprecedented level. As a result, the fast unit delay fault simulator outperforms its multiple delay counterpart by 33–39 percent in speed, and 20–28 percent in memory usage. In other terms, the new fast unit delay fault simulator can realize a performance gain factor of 1500–3900, compared to the conventional unit delay fault-free simulation.

ACKNOWLEDGMENT

The authors are indebted to K. W. Wu, P. Kozak, and E. Pacas-Skewes for their help in the implementation of the fault simulator.

REFERENCES

[1] E. G. Ulrich and T. Baker, "The concurrent simulation of nearly identical digital networks," in *10th Des. Automat. Workshop Proc.*, 1973.
[2] D. M. Schuler and R. K. Cleghorn, "An efficient method of fault simulation for digital circuits modeled from Boolean gates and memories," in *Proc. 14th Des. Automat. Conf.*, 1977.
[3] M. Abramovici, M. A. Breuer, and K. Kumar, "Concurrent fault simulation and functional level modeling," in *Proc. 14th Des. Automat. Conf.*, 1977.
[4] H. N. Nham and A. K. Bose, "A multiple delay simulator for MOS LSI circuits," in *Proc. 17th Des. Automat. Conf.* (Minneapolis, MN), June 23–25, 1980, pp. 610–617.
[5] A. K. Bose, P. Kozak, C-Y Lo, H. N. Nham, E. Pacas-Skewes, and K. W. Wu, "A fault simulator for MOS LSI circuits," in *Proc. 19th Des. Automat. Conf.* (Las Vegas, NV), June 1982.
[6] C-Y Lo, H. N. Nham, and A. K. Bose, "A data structure for MOS circuits," in *Proc. 20th Des. Automat. Conf.* (Miami Beach, FL), June 27–29 1983, pp. 619–624.
[7] C. F. Chen, C-Y Lo, H. N. Nham, and P. Subramaniam, "The second generation MOTIS mixed-mode simulator," in *Proc. 21st Des. Automat. Conf.*, June 1984.
[8] S. K. Jain and V. D. Agrawal, "STAFAN: An alternative for fault simulation," in *Proc. 21st Des. Automat. Conf.*, June 1984.
[9] A. V. Aho, J. E. Hopcroft, and J. D. Ullman, *Data Structures and Algorithms.* Reading, MA: Addison-Wesley, 1983.
[10] R. E. Bryant and M. D. Schustor, "Fault simulation of MOS digital circuits," *VLSI Design*, pp. 24–30, Oct. 1983.
[11] H-C Shih, J. T. Rahmeh, and J. A. Abraham, "FAUST: An MOS fault simulator with timing information," *IEEE Trans. Computer-Aided Design*, vol. CAD-5, Oct. 1986.
[12] R. L. Wadsack, "Fault modeling and logic simulation of CMOS and MOS integrated circuits," *Bell Syst. Tech. J.*, vol. 57, pp. 1449–1473, May–June 1978.
[13] J. Galiay *et al.*, "Physical versus logical fault models MOS LSI circuits: Impact on their testability," *IEEE Trans. Comput.*, vol. C-29, pp. 527–531, June 1980.

Chi-Yuan Lo received the B.S. degree in electrical engineering from National Taiwan University, Taipei, Taiwan, in 1974, and the M.S. degree in the same field from the University of Texas at Austin in 1978.

In 1978, he joined HHB Inc., and was the chief developer of an advanced fault simulation system. In 1980, he joined AT&T Bell Laboratories at Murray Hill, where he was involved in the MOTIS simulator development. Currently, he is a group supervisor responsible for layout verification, symbolic layout compaction, and layout synthesis for integrated circuit design.

*

Hao N. Nham received the B.S. and M.S. degrees in electrical engineering from the University of Texas at Austin, in 1976 and 1978, respectively.

Since 1978, he has been associated with AT&T Bell Laboratories at Murray Hill, where he worked and managed several computer-aided design projects. Currently, he heads a simulation and test department whose activities include logic and fault simulation, timing and circuit analysis, and design for testability.

*

Ajoy K. Bose received the Bachelor of Technology degree in electrical engineering from the Indian Institute of Technology, Kanpur, India, in 1971. He received the M.S. and Ph.D. degrees, in the same field, from the University of Texas at Austin in 1976 and 1977, respectively.

He joined AT&T Bell Laboratories at Murray Hill in 1977. In 1978, he became a supervisor of a simulation and test group, and in 1982, he was appointed head of a simulation, synthesis, and test department. Currently, he heads a department that is responsible for providing layout, synthesis, and schematic capture aids for integrated circuit design.

CONCURRENT FAULT SIMULATION OF MOS DIGITAL CIRCUITS

Michael D. Schuster and Randal E. Bryant

Department of Computer Science
California Institute of Technology
Pasadena, California 91125

ABSTRACT

The concurrent fault simulation technique is widely used to analyze the behavior of digital circuits in the presence of faults. We show how this technique can be applied to metal-oxide-semiconductor (MOS) digital circuits when modeled at the switch-level as a set of charge storage nodes connected by bidirectional transistor switches. The algorithm we present is capable of analyzing the behavior of a wide variety of MOS circuit failures, such as stuck-at-zero or stuck-at-one nodes, stuck-open or stuck-closed transistors, or resistive opens or shorts. We have implemented a fault simulator FMOSSIM based on this algorithm. The capabilities and the performance of this program demonstrate the advantages of combining switch-level and concurrent simulation techniques.

INTRODUCTION

Test engineers use fault simulators to determine how well a sequence of test patterns, when applied to the inputs of an integrated circuit, can distinguish a good chip from a defective one. The fault simulator is given a description of the good circuit, a set of hypothetical faults in the circuit, a specification of the observation points of the test (e.g. the output pins of the chip), and a sequence of test patterns. It then simulates how the good circuit and all of the faulty circuits would behave when the test patterns are applied to the inputs. A fault is considered detected if at any time the simulation of that particular faulty circuit produces, at some observation point, a logic value different than that produced by the good circuit. By keeping track of which faults have been

detected and which have not, the fault simulator can determine the *fault coverage* of the test sequence, which is defined as the ratio of the number of faults detected to the total number simulated. The simulator can also provide the user with information about which faults have not been detected, either because the test sequence failed to exercise the defective part of the circuit, or because the sequence failed to make the effect of such an exercise visible at some observation point. This information guides the engineer in extending or modifying the test sequence to improve its fault coverage. Such a tool is invaluable for developing test patterns for today's complex digital systems.

For a large integrated circuit such as a microprocessor chip, thousands of faults must be simulated to adequately characterize the fault coverage of a test sequence. Furthermore, test sequences can involve thousands of patterns. Hence a simple *serial* simulation, in which the good circuit and each faulty circuit are simulated separately, would require far too much computation. Fortunately, clever algorithms can reduce the amount of computation considerably. A technique known as *concurrent simulation*[1] exploits the fact that a faulty circuit typically differs only slightly from the good circuit. Rather than simulating each circuit separately, only the good circuit is simulated in its entirety. The simulator keeps track of how the network state of each faulty circuit differs from the network state of the good circuit by selectively simulating portions of the faulty network. To the user, it appears as if the program is simulating many circuits concurrently, but the amount of CPU time required is a small factor (e.g. often less than 10 times) greater than the time required to simulate the good circuit alone. Furthermore, the simulator can easily determine when a faulty circuit produces a value different than the good circuit at some observation point without stor-

This research was supported in part by the IBM Corporation and by the Defense Advanced Research Contracts Agency, ARPA Order 3771. Michael Schuster was supported in part by a Bell Laboratories Ph.D. Scholarship.

ing the entire output history of the good circuit simulation. Once a fault has been detected, the simulation of this particular faulty circuit can be dropped, thereby reducing the amount of computation required for the remainder of the simulation. Typically, the faults that cause great differences from the behavior of the good circuit, and hence require the most computational effort, are detected quickly. Consequently, fault dropping greatly improves the overall performance of the simulator.

Most existing logic simulators model a digital circuit as a network of logic gates, in which each gate produces values on its outputs based on the values applied to its inputs, and possibly on the value of its internal state. Some of these simulators extend the simple Boolean gate model, in which only the value 0 or 1 is permitted on each input and output, with additional logic values and special types of gates to model circuit structures such as busses and pass transistors. These simulators are not suitable for modeling faults in MOS digital circuits for two reasons: First, many MOS circuit structures cannot be adequately modeled as a set of logic gates. Creating gate-level descriptions of pass transistor networks, dynamic memory elements, and precharged logic is at best tedious and inaccurate, and at worst impossible, even with extended gate models. The user must translate the logic design by hand into a form compatible with the simulator, and the resulting simulation is inherently biased toward the user's understanding of the functionality of the circuit. Second, logic gate simulators are especially poor at predicting the behavior of a MOS circuit in the presence of faults. Even simple logic gates can become seemingly complex sequential circuits when a fault such as an open-circuited transistor occurs[2]. As a result, fault simulators based on logic gates can model only a limited class of faults, such as the gate outputs and inputs stuck-at-zero or stuck-at-one. Faults such as short circuits across transistors and between wires, or open circuits in transistors or wires, are beyond their capability. Furthermore, even the modeling of stuck-at faults is limited in accuracy when the logic gate description is an artificial translation of the actual circuit structure.

To remedy these problems with logic gate sim-

ulators, we propose that fault simulations of MOS circuits be performed at the *switch level* with the transistor structure of the circuit represented explicitly, but with each transistor modeled in a highly idealized way. This approach has proved successful for logic simulation in programs such as MOSSIM[3] and MOSSIM II[4] because properties such as the bidirectional nature of field-effect transistors and the charge storage capabilities of the nodes in a MOS circuit are modeled directly, rather than by some artificial translation into logic gates. Unlike the precise, but time-consuming algorithms used by circuit simulators, switch-level simulators model the circuit in a sufficiently simplified way that they operate at speeds comparable with conventional logic gate simulators. Furthermore, our switch-level logic model is well suited for modeling a variety of failures in MOS circuits in a reasonably realistic way, because many faults can be viewed as creating new switch-level networks which differ from the switch-level representation of the good circuit. Hence, while the switch-level model has proved successful for logic simulation, it seems especially attractive for fault simulation. Hayes[5] has proposed the Connector-Switch-Attenuator representation of logic circuits for modeling faults, and our switch-level model has essentially the same capabilities.

We have adapted the technique of concurrent simulation to implement a fault simulator for MOS circuits, where the problem is viewed as one of simulating a large number of nearly identical switch-level networks. This program FMOSSIM can simulate a large variety of MOS circuits, under a variety of fault conditions, at much higher speeds than would be possible with serial simulation. Other concurrent fault simulators for MOS have been implemented[6] but these could only model a very limited class of networks. In this paper, we will present an overview of the switch-level model and how different faults can be represented in it. We also discuss our concurrent, switch-level simulation algorithm and present performance results from FMOSSIM.

NETWORK MODEL

The following network model is implemented in the simulators MOSSIM II and FMOSSIM. It provides a more general transistor model than provided by other switch-level simulators, giving better capabilities for fault injection. A switch-level network consists of a set of *nodes* connected by a set of *transistors*. Each node has a state 0, 1, or X, where 0 and 1 represent low and high voltages, respectively. The X state represents an indeterminate voltage arising from an uninitialized node, from a short circuit, or from improper charge sharing. No restrictions are placed on how transistors are interconnected.

Each node is classified as either an *input* node or a *storage* node. An input node provides a strong signal to the network, as does a voltage source in an electrical circuit. Its state is not affected by the actions of the network. Examples include the power and ground nodes Vdd and Gnd, which act as constant sources of the states 1 and 0, respectively, as well as any clock or data inputs.

The state of a storage node is determined by the operation of the network. Much like a capacitor in an electrical circuit, a storage node holds its state in the absence of connections to input nodes. To provide a simple model of charge sharing, each storage node is assigned a discrete *size* from the set $\{\kappa_1, \kappa_2, \ldots, \kappa_q\}$, where the sizes are ordered $\kappa_1 < \kappa_2 < \cdots < \kappa_q$. A larger storage node is assumed to have much greater capacitance than a smaller one. When a set of storage nodes charge share, the states of the largest nodes in the set override the states of the smaller nodes. The number of different sizes required (q) depends on the circuit to be simulated. Most circuits can be represented with just two node sizes. In this representation, high capacitance nodes such as busses assigned size κ_2, and all other nodes are assigned size κ_1.

A transistor is a device with terminals labeled *gate*, *source*, and *drain*. No distinction is made between the source and drain connections — each transistor is symmetric and bidirectional. Because transistors can be either *n-type*, *p-type*, or *d-type*, both nMOS and CMOS circuits can be modeled. A d-type transistor corresponds to a negative threshold depletion mode device. A transistor acts as a resistive switch connecting or disconnecting its source and drain nodes according to its type and the state of its gate node, as shown in Figure 1. Transistor states 0 and 1 represent open (nonconducting) and closed (fully conducting) conditions, respectively. The X state represents an in-

gate state	n-type	p-type	d-type
0	0	1	1
1	1	0	1
X	X	X	1

Figure 1. Transistor state function

determinate condition between open and closed, inclusive.

To model the behavior of ratioed circuits, each transistor is assigned a discrete *strength* from the set $\{\gamma_1, \gamma_2, \ldots, \gamma_p\}$, where strengths are ordered $\gamma_1 < \gamma_2 < \cdots < \gamma_p$. A stronger transistor is assumed to have much greater conductance than a weaker one. When a storage node is connected to a set of input nodes by paths of conducting transistors, its resulting state depends only on the states of the input nodes connected by paths of greatest strength. The strength of a path is defined to equal the strength of the weakest transistor in the path. The total number of strengths required (p) depends on the circuit to be modeled. Most CMOS circuits do not utilize ratioed logic and hence can be modeled with just one transistor strength. Most nMOS circuits require only two strengths, with pull-up loads assigned strength γ_1 and all other transistors assigned strength γ_2.

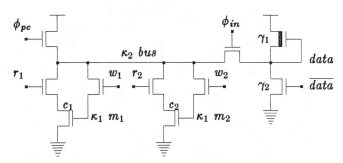

Figure 2. Three transistor dynamic RAM

As an example of a switch-level network, consider the three transistor dynamic RAM circuit shown in Figure 2. The bus node has size κ_2 to indicate that it can supply its state to the size κ_1 storage node (m_1 or m_2) of the selected memory element during a write operation (when w_1 or w_2 is 1) and to the size κ_1 drain node (c_1 or c_2) of the selected storage transistor during a read operation (when r_1 or r_2 is 1). The d-type pull-up transistor in the input inverter has strength γ_1, to indicate that it can drive the bus high only when the strength γ_2 pull-down transistor is not conducting. The strengths of all other transistors in the circuit are arbitrary, since they are not involved in ratioed path formation (except possibly when faults are present).

The switch-level network model strikes a reasonable balance between a detailed electrical model and an abstract logical model. As a result of this abstraction, the model may not predict the true behavior of circuits such as sense amplifiers and arbiters which rely on detailed analog properties. Moreover, the network model does not contain enough detail to accurately model timing behavior, because even in circuits with straightforward logical behavior, timing can be subtle. However, experience has shown that switch-level simulation works quite well for verifying logic designs.

FAULT INJECTION

Faults are represented in FMOSSIM as though extra *fault transistors* were added to the network, much like that proposed by Lightner and Hachtel[7]. In the implementation, however, many of these faults are injected without actually adding fault transistors; nevertheless, the behavior is equivalent to what is described below. The gate nodes of the fault transistors are considered to be extra *fault inputs* to the network that control the presence or absence of the failures. A variety of MOS failures can be modeled with this method. For example, a short circuit between two nodes is modeled by connecting the nodes with a fault transistor that is open in the good circuit and closed in the faulty circuit. Similarly, an open circuit is modeled by splitting a node into two parts and connecting the resulting nodes with a fault transistor that is closed in the good circuit and open in the faulty circuit. By adjusting the strength of the fault transistor, the resistance of the short or open may be modeled in an approximate way. For example, if the strength of the fault transistor is set to γ_{p+1} (i.e. a strength greater than that of any normal transistor), then setting this transistor state to 1 shorts the source and drain nodes together such that they act as a single node. Moreover, because the state of each fault transistor can be controlled independently, both single and multiple faults can be injected.

Figure 3 illustrates the use of fault transistors

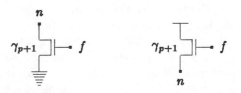

Node n stuck-at-zero   Node n stuck-at-one

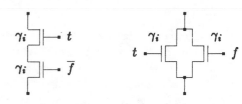

Transistor t stuck-open   Transistor t stuck-closed

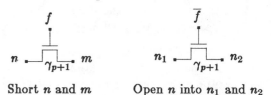

Short n and m Open n into n_1 and n_2

Figure 3. Modeling MOS failures

to create a variety of circuit faults. Those transistors with gate nodes labeled f are normally 0, but are set to 1 to create the fault; the transistors with gate nodes labeled $\overline{f}$ are normally 1, but are set to 0 to create the fault. A stuck-at-zero or stuck-at-one node fault can be modeled by inserting a strength γ_{p+1} fault transistor to short the node to Gnd or to Vdd, respectively. A stuck-closed transistor fault is injected by shorting the transistor's source and drain together with a fault transistor whose strength equals that of the failing transistor. Similarly, a stuck-open transistor fault is modeled by putting a fault transistor in series with it. In FMOSSIM, both stuck-at node states and stuck-at transistor states are implemented without extra fault transistors, while other faults require additional transistors to be inserted into the network.

Although FMOSSIM can model a larger class of faults than can be modeled by logic gate fault simulators, it still provides only a simplified representation of the faulty circuit. For example, the effects of manufacturing defects such as incorrect transistor thresholds, pinholes in the gate oxides, and variations in the circuit delays, cannot be described accurately. The effects of resistive shorts and opens can only be approximated. In fact, even existing circuit simulators cannot model defects that change the basic nature of the devices, such as pinholes in the gate oxides. However, even if the fault models supported by our simulator do not exactly match the failure modes in actual chips, the program can still help the designer in developing a set of test patterns. For circuits implemented in bipolar technologies such as TTL, experience has shown that a test sequence that yields a high level of coverage for single stuck-at-zero and stuck-at-one faults in the logic gate network generally provides a good test of the circuit. It seems reasonable to expect that the test coverage measured by a switch-level fault simulator for an idealized set of faults should reliably predict how well the test sequence will work on a MOS circuit. Such a conjecture, however, can only be confirmed by actual experience in a manufacturing environment.

Many faults in our model have the effect of creating an X state on a node when the good circuit has a 0 or 1. For example, if the control signal w_1 in the circuit shown in Figure 2 is stuck-at-zero, bit m_1 of the memory will never be initialized and will remain at X. On the other hand, if the precharge clock ϕ_{pc} is stuck-at-one, any time we try to read a 1 value out of a memory cell, a short circuit will develop between Vdd and Gnd giving an X on the bus. Whether or not such X's would be detected in an actual test depends on detailed characteristics of the circuit that cannot be predicted at the switch-level, such as the initial voltages of dynamic nodes, how the voltage would divide across a shorting path, and the thresholds of the devices sensing these X values. On one hand, a pessimist might argue that an X in a faulty circuit should be considered undetectable, because there is no guarantee that the X will produce an effect different than the state of the node in the good circuit. On the other hand, a fault that prevents the circuit from being initialized, such as a stuck-at-zero clock line, would clearly be quickly detected. As a compromise FMOSSIM allows the user to specify a *soft detect* limit l such that if in the good circuit some output changes both to 1 and to 0 at least l times each, while the output in a faulty circuit remains at X, then this fault is considered detected. This approach seems to work reasonably well in practice.

BEHAVIORAL MODEL

The operation of a MOS circuit is characterized in the switch-level model in terms of its *steady state response function*[8,9] which can best be explained in terms of an analogy to electrical networks. A MOS transistor behaves as a voltage-controlled, nonlinear resistor where the voltages of its gate, source and drain nodes control the resistance between its source and drain. Suppose in a transistor circuit we could control the transistor resistances independently of the node voltages. For a given setting of the transistor resistances, such a circuit acts as a network of passive elements which, for a given set of initial node voltages, has a unique set of steady state node voltages. Thus a function that maps transistor resistances and initial node voltages to steady state node voltages gives a partial characterization of the behavior of a transistor circuit. The steady state response function provides just this sort of characterization, but in terms of node and transistor states 0, 1, and X. That is, for a given set of initial node and transistor states, the steady state response function yields the set of states which the storage nodes would eventually reach if all transistors were held fixed in their initial states. This function only approximates network behavior, since it does not describe the rate at which nodes approach their steady states nor the effects of the changing transistor states as their gate nodes change state.

In general, a switch-level network may contain nodes and transistors in the X state. Such states arise from improper charge sharing or (transient) short circuits even in properly designed networks. The behavior of a network in the presence of X states must be described in a way that is neither overly optimistic (i.e. ignoring possible error conditions), nor overly pessimistic (i.e. spreading X's beyond the region of indeterminate behavior). This can be accomplished by defining the steady state response of a node to be 0 or 1 if and only if the node would have this unique state regardless of whether each node and transistor in the X state had state 0 or 1; otherwise, the steady state of the node is defined to be X. Rather than computing the steady state for all possible combinations of the nodes and transistors in the X state set to 0 or 1 (a task of exponential complexity), an equivalent two-pass linear time algorithm is used[9] Each pass involves solving a set of equations expressed in a simple, discrete algebra using a relaxation algorithm.

Given a technique for computing the steady state response function, a switch-level logic simulator can be implemented that simulates the operation of the network by repeatedly performing *unit steps* until a stable state is reached. Each unit step involves computing the steady state response of the network, setting the storage nodes to these values, and setting the transistors according to the states of their gate nodes. This simulation technique implements a timing model in which transistors switch one time unit (i.e. one evaluation of the steady state response function) after their gate nodes change state. Such a timing model tells little about the speed of a circuit but usually suffices to describe the circuit's logical behavior. As with other unit delay simulations, this computation may not reach a stable condition due to oscillations in the circuit, and hence an upper bound must be placed on the number of steps simulated.

On a given unit step, often only a small portion of the network changes state, while the rest of the network remains inactive. Most logic simulators exploit this property by recomputing the output of a logic gate only if at least one of the gate's inputs has changed state. A similar effect is achieved in switch-level networks by viewing network activity as creating small *perturbations* of the network state, and only computing the effects of these perturbations incrementally rather than recomputing the state of the entire network. We say that a storage node is *perturbed* if it is the source or drain of a transistor that has changed state, or if it is connected by a transistor in the 1 or X state to an input node that has changed state. Such a perturbation can only affect storage nodes in the *vicinity* of the perturbed node, where two nodes are in the same vicinity if and only if there exists some path of transistors in the 1 or X state between the nodes which does not pass through any input nodes. This definition exploits the *dynamic* locality in the network where the source and drain of a transistor in the 0 state are considered to be electrically isolated. Typically, a vicinity contains only a few nodes, and hence activity remains highly localized.

```
unit-step(P);
    U:=∅;
    for each n ∈ P do
        U:=U ∪ update-vicinity(n);
    P:=∅;
    for each n ∈ U do
        begin
        P:=P ∪ perturb-transistors(n);
        update-node(n);
        end;
    return(P);
end unit-step;
```

Figure 4. Implementation of unit step

Figure 4 shows a simplified implementation of the unit step operation that uses this incremental perturbation technique to recompute only selected parts of the network state. The argument P is a set of perturbed storage nodes derived from either new data and clock inputs to the circuit or from the last unit step. For each of these nodes, *update-vicinity* finds all the nodes in the same vicinity, computes their steady state response, and returns a set of nodes that changed state. These updated nodes are accumulated in the set U. Vicinities are found by a *depth first search*[10] originating at the perturbed node and tracing outward through transistors in the 1 or X state from source to drain until an input node is encountered. As each node is added to the vicinity, it is flagged to avoid duplication and endless cycles. For each updated node n in U, *perturb-transistors* finds all transistors whose gate node is n and checks to see if they have changed state. Nodes perturbed by these changing transistor states are accumulated in a new set P in preparation for the next unit step. Finally, *update-node* sets each updated node to its new state.

CONCURRENT SIMULATION

We have seen that the presence or absence of a fault in a switch-level network is controlled by the state of a fault input node. Suppose the test patterns that specify data and clock input values are extended to include values for the network's fault input nodes. Then the behavior of a set of faulty circuits can be determined by repeatedly simulating patterns that differ only in selected fault input values. Hence, concurrent fault simulation can be viewed as the problem of efficiently applying a large number of nearly identical test sequences to a single network. This viewpoint separates issues of fault modeling from concurrent simulation. For example, since values for fault input nodes are specified on an individual pattern by pattern basis, multiple and intermittent faults are easily modeled without changing the basic simulation algorithm. Furthermore, there are no inherent restrictions requiring that the data inputs of all test sequences be identical. Thus, concurrent simulation is useful not only for simulating faults, but for simulating sets of similar test patterns on a fault-free circuit.

The concurrent simulation algorithm is given a description of the network and a set of *test sequences* $T = \{t_0, \ldots, t_n\}$. A test sequence $t_i \in T$ consists of a sequence of test patterns, each specifying values for the data, clock and fault inputs of the network. The algorithm simulates the network to determine how each node behaves for each test sequence t_i. That is, at any point during the simulation, each node's state s_i in test sequence t_i is found. Since we assume that the behavior of the network differs only slightly from test sequence to test sequence, $s_i = s_0$ for most nodes in the network. This observation is exploited by representing node states compactly as a set of pairs $S = \{\langle t_i, s_i \rangle\}$, called a *state set*, where $\langle t_i, s_i \rangle \in S$ if and only if $i = 0$ or $s_i \neq s_0$. The behavior of the network for test sequence t_0 serves as a reference point, since states are explicitly stored only for test sequence t_0 and those sequences t_i whose states differ from t_0. For this reason, test sequence t_0 is called the *reference sequence*. For fault simulation, the reference sequence corresponds to the good circuit, while test sequences $t_i, i \neq 0$ differ only in selected fault input values, and hence correspond to faulty circuits. A node is said to be *diverged for t_i* if $s_i \neq s_0$. A node is said to be *diverged* if it is diverged for any t_i. If the gate node of a transistor is diverged, then the transistor itself is said to be diverged.

If a node is perturbed due to an input node or transistor changing state for the reference sequence, it is likely that the node is also perturbed for most other test sequences t_i. We exploit this observation by maintaining a set of perturbations of the form $P = \{\langle n_j, t_i \rangle\}$, called the *perturbation set*, where $\langle n_j, t_0 \rangle \in P$ if and only if node n_j is perturbed for the reference sequence t_0 and

$\langle n_j, t_i \rangle \in P, i \neq 0$, if and only if n_j is perturbed for t_i but not for the reference sequence. The perturbation $\langle n_j, t_i \rangle \in P$, where $i \neq 0$, indicates that the network has behaved differently in the area near node n_j for test sequence t_i when compared to its behavior for the reference sequence.

As described above, each unit step of the conventional switch-level simulation algorithm computes a steady state response for each node in the vicinity of a perturbed node, updates those nodes that have new steady states, and returns a set of perturbations for the next unit step. To generalize this operation for concurrent simulation, observe that the perturbation $\langle n_j, t_0 \rangle \in P$ represents a perturbation not only for the reference sequence, but likely for most other test sequences. In general, the steady state response of nodes in a vicinity is a function of both their initial states as well as the states of the transistors whose source or drain node is in the vicinity. Thus, when the steady state response is computed for the nodes in some vicinity as a result of a perturbation for the reference sequence, we must check to see if any of the nodes or transistors are diverged. We expect that most of the time, for most test sequences t_i, nodes within the vicinity will not be diverged for t_i. In this case, the steady state response computation performed for the reference sequence will be valid for t_i, and hence there is no need to duplicate this computation for t_i. However, if some node n_j within the vicinity is diverged for t_i, then the steady state response computation using the states of the nodes and transistors for the reference sequence may not be valid for t_i. To guarantee that an accurate computation be performed for t_i, the perturbation $\langle n_j, t_i \rangle$ is added to P. In effect, we are simply scheduling a steady state response computation that will be performed sometime later. Diverged transistors are handled in a similar manner, for if some transistor with source n_s or drain n_d in the vicinity is found to be diverged for t_i, then the perturbations $\langle n_s, t_i \rangle$ and $\langle n_d, t_i \rangle$ are added to P.

To determine the steady state response for nodes in the vicinity of a perturbation $\langle n_j, t_i \rangle$, where $i \neq 0$, states of the nodes and transistors for test sequence t_i must be found. This involves searching node state sets S for elements of the form $\langle s_i, t_i \rangle$. If such an element is not found, then

1984 CONFERENCE ON ADVANCED RESEARCH IN VLSI, M.I.T.

$$Vdd = m_1 = m_2 = \overline{data} = \{\langle t_0, 1\rangle\}$$
$$Gnd = \phi_{pc} = \phi_{in} = data = \{\langle t_0, 0\rangle\}$$
$$r_2 = w_1 = w_2 = c_1 = c_2 = \{\langle t_0, 0\rangle\}$$
$$bus = \{\langle t_0, 1\rangle, \langle t_1, 0\rangle\}$$
$$r_1 = f_1 = \{\langle t_0, 0\rangle, \langle t_1, 1\rangle\}$$
$$f_2 = \{\langle t_0, 0\rangle, \langle t_2, 1\rangle\}$$

Figure 5. Initial Node States

the state for the reference sequence is used. To reduce search time, elements in both the state sets S and perturbation set P are kept sorted by test sequence.

As an example of this simulation technique, consider the circuit shown in Figure 2. An operation that sets node m_2 to 0 will be described. Suppose initially that nodes Vdd, m_1, m_2, bus, and $\overline{data}$ have state 1 and all other nodes have state 0. Two fault transistors are added to the network, one connecting node m_2 to Vdd whose gate is fault input f_1, the other connecting node r_1 to Vdd whose gate is f_2. For the reference sequence, both of these fault input nodes have state 0 so that the faults are absent. For test sequence t_1, f_1 has state 1 to inject fault r_1 stuck-at-one. For test sequence t_2, f_2 has state 1 to inject fault m_2 stuck-at-one. Due to the fault injected by t_1, bus and Gnd are connected by conducting transistors, hence bus is initially 0 for t_1. The representation of these initial states is shown in Figure 5.

To set m_2 to 0, nodes ϕ_{in} and w_2 must be set to 1. These changes perturb bus, $data$, and m_2, since they are connected to the source or drain of transistors that have changed state. The vicinity for each of these perturbed nodes contains bus, $data$, m_2, Vdd, and Gnd, and so their steady state responses are determined. All three storage nodes have steady states 0 due to the connection to Gnd through transistors whose gates are ϕ_{in} and $\overline{data}$. The states of Vdd and Gnd are unchanged since they are input nodes. Notice that the pull-up connection between $data$ and Vdd has no effect on the steady state of $data$ since the strength of this connection, which is γ_1, is less than the strength γ_2 pull-down connection between $data$ and Gnd.

The steady state computation just described was performed relative to the reference sequence, since node states for the reference sequence were

$$Vdd = m_1 = \phi_{in} = w_2 = \overline{data} = \{\langle t_0, 1\rangle\}$$
$$Gnd = \phi_{pc} = data = \{\langle t_0, 0\rangle\}$$
$$r_2 = w_1 = c_1 = c_2 = \{\langle t_0, 0\rangle\}$$
$$bus = \{\langle t_0, 0\rangle, \langle t_2, \mathbf{X}\rangle\}$$
$$r_1 = f_1 = \{\langle t_0, 0\rangle, \langle t_1, 1\rangle\}$$
$$m_2 = f_2 = \{\langle t_0, 0\rangle, \langle t_2, 1\rangle\}$$

Figure 6. Final Node States

used to determine which nodes were within the vicinity as well as their steady state responses. This computation may be invalid for sequences t_1 or t_2 since bus has state 0 for t_2 and m_2 is connected to a conducting fault transistor for t_1. So that the appropriate steady state response computations will be performed for both t_1 and t_2, the perturbations $\langle bus, t_1\rangle$ and $\langle m_2, t_2\rangle$ are generated as the vicinity is found.

Consider the effects of perturbation $\langle m_2, t_2\rangle$. A vicinity containing bus, $data$, m_2, Vdd, and Gnd is found, as in the simulation for the reference sequence. The steady state response of bus depends on the strengths of the transistors whose gates are ϕ_{in} and w_2. If both of these transistors have strength γ_1, $data$ stays 0 but bus becomes X due to the short between Gnd and Vdd through the fault transistor connected to m_2.

Now consider the effects of the perturbation $\langle bus, t_1\rangle$. In this case, the vicinity contains node c_1, in addition to those found above. The short between bus and Gnd has no effect, and c_1, m_2, bus, and $data$ all have steady state responses equal to those in the good circuit. The representation of the final node states is shown in Figure 6.

In this example, we have seen that faults may affect the steady state response of nodes as well as which nodes are contained within a vicinity. By explicitly generating perturbations for diverged nodes and transistors when a vicinity in the good circuit is simulated, we exploit the locality of activity in each faulty circuit independent of activity in other circuits. Furthermore, this technique selectively simulates only differing portions of a faulty circuit, and hence simulation proceeds quickly.

PERFORMANCE RESULTS

As a test case for evaluating the performance of FMOSSIM, we simulated a 64 bit dynamic RAM

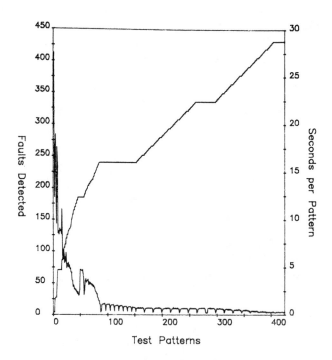

Figure 7. Performance on Memory Circuit

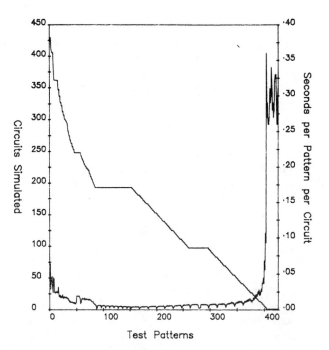

Figure 8. Effective Concurrency

circuit containing 374 transistors. This circuit incorporates a variety of MOS structures such as logic gates, bidirectional pass transistors, dynamic latches, precharged busses, and three-transistor dynamic memory elements. The circuit was simulated with 428 faults — each storage node stuck-at-zero, each storage node stuck-at-one, and pairs of adjacent busses shorted together. To validate the program, we also simulated other faults, including stuck-open and stuck-closed transistors. The simulator was implemented in the Mainsail programming language[11] and run on a DEC-20/60.

Figure 7 illustrates the performance of FMOS-SIM when simulating a test sequence consisting of a marching test[12] of the memory, together with special tests for the control logic. The curve climbing diagonally upward indicates the total number of faults detected as the test progresses. All faults were detected after 407 patterns. The falling curve indicates the CPU time required to simulate each pattern. This time starts at 27 seconds when the circuits are initialized. After 100 patterns, it drops to around 1 second as faults were detected and the simulations of these circuits were dropped. This time finally reaching 0.3 seconds at the end of the simulation, when only the good circuit is being simulated.

Figure 8 illustrates the performance advantage of concurrent simulation over simulating each faulty circuit separately. The curve falling diagonally to the right indicates the number of circuits being simulated as the test proceeds. The other curve indicates the CPU time required to simulate each pattern divided by the number of circuits being simulated for that pattern. This curve starts at about 0.05 seconds per pattern, drops to a low of 0.005 seconds once those faults causing major differences from the good circuit are dropped, and finally climbs back to 0.3 seconds when only the good circuit is being simulated. Considering that simulating a single circuit requires about 0.3 seconds per pattern, the effective benefit of simulating all of the circuits concurrently starts at 6 times serial simulation, rises to 60 times, and drops back down to 1.

Over the entire test sequence, simulating the good machine alone requires 2.5 CPU minutes. Our fault simulation requires 11 CPU minutes, whereas simulating each faulty circuit serially until it produces a different result than the good circuit would take almost 6 hours. Thus, in this case, concurrent simulation has a thirty-fold net advantage over serial simulation. Such a performance gain is clearly worth the effort.

1984 CONFERENCE ON ADVANCED RESEARCH IN VLSI, M.I.T.

JANUARY 24, 4:00 P.M.

CONCLUSION

Our experience with FMOSSIM has shown that it is a very useful tool for developing test sequences. Even when developing a test for a small section of an integrated circuit (such as an ALU or a register array), the fault simulator provides information that is hard to obtain by any other means. It quickly directs the designer to those areas of the circuit that require further tests. For example, in developing test sequences for the memory design described previously, we discovered that a simple marching test provided high coverage in the memory array itself, but that testing the control logic and peripheral circuits such as the input and output latches was more difficult.

It remains to be seen how the performance characteristics of FMOSSIM will vary as the size of the circuit and the number of faults to be simulated grows large. Even if it becomes impractical to run full-chip fault simulations with large numbers of faults, the program could still produce useful results by simulating portions of the chip, by eliminating faults that produce effects identical to other faults, or by simulating only a subset of the possible faults selected at random.

REFERENCES

[1] E. Ulrich, T. Baker, "The Concurrent Simulation of Nearly Identical Digital Networks," *Design Automation Workshop Proc.*, June 19-73, pp. 145–160, and *IEEE Computer*, April 1974, pp. 39–44.

[2] R. Wadsack, "Fault Modeling and Logic Simulation of CMOS and MOS Integrated Circuits," *Bell System Technical Journal*, Vol. 57, May-June 1978, pp. 1449–1473.

[3] R. Bryant, "MOSSIM: A Switch-Level Simulator for MOS LSI," *18th Design Automation Conference Proceedings*, July 1981, pp. 786–790.

[4] R. Bryant, M. Schuster, D. Whiting, *MOSSIM II: A Switch-Level Simulator for MOS LSI, User's Manual*, Technical Report 5033, Department of Computer Science, California Institute of Technology, March 1982.

[5] J. Hayes, "A Fault Simulation Methodology for VLSI," *19th Design Automation Conference Proceedings*, July 1982, pp. 393–399.

[6] A. Bose, *et al*, "A Fault Simulator for MOS LSI Circuits," *19th Design Automation Conference Proceedings*, July 1982, pp. 400–409.

[7] M. Lightner, G. Hachtel, "Implication Algorithms for MOS Switch Level Functional Macromodeling, Implication and Testing," *19th Design Automation Conference Proceedings*, July 1982, pp. 691–698.

[8] R. Bryant, "A Switch-Level Model of MOS Logic Circuits," in J. Gray, ed., *VLSI 81*, Academic Press, August 1982, pp. 329–340.

[9] R. Bryant, *A Switch-Level Model and Simulator for MOS Digital Systems*, Technical Report 5065, Department of Computer Science, California Institute of Technology, January 1983.

[10] A. Aho, J. Hopcroft, and J. Ullman, *The Design and Analysis of Computer Algorithms*, Addison Wesley, 1974.

[11] Xidak, Inc. *Mainsail Language Manual*, Menlo Park, CA., 1982.

[12] Winegarden, S., and D. Pannell, "Paragons for Memory Test," *1981 IEEE Test Conference*, pp. 44–48.

Fault Simulation with the Parallel Value List Algorithm

Kyushik Son, GenRad Inc., Santa Clara, CA

Large complex circuits place heavy demands on most CAE tools, but on fault simulators in particular. With higher circuit complexity, both memory usage and execution speed can determine the effectiveness of a simulator. However, in most commercial simulators, these factors are often mutually exclusive. A fault simulation technique using the parallel-value-list (PVL) algorithm provides both fast execution speed and efficient memory usage by combining the advantageous features of the parallel and concurrent algorithms. GenRad's HILO-3 Universal Logic Simulation System offers the first commercial implementation of the PVL algorithm. This article reviews the parallel and concurrent approaches, the PVL algorithm, and the contrasts and trade-offs among the three methods.

A fault simulator evaluates test patterns by applying them to a circuit model containing faults. A test pattern "detects" a fault when a circuit output value differs from the good-circuit (fault-free) value. The simulator then reports the percentage of faults detected by the test vectors, and it provides other fault statistics. The simulation results help the design engineer determine whether a circuit design is testable, and they guide the test engineer in developing an effective test set for a circuit.

Fault-simulation algorithms differ in the way in which they store, organize, and propagate fault values. Commercial simulators vary in how effectively they implement an algorithm and in the types of features they offer.

Almost all commercially available simulators use either the parallel or concurrent algorithms. The parallel fault-simulation method evaluates a given number of faults at one time—i.e., in parallel (Seshu, 1965). The algorithm stores fault values densely, packing them into individual bits in a machine word, or a set of machine words. The number of faults that the simulator can process per pass is a multiple of the word length of the host computer.

The concurrent algorithm stores faults in individual cells, rather than in groups (Ulrich and Baker, 1973). However, the concurrent approach retains and propagates only those faults that remain active in a circuit. The algorithm can process all faults in one pass.

The new PVL technique stores faults in densely packed groups, as in the parallel algorithm, but it propagates only

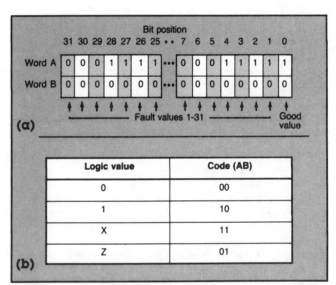

FIGURE 1. Parallel fault data structure (a) and coding of logic values (b).

active fault groups, as in the concurrent approach (Moorby, 1983). Using features from the parallel and concurrent algorithms, the PVL technique avoids many of the pitfalls associated with both approaches.

The Parallel Algorithm

The word length of the host computer determines the number of faults that a parallel fault simulator can process at one time. The data structure for the HILO-2 parallel simulator accommodates 31 fault values and a fault-free value, as shown in Figure 1. Each bit position in the paired words corresponds to a particular fault at a particular location, for example, WIRE1 stuck-at-zero. Stored at each bit position is a code representing the logic value resulting from that fault on a particular element terminal. For example, the simulator stores in Word A, Position 4 and in Word B, Position 4 the 2-bit code for the logic value for Fault 4 at a terminal.

The parallel method does not necessarily limit the number of faults-per-pass to the machine word length. By combining several word pairs, the simulator can process a greater number of faults per pass. HILO-2, for example, processes five

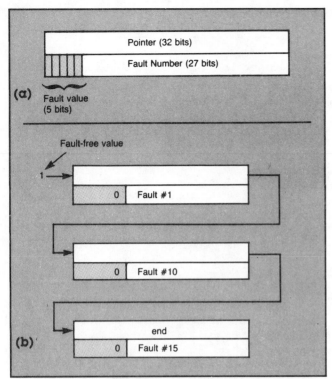

FIGURE 2. Concurrent algorithm fault cell (α) and linked list structure (b).

32-bit word pairs per pass, but the user can extend the pass size to any multiple of 32 bits.

A parallel simulator propagates faults by performing group operations on entire words. When propagating faults through a two-input AND gate, for example, the simulator performs a logical AND operation on each bit in the words that store the fault values for the two inputs. Such an operation is a basic function of any computing machine, and thus the algorithm can perform it rapidly.

The Concurrent Algorithm

A concurrent simulation algorithm organizes fault values in a linked-list data structure. A fault cell consists of a fault value, a fault number, and a pointer to the next active fault, as shown in Figure 2. The linked list contains only active faults, that is, those fault values differing from the fault-free value.

The number of bits required per fault cell varies, depending on the number of logic values supported, the word size of the host machine, and the number of total faults supported. For a concurrent 15-value simulator running on a 32-bit computer, a fault cell might typically require 64 bits: 5 bits for the fault value, 27 bits for the fault number, and 32 bits for the pointer to the next fault cell.

The linked-list data structure used in concurrent simulation organizes memory effectively. The algorithm retains active faults, deleting inactive faults from the linked list by changing pointer values. The algorithm deletes an inactive fault value by modifying the pointer in the previous fault on the list to point to the next fault on the list, skipping the inactive fault.

The Parallel-Value-List Algorithm

The PVL fault-data structure is a hybrid of parallel and concurrent structures, as shown in Figure 3. PVL associates a

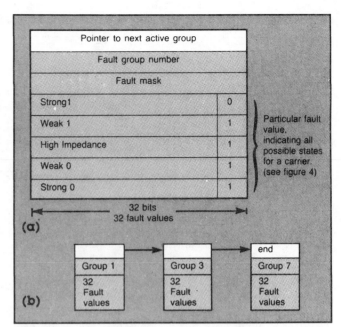

FIGURE 3. PVL fault-group structure as implemented in HILO-3 (α); parallel value lists in linked-list data structure (b).

pointer and a fault-group number with a group of faults stored in parallel. In the HILO-3 implementation of PVL, the width of each fault group is 32 bits, with each bit position corresponding to a particular fault in the circuit. The pointer indicates the next fault group in the list. The algorithm ranks fault groups in ascending order. The HILO-3 data structure also includes a 32-bit fault mask that aids functional fault simulation, and excludes from further simulation the faults detected on the circuit output by previous tests.

The algorithm stores fault values vertically in five words, each of which represents a different logic value. The HILO-3 simulator employs five states: 1 for Strong 1, H for Weak 1, Z for High Impedance, L for Weak 0, and 0 for Strong 0 (Flake et al., 1983). The simulator sets a bit for each logic value possible for the carrier. Figure 4 shows the 15 logic values the HILO-3 uses to represent all possible levels of ambiguity. For example, the value D indicates that logic values 0, W, Z, or H could be present on the carrier, but not 1.

The PVL algorithm propagates faults in groups. The algorithm assigns a fault group to a wire if at least one fault value in the group differs from the fault-free value on that wire. The fault activity within a fault group generally varies, depending on the location of the wire within the circuit and the configuration of the circuit. HILO-3 constructs fault groups from faults occurring in the same general location. For example, a group containing faults on wires 1, 2, and 3 would most probably not contain faults for wire 329.

For a given fault-free value on the input terminal of an element, the simulator assigns specific fault groups to that input. It assigns only those groups containing fault values differing from the fault-free value. It ignores the fault groups containing all values equal to the fault-free value.

In fault propagation, PVL considers a variety of factors: the circuit element type, the fault-free values on the element terminals, and the fault groups active on those terminals. The algorithm then determines which fault groups to propagate

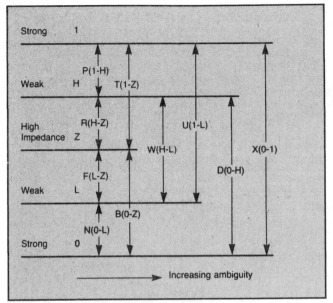

FIGURE 4. HILO-3 logic values.

through the element. Depending on the type of element, PVL performs set-union or set-intersection operations on the fault groups present on the terminals. The effect of the set operation is to propagate to the output of the element only those groups producing fault values differing from the fault-free value on the element output. PVL evaluates the fault groups by performing the appropriate Boolean operation on the values stored in the groups. (For a specific case, see "PVL Fault Propagation: An Example," on pp. 42-43.)

When the algorithm schedules a change in the fault-free value of a wire, it removes the previous fault groups from the wire and assigns a new set of active fault groups. PVL then propagates the new fault groups to the element output.

The PVL algorithm does not propagate a fault group to the element output unless the evaluation produces a fault value differing from the fault-free value, so only active fault groups propagate to the output of the circuit model. A fault group active in one part of the circuit may not remain active, so it may not appear on the circuit outputs.

A fault mask within the HILO-3 data structure allows the simulator to keep track of individual faults that have been detected at the output of the circuit. When all faults within a fault group have been detected, the simulator then discards the fault group, no longer using it in the simulation.

When a fault group does propagate to the circuit output, the simulator searches the group for active faults. The simulator then records those faults as detected faults. The HILO-3 simulator offers a wide range of fault-reporting options, and user control over parameters, such as the number of times a fault should be detected before it is dropped from further simulation.

Contrasts

All three algorithms exhibit both strengths and weaknesses. While each algorithm theoretically performs best under certain conditions, the actual implementation of any algorithm affects its performance. Simulator performance depends on a variety of factors. These factors include the efficiency of the implementation and the size, type, and complexity of the

circuit being simulated.

Dense data storage is the main advantage of parallel fault algorithms. For example, parallel storage for 32 faults could consume less than one-tenth as much memory as concurrent storage, depending on the degree of fault activity.

Predictable memory usage is another advantage of the parallel method. The parallel technique ordinarily performs fault simulation in multiple passes with a fixed number of faults per pass. A parallel simulator usually restricts the number of faults per pass to a multiple of the machine word size. A parallel version of the HILO simulator, HILO-2, simulates 159 faults per pass (default). The total number of faults possible in a given circuit, the word size of the host computer, and the number of faults per pass are predetermined, so the memory requirements per pass for a parallel simulation are fixed and predictable.

The parallel approach also evaluates faults rapidly. The simulator quickly propagates all faults under consideration in a given pass by performing machine operations on entire words.

Although the parallel approach does evaluate faults rapidly, commercial parallel simulators may execute slowly under certain conditions. The parallel algorithm processes all faults on each wire, regardless of whether any of their fault values differ from the fault-free value. For high fault activity throughout a circuit, the parallel algorithm performs well. For low fault activity, however, parallel simulators do not perform as efficiently as concurrent simulators. When there are only a few active faults, the parallel method devotes the majority of simulation run-time and memory to storing and evaluating fault values that produce no detectable effect on the output.

The main advantage of the concurrent approach is speed. Because a concurrent simulator processes only the active faults, it often requires less simulation run-time than does a parallel algorithm.

The advantages of the concurrent approach become particularly evident with low fault activity. Because only a small percentage of the total faults are active at a given element terminal, the simulator requires a small fraction of the memory and run-time necessary to simulate all faults.

With heavier fault activity spread throughout the circuit, a concurrent simulator can perform less efficiently. The concurrent data structure requires considerably more memory per fault than the parallel structure, so heavy fault activity in a complex circuit can consume large amounts of memory.

Memory requirements for a concurrent simulation are difficult to predict in advance. A concurrent algorithm stores and processes only active faults, but the number of faults active at a given wire can range from zero to hundreds of thousands. Within a single circuit, fault activity can vary enormously from wire to wire. Thus, the memory resources available on a given machine may or may not accommodate the requirements of a particular simulation.

The concurrent algorithm can process any number of faults per wire, so concurrent simulation theoretically requires only a single pass. In fact, the algorithm's unpredictable memory usage usually requires multiple-pass simulation, with a limited number of faults covered per pass, in order to reduce the amount of memory required.

By combining the linked-list data structure used in the

PVL Fault Propagation: An Example

The example in Figure A employs a simplified version of the PVL technique, using four-value logic and eight-bit words. The example shows PVL fault propagation through two gates within a larger circuit. NAND gate Gate 1 has inputs Wire A and Wire B, and output Wire C. NAND gate Gate 2 has inputs Wire C and Wire D, and output Wire E. The fault values are stored vertically, with 00 representing logic zero, 10 representing logic one, 01 representing a high-impedance state, and 11 representing an X (either zero or one).

At Gate 1, the algorithm has assigned active fault groups G1

and G2 to Wire A, and G2 and G3 to Wire B. The fault-free values on both wires equal logic one. On Wire A, G1 contains zero values in bit positions P0, P1, P2, P3, and P6, as defined in the diagram. G2 contains a zero in P5. On Wire B, G2 contains X faults in positions P1 and P3. G3 contains an X in P5, and zeros in P0, P2, and P7. Other values in the fault groups equal the fault-free value.

To propagate the fault groups, the simulator examines the fault-free value on the inputs, and the gate type. For a NAND gate with fault-free values of logic one on both inputs, the

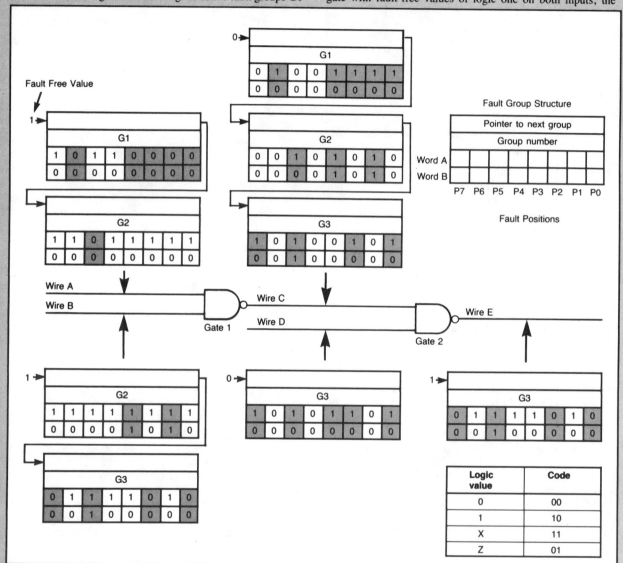

FIGURE A. Fault propagation with parallel value lists.

concurrent approach with the dense fault-storage method used in the parallel approach, the PVL algorithm directly addresses problems encountered in both types of fault simulators.

PVL Algorithm Benefits

PVL eliminates the major drawback of parallel simulation: processing of all faults, regardless of their activity. PVL

divides the total fault set into fault groups and processes only those groups containing active faults. At any one time, the algorithm assigns to a wire and propagates only a fraction of the total fault set, thus reducing simulation run-time. The algorithm also minimizes run-times by reducing the number of passes needed to simulate all faults. In the HILO-3 implementation of the PVL algorithm, the user may simulate all simulator performs a set-union operation on the fault group at the gate inputs. The set union includes the group present on Wire A only, the group present on Wire B only, and the group present on both Wire A and Wire B. Thus, G1, G2, and G3 all propagate on the gate output.

The simulator then evaluates the fault groups. The fault-free value of logic one on each wire causes the simulator to copy and invert the fault values stored in G1 and G3. The operation is equivalent to performing a NAND operation between each fault value in the group and the fault-free value. The simulator then combines the fault values in G2 on Wire A with the fault values in G2 on Wire B with a NAND operation. The operation results in X values in P1 and P3, and a one in P5 of G2. G1 contains values of logic one in positions P0, P1, P2, P3, and P6. G3 contains an X in P5 and ones in P0, P2, and P7. The remaining faults in the groups equal the fault-free value of zero for Wire C.

At Gate 2, fault groups G1, G2, and G3 reside on Wire C, and G3 resides on Wire D. G3 contains a one in P0, P2, P3, P5, and P7 on Wire D. With fault-free values of zero on both input terminals to Gate 2 (a NAND gate), the simulator performs a set-intersection operation on the groups present on the gate input wires. The intersection operation propagates G3, because it resides on both gates, but omits G1 and G2, because they reside on only one wire. Because the fault-free value on Wire D equals zero and Gate 2 is a NAND gate, fault values of one in groups G1 and G2 would produce the same value on Wire E as would the values equal to zero. That is, a fault value and the fault-free value on Wire C would produce the same output on Wire E. Because only fault values that can be detected on the circuit output are of interest to the simulator, the algorithm does not propagate those groups containing faults whose effects are indistinguishable from those of the fault-free value.

The simulator evaluates the faults at Gate 2 by combining the fault values in G3 on Wire C with those in G3 on Wire D with a NAND operation. On Wire E the fault-free value equals one. G3 on Wire E contains an X value in P5, and zeros in positions P0, P2, and P7. The simulator then propagates the group, including its three active fault values and the X value, to the next stage of the circuit.

In the example, the PVL simulator would use less memory than the concurrent approach and, if the sample circuit were part of a larger circuit, less memory than the parallel algorithm as well. In a parallel simulation, the algorithm would assign not only the faults active in this particular section of the circuit, but all the faults possible for the entire circuit. Assuming that a concurrent simulator uses two words per fault cell, the PVL algorithm would use substantially less memory to simulate the sample circuit. On Wire C, for example, PVL uses 12 words in representing 12 active faults, whereas the concurrent would use 22 words. On each wire, PVL uses less memory for fault storage.

time in evaluating 32 faults stored in a PVL fault group than it would in evaluating a few faults stored in a concurrent list.

PVL retains the speed advantage of the concurrent algorithm, because it processes only active groups, and because the linked-list structure speeds fault-group assignments in the fault propagation process. In some instances, the PVL algorithm gains additional speed advantages from its efficient use of memory.

PVL uses less memory per fault than the concurrent algorithm. However, for extremely low fault activity, PVL may use more memory to store fault values than the concurrent algorithm. The large fraction of inactive faults stored in the fault groups accounts for the higher memory usage. Except for very minimal fault activity, the PVL algorithm generally uses the same or less memory as the concurrent approach does for fault storage.

With heavy fault activity, PVL gains both speed and memory advantages over the concurrent algorithm. The individual operations required to evaluate a concurrent fault list take more time than the group operations used in PVL, so long concurrent fault lists can take longer to evaluate. In addition, PVL can represent a large number of faults in a given location by only a small number of fault groups. Therefore, the same fault activity in a concurrent simulation could consume considerably more computing resources in handling the pointer and fault-number structures called for by a long fault list. □

Acknowledgments

The author would like to thank Joan Frazer, Kathy Abelson, Brian Bailey, and R.G. Bennetts for their assistance in preparing this article.

References

Flake, P.L., P.R. Moorby, and G. Musgrave. 1983. "An Algebra for Logic Strength Simulation," *20th Design Automation Conference*, Miami Beach, FL.

Moorby, P.R. 1983. "Fault Simulation Using Parallel Value Lists," *International Conference on Computer-Aided Design*, Santa Clara, CA.

Seshu, S. 1965. "On an Improved Diagnosis Program," *IEEE Transactions on Electronic Computers* (Short Notes), Vol. EC-14.

Ulrich, E.G., and T. Baker. 1973. "The Concurrent Simulation of Nearly Identical Networks," *10th Design Automation Conference*, Portland, OR.

About the Author

Kyushik Son is an engineering project leader at GenRad's Design Engineering Group in Milpitas, CA. He is currently working on a testability analysis project. Before his employment at GenRad, he was associated with GTE Laboratories and Digital Equipment Corp., where he worked on various computer-aided design projects. He has a B.S. from Seoul National University, an M.S. from Southern Methodist University, and a Ph.D. from Oakland University in Rochester, Michigan.

faults in one pass, or he may specify the number of faults to be simulated in each pass.

The dense storage scheme used in parallel simulation enhances the performance of a PVL simulator. Because the simulator evaluates fault groups by using machine-level operations, the inactive faults in a group do not pose a problem in terms of execution time. A computer might consume no more

Statistical Fault Analysis

As VLSI circuits grow in complexity, fault simulation costs get increasingly burdensome. Stafan provides an effective, efficient alternative.

Sunil K. Jain and Vishwani D. Agrawal
AT&T Bell Laboratories

Although fault analysis is essential to VLSI design, current methods typically suffer either from undue complexity or imprecision. Fault simulation techniques, though exact, can consume CPU time and memory at a rate increasing at least as the square of the number of gates in the circuit.[1] For VLSI circuits, this is a serious limitation. One approach that reduces such complexity involves the random sampling of faults.[2] This method requires simulation of a randomly selected subset of faults to give an estimate of the fault coverage, whose accuracy depends only upon the number of simulated faults, not on the total number of faults in the circuit. Unfortunately, fault sampling techniques fall short in that they assume the availability (or development) of a complete fault simulation program and they give absolutely no information about the detectability of

the faults that were not sampled. A list of undetected faults is desirable for test vector development and for checking redundancies.

This article describes a statistical fault analysis technique, called Stafan, which involves only fault-free simulation. Fault-free (or true-value) simulation is essential for design verification, is considerably less complex than fault simulation, and is used in the present method to calculate the probability of detection for each stuck fault in the circuit from the signal statistics. In a recent work[3] fault detection probabilities were computed for random stimuli. In general, upper and lower bounds for the detection probabilities could be obtained. These bounds could be narrowed down at the cost of greater amount of computation time. However, the method could handle only combinational circuits.

By contrast, Stafan can compute the detection probabilities for the given stimuli (vector set) with which the fault-free simulation is carried out. No elaborate software development is needed, and the calculation adds only a small overhead to the fault-free simulation cost. Furthermore, the method is not limited to combinational circuits. It produces an estimate of fault coverage by the vector stimuli used in simulation. Since the estimate is statistical, higher ac-

Summary

Statistical Fault Analysis, or Stafan, is proposed as an alternative to fault simulation of digital circuits. This method defines controllabilities and observabilities of circuit nodes as probabilities estimated from signal statistics of fault-free simulation. Special procedures deal with these quantities at fanout and feedback nodes. The computed probabilities are used to derive unbiased estimates of fault detection probabilities and overall fault coverage for the given set of input vectors. Among Stafan's advantages, fault coverage and the undetected fault data obtained for actual circuits are shown to agree within five percent of fault simulator results, yet CPU time and memory demands fall far short of those required in fault simulation. The computational complexity added to a fault-free simulator by Stafan grows only linearly with the number of circuit nodes.

An earlier version of this article appeared in the *ACM/IEEE 21st Design Automation Conference Procedings*, June 1984.

Reprinted from *IEEE Design & Test of Computers*, Volume 2, Number 2, February 1985, pages 38-44. Copyright © 1985 by The Institute of Electrical and Electronics Engineers, Inc. All rights reserved.

curacy can be expected for larger circuits. Another technique known as critical path tracing[4] has been proposed as an alternative to fault simulation, but it too can analyze only the circuits that are basically combinational.

Stafan makes use of the concepts of *controllability* and *observability*.[5,6] These terms are redefined as probabilities of controlling and observing the lines. Controllability of a line is estimated by collecting the statistics of activity on that line. Observability is then computed from the estimated controllabilities. The product of the appropriate controllability and observability gives the detection probability of a fault. Faults can be graded in terms of their detection probabilities and the faults with lower detection probabilities are the likely ones to be left undetected by the vector set. A simple calculation leads to fault coverage.

Theory

Consider the logic model of the circuit as is often used by simulators.[7] In this model the circuit is described in terms of single-output boolean (AND, OR, NAND, NOR, and NOT) gates. The gates are connected by paths, called *lines*. The primary output line values are specified by *input vectors*. The simulator then computes the logical values (zero or one) for all other lines. We will consider the stuck-type ($s-a-1$ and $s-a-0$) faults on input and output lines of each gate.

Let us define the following quantitites for each line:

• $C1(l)$ or *one-controllability* of line l is the probability of line l having a value of one on a randomly selected vector.

• $C0(l)$ or *zero-controllability* of line l is the probability of line l having a value of zero on a randomly selected vector.

• $B1(l)$ or *one-observability* of line l is the probability of observing the line l at a primary output when the alue of line l is one. This is the conditional probability of sensitiz-

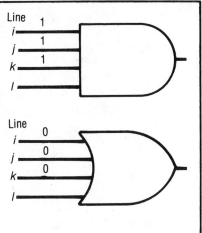

Figure 1. Sensitization of path from line l to gate output.

ing a path from line l to a primary output, given that the value of line l is one. Similarily,

• $B0(l)$ or *zero-observability* of line l is the path sensitization probability from line l to a primary output when the value of line l is zero.

Statistical estimation of controllabilities. Suppose we simulate N input vectors and for every line in the circuit keep two counters in the fault-free simulator. These counters are called the one-counter and the zero-counter, respectively. Whenever a line assumes a value one or zero, its one-counter or the zero-counter is incremented. Most simulators use three values: zero, one and unknown (X). When the line value is X, none of the counters is incremented. If the simulator also generates the high-impedance state on a line, then the same counter that was incremented on the previous vector is incremented again. After simulating N vectors, the one- and zero-controllabilities are estimated as

$$C1(l) = \frac{one\text{-}count}{N}$$

and

$$C0(l) = \frac{zero\text{-}count}{N}$$

Computation of observabilities. To compute observability, the simulator keeps an additional sensitization

counter for each input line of a gate. This counter is incremented on a vector only if a path from the corresponding line to the gate output is sensitized. Figure 1 gives two examples of input states for which the sensitization counter of the line l is incremented. After N vectors are simulated, the one-level path sensitization probability for line l is estimated as

$$S(l) = \frac{sensitization\text{-}count}{N}$$

For observability computation, first the one- and zero-observabilities $B1$ and $B0$ for all primary output lines are set to unity. Next the procedures described below for propagating observabilities from a gate output to inputs is used until the observabilities of all lines have been obtained.

Consider the four-input AND gate shown in Figure 2. Lines i, j, k and l are the input lines and m is the output line. Suppose the controllabilities of all the lines of this gate are known and the observabilities, $B1(m)$ and $B0(m)$, of its output line have been calculated. We illustrate the procedure of propagating the observabilities to the inputs of this gate by computing the observabilities, $B1(l)$ and $B0(l)$, for the line l. As shown in Figure 2, an input of one on line l is observed at the output line m whenever a 1111 pattern occurs at the input of the AND gate.

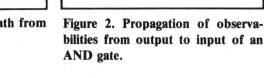

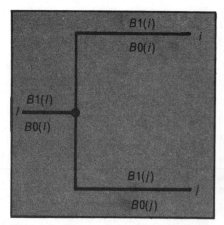

Figure 3. Observabilities at a fanout.

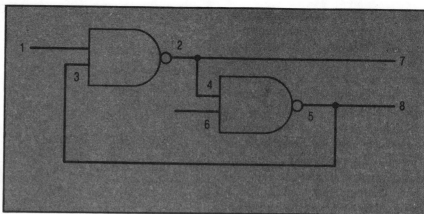

Figure 4. NAND flip-flop.

Since the occurrence of this pattern is also the condition for an output of one at m, the probability of this pattern is the same as one-controllability, $C1(m)$, of the output line m. Also, $C1(m)$ is the joint probability of two events: (1) line l equals one and (2) its value is observable at m. Since the probability that line l equals one is $C1(l)$, the conditional probability[8] of the second event (observing l at m), given that the first event (line l is one) has occurred, is obtained as $C1(m)/C1(l)$. Once line l is observed at m, its observability with respect to the circuit output can be computed as

$$B1(l) = B1(m) \cdot C1(m)/C1(l)$$

Similarly, when l is zero, observation of l at m requires a 1110 pattern at the input of the AND gate. The probability that this pattern will occur is $S(l) - C1(m)$. This is because $S(l)$ corresponds to both patterns 1111 and 1110 while $C1(m)$ corresponds just to 1111. Thus the zero-observability of line l is

$$B0(l) = B0(m) \cdot \frac{S(l) - C1(m)}{C0(l)}$$

Observabilities of other gate types can be obtained in a similar manner.[9] However, two other situations frequently occur in logic circuits. These are discussed below.

Fanouts. Consider the line l which fans out into two lines i and j as shown in Figure 3. Here we analyze one-observabilities, recognizing that

similar arguments apply to zero-observabilities. $B1(i)$ and $B1(j)$ are the observabilities of lines i and j, respectively. The value of line l can be observed through either line i or line j. If the paths connecting lines i and j to observable outputs are independent, then the observability of l is the probability of the union of two events with probabilities $B1(i)$ and $B1(j)$. On the other hand, the two paths may be so correlated that either both are simultaneously sensitized or none is sensitized. In this case, assuming that the more probable path can be used, the observability of l is at least equal to the larger of $B1(i)$ and $B1(j)$. Similarly, if line l fans out to m branches, then

$$\max_{1 \leqslant k \leqslant m} [B1(i_k)] \leqslant B1(l) \leqslant \bigcup_{k=1}^{m} B1(i_k)$$

where the upper bound on the right-hand side is the union of observable path events.[8] Actual computation of these bounds would require a detailed analysis of the circuit topology, and these bounds would depend upon the degree of reconvergence of the fanouts. However, any advantage gained from such an analysis would depend upon how wide this range is. For simplicity, we introduce an arbitrary constant α such that

$$B1(l) = (1 - \alpha) \max_{1 \leqslant k \leqslant m} [B1(i_k)]$$

$$+ \alpha \bigcup_{k=1}^{m} B1(i_k)$$

When $\alpha = 0$, $B1(l)$ is minimum and $\alpha = 1$ corresponds to the upper

bound. In the general case, the value of α may differ for different fanout branches. Later we experimentally study the sensitivity of the fault analysis to the value of α and determine its suitable value for actual circuits.

Feedback. Feedback loops allow storage of signal (state) values, and this complicates computation of observabilities. Here we demonstrate the calculation of observability in a feedback situation by the NAND flip-flop circuit of Figure 4. Suppose the observabilities of lines 7 and 8 and the controllabilities of all lines have been computed. This leaves the observabilities of lines 1 through 6 to be determined. Assuming that the signals on lines 1 and 6 are independent, we establish an iterative procedure for determining the observabilities of lines 2, 3, 4, and 5. Suppose we cut the feedback loop at line 4 and trace the circuit along the lines 2, 3, and 5 until we again arrive at 4; at this point the structure, consisting of lines 4, 2, 3, 5, and 4, is duplicated as shown in Figure 5. Suppose $B1_0(4) = 0$ is the zero-order value of one-observability of line 4. Then $B1_0(2) = B1(7)$. Observabilities $B0_0(3)$, $B0_0(5)$, $B1_1(4)$ and $B1_1(2)$ can be obtained from formulae given in the previous sections above. We proceed in the same manner to calculate $B0_1(3)$, $B0_1(5)$, $B1_2(4), \ldots$, until the successive iterations produce identical values. It can be verified that

IEEE DESIGN & TEST

such iterations converge to a unique value. Thus $B1(4)$, $B1(2)$, $B0(3)$ and $B0(5)$ are computed. Similarly, starting with $B0_0(4) = 0$, the values of $B0(4)$, $B0(2)$, $B1(3)$ and $B1(5)$ can be calculated. Once these are available, observabilities of lines 1 and 6 follow easily.

In this analysis of feedback, we assume that signals 1 and 6, which sensitize the feedback loop, are independent. Sensitization of the loop corresponds to storing the values of signals in the feedback (provided the number of inversions around the loop is even; an odd number of inversions gives rise to oscillations, invalidating the fault analysis). In a clocked circuit, signals 1 and 6, which are derived from the same clock signal, cannot be assumed to be independent. In order to adequately analyze such a circuit, we must calculate the *loop-sensitization probability*, L. This can be done by identifying all the input signals of the gates forming a loop and removing from them the output signals that form the feedback. For example, in Figure 4 the input signals are 1, 3, 4, and 6. If we remove output signals 3 and 4, we are left with signals 1 and 6. In order to sensitize the loop, signals 1 and 6 are simultaneously set to "logic one." In the fault-free simulator, if we set up a loop counter for each loop to count occurrences of loop-sensitization states, then we can estimate the loop-sensitization probability after simulation of N vectors as

$$L = \frac{loop\text{-}count}{N}$$

Consideration of calculations for line 2 in Figure 4 illustrates the application of the probability L. Assuming that the circuit has been converted into a combinational circuit by removing line 3, we can observe line 2 through either line 7 or lines 4 and 8. Then, supposing that the one-observability of line 2 due to these two observation paths is $B1'(2)$, we can reconnect line 3 to consider the effect of the feedback loop. With probability L, the value of line 2 propagates

through the loop (lines 4, 5, 3, and 2) and reappears at 2 for a possible observation during subsequent time frames. Thus the total one-observability of line 2 is

$$B1(2) = B1'(2) + [1 - B1'(2)] \cdot L \cdot B1(2)$$

The first term on the right-hand side accounts for observation in the current time frame. The second term accounts for the event that line 2 is not observed in the current time frame but its value is stored in the flip-flop due to the sensitization of loop. Further simplifying, we get

$$B1(2) = \frac{B1'(2)}{1 - [1 - B1'(2)] \cdot L}$$

Other observabilities can be obtained in a similar manner.

Computation of fault-detection probability.

Consider the fault "line l stuck-at-1." To detect this fault, line l must be set to a value of zero and then its value should be observed at a primary output. Thus the probability of detection of this fault is given by the equation

$$D1(l) = B0(l) \cdot C0(l)$$

Since $B0(l)$ is the conditional probability of observing the line l when its

value is set to zero and $C0(l)$ is the probability of setting l to zero, the above product is the joint probability of the required events. Similarly, the probability of detecting the fault "line l struck-at-0" can be calculated as

$$D0(l) = B1(l) \cdot C1(l)$$

If, for a given fault, the detection probability is x, then the probability of detecting this fault by a set of N vectors is $X(N) = 1 - (1 - x)^N$. This is just one minus the probability that none of the N vectors detect the fault.

Unbiasing the fault detection probability. Suppose we simulate N vectors and from the statistical data collected during simulation obtain the detection probabilities of all faults. The probabilities thus computed are statistical estimates and can be regarded as random variables whose values converge to their exact values as N tends to infinity. With a finite N, however, the estimated value of detection probability, x, will contain a random error. Earlier work indicated that this error leads to a biased estimation of fault coverage.[9] As shown there, the unbiasing requires

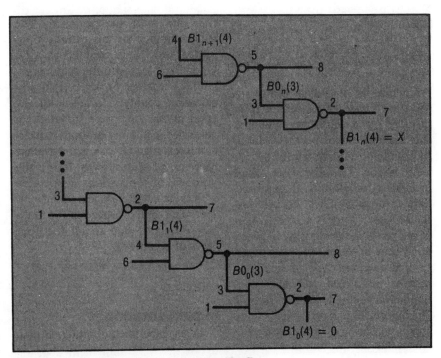

Figure 5. Iterative analysis of NAND flip-flop.

modifying the probability of detection by N vectors as

$$X(N) = 1 - \frac{(1 - x)^N}{W(x)}$$

where*

$$W(x) = 1 + \frac{N - 1}{6} \beta^2 \frac{x}{1 - x}$$

where β is a constant of proportionality which is determined empirically.

Fault coverage. Consider a circuit with K faults and V test vectors. We divide the set of vectors into l subsets, each containing $V/l = N$ vectors, and then calculate the fault coverages $F(N)$, $F(2N)$,...,$F(lN)$. For the i-th fault, we compute the detection probabilities from the N-vector statistics in each subset as x_{i1}, x_{i2},...,x_{ij},...,x_{il}. The probability of detecting this fault by the first j vector subsets is given by the formula[9]

$$f_i(jN) = 1 - \prod_{m=1}^{j} \frac{(1 - x_{im})^N}{W(x_{im})}$$

where the right-hand side consists of one minus the probability of not detecting the i-th fault by the vector sets 1 through j. The cumulative fault coverage, i.e., the fraction of faults covered by the first j vector subsets, is obtained from the following formula[9]:

$$F(jN) = \frac{1}{K} \sum_{i=1}^{K} f_i(jN)$$

Complexity of Stafan. Stafan requires two types of operations to be included in a fault-free simulator. The first type, involving the updating of counters, must be performed on every vector. The other type, which includes computation of controllabilities, observabilities, etc., is performed once every N vectors, where N can be chosen arbitrarily. In general, N can be large. In the extreme case, the second type of operation may be performed only once after simulation through all the vectors. Operations like loop identification and initialization of counters are also performed only once during preprocessing. Thus Stafan's main overhead in the fault-free simulator is due to the first type of operation.

These operations and their relative complexities are listed in Table 1. Each counter is updated after examining certain line values. The number G is the total number of gates in the circuit. Every gate output line has a zero-counter and a one-counter. Each counter requires two operations: (1) examine the line value and (2) update the counter. Thus there are $2G$ operations for each type of counter. In practice, some of these operations may overlap. If n_f is the average number of inputs per gate, then the number of sensitization counters is $n_f G$. In order to update this counter for a gate-input line, all other inputs of this gate must be examined. The total number of operations connected with these counters is $n_f^2 G$. Updating a loop counter requires examining whether or not certain sensitization counters for each of the gates in the loop were updated. In general, the number of loops in a circuit is less than G. If n_l is the average number of gates in a loop, the number of operations associated with these counters is less than $(n_l + 1)G$. The total overhead in the fault-free simulator due to all the four types of counters is

$$overhead \propto G(4 + n_f^2 + an_l + a)$$

where $a < 1$.

Implementation

In an experimental study, Stafan algorithms were implemented in an existing MOS simulator.[10] Since this simulator was also capable of simulating circuits at gate level with stuck-at-0 and stuck-at-1 faults, it was possible to compare its fault simulation results with Stafan fault coverage estimation.

In the implementation it was necessary to set the values of the empirical constants α and β. For calculation of observabilities at fanouts, a suitable value of constant α was determined by an experiment conducted on a large circuit. A value $\alpha = 1$ showed good agreement with the fault simulation result. Notice that this corresponds to the assumption that the fanout branches are independent. In fact the results were rather insensitive to the actual value of α. The other empirical constant, β, was used to unbias the fault detection probabilities. Again, by experimentation with an actual circuit, it was found that the value $\beta^2/6 = 5.0$ produced a good match with fault simulation results. Thus set in the analysis, these values of α and β produced consistently good results in trials on several other circuits. In this implementation the feedback in the cross-coupled gates was handled using the loop-sensitization probability. But the larger feedback loops were processed by the iterative procedure.

Results

Results obtained by Stafan on several circuits varying in size from 102 gates to 2723 gates are summarized in Table 2. The plots of fault coverage versus number of vectors for two of

Table 1.
Operations performed in Stafan.

Counter	Required for	Number of values examined	Number of counters	Number of operations
zero-counter	every gate	1	G	$2G$
one-counter	every gate	1	G	$2G$
sensitization-counter	every gate-input line	$n_f - 1$	$n_f G$	$n_f^2 G$
loop-counter	every loop	n_l	$< G$	$< (n_l + 1)G$

---

*This equation was in error in the original paper. It appears corrected here.

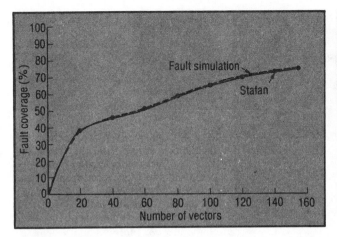

Figure 6. Fault coverage for a 64-bit ALU.

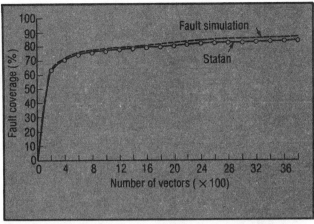

Figure 7. Fault coverage for circuit A, a sequential circuit with 1983 gates.

the circuits are shown in Figures 6 and 7. Figure 6 shows the fault coverage plot for a 64-bit arithmetic logic unit, or ALU, and Figure 7 shows the fault coverage for a sequential circuit with 1983 gates. From the graphs it can be seen that the Stafan fault coverage estimation closely follows the actual fault coverage obtained from a fault simulator. Different periods (N) of analysis were taken for various circuits. It was found that the period of analysis has a very small effect on the final fault coverage estimates. From the data in Table 2, it is evident that Stafan is a very effective technique for small to large circuits. Average deviation of Stafan fault coverage

from the actual fault simulator result varies from 0.29 percent to 3.65 percent.

To determine how accurately the detection probabilities would predict the undetected faults, all the 4376 faults of the 64-bit ALU were graded in terms of their cumulative detection probabilities as obtained after simulation through 155 vectors. The faults, ordered in terms of decreasing detection probability, are shown in Figure 8. Since the estimated fault coverage was 75.09 percent, the first 3286 faults in this graded list were assumed to be detected. This left the 1090 faults, with detection probabilities less than 0.53, as undetected. Comparison with fault simulation

results showed that of these 1090 faults, 1036 were indeed undetected. Also, among the 3286 faults that were assumed to be detected by Stafan, only 46 faults were actually reported as undetected by the fault simulator.

In this article we have presented a statistical alternative to fault simulation which can handle large circuit complexity. Preliminary experiments on actual logic circuits indicate good results not only for fault coverage but also for finding the faults that remain undetected by a vector set. There are, however two parameters used in the analysis, α and β, which must be determined

**Table 2.
Stafan results.**

Circuit	Number of gates	Primary inputs/ ouputs	Flip-flops	Number of vectors	Number of faults	Period of estimation in Stafan (N)	Final Coverage Fault simulation percent	Stafan percent	Average difference
4-bit ALU	102	14/8	0	52	263	10	96.57	96.25	0.47
64-bit ALU	1827	134/69	0	155	4376	20	75.30	75.09	0.29
4-bit multiplier	359	12/10	15	1111	741	100	93.12	86.80	3.37
circuit A	1983	38/34	86	3842	5060	200	86.44	83.61	1.24
circuit B	2723	64/64	98	3636	5856	200	71.26	72.57	3.65

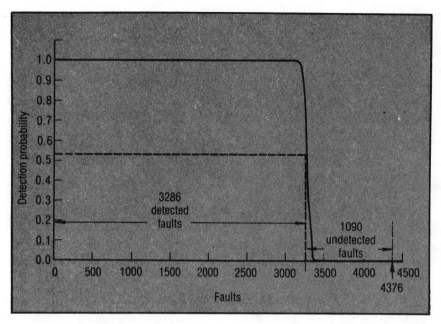

Figure 8. Detection probabilities for faults in a 64-bit ALU after simulating 155 vectors.

Sunil K. Jain received the Bachelor of Technology degree from the Indian Institute of Technology, Kanpur, India in 1980, and the MS degree from Lehigh University, Pennsylvania in 1982. He has worked on computer-aided design and testing of VLSI circuits at AT&T Bell Laboratories, Murray Hill, New Jersey. His interests include design for testability, built-in test, high level design verification and logic synthesis.

empirically. While β can be determined by a comparison with fault simulation results, α may, in general, depend upon the structure of the circuit. Fortunately, in the experiments that we have conducted, the results seem to be only mildly affected by the value of α. □

Vishwani D. Agrawal is the supervisor of the test and design verification group at AT&T Bell Laboratories in Murray Hill, New Jersey. Before joining Bell Laboratories, he worked at TRW Defense and Space Systems Group in California and at the Indian Institute of Technology in New Delhi, where he was an assistant professor. He received a BE in telecommunications engineering from the University of Roorkee, an ME in electrical communication engineering from the Indian Institute of Science, and a PhD in electrical engineering from the University of Illinois.

References

1. P. Goel, "Test Generation Costs Analysis and Projections," *Proc. 17th Design Automation Conf.,* June 1980, pp. 77-84.

2. V. D. Agrawal, "Sampling Techniques for Determining Fault Coverage in LSI Circuits," *J. Digital Systems,* Vol. 5, Fall 1981, pp. 189-202.

3. J. Savir, G. Ditlow, and P. H. Bardell, "Random Pattern Testability," *Digest of Papers 13th Ann. Fault-Tolerant Computing Symp.,* June 1983, pp. 80-89.

4. M. Abramovici, P. R. Menon, and D. T. Miller, "Critical Path Tracing —An Alternative to Fault Simulation," *Proc. 20th Design Automation Conf.,* June 1983, pp. 214-220.

5. J. E. Stephenson and J. Grason, "A Testability Measure for Register Transfer Level Digital Circuits," *Digest of Papers 6th Int'l Fault Tolerant Computing Symp.,* June 1976, pp. 101-107.

6. L. H. Goldstein, "Controllability/ Observability Analysis of Digital Circuits," *IEEE Trans. Circuits and Systems,* Vol. CAS-26, Sept. 1979, pp. 685-693.

7. S. G. Chappell, C. H. Elmendorf, and L. D. Schmidt, "LAMP: Logic-Circuit Simulator," *Bell System Tech. J.,* Vol. 53, Oct. 1974, pp. 1451-1476.

8. K. S. Trivedi, *Probability and Statistics with Reliability, Queueing, and Computer Science Applications,* Prentice-Hall, Englewood Cliffs, N.J., 1982.

9. S. K. Jain and V. D. Agrawal, "STAFAN: An Alternative to Fault Simulation," *Proc. 21st Design Automation Conf.,* June 1984, pp. 18-23.

10. A. K. Bose et al., "A Fault Simulator for MOS LSI Circuits," *Proc. 19th Design Automation Conf.,* June 1982, pp. 400-409.

The authors may be contacted at AT&T Bell Laboratories, 600 Mountain Avenue, Murray Hill, NJ 07974.

Sampling Techniques for Determining Fault Coverage in LSI Circuits

VISHWANI D. AGRAWAL*

Abstract—Two statistical sampling procedures for determining fault coverage in digital circuits are described. Since these procedures require simulation of only a fraction of the total faults, much less effort is needed than for the conventional method of simulating all faults. Formulas for sample size and the confidence range are derived, and their use is illustrated by examples. In the first method a fixed number of faults are simulated. The second method is based on sequential sampling where the result of fault simulation is continuously monitored as the number of sample faults is increased. Sampling is stopped when the required confidence range is achieved. In either procedure, the number of sampled faults depends only upon the desired confidence range and not on the circuit size. For any large circuit, reasonably good results can be obtained by simulating 1000 to 2000 faults.

Index Terms—Logic testing, fault coverage, test generation, statistical methods.

1. INTRODUCTION

Test patterns for large logic circuits are often determined from a knowledge of the circuit function. A fault simulator is then used to find the effectiveness of the test patterns in detecting hardware faults. The hardware faults normally considered are the stuck-at-0 and stuck-at-1 on all the lines in the circuit. A coverage of these faults in excess of 80 percent may be considered acceptable for some applications, although, in general, a higher coverage is desirable.

Fault simulation of large circuits can be very expensive. Statistical sampling techniques require simulation of only a small subset of the total faults and hence significantly reduce the cost of fault coverage analysis. Some applications of sampling techniques have been reported [1–4], but they have not gained popularity. Conventional sampling techniques are designed to produce an accept or reject type of decision. For example, it is easy to devise a sampling procedure to accept the tests only if the fault coverage is above 80 percent. In the fault coverage analysis, however, one is interested in finding out what the actual fault coverage is. Thus, the sampling analysis should indicate that the fault coverage is above a percentage p_1 but below percentage p_2. Also, instead of the values of p_1 and p_2 only the range p_2-p_1 may be specified. The statistical techniques developed in this paper fulfill such need.

Of the two methods described, the first requires simulation of a fixed number of faults. A simple analysis is given to determine this number from the required confidence range (p_2-p_1). The second method is based upon sequential sampling [5] which is, in general, considered more efficient than the fixed sample size method. The sequential method requires simulation of several samples each consisting of a small number of faults. Such a method would be ideally suited to parallel simulators which simulate a small number of faults in each pass ([6], section 4.6.2).

2. FIXED SAMPLE SIZE METHOD

In the first method, referred to here as the *fixed sample size method*, the fault coverage is evaluated by simulating a few randomly selected faults. The number of detected (or undetected) faults in the sample divided by the total number of faults sampled is treated as a random variable which is used to estimate the fault coverage. Using the value of this random variable obtained in a sampling experiment, we determine a range of values such that the probability of actual fault coverage being out of this range would be very small. Let us consider a circuit which has M faults. We randomly* pick N faults ($N < M$) and simulate them using the given test patterns. If n among these N faults are undetected, then we might conclude that the expected value (or the mean square estimate) of fault coverage is $1 - n/N$. However, we would like to have a confidence level for our result.

Consider the statistician's favorite model of M balls, m red (undetected faults) and $M - m$ black (detected faults). A group of N balls is chosen at random. The probability q_n of having n red balls in the sample is given by the hypergeometric distribution ([7], pp. 43–44):

$$q_n = \frac{\binom{m}{n}\binom{M-m}{N-n}}{\binom{M}{N}}. \tag{1}$$

For large M and N, q_n is closely approximated by the Gaussian formula [8] with

---

* Bell Laboratories, Murray Hill, New Jersey 07974.

0195-4350/81/0900-0189 $02.52/0

---

* In general, faults may be correlated since several faults would be detected by the same pattern. Still, in a sampling experiment the fault samples are independent since the event that a fault is sampled is completely independent of the fact that any other fault was also sampled.

average, $a(p) = N(1 - p)$, (2)

and

variance, $\sigma^2(p) = Np(1 - p)\left[1 - \dfrac{N}{M}\right]$, (3)

where $p = 1 - \dfrac{m}{M}$ is the true fault coverage expressed as a fraction of all faults. In the sampling experiment, p is unknown. Define p_{min} as the lowest fault coverage for which the probability of obtaining fewer than n undetected faults in a sample of size N is no greater than ϵ. If ϵ is chosen sufficiently small, say $\epsilon = 0.001$, then n undetected faults would indicate that the fault coverage for all practical purposes is greater than p_{min}. Similarly, we can also define a p_{max} as the highest fault coverage such that the probability of obtaining more than n undetected faults in a sample of size N is again less than ϵ. Now the fault coverage p can, for practical purposes, be assumed to be bounded:

$$p_{min} \leqslant p \leqslant p_{max}$$ (4)

These definitions of p_{min} and p_{max} are illustrated in Fig. 1.

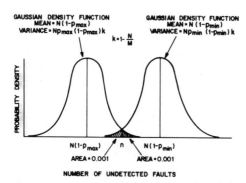

Fig. 1. Interpretation of maximum and minimum fault coverage (p_{max} and p_{min}) corresponding to the number (n) of undetected faults in the sample

Since the random variable n can be assumed to be Gaussian with mean and variance given by (2) and (3), we have

$$\frac{1}{2} - \text{erf}\left[\frac{a(p_{min}) - n}{\sigma(p_{min})}\right] = \epsilon$$ (5)

and

$$\frac{1}{2} - \text{erf}\left[\frac{n - a(p_{max})}{\sigma(p_{max})}\right] = \epsilon$$ (6)

where ([9] pp. 64–65)

$$\text{erf}(x) = \frac{1}{\sqrt{2\pi}} \int_0^x e^{-\frac{y^2}{2}} \, dy$$ (7)

Now using $\epsilon = 0.001$, since $\frac{1}{2} - \text{erf}(3.0) = 0.001$, from (5) and (6) we get*

$$n = a(p_{min}) - 3\sigma(p_{min})$$ (8)

and

$$n = a(p_{max}) + 3\sigma(p_{max})$$ (9)

Substituting from (2) and (3) and solving the quadratic equations in p_{max} and p_{min}, one can easily obtain the following result:

$$p_{\substack{max \\ min}} = \frac{2N^2 - 2nN + 9Nk \pm \sqrt{81N^2k^2 - 36n^2Nk + 36nN^2k}}{2N^2 + 18Nk}$$ (10)

where

$$k = 1 - \frac{N}{M}.$$

We thus have a range, p_{min} to p_{max}, in which the true fault coverage will lie with a high probability. It is convenient to express this range as $p_{av} \pm \Delta p$, where

$$p_{av} = \frac{p_{max} + p_{min}}{2}$$ (11)

and

$$\Delta p = \frac{p_{max} - p_{min}}{2}.$$ (12)

Sample Size

Let us assume that the sample size (N) is much smaller than the total number (M) of faults. It is only in such cases that one would use a sampling technique. We can, therefore, assume that $k = 1 - N/M$

---

* This is similar to the three-sigma limit often used in statistics which implies that for practical purposes a Gaussian random variable can be assumed to be bounded within an interval, mean $\pm 3 \times$ standard deviation (σ).

≈ 1. Note that in (3) this approximation will increase the variance leading to a pessimistic (or safe) result. For $N = 100$, p_{max} and p_{min} as computed from (10) are shown in Fig. 2 as a function of the fraction (n/N) of undetected faults. The range between p_{min} and p_{max} is shown by the shaded region in the figure. Fig. 2 also shows this range for $N = 1000$. Indeed, the accuracy of result can be increased to any desired value by increasing N. But a suitable value of N can be selected from Figs. 3 and 4 which were obtained from equations (10), (11), and (12). Clearly, if $N \geqslant 1000$, the average fault coverage p_{av} coincides with sample fault coverage, $1 - n/N$. Also, the uncertainty range is smaller than ± 5 percent. The uncertainty range is widest when the fault coverage is around 50 percent. For a fault coverage of 95 percent, the range of uncertainty is only 2 percent.

until a decision is made. In practical cases, instead of simulating a single fault each time, one may simulate a small set of faults.

The theory of sequential sampling was developed by Wald [5]. Only the main results of this theory, as applied to fault coverage analysis, will be stated here. Consider the graph of Fig. 5 where the number of

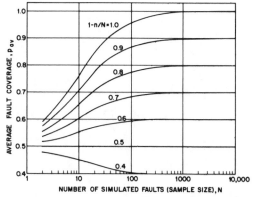

Fig. 3. Average fault coverage as a function of sample size for various values of sample fault coverage $(1 - n/N)$

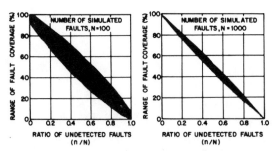

Fig. 2. Range of fault coverage (shaded region) as a function of fractional undetected faults (n/N) in a sample of N faults for $N = 100$ and $N = 1000$

3. SEQUENTIAL SAMPLING

The use of sequential sampling in logic fault analysis has been suggested by Case [2]. In this method a single randomly selected fault is simulated with all the test patterns. Either the fault is detected or not detected. Based on this result, one tries to make a decision regarding the fault coverage. If the decision cannot be made, another fault is simulated, and the result is examined again. This process is continued

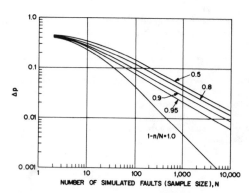

Fig. 4. Spread of fault coverage range on either side of the average fault coverage of Fig. 3

* Notice that our $p0$ and $p1$ are complements of Wald's $p0$ and $p1$. In Wald's analysis, $p0$ and $p1$ ($p0 < p1$), are the fractions of bad items in a lot. Our $p0$ and $p1$ are fractions of covered (or good) faults. In both cases α and β have the same meaning. Equations (13–15) were obtained by substituting $1 - p0$ for $p0$ and $1 - p1$ for $p1$ in Wald's expressions.

undetected faults can be plotted as a function of the number of simulated faults. In a sampling experiment, as more and more faults are sampled, the number of undetected faults traces a curve starting from the origin. According to Wald's theory, two parallel lines A and B are drawn. If the sampling curve crosses the line B, we conclude that the fault coverage is below some percentage $p0$ (90 percent in Fig. 5). If it crosses A, we conclude that fault coverage is higher than $p1$ (86.7 percent). As long as the sampling curve stays between the two parallel lines, sampling is continued. The two parallel lines are drawn from the intercepts $h0$, $h1$ and the slope s computed from the following formulas* ([5], page 94):

$$h0 = \frac{1}{D} \log \frac{\beta}{1-\alpha} \qquad (13)$$

$$h1 = \frac{1}{D} \log \frac{1-\beta}{\alpha} \qquad (14)$$

$$s = \frac{1}{D} \log \frac{p0}{p1} \qquad (15)$$

$$D = \log \frac{1-p1}{1-p0} - \log \frac{p1}{p0} \qquad (16)$$

where α, β, $p0$, and $p1$, $(p0 > p1)$ are defined as follows: if the sampling curve crosses line B, then the probability of the fractional fault coverage being above $p0$ is less than α, and if the sampling curve crosses A, then the probability of fault coverage being below $p1$ is less than β. Apparently, in the language of quality control analysis, α and β represent the risks of rejecting a good lot and accepting a bad lot, respectively. In Fig. 5, $\alpha = \beta = 0.01$. For the pair of lines A and B, $p1 = 0.867$, $p0 = 0.9$.

In [2], a crossing of the line A was assumed to indicate a fault coverage better than $p0$ while the crossing of B was interpreted as a fault coverage below $p1$. Since $p1 < p0$, if the true fault coverage is between $p0$ and $p1$, no decision will ever be made. This is not true in sequential analysis; it always leads to a decision. A closer examination of Wald's theory [5] indicates that crossing of A (drawn as solid line), also known as acceptance, only means that $\text{Prob}(p < p1) < \alpha$. For a sufficiently small α, acceptance would be practically equivalent to $p > p1$. Similarly, a crossing of B (drawn as dashed line), or rejection, should mean $p < p0$. These two regions, as shown in Fig. 6, overlap because $p1 < p0$. It is this overlap which assures a decision in sequential sampling if the sampling is continued long enough. The decision would, however, give either a lower or an upper bound of the fault coverage. In order to have both the bounds, we must make more than one decision.

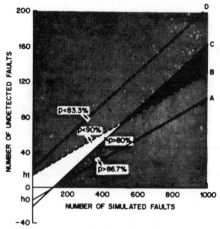

Fig. 5. Decision regions for sequential analysis

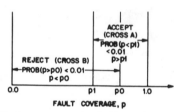

Fig. 6. Fault coverage associated with a decision in sequential analysis

Let us now add a pair of parallel lines C and D to Fig. 5; for these lines $\alpha = \beta = 0.01$, $p0 = 83.3$ percent, and $p1 = 80.0$ percent. If the sampling curve enters the shaded region between the lines B and C, then it must have crossed B ($p < 90$ percent) and C ($p > 80$ percent), and we would conclude that 80 percent $< p < 90$ percent.

The graph of Fig. 7 was drawn to analyze any fault coverage between 56.7 and 96.7 percent. As we have seen in Fig. 6, if the true value of p lies between $p0$ and $p1$, either decision, accept or reject, is possible. If, however, $p > p0$ or $p < p1$, only one decision is possible. We should, therefore, draw the decision regions in such a way that for any given p, there will be one pair with $p0 < p$ and another with $p1 > p$. This will assure two decisions, one "greater than" and the other, "less than." To obtain such decision regions, the range 53.3 to 96.7 was divided into intervals of 3.33, and for each adjacent pair of numbers a set of parallel lines ($\alpha = \beta = .01$) were drawn using (13), (14), and (15). This gives a separation of about 10 percent between the upper and lower bounds. The dashed lines in Fig. 7 are used to obtain the upper bound and the solid lines the lower bound. Thus, the

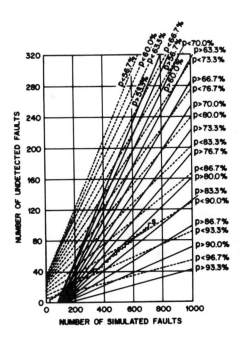

Fig. 7. Graph for sequential analysis of fault coverage in the range 56.7–96.7 percent

sampling curve marked "S" indicates a fault coverage between 80 and 90 percent.

4. EXAMPLES

Two examples will be given to illustrate the above sampling techniques. The circuit considered in the first example was an actual MOS LSI circuit having 2629 gates and a total of 9073 "stuck-at" faults. After *fault collapsing* ([6], Section 2.5), 5904 faults remained. The circuit, which had 18 primary inputs and 19 primary outputs, was highly sequential and also contained asynchronous logic. A test set of 1087 input patterns was evaluated. Simulation of all the 5904 faults using the LAMP simulator [10] required 2225 CPU seconds on IBM370 and the fault coverage was found to be 69.3 percent. Next, 17 percent of the total faults were randomly selected. As a result, 1003 faults were simulated of which 274 were found undetectable. From Figs. 3 and 4, this indicates a fault coverage range 71 ± 4 percent which compares favorably with the actual fault coverage of 69.3 percent obtained from simulation of all faults. However, the simulation CPU time for the 1003 faults was only 184 seconds or about 8 percent of the time needed for simulation of all faults.

In order to evaluate the fault coverage by the sequential sampling method, random samples of 50 to 60 faults were taken. The faults contained in the samples were mutually exclusive, i.e., a fault which was sampled once was not included in any other sample. Faults in each sample were simulated on the LAMP simulator using the same set of 1087 test patterns. The number of undetected faults in the 17 fault samples that were simulated varied between 12 and 20, and this is plotted by a stepped curve in Fig. 8. This figure is the same as Fig. 7 except that only some of the lines intersected by the sampling curve are shown. After nine samples (or about 500 faults) the fault coverage appears to be between 63.3 and 80.0 percent. After 15 samples (i.e., about 800 faults) the coverage is between 66.7 and 80.0 percent. After 17 samples containing 924 faults, the fault coverage appears to be between 66.7 and 76.7 percent.

On an average, the simulation time for a sample was about 44 seconds. Thus, the total time of this sequential sampling run was 748 seconds. This time is significantly higher than the time required for the fixed size sample reported above. This is because LAMP [10] is a deductive simulator in which the computation time depends on the average size of fault list (list of faults active at any time) and not on the total number of faults being simulated ([6], section 4.6). The minimum overhead or preparation time of the simulator is high, but the total time of simulation increases slowly with the number of faults. Therefore, it is advantageous to include all faults in one run as opposed to running the simulator several times with fewer faults.

A parallel simulation, on the other hand, is a natural multipass

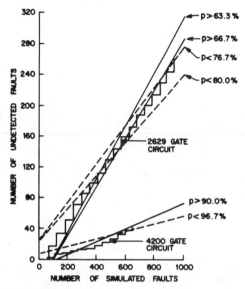

Fig. 8. Fault coverage analysis of example circuits by sequential sampling

Next, for sequential sampling, twelve samples, each consisting of 50 to 60 faults, were simulated. The result is shown in Fig. 8. At the sixth sample, the sampling curve crosses the solid line marked $p > 90.0$ percent, and at the eleventh sample the dotted line marked $p < 96.7$ percent is crossed. Thus, the fault coverage is found to be in the range 90.0 to 96.7 percent. The CPU time required for simulating the twelve samples was about the same as that required for simulating all the faults. As explained earlier, in terms of computation time, sequential sampling is not as attractive for use with a deductive simulator.

In later work, more test patterns were added to the test set of the multiplier circuit to raise the fault coverage to 97.7 percent (as found by simulating all faults.) When 1004 randomly sampled faults were simulated, 24 faults were found to be undetectable by the new test set. This gives a fault coverage in the range 97.43 ± 1.3 percent.

process. The number of faults simulated in one pass usually depends on the word size of the computer. If the faults simulated in each pass are randomly selected, one can analyze the result after each pass and report the range of fault coverage. It is also possible to let the simulator monitor this range automatically and stop itself when the range has been narrowed to some pre-specified value. The extra computation time for doing this in a parallel simulation would be almost negligible.

As a second example, consider another LSI circuit, a 16-bit integer multiplier having 4200 gates. Most of the circuit was combinational with the exception of the synchronously clocked input and output registers. The circuit had 14,745 uncollapsed and 9142 collapsed faults. A test set of 400 patterns was evaluated on the LAMP simulator. Of the randomly selected 1004 faults (11 percent of the collapsed faults) that were simulated, 65 were not detected. From (10), (11), and (12) (also Figs. 3 and 4), this gives a fault coverage range of 93.18 ± 2.2 percent. Simulation of all 9142 faults produced a fault coverage of 94.03 percent. The CPU time required for the sampling run was only 25 percent of that used for simulation of all faults.

5. DISCUSSION OF SAMPLING MECHANISM

Practical circuits contain many different types of faults other than the "single stuck-at" faults. Among these are the "multiple stuck-at" faults and certain technology dependent faults considered by Wadsack [11, 12]. One might, therefore, argue as to how good the tests are that are known to detect a certain percentage of "single stuck-at" faults. We can only say that the "single stuck-at" faults represent a sample of all possible faults, and if we take a sufficiently large number of these (1000 or more) we might be able to say that our tests should detect a similar percentage of all possible faults. This argument is, however, applicable to test patterns that are functionally generated and hence do not necessarily favor the "single stuck-at" faults. Unfortunately, we cannot provide any supporting data for this argument other than saying that this sampling mechanism may be a possible reason for the success of the "single stuck-at" fault technique in practice.

One reason for recommending the use of sampling techniques in the present application is that we are most often dealing with a less than 100 percent fault coverage. The justification for using tests with less than 100 percent fault coverage is that they have produced acceptable results. Why this happens is not clearly understood. It might be that on an LSI chip, since the circuit density is usually high, the occurrence of an isolated single fault during chip fabrication is very unlikely. In other words, a physical defect on the chip could affect a chip area covering several logic fault sites giving rise to a multiple fault situation. Single fault detection test sets are often found to be adequate since they are relatively good for *detection* of multiple faults ([6], page 21) and fault *location* is not generally desired for single chip circuits. A multiple fault may be considered a cluster of single faults, and as long as some of these faults are covered by the single fault test sequence, the chip test result may be reliable. This phenomenon of fault clustering and its influence on the performance of tests with less than 100 percent fault coverage require further study.

6. CONCLUSION

The two methods of fault sampling presented above can be used with any fault simulator. Sequential sampling is ideally suited to a multipass simulator (e.g., parallel simulator). As the example given above shows, sampling methods can result in a considerable saving in the computation time of fault simulation. Also, the storage requirement of a fault simulator rapidly increases with the number of faults being simulated. Thus, if a sampling method is used, much larger circuits can be evaluated with the given resources than would be possible when all faults were simulated.

As the analysis shows, for reasonable accuracy, one should simulate about 1000 faults. Sampling methods should, therefore, be useful for large circuits having several thousand faults. In preliminary stages of test pattern generation, smaller samples can also be used to advantage. If the fault coverage is low, many of the sample faults will be undetected. By examining these, one would know which sections of circuit contain the majority of undetected faults. Functional patterns which would exercise these sections can then be included in the test set. On the other hand, if one uses an algorithmic method for generating tests for the undetected faults, a totally independent sample fault set should be used in subsequent sampling.

7. REFERENCES

[1] Butler, T. T.; Hallin, T. G.; Kulzer, J. J.; and Johnson, K. W. LAMP: application to switching system development. *B.S.T.J.* Vol. 53. October 1974, pp. 1535–1555.

[2] Case, G. R. A statistical method for test sequence evaluation. *Proceedings of 12th Design Automation Conference.* Boston, MA. June 23–25, 1975, pp. 257–260.

[3] Schuler, D. M.; Ulrich, E. G.; Baker, T. E.; and Bryant, S. P. Random test generation using concurrent logic simulation. *Proceedings of 12th Design Automation Conference.* Boston, MA. June 23–25, 1975, pp. 261–267.

[4] Gay, F. A. Evaluation of maintenance software in real-time systems. *IEEE Trans. on Computers.* Vol. C-27. June 1978, pp. 576–582.

[5] Wald, A. *Sequential Analysis.* New York: Dover, 1973.

[6] Breuer, M. A. and Friedman, A. D. *Diagnosis and Reliable Design of Digital Systems.* Rockville, MD: Computer Science Press, 1976.

[7] Feller, W. *An Introduction to Probability Theory and Its Applications.* Vol. 1. New York: Wiley, Third Edition; 1968.

[8] Govindarajulu, Z. Normal approximations to the classical discrete distributions. *Classical and Contagious Discrete Distributions.* G. P. Patil (editor). Calcutta: Statistical Publishing Society, 1965, pp. 79–108.

[9] Papoulis, A. *Probability, Random Variables and Stochastic Processes.* New York: McGraw-Hill, 1965.

[10] Chang, H. Y.; Smith, Jr., G. W.; and Walford, R. B. LAMP: system description. *B.S.T.J.* Vol. 53. October 1974, pp. 1431–1449.

[11] Wadsack, R. L. Fault modeling and logic simulation of CMOS and MOS integrated circuits. *B.S.T.J.* Vol. 57. May-June 1978, pp. 1449–1474.

[12] Wadsack, R. L. Fault coverage in digital integrated circuits. *B.S.T.J.* Vol. 57. May-June 1978, pp. 1475–1488.

Reprinted from *IEEE Transactions on Computers*, Volume C-30, Number
12, December 1981, pages 987-988. Copyright © 1981 by The Institute of
Electrical and Electronics Engineers, Inc. All rights reserved.

Defect Level as a Function of Fault Coverage

T. W. WILLIAMS AND N. C. BROWN

Abstract—This correspondence presents a single equation relating the defect
level of LSI chips to the yield and stuck-at-fault coverage with some assumptions. It is assumed that the faults occur randomly on the chips, which implies
no clustering. This concept is extended to modules on boards.

Index Terms—Fault coverage, stuck-at-fault, testing, yield.

INTRODUCTION

When testing chips on a wafer, it has been found in the past that
a very good test is required to separate the "good" chips from the
"bad" chips when the percent of "bad" chips is high. This has led to
conjecture of the relation of defect level shipped to the fault coverage.
As a result, some questions have arisen to the shape of such a graph.
A short analysis of this defect level as a function of testability was
given in the appendix of a paper by Thomas [1]. Analysis of fault
cluster has been given by Muehldorf [2], [3]. This technique uses a
significant amount of information about the technology and the topology of the particular design. It has been proposed by Wadsack [4]
that the two variables are linearly related. The purpose of this correspondence is to state some assumptions, and based on these assumptions, determine the defect level for faults as a function of fault
coverage and yield. By definition, the fault coverage T is the number
of stuck-at-faults tested m, divided by the total number stuck-at-faults
n, assumed.

ASSUMPTIONS AND DERIVATIVES

Assume that a given chip has exactly n stuck-at-faults which can
be modeled with the standard stuck-at-fault assumption [5]. Furthermore, let m be the number of the n faults which are tested ($m \leq
n$). Finally, assume that the probability of a fault occurring is inde-
pendent of whether any other fault has occurred or not, and that all

Manuscript received December 1, 1980; revised June 10, 1981.
T. W. Williams is with General Technology Division, IBM, Boulder, CO
80302.
N. C. Brown is with General Products Division, IBM, Tucson, AZ
85702.

faults are equally likely with probability P_n. This gives rise to a uniform distribution of faults. Since independence is assumed, the
probability of a chip being all good is

$$(1 - P_n)^n \tag{1}$$

which is the product of the probability of each possible fault being
absent, i.e., no defects. The probability of having a chip with exactly
k faults in it can be found from the binomial distribution to be

$$\binom{n}{k} (1 - P_n)^{n-k} P_n^k = \frac{n!}{k!(n-k)!} (1 - P_n)^{n-k} P_n^k. \tag{2}$$

If m faults out of the n possible faults are tested, the question of
whether all m of the faults tested test good, can be answered by using
the hypergeometric distribution. Thus, the probability of testing m
of the faults out of n with no defects found where there are k faults
is equal to

$$= \begin{cases} \dfrac{\binom{n-k}{m}}{\binom{n}{m}} = \dfrac{\dfrac{(n-k)!}{m!(n-k-m)!}}{\dfrac{n!}{m!(n-m)!}} & \text{for } n-k-m \geq 0 \\ 0 & n-k-m < 0. \end{cases} \tag{3}$$

The probability of accepting a chip with k faults when testing m of
the n is equal to

$$= \begin{cases} \dfrac{\binom{n}{k} (1 - P_n)^{n-k} P_n^k \binom{n-k}{m}}{\binom{n}{m}} & n-k-m \geq 0 \\ 0 & n-k-m < 0. \end{cases} \tag{4}$$

The term in (4) can be reduced to

$$= \begin{cases} \binom{n-m}{k} (1 - P_n)^{n-k} P_n^k & n-k-m \geq 0 \\ 0 & n-k-m < 0. \end{cases} \tag{5}$$

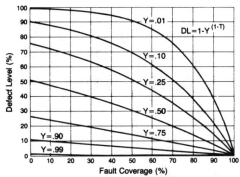

Fig. 1. Defect level as a function of fault coverage.

The probability of accepting a chip with one or more faults P_a, is equal to

$$P_a = \sum_{k=1}^{n-m} \binom{n-m}{k} (1-P_n)^{n-k} P_n^k. \tag{6}$$

Using the identity shown in (7), (6) can be reduced as shown in (8).

$$1 = [(1-P_n) + P_n]^{n-m} = \sum_{k=0}^{n-m} \binom{n-m}{k} (1-P_n)^{n-m-k} P_n^k. \tag{7}$$

Thus

$$\begin{aligned}
P_a &= \sum_{k=1}^{n-m} \binom{n-m}{k} (1-P_n)^{n-k} P_n^k \\
&= (1-P_n)^m \sum_{k=1}^{n-m} \binom{n-m}{k} (1-P_n)^{n-m-k} P_n^k \\
&= (1-P_n)^m [1 - (1-P_n)^{n-m}] \\
&= (1-P_n)^m - (1-P_n)^n.
\end{aligned} \tag{8}$$

The defect level (DL) is equal to the probability that a bad chip is accepted, divided by the probability of accepting a bad chip plus the probability of a good chip, which under our assumptions will always be accepted.

$$DL = \frac{P_a}{(1-P_n)^n + P_a}. \tag{9}$$

Substituting (8) into (9) yields (10) for DL.

$$DL = 1 - (1-P_n)^{n-m}. \tag{10}$$

The yield of a process Y is the probability of a totally good chip. Since the probability of a good chip is $(1-P_n)^n$, it follows that

$$Y = (1-P_n)^n. \tag{11}$$

Substituting (11) into (10) yields

$$DL = 1 - Y^{(1-\frac{m}{n})}. \tag{12}$$

Again, by definition the fault coverage T is the number of faults tested m, divided by the total number faults n. Thus, (12) can be put in terms of yield Y, and fault coverage T, which is as follows:

$$DL = 1 - Y^{(1-T)}. \tag{13}$$

Fig. 1 shows a family of curves with different yields. Clearly, (13) is not linear in T as suggested in [4]. However, for high yield process, the curve "looks" almost like a straight line.

Now that this problem has been solved with the full power of distributions, the following derivation using conditional probability is quite straightforward. Let A be the event that all stuck-at-faults are good in the chip, and B the event that m out of the n have been tested and found to be good. Therefore, the conditional probability equation is

$$P(A \mid B) = \frac{P(A \cap B)}{P(B)}. \tag{14}$$

The $P(A \cap B) = (1-P_n)^n$ and the $P(B) = (1-P_n)^m$. Therefore, the DL is

$$DL = 1 - P(A \mid B) = 1 - \frac{(1-P_n)^n}{(1-P_n)^m}. \tag{15}$$

Equation (15) is exactly what was obtained in (10), and hence, yields

$$DL = 1 - Y^{(1-T)}. \tag{16}$$

Equation (16) can be used to estimate the defect level at the board, if the modules on the board are equally likely to have a fault and are independent with no manufacturing defects induced. (The manufacturing defects could also be added with a bit more complication.) If a board contains 40 modules each, with a defect level of 1.5 percent, then the probability that the card will be good is

$$(1 - 0.015)^{40} = 0.546. \tag{17}$$

Hence, about half (0.454) of the boards will have one or more faulty components. The defect level for the board DL_B after testing with a test T is

$$DL_B = 1 - (0.546)^{(1-T)}. \tag{18}$$

Using (18), boards with a defect level of 10 percent require a level of fault coverage of 82.6 percent, whereas a board with 1 percent defect level requires fault coverage of 98.3 percent.

This technique gives estimates for quick calculations. If process defects and probability density functions are known, then a better estimate of the defect levels can be obtained [2], [3].

CONCLUSION

With VLSI, there is more and more interest in the defect level of product as a function of yield and fault coverage. The motivation for this interest is cost driven. This correspondence has presented two techniques for obtaining the equation for defect level as a function of fault coverage and yield of a process. Another application of this equation to board defect level has been shown. The key point about this equation is that defect level is exponentially related to fault coverage.

REFERENCES

[1] J. J. Thomas, "Establishing test requirements for digital networks," presented at the 1973 WESCON, session 10.
[2] E. I. Muehldorf, "A quality measure for LSI components," *IEEE J. Solid-State Circuits*, vol. SC-9, pp. 291–297, Oct. 1974.
[3] ——, "Fault clustering: Modeling and observation on experimental LSI chips," *IEEE J. Solid-State Circuits*, vol. SC-10, pp. 237–244, Aug. 1975.
[4] R. L. Wadsack, "Fault coverage in digital integrated circuits," *Bell Syst. Tech. J.*, vol. 57, pp. 1475–1488, May–June 1978.
[5] H. Y. Chang, E. Manning, and G. Metze, *Fault Diagnosis of Digital Systems.* New York: Wiley-Interscience, 1970.

Characterizing the LSI Yield Equation from Wafer Test Data

SHARAD C. SETH, SENIOR MEMBER, IEEE, AND VISHWANI D. AGRAWAL, SENIOR MEMBER, IEEE

Abstract—The results of production test on LSI wafers are analyzed to determine the parameters of the yield equation. Recognizing that a physical defect on a chip can produce several logical faults, the number of faults per defect is assumed to be a random variable with Poisson distribution. The analysis provides a relationship between the yield of the tested fraction of the chip area and the cumulative fault coverage of test patterns. The parameters of the yield equation are estimated by fitting this relation to the measured yield versus fault coverage data.

I. Introduction

THE established approach to yield estimation of LSI chips is based upon an assumed defect–density distribution over a wafer. The yield equation, i.e., the yield versus chip area relationship, is expressed in terms of the parameters of this distribution which are estimated either from monitor wafers [1] or from a few carefully placed test chips on each wafer [2]–[4]. The monitors or test chips are designed to detect commonly known types of *physical defects*, such as opens and shorts in the layers of diffusion, polysilicon, and metal or the *parametric irregularities*. Once the distribution of defect–density is determined, the chip yield can be calculated. The parameters of yield equation not only vary from wafer-to-wafer or lot-to-lot but also undergo variations within a wafer. A continuous monitoring is, therefore, desirable.

In addition to parametric testing the wafer test also includes the functional testing of *all* the chips on the wafer. It was shown in [5] that the chip failure data thus obtained can be analyzed to estimate the *reject ratio*, that is, the fraction of bad chips passed as good by the tests. In this paper, we show that further use can be made of the same data in characterizing the yield equation. A compound model is introduced in which each physical defect is assumed to produce a random number of *logical faults*. The parameters of the model are derived from the functional test process. These test data reflect the effect of fault distribution over all the chips on a wafer instead of a few defect monitors.

II. Analysis

Let x be the random variable denoting the number of physical defects on a chip. Following Stapper [6] we will assume that x has a *negative binomial distribution* given by [7, p. 18]:

Manuscript received December 2, 1982; revised October 18, 1983.
S. C. Seth is with the Department of Computer Science, University of Nebraska, Lincoln, NE 68588.
V. D. Agrawal is with Bell Laboratories, Murray Hill, NJ 07974.

$$p_1(x) = \text{Prob(number of defects} = x)$$

$$= \binom{x + a - 1}{x} (Ab)^x (1 + Ab)^{-x-a} \tag{1}$$

where A is the chip area, and $a \geqslant 0$, and $b > 0$ are two parameters. Further, we assume that each physical defect can produce several faults, such as stuck-at-1's, stuck-at-0's, etc. Suppose a given chip has x defects and the ith defect causes k_i faults. Then the total number of faults on the chip is

$$n = \sum_{i=1}^{x} k_i.$$

We assume that the random variables k_i are independent and that their values occur with probabilities given by a Poisson distribution having mean c. Then the total number of faults in the presence of x defects will have a distribution which is the x-fold convolution of identical Poisson distributions. This is known to be a Poisson distribution also [8, p. 268] with mean cx. Thus

$$p_2(n|x) = \text{Prob(number of faults)} = n|x \text{ defects)}$$

$$= \frac{(cx)^n}{n!} e^{-cx}. \tag{2}$$

With the help of (1) and (2) we can express a *generalized distribution* [7, p. 21] for the number of faults on a chip:

$$p_3(n) = \text{Prob(number of faults} = n)$$

$$= \sum_{x=0}^{\infty} p_2(n/x) p_1(x). \tag{3}$$

Next, we will derive the probability generating function (p.g.f.) for $p_3(n)$ which is defined as

$$G_3(s) \triangleq \sum_{n=0}^{\infty} p_3(n) s^n \tag{4}$$

where s is the transformation variable (see [8, p. 264]. Substituting from (3), we get,

$$G_3(s) = \sum_{n=0}^{\infty} \sum_{x=0}^{\infty} p_2(n|x) p_1(x) s^n$$

$$= \sum_{x=0}^{\infty} p_1(x) \sum_{n=0}^{\infty} p_2(n|x) s^n.$$

Reprinted from *IEEE Transactions on Computer-Aided Design*, Volume CAD-3, Number 2, April 1984, pages 123-126.

The inner summation in the last expression represents the p.g.f. of the Poisson distribution [7, p. 14] which is $e^{cx(s-1)}$. Therefore,

$$G_3(s) = \sum_{x=0}^{\infty} p_1(x) e^{cx(s-1)}$$

$$= \sum_{x=0}^{\infty} p_1(x) t^x \quad \text{where} \quad t = e^{c(s-1)}$$

$$= G_1(t)$$

where G_1 represents the p.g.f. of the negative-binomial distribution p_1. This has the closed-form expression ([7, p. 17])

$$G_1(t) = (1 + Ab - Abt)^{-a}$$

which, upon substitution of the expression for t, yields the desired p.g.f. as

$$G_3(s) = [1 + Ab(1 - e^{c(s-1)})]^{-a}. \tag{5}$$

If f is the fault coverage expressed as a fraction of total faults, then $1 - f$ will be the probability of a randomly selected fault remaining undetected by the tests. When the chip has n faults, the probability of none of them being detected by the tests can be approximated as $(1 - f)^n$. This approximation is accurate under quite general conditions as shown in [9]. Now since n is a random variable with probability density $p_3(n)$, the apparent yield of chips that pass the tests will be

$$y + Y_{bg}(f) = \sum_{n=0}^{\infty} p_3(n)(1 - f)^n$$

where the left-hand side simply indicates that the apparent yield is composed of the true yield y and the yield $Y_{bg}(f)$ of bad chips tested as good. From the definition of probability generating function given by (4) the above expression is equivalent to $G_3(1 - f)$. Thus using (5), we get

$$y + Y_{bg}(f) = [1 + Ab(1 - e^{-cf})]^{-a}. \tag{6}$$

Obviously, for a complete fault coverage ($f = 1$), Y_{bg} is zero. Thus the yield is given by

$$y = [1 + Ab(1 - e^{-c})]^{-a}. \tag{7}$$

Reject ratio, which is defined as the fraction of bad chips among those that are tested good can be computed from (6) and (7) as follows:

$$r(f) = \frac{Y_{bg}(f)}{y + Y_{bg}(f)} = 1 - \left[\frac{1 + Ab(1 - e^{-c})}{1 + Ab(1 - e^{-cf})}\right]^{-a}. \tag{8}$$

Let $P(f)$ represent the fraction of chips rejected by test patterns with cummulative fault-coverage f, then,

$$P(f) = 1 - y - Y_{bg}(f) = 1 - [1 + Ab(1 - e^{-cf})]^{-a}. \tag{9}$$

III. Estimation of Parameters

The wafer test data for an LSI chip was analyzed. This chip contained approximately 2700 transistors. The chip-failure data was combined with the results from fault simulation to obtain a plot of the fraction $P(f)$ of failing chips versus the

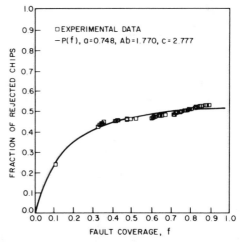

Fig. 1. Wafer-test data: Fraction of rejected chips as a function of fault coverage.

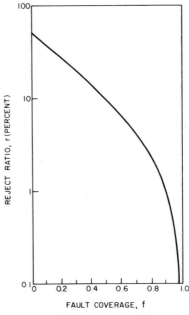

Fig. 2. Reject ratio versus fault coverage as computed from (8) using the estimated parameters $a = 0.748$, $Ab = 1.77$, and $c = 2.777$.

fault coverage f (see [5] for further details of this procedure.) The resultant data are shown as the points in Fig. 1. A weighted least squares procedure was used to estimate the parameters a, Ab, and c in (9) that best fit these data [10]. The results were as follows:

$$a = 0.748, \quad Ab = 1.770, \quad \text{and} \quad c = 2.777.$$

From (7) the yield for these values of the parameters is 48 percent which agrees closely with the expected yield for this chip. The reject ratio for the tests, which have a 90-percent fault coverage, is about one percent as computed from (8) (see Fig. 2). Also for a 0.1-percent reject ratio ($r = 0.001$), about 99-percent fault coverage will be required.

IV. Yield and Fault Coverage

Stapper's yield equation is written as [6]

$$y = [1 + A\bar{D}(\sigma/\mu)^2]^{-(\mu/\sigma)^2} \tag{10}$$

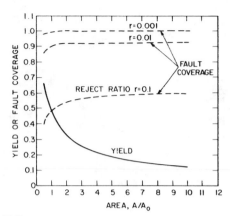

Fig. 3. *Yield Equation:* Yield versus area (solid curve) computed from the estimated parameters, $a = 0.748$, $A_0 b = 1.77$, $c = 2.777$. The normalizing area A_0 is the area of the chip of Fig. 1. The dashed curves are the computed fault coverages required for reject ratios of 10-, 1-, and 0.1-percent.

where $\bar{D}$ is the average defect density and σ/μ is the coefficient of variation of the defect density. A is the chip area. Comparing (10) and (7), we get

$$\sigma/\mu = \sqrt{1/a}$$

and

$$A\bar{D} = Ab(1 - e^{-c})a. \tag{11}$$

For the chip considered in the previous section, $\sigma/\mu = 1.16$ and $A\bar{D} = 1.93$. These values are of the same order as those given in [6]. Fig. 3 shows a yield versus area curve (solid line) as computed from these values. The normalizing area A_0 in this graph is the area of the chip whose test results were analyzed in the previous section.

For a given reject ratio r, (8) can be solved to give the required fault coverage,

$$f = -\frac{1}{c} \ln \left[1 + \frac{1 - (1 - r)^{1/a} \{1 + Ab(1 - e^{-c})\}}{Ab} \right]. \tag{12}$$

The fault coverages as computed from this formula are shown in Fig. 3 by dashed curves. It is interesting to note that as the area increases, for a given reject ratio, the required fault coverage converges to a fixed value. For example, a 1-percent reject ratio ($r = 0.01$) would require about 93-percent fault coverage. These results are, of course, valid for the chips that are fabricated in the same technology and design-style as the one from which the parameters were estimated. For finer features, one would expect the average number c of logical faults per physical defect to be larger and in that case equation (12) will give a lower fault coverage requirement for the same given reject ratio.

Normally, the yield equation is characterized by fitting (10) to the experimental data on yield versus area obtained from several chips of varying areas. In our analysis the characterization of the yield equation is accomplished from the data on just one type of chips. This is not surprising because the measured rejected fraction (or 1-yield), $P(f)$ given by (9), contains the effect of yield variation as the tested area of chip increases.

To illustrate this we use (11) and rewrite (9) as

$$P(f) = 1 - [1 + A_f \bar{D}(\sigma/\mu)^2]^{-(\mu/\sigma)^2}$$

where A_f is the tested area given by

$$A_f = A \cdot \frac{1 - e^{-cf}}{1 - e^{-c}}.$$

Thus the $P(f)$ versus f relation can also be thought of as 1-yield versus tested area. Notice that A_f is a nonlinear function of f since in our model, a defect can cause several faults. The special case of a single fault per defect can be analyzed by assuming $c \ll 1$ so that the probability of more than one fault is very small. In this case $A_f = Af$ as has been discussed in [11].

V. Conclusion

Traditionally chip failure data has been used just to identify good chips from the bad ones. We have shown that such data, in combination with results from a fault simulator, can be used also to characterize important aspects of processing and testing. The yield equation derived in this paper is based on the distinction between physical defects and logical faults. The parameters of this equation are derived from the wafer-level test data.

Briefly, the advantages of the proposed approach are as follows:

(1) Since the yield equation is characterized at the functional test level, it is capable of taking the technology-dependent factors into account.

(2) No additional effort is required for data collection since the wafer-level tests for both yield characterization and production testing are the same.

(3) The results of analysis may be used differently for a new and mature process. For a new process the parameters of the yield equation may be monitored closely for an unexpected deviation from the norm and used to raise an alert in case of such a deviation. For a mature process, the yield equation could be used to estimate the yield and the required fault coverage of a future chip with a different area.

Acknowledgment

The authors are grateful to J. E. Iwersen for useful technical discussions and express their thanks to C. M. Roman for providing the wafer-test data.

References

[1] C. H. Stapper, "LSI yield and process monitoring," *IBM J. Res. Develop.*, vol. 20, pp. 228–234, May 1976.
[2] M. G. Buehler and L. W. Linholm, "Role of test chips in coordinating logic and circuit design and layout aids for VLSI," *Solid State Technol.*, vol. 24, pp. 68–74, Sept. 1981.
[3] D. S. Perloff *et al.*, "Microelectronic test chips in integrated circuit manufacturing," *Solid State Technol.*, vol. 24, pp. 75–80, Sept. 1981.
[4] U. Kaempf, "Automated parametric testers to monitor the integrated circuit process," *Solid State Technol.*, vol. 24, pp. 81–87, Sept. 1981.
[5] V. D. Agrawal, S. C. Seth, and P. Agrawal, "Fault coverage requirement in production testing of LSI circuits," *IEEE J. Solid-State Circuits*, vol. SC-17, pp. 57–61, Feb. 1982.

[6] C. H. Stapper, "On a composite model to the IC yield problem," *IEEE J. Solid-State Circuits*, vol. SC-10, pp. 537–539, Dec. 1975.

[7] A. Rogers, *Statistical Analysis of Spatial Dispersions*. London, England: Pion Limited, 1974.

[8] W. Feller, *An Introduction to Probability Theory and Its Applications*, vol. I. New York: Wiley, 1968.

[9] V. D. Agrawal, S. C. Seth, and P. Agrawal, "LSI product quality and fault coverage," in *Proc. 18th Design Automation Conf.*, (Nashville, TN), June 29–July 1, 1981, pp. 196–203.

[10] S. C. Seth and V. D. Agrawal, "Forecasting reject rate of tested LSI chips," *IEEE Electron Device Lett.*, vol. EDL-2, pp. 286–287, Nov. 1981.

[11] I. I. Eldumiati and R. N. Gadenz, "Logic and fault simulation," *Bell Syst. Tech. J.*, vol. 60, pp. 1463–1473, Sept. 1981.

*

Sharad C. Seth (S'66–M'70–SM'82) received the B.E. degree in electronics and telecommunications from Jabalpur University, Jabalpur, India, in 1964, the M.Tech. degree in electrical engineering from the Indian Institute of Technology, Kanpur, India, in 1966, and the Ph.D. degree in electrical engineering from the University of Illinois, Urbana, in 1970.

Since 1970 he has been on the faculty of the Department of Computer Science, University of Nebraska, Lincoln, and is currently a Professor. He held visiting positions at the Indian Institute of Technology, Kanpur, India, during the years 1974–1975 and 1982–1983 and at Bell Laboratories, Murray Hill, NJ, during the summers of 1980 and 1982. His current research interests are in the areas of VLSI testing and design and reliability analysis of fault-tolerant systems.

Dr. Seth is a member of the ACM and the Computer Society of India.

*

Vishwani D. Agrawal (S'68–M'70–SM'80) received the B.Sc. degree from Allahabad University, Allahabad, India, in 1960, the B.E. (honors) degree from Roorkee University, Roorkee, India, in 1964, the M.E. degree from the Indian Institute of Science, Bangalore, India, in 1966, and the Ph.D. degree from the University of Illinois, Urbana, Illinois, in 1971.

His experience includes teaching (1966–1967) in the Department of Electrical Engineering, Indian Institute of Technology, New Delhi, India; research (1967–1970) at the Antenna Laboratory, University of Illinois, Urbana; digital test technique development for Illiac IV Project (1970–1971) at the Automation Technology, Inc., Champaign, IL; electromagnetic pulse (EMP) experimentation (1971–1972) at E.G. and G., Inc., Albuquerque, NM; teaching and research (1972–1975) at the School of Radar Studies, Indian Institute of Technology, New Delhi, India; and spacecraft antenna design (1975–1978) at TRW Defense and Space Systems Group, Redondo Beach, CA. Since 1978, he has been working on computer-aided design and testing of LSI circuits at the Bell Laboratories, Murray Hill, NJ, where he is now the supervisor of Test Aids Group. He was co-recipient of the Best Applications Paper Award from the IEEE Antennas and Propogation Society in 1979, and his paper, coàuthored with M. R. Mercer, has won him the Best Paper Award at the 1982 IEEE International Test Conference.

Dr. Agrawal is a fellow of the Institution of Electronics and Telecommunication Engineers (India).

Chapter V: Testability Analysis

How do you define testability? Pose this question to 10 digital engineers and you will have not one but 10 definitions. The reason is that the perception of testability is highly dependent on one's involvement with testing. For example, a design engineer might consider the complexity of test vector generation as a measure of circuit testability. To a test engineer, testability may mean compatibility of design with the test equipment. Quality engineers often relate testability to fault coverage.

The following definition is based on common sense: *Testability is the property of a circuit that makes it easy (and sometimes, possible!) to test.* The primary objective of testability analysis is to give an early warning about the testing problems that lie ahead. It should also provide guidance in improving the testability. To be useful, testability analysis should be simpler than actual test generation or fault simulation.

To accomplish these goals, testability analysis is normally assumed to have the following attributes:

- *Topological analysis:* Only the structure of circuit is analyzed. No test vectors are involved (this allows the use of analysis in the very early phase of design). Testability analysis is a static form of analysis as compared to simulation, which is a dynamic analysis.

- *Linear complexity:* The analysis should be linear (or almost linear) in circuit size. Otherwise, one could use test generation or fault simulation, both of which have higher complexity but provide the necessary test data.

1: Overview of Techniques

Most of the work on testability analysis has been reported during the last two decades. Stephenson and Grason [Step76] defined testability measures. For every node in the circuit, they defined two quantities, *controllability* and *observability,* as indicators of controlling and observing that node. These parameters, with values between 0 and 1, were computed for all nodes in the circuit by using the functional behavior of the modules. Signal correlations due to fanouts were neglected, and the testability of a node was defined as the geometric mean of its controllability and observability. Attempts at interpreting the results met only with limited success. However, this work showed that testability analysis tools are possible [Gras79].

The first popular computer-aided design (CAD) tool for testability analysis was SCOAP, developed by Goldstein [Gold79, Gold80]. It provided several improvements over the previous work. First, the analysis was performed at the gate level instead of the register-transfer level. This made SCOAP results easier to relate to the faults that are commonly modeled at the gate level. Second, Goldstein recognized that the controllability of a signal may be dependent on the specific logic value. For example, it is easier to control the output of an AND gate to 0 than to 1. Separate 0- and 1-controllabilities were, therefore, defined. In all, three combinational and three sequential measures are computed by SCOAP for each node in the circuit. Numerical values of these measures range between zero and infinity and are assumed to represent the *effort* required in controlling/observing the node. Higher values denote greater effort. Third, the analysis complexity was kept almost linear in the number of nodes by neglecting signal correlation. This, however, became the stumbling block for SCOAP since signal correlations caused by reconvergent fanouts are the main reason why test generation is difficult.

Analysis of SCOAP results has shown its potential in identifying circuits that are difficult to test, although the results are not always reliable [Agra82]. Production-level CAD tools have been developed for use in very large scale integration (VLSI) design [Sing84]. Several other algorithms that fall in the same class as SCOAP have been reported in the literature [Chan74, Kovi81, Benn81, Rati82].

There are two main problems with SCOAP-like testability measures. First, a certain arbitrariness in the definition of controllability and observability measures makes calibration difficult. SCOAP can compare the testability of two circuits but can not tell how testable a given circuit is. Second, the assumption of independence of signals produced by the same fanout limits accuracy. These problems have led to the use of probabilistic definition of testability.

An alternative to SCOAP-like measures of controllability and observability is to define these terms as probabilities. Consider application of a random input vector to a combinational circuit. For a line l in the circuit, the probability of the event "signal value on l is set to 1 by a random vector" is called the 1-*controllability* of line l and denoted as $C1(l)$. When a long sequence of random vectors is applied to the circuit, $C1(l)$ is the expected fraction of times that a 1 will appear on line l. The zero controllability of a line is defined in a similar way. The probability of the event "fault l s-a-0 is detected by a random input" is called the 0–*detectability* of line l and is denoted as $D0(l)$. The detection of the fault l s-a-0 by the random vector requires simultaneous occurrence of two events: "line l is set to 1" and "a path from line l is sensitized to a circuit output" (see discussion of path sensitization in Chapter III). The probability of the second event is called the 1–*observability* of line l which is denoted as $B1(l)$. Then the relation

$$D0(l) = C1(l) \cdot B1(l)$$

represents the condition stated above for detection of l s-a-0.

Parker and McCluskey [Park75a, Park75b] developed procedures for computing line controllabilities (which they called *signal probabilities*) in combinational circuits. In their approach, the probability of a signal assuming a value 1 is computed from a Boolean expression for that signal written in terms of primary input variables Fault detection probability is obtained as the probability of the exclusive-or function of the good and the faulty outputs assuming a value 1 (see reprint of their paper in this chapter.)

Fike [Fike75] additionally defined a *transmission probability* for each line as the probability of sensitizing a path from that line to a primary output (in terms of the notation above, the transmission probability of line l is the sum $D0(l) + D1(l)$.) The computation of line detectabilities in the presence of reconvergent fanouts by Fike's method would require exhaustive simulation and thus would be pointless. Other authors have called this transmission probability as observability. Savir [Savi83] showed that the derivation of detectability by multiplying controllability and observability could produce incorrect result. Jain and Agrawal [Jain85], in their work on statistical fault analysis, defined separate 0 and 1 observabilities for each line, as we have done above. This makes it possible to express detectability correctly as a product of appropriate controllability and observability (see the above equation).

Parker and McClusky's work led to several applications of probabilistic analysis [Ogus75, Shed75, Magn77, Bass80]. Complexity of symbolic computation for large circuits, however, restricted its applicability. This motivated the later work on numeric and approximate methods. Savir *et al.* [Savi84] formulated a *cutting algorithm* in which every fanout line is cut and initialized to a controllability range [0,1]. The modified network thus becomes free from reconvergent fanouts, and controllability range for every line can be obtained. The price paid for this computational tractability is that only upper and lower bounds on controllability can be obtained. The lower bounds are useful in providing a conservative estimate on the length of random-pattern tests for adequate fault coverage, although the estimate may be unduly pessimistic if the bounds are not close to the exact values. Brglez devised a probabilistic testability algorithm, COP [Brgl84a], and showed that reasonable accuracy could be obtained in some cases by neglecting signal correlation.

Recently, accurate methods for probabilistic analysis have received attention. Bass and Grundmann [Bass81] showed that in a combinational network, when just the inputs involved in producing reconvergent fanout signals are set to 0 or 1, all other signals in the network become mutually independent. Thus, an exact computation is possible for cases with partially enumerated inputs. In another recent work [Seth85], the circuit is covered by smaller blocks and a partial enumeration technique is used on each block. These blocks, called *supergates,* completely include reconvergent fanouts. Based on this covering, algorithms to exactly compute detection probabilities have also been derived [Seth86]. These algorithms avoid taking exclusive-or between the good and the faulty circuits [Park75a] or inserting auxiliary AND gates as suggested by Savir *et al.* [Savi84]. Their computational cost, however, is exponential in the number of reconvergent fanouts in any covering block. In the worst case, the whole circuit may be covered by a single block and all its inputs could be reconvergent thus leading to an exhaustive procedure. In such cases, approximations may be necessary. Further, with the suggested approximations, errors in the computed values could be positive or negative.

2: SCOAP

Most popular among testability algorithms has been SCOAP (Sandia Controllability and Observability Analysis Program.) SCOAP [Gold79, Gold80] computes six quantities for every node in the circuit. These quantities relate to the effort of controlling and observing the node. For a node x, the six quantities are defined as follows:

1. Combinational zero controllability $CC^0(x)$
2. Combinational one controllability $CC^1(x)$
3. Combinational observability $CO(x)$
4. Sequential zero controllability $SC^0(x)$
5. Sequential one controllability $SC^1(x)$
6. Sequential observability $SO(x)$

The number of other nodes that must be set to either control or observe a particular node determines the combinational measures for that node. Sequential measures, on the other hand, depend on the number of time frames (e.g., clock cycles) required to control or observe a node. For all primary inputs of the circuit, both combinational controllabilities are defined as unity and both sequential controllabilities as zero. Also, both observabilities for all primary outputs are set to zero. To understand how these measures are computed for other nodes of the circuit, consider the AND gate shown in Figure 5.1. Since the gate is combinational, only combinational measures are relevant.

All node controllabilities are calculated first and used in the calculation of node observabilities. The

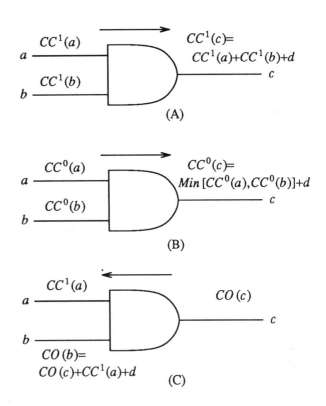

Figure 5.1: Combinational measures in SCOAP.

calculation of controllabilities proceeds from input to output. In Figure 5.1A the combinational one-controllability of the output line c is computed as the sum of the one-controllabilities of the input lines. Intuitively, this computation is obvious if controllability of a node is equated with the effort to set that node to the specified value. Thus, in order to set line c to 1 both lines a and b must be set at 1. The quantity d is added as the depth factor, again, based on the intuition that the farther removed a node is from the primary input the harder it is to control. The exact value chosen for d is somewhat arbitrary; Goldstein [Gold79] suggests choosing $d=1$. In Figure 5.1B line c can be set to zero by setting either a or b to zero, whichever is easier. Thus, the minimum of the zero-controllabilities for lines a and b is added to the depth factor d to derive zero-controllability of c. Observability calculation starts with *a priori* definition of observabilities for primary outputs. The observability of a gate input is defined in terms of the observability of the gate output and the controllabilities of the other inputs of the gate. Recursive application of these definitions allows computation of observabilities for all the nodes in the circuit. Figure 5.1C illustrates the calculation of observability of an input to an AND gate: For observing line *b*, set line *a* to 1 and observe *c*. A node in the circuit will be harder to control or observe the higher its corresponding measure is.

The sequential measures are defined and computed in a similar way but, as was already mentioned, they represent the length of input sequences required to control or observe a node. Thus combinational elements add nothing to sequential measures. For a flip-flop the output sequential controllabilities will be determined by the sequential controllabilities of its data and clock inputs and a sequential depth factor.

2.1: Applications of SCOAP

The overall complexity of computation in SCOAP is almost linear in the number of gates, which makes it an attractive testability audit tool. Actual experience has shown the sequential measures to be less valuable than the combinational ones. Analytical approaches to relate the testability measures to data on fault coverage or fault detection have not met with much success. Studies [Agra82] of correlation between fault detection data and testability measures show the measures to be quite poor at predicting which individual faults will remain undetected and which will be detected. However, testability measures *can* be effective in approximately predicting relative coverage levels of specific fault sets. The general information provided at the entire circuit level may be even better.

In practice, designers use testability measures to find portions of poor controllability or observability in their circuits, as identified by large values. Proper modifications in the circuit lead to reduction of these values. The testability of the stuck-type faults on a node *x* is defined as:

$$T(x\ stuck-at-0) = CC^1(x) + CO(x)$$

$$T(x\ stuck-at-1) = CC^0(x) + CO(x)$$

These equations reflect the requirement that to detect a stuck-type fault on a line it must be set at the opposite value *and* observed.

The solid line in Figure 5.2a shows node testabilities computed by SCOAP in the form of a histogram for a complex VLSI circuit. Notice that testability represents the effort of testing and, therefore, nodes with high testability values are the most difficult to test. An examination of the nodes with large testability values (above 1.5k) showed that they were clustered in a portion of circuit with poor observability.

An experiment was conducted to determine SCOAP's responsiveness to circuit modifications. A simple modification, as shown in Figure 5.2b, allows the signals to be observed at a primary output through a test multiplexer. Although such a design is rather expensive to be practical, it certainly improves observability. The testability histogram of the modified circuit, shown with dotted line in Figure 5.2a, clearly indicates the testability improvement.

Empirical study has shown the use of testability analysis in predicting the test length. In this work the overall circuit *testability index* is defined as [Sing84]:

$$Testability\ Index = \log \sum_{all\ f_i} T(f_i)$$

Actual number of test vectors (for 90 percent fault coverage) for several circuits are shown in Figure 5.3 as a function of their testability index.

3: Probabilistic Testability

We defined the probabilistic measures of testability in Section 1. Using a simple example, we will now illustrate the computations. Consider the circuit in Figure 5.4A. The binary values on the lines show the result of exhaustive simulation. Based on the result of simulation, the signal controllabilities can be easily computed. One-controllabilities are shown in Figure 5.4A. Now suppose we wish to obtain the controllabilities without simulation. We first compute the 1-controllability of line *e* as 1/4 by multiplying the 1-controllabilities (both 1/2) of lines *a* and *b*. This is because both *a* and *b* should be 1 for *e* to be 1. The 1-controllability of line *f* is one minus the 0-controllability of *b*. It is, therefore, 1/2. A 1 output from the OR gate requires that both its inputs not be simultaneously 0. Since the 0-controllabilities of these inputs are 3/4 and 1/2, a simple-minded computation will give the 1-controllability of *g* as 1 − 3/8 = 5/8. This is, of course, wrong since exhaustive simulation gives 3/4.

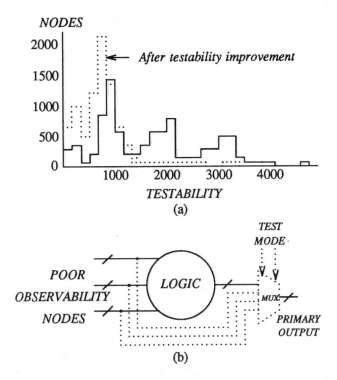

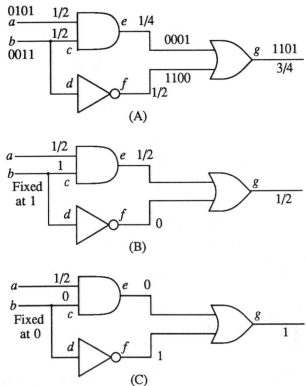

Figure 5.4: Computing probabilistic controllability.

Figure 5.2: SCOAP-guided testability improvement.

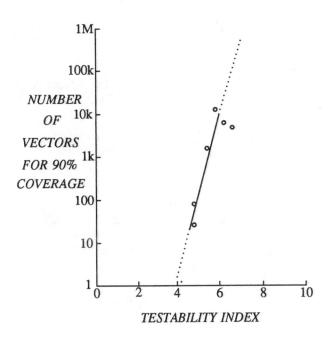

Figure 5.3: Test vectors vs. testability index.

The reason for error is the reconvergent fanout in this circuit that makes the signals *e* and *f* correlate. Their probabilities, therefore, can not be multiplied.

Accurate computation of controllabilities in presence of reconvergent fanouts requires much more

careful consideration. In this simple example, lines *e* and *f* can be made independent by setting the line *b* to fixed values. When *b* is set to 1, simple computation as described above will produce the 1-controllability of *g* as 1/2. This is shown in Figure 5.4B. Similarly, setting *b* to 0 in Figure 5.4C, the output 1-controllability is obtained as 1. These two are conditional controllabilities, and combining them, after weighting with appropriate controllabilities of *b*, gives the correct 1-controllability of *g* as $1/2 \times 1/2 + 1 \times 1/2 = 3/4$.

This simple example illustrates the testability analysis known as PREDICT (Probabilistic Estimation of Digital Circuit Testability). PREDICT [Seth85, Seth86] also includes special procedures for computing observabilities. This chapter includes reprints describing some of the other methods of computing probabilistic testability mentioned in Section V.1 [Savi84] and COP [Brgl84a].

Another class of methods for computing testability can be termed as *statistical*. Simulation data are used to obtain statistical estimates of controllability and observability. One such method, STAFAN [Jain85], as discussed in Chapter IV, computes signal controllabilities from true-value simulation and then approximates observabilities deductively. Another method, known as parallel pattern evaluation and single fault propagation (PPSFP), has been successfully used for computing fault detection probabilities in circuits with scan design [Waic85].

4: Further Applications

We have given two applications of SCOAP in Section V.2.1. Testability analysis has also been used to improve the search heuristics of test generation programs [Agra85a, Brgl84b, Pate86]. Attempts at testability-based static analysis of fault coverage have also been quite successful in the case of combinational circuits [Agra85b, Brgl85]. In 1984, at the International Test Conference, a panel on *Will Testability Analysis Replace Fault Simulation?* concluded with a clear identification of two problems: (1) Fault simulation will be too expensive for the million-device chips of the future and (2) Improvements are needed in the testability analysis techniques. Another application of testability analysis in guiding design for testability is described in [Tris84].

5: Conclusion

Most work on testability analysis is of recent origin. Testability measures like SCOAP have been widely studied. Still their real application is not clearly understood by designers. In this chapter, we have attempted to give a flavor of this work. It is hoped, this brief introduction will provide an incentive for more investigation which, we feel, is urgently needed.

6: Selected Reading

In this chapter we have reprinted six papers. Goldstein's paper [Gold79] presents his work on SCOAP. The second paper by Singer [Sing84] describes the implementation of SCOAP as a tool in VLSI design environment. A serious reader may supplement these with additional papers. We recommend two. Some implementation details of SCOAP appear in [Gold80], and a paper by Agrawal and Mercer [Agra82] deals with the understanding of testability measures. It also gives a method of evaluating fault coverage.

The last four papers of this chapter are on more accurate probabilistic analyses [Park75b, Savi84,

Brgl84a, Seth85]. So far this problem has only been satisfactorily considered for combinational circuits.

7: References

[Agra82] V. D. Agrawal and M. R. Mercer, "Testability Measures -- What Do They Tell Us?," *International Test Conf. Digest of Papers*, Philadelphia, PA, pp. 391-396, November 1982.

[Agra85a] V. D. Agrawal, S. C. Seth, and C. C. Chuang, "Probabilistically Guided Test Generation," *Proc. of Int. Symp. Circuits and Systems (ISCAS)*, pp. 687-689, May 1985.

[Agra85b] V. D. Agrawal and S. C. Seth, "Probabilistic Testability," *Int. Conf. on Computer Design (ICCD-85)*, Port Chester, NY, pp. 562-565, October 1985.

[Bass80] S. C. Bass, "The Application of Probabilistic Modeling to the Design and Fault Analysis of Digital Networks," *Proc. Int. Symp. on Circ. Syst. (ISCAS)*, Houston, Texas, pp. 753-756, April 1980.

[Bass81] S. C. Bass and J. W. Grundmann, "Expected Value Analysis of Combinational Logic Networks," *IEEE Trans. on Circ. Syst.*, Vol. CAS-28, pp. 367-382, May 1981.

[Benn81] R. G. Bennetts, C. M. Maunder, and G. D. Robinson, "CAMELOT: A Computer-Aided Measure for Logic Testability," *IEE Proc.*, Vol. 128, Pt. E, pp. 177-189, September 1981.

[Brgl84a] F. Brglez, "On Testability Analysis Of Combinational Networks," *Proc. Int. Symp. Circuits and Systems (ISCAS)*, Montreal, Canada, pp. 221-225, May 1984, **see reprint in this chapter**.

[Brgl84b] F. Brglez, P. Pownall, and R. Hum, "Application of Testability Analysis from ATPG to Critical Delay Path Tracing," *Proc. Int. Test Conf.*, Philadelphia, PA, pp. 705-712, October 1984.

[Brgl85] F. Brglez, "A Fast Fault Grader : Analysis and Applications," *Proc. Int. Test Conf. (ITC-85)*, Philadelphia, PA, pp. 785-794, Nov. 1985.

[Chan74] H. Y. Chang and G. W. Heimbigner, "Controllability, Observability, and Maintenance Engineering Technique (COMET)," *Bell Syst. Tech. J.*, Vol. 53, pp. 1505-1534, October 1974.

[Fike75] J. L. Fike, "Predicting Fault Detectability in Combinational Circuits − A New Design Tool?," *Proc. 12th Des. Auto. Conf.*, pp. 290-295, 1975.

[Gold79] L. H. Goldstein, "Controllability /

Observability Analysis of Digital Circuits," *IEEE Trans. on Circuits and Systems*, Vol. CAS-26, pp. 685-693, Sept 1979, **see reprint in this chapter.**

[Gold80] L. H. Goldstein and E. L. Thigpen, "SCOAP: Sandia Controllability/Observability Analysis Program," *Proc. 17th Des. Auto. Conf.*, Minneapolis, MN, pp. 190-196, June 1980.

[Gras79] J. Grason, "TMEAS, A Testability Measure Program," *Proc. 16th Des. Auto. Conf.*, San Diego, CA, pp. 156-161, June 1979.

[Jain85] S. K. Jain and V. D. Agrawal, "Statistical Fault Analysis," *IEEE Design & Test of Computers*, Vol. 2, pp. 38-44, Feb. 1985, **see reprint in Chapter IV.**

[Kovi81] P. G. Kovijanic, "Single Testability Figure of Merit," *Int. Test Conf., Digest of Papers*, Philadelphia, PA, pp. 521-529, October 1981.

[Magn77] B. Magnhagen, "Practical Experiments from Signal Probability Simulation of Digital Designs," *Proc. 14th Des. Auto. Conf.*, New Orleans, Louisiana, pp. 216-219, June 1977.

[Ogus75] R. C. Ogus, "The Probability of a Correct Output from a Combinational Circuit," *IEEE Trans. Computers*, Vol. C-24, pp. 534-544, May 1975.

[Park75a] K. P. Parker and E. J. McCluskey, "Analysis of Logic Circuits with Faults Using Input Signal Probabilities," *IEEE Trans. Computers*, Vol. C-24, pp. 573-578, May 1975.

[Park75b] K. P. Parker and E. J. McCluskey, "Probabilistic Treatment of General Combinational Networks," *IEEE Trans. Computers*, Vol. C-24, pp. 668-670, June 1975, **see reprint in this chapter.**

[Pate86] S. Patel and J. Patel, "Effectiveness of Heuristics Measures for Automatic Test Pattern Generation," *Proc. Des. Auto. Conf.*, Las Vegas, Nevada, pp. 547-552, June 1986.

[Rati82] I. M. Ratiu, "VICTOR: A Fast VLSI Testability Analysis Program," *Int. Test Conf. Digest of Papers*, Philadelphia, PA, pp. 397-401, November 1982.

[Savi83] J. Savir, "Good Controllability and Good Observability Do Not Guarantee Good Testability," *IEEE Trans. Computers*, Vol. C-32, pp. 1198-1200, December 1983.

[Savi84] J. Savir, G. S. Ditlow, and P. H. Bardell, "Random Pattern Testability," *IEEE Trans. Computers*, Vol. C-33, pp. 79-90, January 1984, **see reprint in this chapter.**

[Seth85] S. C. Seth, L. Pan, and V. D. Agrawal, "PREDICT – Probabilistic Estimation of Digital Circuit Testability," *Fault-Tolerant Comp. Symp. (FTCS-15) Digest of Papers*, Ann Arbor, MI, pp. 220-225, June 1985, **see reprint in this chapter.**

[Seth86] S. C. Seth, B. B. Bhattacharya, and V. D. Agrawal, "An Exact Analysis for Efficient Computation of Random-Pattern Testability in Combinational Circuits," *Fault-Tolerant Computing Symp. (FTCS-16) Digest of Papers*, Vienna, Austria, pp. 318-323, July 1986.

[Shed75] J. J. Shedletsky and E. J. McCluskey, "The Error Latency of a Fault in a Combinational Digital Circuit," *Fault-Tolerant Computing Symp. (FTCS-5) Digest of Papers*, Paris, France, pp. 210-214, June 1975.

[Sing84] D. M. Singer, "Testability Analysis of MOS VLSI Circuits," *Proc. Int. Test Conf.*, Philadelphia, PA, pp. 690-696, Oct. 1984, **see reprint in this chapter.**

[Step76] J. E. Stephenson and J. Grason, "A Testability Measure for Register Transfer Level Digital Circuits," *Fault-Tolerant Computing Symp. (FTCS-6) Digest of Papers*, Pittsburgh, PA, pp. 101-107, June 1976.

[Tris84] E. Trischler, "ATWIG, An Automatic Test Pattern Generator with Inherent Guidance," *Proc. Int. Test Conf.*, Philadelphia, PA, pp. 80-87, October 1984.

[Waic85] J. A. Waicukauski, E. B. Eichelberger, D. O. Forlenza, E. Lindbloom, and T. McCarthy, "A Statistical Calculation of Fault Detection Probabilities by Fast Fault Simulation," *Proc. Int. Test Conf.*, Philadelphia, PA, pp. 779-784, November 1985.

Controllability/Observability Analysis of Digital Circuits

LAWRENCE H. GOLDSTEIN, MEMBER, IEEE

Reprinted from *IEEE Transactions on Circuits and Systems,* Volume CAS-26, Number 9, September 1979, pages 685-693. Copyright © 1979 by The Institute of Electrical and Electronics Engineers, Inc. All rights reserved.

Abstract—The testability of a digital circuit is directly related to the difficulty of controlling and observing the logical values of internal nodes from circuit inputs and outputs, respectively. This paper presents a method for analyzing digital circuits in terms of six functions which characterize combinational and sequential controllability and observability.

I. INTRODUCTION

AS LSI circuits become larger, the need for designing them with testability in mind becomes more acute. To accomplish this objective, it is necessary to quantify the testability of a circuit in some manner. This quantitative measure of testability can then be used to aid in partitioning circuits to make systems more testable.

Such testability measures as gate count, number of test vectors needed to achieve a given fault coverage and controllability/observability (C/O) matrices for linear-sequential machines have been considered and compared for consistency by Dejka [1]. Unfortunately, all of these measures have problems: gate count is too crude; test sequence length is too difficult to determine in general; and most practical circuits are not linear-sequential machines.

Stephenson and Grason [2] developed testability measures normalized between zero and one for register-transfer-level digital circuits and compared their predictions with actual test-generation effort required for digital circuits of various sizes. There appeared to be good correlation between testability values and actual test-generation effort. Breuer [3] worked on characterizing the costs associated with setting lines internal to a digital circuit to specified logical values and driving these values to primary outputs. These measures are not normalized and their values tend to increase as the testability of the circuit decreases. They were developed specifically for the purpose of improving the efficiency of automated test-sequence generation by providing estimates of the difficulty of justification and propagation operations in a D-algorithm-type approach.

Other approaches to the testability problem include design for testability using LSSD [4], analysis and system reorganization to enhance testability using COMET [5], and diagnosability theory for digital systems [6].

Manuscript received November 21, 1978; revised March 27, 1979.
The author is with Division 2113, Sandia Laboratories, Albuquerque, NM 87185.

II. PRELIMINARIES

This paper will develop six functions to characterize the C/O properties of the internal nodes of a digital circuit. The intent is to provide a quantitative measure of the difficulty of controlling and observing the logical values of internal nodes from consideration of circuit topology alone without analyzing particular sequences of input and state vectors. Ideally, the measures should be easy to compute and accurately characterize the C/O properties of interest.

The digital circuits under consideration are composed of combinational and sequential standard cells or modules contained in a standard cell library. This library includes basic elements such as AND gates, OR gates, inverters, buffers, flip-flops, as well as more complex logical functions created by combining basic elements. Depending upon the level of integration utilized, standard cells may be packaged independently (SSI or MSI) or connected on a single IC by a layout program (LSI). The functions selected for implementation as standard cells depend upon both the technology (functions easy to realize in MOS, I^2L, etc.) and the type of design work underway (frequently used functions). While the analysis presented in this paper assumes the existence of a standard cell library, it places no restrictions upon its contents.

The C/O functions to be described are divided into two sets—combinational and sequential. Combinational 0 and 1 controllabilities of an internal node N, $CC^0(N)$ and $CC^1(N)$, are related to the minimum number of combinational node assignments in the circuit required to justify a 0 or 1, respectively, on node N. A "combinational node" is defined as either a primary input node or an output node of a combinational standard cell. The combinational observability of N, $CO(N)$, is related to both the number of combinational standard cells between node N and a primary output terminal and the minimum number of combinational node assignments required to propagate the logical value on node N to a primary output of the circuit.

Sequential 0 and 1 controllabilities of a node N, $SC^0(N)$ and $SC^1(N)$, estimate the minimum number of sequential nodes that must be set to specified logical values in order to justify a 0 or 1, respectively, on node N. A "sequential node" is an output node of a sequential standard cell. These sequential controllabilities provide a measure of the number of time frames required to control nodes that are deeply embedded in a digital network from the primary inputs. If it is possible to exploit parallelism inherent in the circuit to simultaneously control groups of sequential nodes, the acutal number of time frames needed to set a node of the circuit to a specified logical value may be less than the estimate provided by the sequential controllability measures. In this sense, the sequential controllabilities estimate an upper bound. Analogously, the sequential observability of node N, $SO(N)$, is related to both the number of sequential standard cells between node N and a primary circuit output and the number of sequential standard cells that must be controlled in order to propagate the logical value of N to an output.

III. MOTIVATION

A. Combinational Testability Measures

The combinational 0 and 1 controllabilities and combinational observabilities mentioned in the preceding section can be viewed as cost functions measuring the difficulty in a spatial sense of accomplishing the complete set of node justifications required to control or observe a specified node in the circuit. This approach is philosophically related to that of Breuer [3] in its utilization of the cost function concept but supplants Breuer's method by providing a more accurate and consistent relationship of cell depths and functions to controllability and observability costs and by dichotomizing these costs into spatial and temporal components (combinational and sequential testability measures, respectively).

Quantitatively, the magnitude of the combinational e controllability, $e \in \{0,1\}$, of node A in a given logic circuit can be positively correlated with the percentage of nodes in the circuit that must be set to specified logical values in order to justify a logical value e on node A. As an example, consider a set of two-input AND gates interconnected as a binary tree with output node OUT. For a tree depth of k, there will be 2^k primary inputs, $2^k - 1$ AND gates, and $2^{k+1} - 1$ nodes in the circuit. In order to set node OUT to a logical 1, every node in the circuit must be set to a logical 1, and $CC^1(\text{OUT}) = 2^{k+1} - 1$, an exponential function of tree depth. However, only one primary input and only $k + 1$ nodes total must be set to logical 0 in order to force OUT to 0. Therefore, $CC^0(\text{OUT}) = 1 + k$, a linear function of tree depth. This result agrees with the intuitively reasonable observation that it is substantially easier to set the output of a tree of AND gates to a logical 0 than to set it to a logical 1.

1) Relationship to Signal Probabilities: Additional corroboration for the reasonableness of the approach presented in this paper comes from the work of Parker and McCluskey on signal probabilities [7]. If the justification of an internal node A in a circuit to a logical value 1, for example, is very difficult to accomplish, then $CC^1(A)$ will be computed to be a large positive integer. The analysis of Parker and McCluskey generates the result that the probability of node A being a logical 1 will be near 0 for equal input signal probabilities. On the other hand, an easy node justification will have a smaller combinational controllability number and a larger signal probability (nearer 1) associated with it. In the case of the AND gate binary tree example, for equally likely logical values on all of the circuit input lines, $P(\text{OUT} = 1) = (1/2)^{2^k}$ and $P(\text{OUT} = 0) = 1 - (1/2)^{2^k}$, where $CC^1(\text{OUT}) = 2^{k+1} - 1$ and $CC^0(\text{OUT}) = 1 + k$, as derived earlier.

Although the correlation discussed in the preceding paragraph between signal probabilities and the controllability measures defined in this paper does exist, there is a basic difference in objective between the two approaches. The C/O numbers computed by the algorithm presented here are an inherent property of the topology of the circuit under consideration. As discussed by Keiner [8] inherent testability is a deterministic property of the circuit design that excludes test stimulus/response considerations. When the environment within which the circuit operates is taken into consideration, probabilistic measures such as those discussed by Parker and McCluskey become more meaningful.

2) Minimum Cost Approach: In general, there are a number of alternative mechanisms for accomplishing a specified node justification in a circuit. Each distinct alternative will have a cost associated with it. The costs actually utilized in the analysis presented in this paper to characterize node controllabilities and observabilities are the minima over the sets of alternatives of the costs associated with each alternative. This approach is motivated by the observation that the cost of controlling a node in a digital circuit will depend only upon the method actually chosen to accomplish the control. Since the best alternative is the easiest to accomplish, it will have the minimum cost. Costs of alternatives not chosen are not relevant.

The minimum cost approach proposed in this paper contrasts with the testability analysis technique discussed by Stephenson and Grason [2]. Their objective in the formulation of controllability transfer factors (CTF's), for example, for logical components is to characterize the uniformity of a module's input–output mapping. These factors are normalized between 0 and 1 with values near 0 corresponding to less uniform I/O maps and CTF's near 1 being produced by more uniform maps. Their reasoning is that the greater the deviation from uniformity of a logical component's input–output mapping the more difficult it will be to obtain particular output values and, hence, the less controllable the component will be. This is basically an averaging approach, and it tends to obscure the relative difficulties of accomplishing distinct logical justifications on a component's output nodes.

As a specific example of the contrast between CTF's and combinational controllability measures, consider 2- and 3-input AND gates. The CTF's of 2- and 3-input AND gates are 1/2 and 1/4, respectively, indicating that a

3-input AND gate is less controllable than a 2-input AND gate. The combinational 0 and 1 controllabilities for these same two gates, when their inputs are primary inputs of the circuit, are 2 and 3 for the 2-input AND gate and 2 and 4 for the 3-input AND gate. Notice that these combinational controllability measures preserve the information that the loss of controllability in adding one input to a 2-input AND gate is caused by the increased difficulty of setting the output node to a logical 1. The 0 controllability of the output node is not affected.

3) Treatment of Reconvergent Fanout: For circuits with reconvergent fanout, the combinational controllability and observability numbers defined in this paper measure the minimum number of combinational node assignments in the equivalent tree circuit required to accomplish the necessary logical justifications. This approach to the definition of testability measures accomplishes two objectives:

1) reduces the complexity of testability analysis from an exponential to a linear function of circuit size, making computer program implementation feasible for large circuits, and
2) produces an exact analysis for circuits without reconvergent fanout and provides a useful approximate analysis in the general case which is a consistent extension of the procedure for circuits with no reconvergent fanout.

The combinational testability measures as defined can be used to flag potentially uncontrollable nodes. If node A is 0 or 1 uncontrollable because either it or one of its predecessors is not properly connected to the primary inputs of the circuit, its combinational 0 or 1 controllability will be computed to be ∞. However, if node A is, for example, 1 uncontrollable because of reconvergent fanout, its combinational 1 controllability will not be computed to be infinite. Proving that node A is 1 uncontrollable requires the exploration of all possible control mechanisms for node A, an exponentially complex process in general. Since this approach is not feasible for very large circuits, it is worthwhile to investigate the information obtainable about circuit testability with a linear computational effort.

Using a linear complexity algorithm, it can be determined that $CC^1(A)$ is an integer larger than the total number of combinational nodes in a subcircuit containing node A and its predecessor fanout point. The interpretation of this result is that distinct nodes in the equivalent tree circuit corresponding to the same node in the actual circuit must be assigned to different logical values in order to set node A to a logical 1. This inconsistent multiple assignment condition leads to node uncontrollability. It is also possible for a multiple assignment to be logically consistent. The reduction in computational complexity of the testability analysis approach presented in this paper over exhaustive search is related to the fact that the logical consistency of multiple node assignments is not completely resolved in circuits possessing reconvergent fanout. However, since nodes with large combinational controllability numbers may in fact be uncontrollable, they can be identified by this analysis and examined more closely by design engineers. Similar comments apply to the interpretation of the observability measures.

B. Sequential Testability Measures

The sequential 0 and 1 controllabilities and sequential observabilities defined in Section II are cost functions measuring the difficulty in a temporal sense of accomplishing the node justifications required to control or observe a specified node in the circuit. Since a combinational circuit possesses no sequential standard cells, all of its sequential controllability and observability numbers are zero. The interpretation of this result is that any possible node justification in a combinational circuit can be accomplished within one time frame.

For the case of general sequential circuits, the sequential controllability numbers estimate the number of sequential modules that must be set to specified logical values in order to accomplish the necessary node justifications. If the sequential cells in a circuit are interconnected serially, the logical justification of each successive sequential node will take one additional time frame, and the sequential controllability numbers will measure the number of time frames required to accomplish the desired operations. If it is possible to exploit circuit parallelism to simultaneously control groups of sequential nodes, then the actual number of time frames required to accomplish certain node justifications may be less than the estimate provided by the sequential controllability numbers. However, these sequential testability measures can always be interpreted as temporal cost functions.

The combinational controllability and observability numbers for a sequential circuit can still be viewed as spatial cost functions, but now that cost may be spread over a number of time frames instead of concentrated in one time frame as in the case of combinational circuits.

IV. QUANTITATIVE TESTABILITY ANALYSIS

A. Primary Inputs and Outputs

If I is a primary input node of a digital circuit, then the controllabilities of node I are defined as follows:

$$CC^0(I) \triangleq 1 \tag{1}$$

$$CC^1(I) \triangleq 1 \tag{2}$$

$$SC^0(I) \triangleq 0 \tag{3}$$

and

$$SC^1(I) \triangleq 0. \tag{4}$$

Equations (1) and (2) follow from the consideration that a primary input is a combinational node that requires exactly one node assignment to set to either 0 or 1. Since it is not necessary to control any sequential nodes in the justification of a primary input, $SC^0(I)$ and $SC^1(I)$ are defined to be 0.

A primary output node U of a digital circuit can be observed without the necessity of either controlling or observing any other nodes in the circuit. Therefore, $CO(U)$ and $SO(U)$ can be consistently defined to be 0.

$$CO(U) \triangleq 0 \qquad (5)$$

and

$$SO(U) \triangleq 0. \qquad (6)$$

B. Standard Cells

In analyzing the controllability of standard cells, we are interested in determining the difficulty of setting cell output nodes to specified logical values in terms of the corresponding quantities for cell input nodes. The observability of standard cell input nodes depends upon both the cell output node observabilities and the controllabilities of the input nodes and output nodes.

To compute the controllability of a standard cell output node, all possible input assignments that accomplish the desired output node justification are examined, and a number equal to the sum of the controllabilities associated with each of the input assignments considered is computed. The minimum of these numbers, incremented by the cell depth, is defined to be the output node controllability.

In this paper, all cell depths will be defined to be either 0 or 1. The "combinational depth" of a combinational standard cell is defined to be 1, and its "sequential depth" is defined to be 0. The combinational depth of a sequential standard cell is defined to be 0, and its sequential depth is defined to be 1. Note that it is possible to define cell depths to be greater than 1. In fact, for multiple-output standard cells, the depths of different outputs may be defined to be different. However, for the definitions utilized in this paper, the node controllabilities and observabilities have relatively straightforward interpretations.

For a node N in a tree-like interconnection of standard cells, $CC^e(N)$ $[SC^e(N)]$, $e \in \{0, 1\}$, is equal to the minimum number of combinational (sequential) node assignments required to set node N to a logical value e. This result is obvious for primary input nodes and can be proven by mathematical induction for the other nodes in the circuit. The combinational and sequential controllability numbers computed for more general circuits have a similar interpretation with respect to the equivalent tree circuit. Finally, combinational and sequential observabilities have an analogous interpretation.

In order to determine the observabilities of a standard cell input node, all of the cell input assignments that sensitize one or more cell outputs to changes in the specified input are considered. The observability of the input node is defined as the observability of the easiest to observe sensitized output plus the sum of the controllabilities of the minimum cost sensitizing input assignment plus the cell depth.

As an example, consider the C1130, a 3-input NOR combinational standard cell. The C1130 cell with output Y and inputs X_1, X_2, and X_3 realizes the logical function $Y = (X_1 + X_2 + X_3)'$. In order to assign Y to 1, it is necessary to set all three input nodes to 0. Hence,

$$CC^1(Y) = CC^0(X_1) + CC^0(X_2) + CC^0(X_3) + 1 \qquad (7)$$

and

$$SC^1(Y) = SC^0(X_1) + SC^0(X_2) + SC^0(X_3). \qquad (8)$$

Notice that the combinational depth of the C1130 is equal to 1 and its sequential depth equals 0. The output Y can be set to 0 in three distinct ways: $X_1 = 1$, $X_2 = d$, $X_3 = d$; $X_1 = d$, $X_2 = 1$, $X_3 = d$; and $X_1 = d$, $X_2 = d$, $X_3 = 1$; where "d" represents "do not care." Therefore,

$$CC^0(Y) = \min \left[CC^1(X_1), CC^1(X_2), CC^1(X_3) \right] + 1 \qquad (9)$$

and

$$SC^0(Y) = \min \left[SC^1(X_1), SC^1(X_2), SC^1(X_3) \right]. \qquad (10)$$

Observing input X_i requires the observation of output Y while the other two inputs are maintained at logical 0. Thus the observability equations for cell C1130 can be written

$$CO(X_i) = CO(Y) + CC^0(X_j) + CC^0(X_k) + 1 \qquad (11)$$

and

$$SO(X_i) = SO(Y) + SC^0(X_j) + SC^0(X_k) \qquad (12)$$

where i, j, k are distinct elements of the set $\{1, 2, 3\}$.

The C1130 combinational controllability equations presented in (7) and (9) can be written in matrix form as follows:

$$
\begin{bmatrix} CC^0(Y) \\ CC^1(Y) \end{bmatrix} =
\begin{bmatrix} 0 & 1 & 0 & 0 & 0 & 0 & 1 \\ & & & \text{min} & & & \\ 0 & 0 & 0 & 1 & 0 & 0 & 1 \\ & & & \text{min} & & & \\ 0 & 0 & 0 & 0 & 0 & 1 & 1 \\ 1 & 0 & 1 & 0 & 1 & 0 & 1 \end{bmatrix}
\begin{bmatrix} CC^0(X_1) \\ CC^1(X_1) \\ CC^0(X_2) \\ CC^1(X_2) \\ CC^0(X_3) \\ CC^1(X_3) \\ 1 \end{bmatrix}.
$$
$$(13)$$

The output controllability vector on the left is computed by multiplying the input controllability vector by the combinational controllability matrix. Whenever a "min" is encountered, the scalar product of the next row of the matrix with the input vector is formed, and the minimum of that result and the previously computed result becomes the entry for the current component of the controllability output vector. Multiple minima are handled in an analogous fashion. If no "min" word is encountered, the next output vector component is computed.

Notice that the matrix utilized in (13) consists of entirely 0's, 1's, and "min's." It can be compactly represented in a cell library entry by writing each binary line as an octal number and each "min" line as an M. The resulting library entry line for the C1130 combinational controllability (CC) matrix has the form:

$$41 \quad M \quad 11 \quad M \quad 3 \quad 125. \quad (14)$$

Analogous analyses can be performed for the combinational observability (CO), sequential controllability (SC), and sequential observability (SO) properties of cell C1130, resulting in a complete controllability/observability library entry of the form:

```
Name    C1130
CC    41      M    11   M   3   125
CO    1025        1105  1121
SC    40      M    10   M   2   124
SO    1024        1104  1120
End.                                        (15)
```

Each combinational and sequential cell of interest can be analyzed in the manner indicated above, and entries of the form presented for the C1130 can be made in the library.

For a second example, consider the C1490, a resettable negative-edge-triggered D-flip-flop sequential standard cell. In order to set the output Q of a C1490 to 1, it is necessary to set the D input to 1, hold the reset line R at 0, and generate a falling edge on the clock line, C. Therefore, the 1 controllability equations for Q can be written:

$$CC^1(Q) = CC^1(D) + CC^1(C) + CC^0(C) + CC^0(R) \quad (16)$$

and

$$SC^1(Q) = SC^1(D) + SC^1(C) + SC^0(C) + SC^0(R) + 1. \quad (17)$$

Notice that the difficulty of generating a falling edge on the clock line is represented in (16) by $CC^1(C) + CC^0(C)$, since it is necessary first to set the clock line to 1, then force it to 0.

There are two distinct mechanisms for setting Q to 0. Either the reset line can be used while maintaining the clock line at a logical 0, or a 0 value can be clocked into the flip-flop from the D-input line. Consequently, the 0-controllability equations for Q can be written:

$$CC^0(Q) = \min \left[CC^1(R) + CC^0(C) \right.$$
$$\left. CC^0(D) + CC^1(C) + CC^0(C) + CC^0(R) \right] \quad (18)$$

and

$$SC^0(Q) = \min \left[SC^1(R) + SC^0(C) \right.$$
$$\left. SC^0(D) + SC^1(C) + SC^0(C) + SC^0(R) \right] + 1. \quad (19)$$

The D-input line value can be observed at the Q output of the flip-flop by generating a falling edge on the clock line while holding the reset line low.

$$CO(D) = CO(Q) + CC^1(C) + CC^0(C) + CC^0(R) \quad (20)$$

and

$$SO(D) = SO(Q) + SC^1(C) + SC^0(C) + SC^0(R) + 1. \quad (21)$$

The reset line R can be observed at Q by setting the flip-flop to a logical 1 and then using the reset line to force it to a logical 0.

$$CO(R) = CO(Q) + CC^1(Q) + CC^0(C) + CC^1(R) \quad (22)$$

and

$$SO(R) = SO(Q) + SC^1(Q) + SC^0(C) + SC^1(R) + 1. \quad (23)$$

Finally, the clock line can be indirectly observed at the flip-flop output by either setting the flip-flop to 1 and clocking in a 0 or resetting the flip-flop to 0 and clocking in a 1.

$$CO(C) = \min \left[CO(Q) + CC^0(R) + CC^1(C) \right.$$
$$+ CC^0(C) + CC^0(D) + CC^1(Q)$$
$$CO(Q) + CC^0(R) + CC^1(C)$$
$$\left. + CC^0(C) + CC^1(D) + CC^0(Q) \right] \quad (24)$$

and

$$SO(C) = 1 + \min \left[SO(Q) + SC^0(R) + SC^1(C) \right.$$
$$+ SC^0(C) + SC^0(D) + SC^1(Q)$$
$$SO(Q) + SC^0(R) + SC^1(C)$$
$$\left. + SC^0(C) + SC^1(D) + SC^0(Q) \right]. \quad (25)$$

C. Controllability/Observability Calculation Algorithm for a Circuit

Calculate circuit node controllabilities.

Initializations: For all primary input nodes I, set

$$CC^0(I) = CC^1(I) = 1$$

$$SC^0(I) = SC^1(I) = 0.$$

For all other nodes N, set

$$CC^0(N) = CC^1(N) = \infty$$

$$SC^0(N) = SC^1(N) = \infty.$$

Working from primary inputs to circuit outputs, use standard cell controllability equations to map cell input node controllabilities into cell output node controllabilities.

Iterate on the above step until the controllability numbers stabilize (to handle feedback loops external to standard cells, etc.).

Since this is an integer algorithm, and the controllability numbers are monotonically nonincreasing from iteration to iteration, we are always guaranteed that the algorithm converges. Practically, only two or three iterations are usually necessary for the controllability numbers to stabilize.

Calculate circuit node observabilities.

Initializations: For all primary output nodes U, set

$$CO(U) = 0$$
$$SO(U) = 0.$$

For all other nodes N, set

$$CO(N) = SO(N) = \infty.$$

Working from primary outputs to circuit inputs, use standard cell observability equations together with the previously computed node controllabilities to map cell output node observabilities into cell input node observabilities. Note that the observability of a fanout point is defined to be equal to the minimum of the observabilities of the nodes to which it fans out.

Iterate on the above step until the observability numbers stabilize.

If, after application of the above algorithm to a given digital circuit, there remains a node N with an infinite e-controllability number, $e \in \{0, 1\}$, then that node is e-uncontrollable. $CC^e(N) = \infty$ or $SC^e(N) = \infty$ is a sufficient but not necessary condition for the e uncontrollability of N. Similarly, $CO(N) = \infty$ or $SO(N) = \infty$ is a sufficient but not necessary condition for the unobservability of node N. As was discussed in the section on motivation, this type of untestability results from the existence in the circuit of nodes which are not properly connected to either primary inputs or outputs.

Program Implementation

In order to help evaluate the computational practicality of this testability analysis approach, working versions of the algorithms presented in the preceding section were implemented on a DEC-10 computer system. The algorithms as programmed were stable, and run times on the order of 0.75 min for 30 cell circuits and 3.5 min for 200 cell circuits were typical. When compared with multihour execution times for test-sequence-generation programs, these run times on the order of several minutes to accomplish the testability analysis of complex sequential circuits appear quite attractive.

V. EXAMPLE-7-STAGE-FEEDBACK SHIFT REGISTER

As an example of the analysis discussed in the preceding sections, consider the 7-stage-feedback shift-register circuit in Fig. 1. Application of the combinational controllability calculation algorithm to the circuit in Fig. 1 yields the combinational controllability profiles in Fig. 2. These

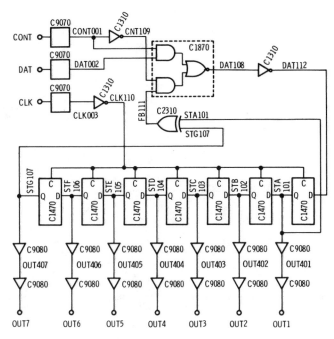

Fig. 1. 7-stage-feedback shift-register circuit.

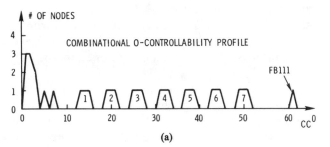

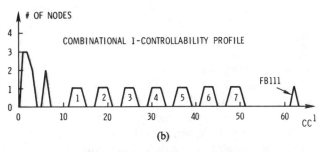

Fig. 2. Combinational controllability profiles of the 7-stage-feedback shift-register circuit. (a) Combinational 0-controllability profile. (b) Combinational 1-controllability profile.

profiles summarize circuit controllability information by plotting 0 or 1 controllability on the x axis versus the number of nodes possessing that controllability on the y axis. The result is a controllability density plot which can be used to characterize the overall controllability of the circuit, pinpoint the least controllable nodes, and suggest circuit modifications to enhance controllability.

For the 7-stage-feedback shift-register circuit, nodes near the primary inputs are highly controllable and appear between $CC = 0$ and $CC = 10$ on the controllability profiles. Each flip-flop in the shift register has a group of nodes associated with it that appear as a bump in the

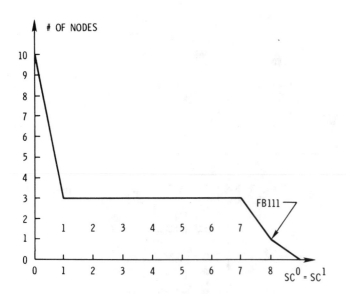

Fig. 3. Sequential controllability profiles of the 7-stage-feedback shift-register circuit.

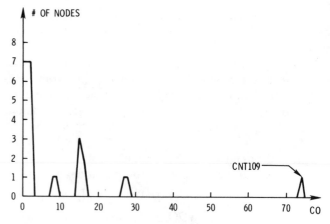

Fig. 4. Combinational observability profile for the 7-stage-feedback shift-register circuit.

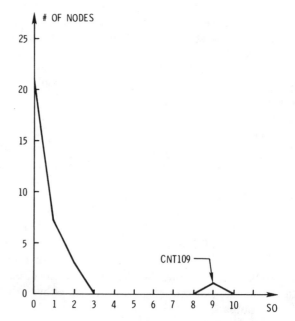

Fig. 5. Sequential observability profile for the 7-stage-feedback shift-register circuit.

profiles. Bumps one through seven correspond to flip-flops STA101 through STG107 in the profiles. The least controllable node in the circuit is FB111, the output of the feedback exclusive OR gate. This result is obvious from the observation that the inputs to the exclusive OR are the least controllable flip-flop output and one other flip-flop output.

The sequential 0 and 1 controllability profiles for the 7-stage-feedback shift-register circuit in Fig. 1 are identical and are presented in Fig. 3. These profiles are identical in this case because the input multiplexing circuitry allows any of the flip-flops in the circuit to be set to logical 0 or logical 1 with equal temporal facility. (The same number of sequential nodes must be controlled in either case.)

All of the combinational nodes near primary inputs have 0-sequential controllability and account for the peak in the sequential controllability profiles at $SC=0$. The nodes associated with flip-flops one through seven form a plateau in the sequential controllability profile between $SC=1$ and $SC=7$. Again, FB111 appears furthest to the right on the profile (at $SC=8$) indicating that it is the least-controllable node in the circuit from a sequential controllability point-of-view, as well as from a combinational controllability evaluation.

The combinational observability profile for the 7-stage-feedback shift-register circuit is presented in Fig. 4. The large peak near the origin represents outputs of flip-flops and their associated buffers. Each flip-flop output fed through two buffers is a primary output of the circuit. The other peaks in the profile correspond to nodes closer to primary inputs of the circuit. CNT109 is substantially less observable than any other node in the circuit, as indicated by the peak at $CO=74$. While this fact is not immediately obvious from the schematic, it can be understood by observing that CNT109 is one input of the AND gate whose other input is FB111, the least-controllable node in the circuit. If one additional output pad was available to

enhance the observability of the circuit, a logical location for it would be at CNT109.

Finally, the sequential observability profile for the 7-stage-feedback shift-register circuit is presented in Fig. 5. Since most nodes in the circuit have a very small sequential depth from the primary outputs, a large peak near $SO=0$ appears in the profile. CNT109 is again flagged as the least observable node by the peak at $SO=9$.

VI. EVALUATION OF THE CONTROLLABILITY/OBSERVABILITY MEASURES

Relationships between the controllability/observability measures presented in this paper and related approaches [2], [3], [7] have been discussed in the motivation section. In this section, correlations between the testability measures and inherent testability properties of a digital circuit will be presented.

It is apparent from Fig. 1 that the 7-stage-feedback shift-register circuit analyzed in the previous section is testable in the sense proposed in [4]. By setting primary input CONT to 1, the shift register can be initialized to any state through the primary circuit input DAT. Call this circuit C_1. If the input multiplexing section of C_1 is replaced by an OR gate with inputs FB111 and DAT and output DAT112, the only state to which the shift register can be initialized is 1111111, an obvious decrease in intrinsic controllability. Call this less-controllable circuit C_2.

If the maximum combinational controllability number CC_{max} is used as a figure of merit for the controllability of the circuit, it can be seen that CC_{max} exhibits the desired behavior for the two circuits defined above. Specifically,

$$CC_{max}(C_1) = 62 \qquad (26)$$

and

$$CC_{max}(C_2) = 106. \qquad (27)$$

As circuit controllability decreases, CC_{max} increases in the manner indicated in (26) and (27).

A circuit C_3 can be derived from C_1 by adding a sufficient number of primary inputs and multiplexers to control each flip-flop independently. This structure is inherently more controllable than C_1, and

$$CC_{max}(C_3) = 19 \qquad (28)$$

better than three times smaller than $CC_{max}(C_1)$. The enhanced controllability of C_3 over C_1 leads to improved observability properties for circuit C_3 as well since logical values can be propagated to primary outputs more easily. These intrinsic observability characteristics of circuits C_1 and C_3 are reflected by their maximum combinational observability numbers:

$$CO_{max}(C_1) = 74 \qquad (29)$$

and

$$CO_{max}(C_3) = 33. \qquad (30)$$

The more observable circuit C_3 has a CO_{max} better than two times smaller than $CO_{max}(C_1)$. By making the least-observable node in C_3 a primary output, the resulting configuration becomes even more observable and its CO_{max} is further reduced to 22. Sequential testability measures exhibit similar behavior.

While maximum controllability and observability numbers were used in this analysis to correlate with inherent circuit testability properties, other aspects of the controllability/observability profiles can provide additional information. Means, moments, and cumulative distributions can be derived from the node testability numbers to highlight various properties of the profiles; and measures of multimodality may be used to identify sections of the circuit that may be difficult to test. However, the key result to emphasize in this section is that the controllability and observability measures computed by the algorithms presented in this paper correlate well with intrinsic controllability and observability properties of the circuits analyzed.

VII. Use of the Controllability/Observability Measures

The testability measures presented in this paper can be utilized in two distinct modes: 1) to guide redesign for the purpose of enhancing circuit testability, and 2) to guide vector-generation algorithms as part of the test-sequence-generation process. While being used as a feedback tool for the design engineer, these measures identify potentially uncontrollable or unobservable nodes and order all of the nodes in the circuit according to the six parameters discussed. As the designer rearranges circuit topology and possibly adds test points, he can observe the effect of these actions on the testability profiles and factor this information into the design process.

As an aid for automated test-sequence-generation programs, these measures can be used to order the alternatives in decisions that must be made during the vector-generation process. For example, an ATG program will be more likely to quickly succeed in propagating an internal logical value to a primary output of the circuit if it has access to node observability information than if it must make random choices at each decision point. This intelligent guidance of the vector-generation process has the potential of substantially improving the performance of automated test sequence generation.

VIII. Conclusions

Six measures have been presented which characterize the controllability and observability of a digital circuit: combinational 0 and 1 controllability, sequential 0 and 1 controllability, combinational observability, and sequential observability. The dichotomization of these measures into spatial and temporal components has been discussed as well as their relationship to other testability measures proposed in the past. While motivating the treatment of circuits with reconvergent fanout, the relative complexities of this testability analysis and an exact treatment were compared, and the areas within which information was sacrificed to reduce the complexity of the problem were identified.

Section IV of the paper described required initializations, treatment of standard cells and development of a standard cell library, algorithms for the calculation of circuit node controllabilities and observabilities, and implementation of the algorithms in a working computer program. The controllability and observability of a 7-stage-feedback shift register was thoroughly analyzed and profiles were presented that allow visualization of these properties at a glance. This example was then extended for the purpose of correlating the testability measures derived with intrinsic controllability and observability properties of the circuits analyzed. Finally, use of the controllability/observability measures to guide design for testability and automated test-sequence-generation was discussed.

REFERENCES

[1] W. J. Dejka, "Measure of testability in device and system design," *Proc. 20th Midwest Symp. Circuits Syst.*, Aug. 1977, pp. 39–52.

[2] J. E. Stephenson and J. Grason, "A testability measure for register transfer level digital circuits," *Proc. 6th Fault Tolerant Computing Symp.*, June 1976, pp. 101–107.

[3] Breuer *et al.* "TEST/80—An advanced ATG system for digital circuits," Rep. 1–77.

[4] E. B. Eichelberger and T. W. Williams, "A logic design structure for LSI testability," *Proc. 14th Design Automation Conf.*, June 1977, pp. 462–468.

[5] H. Y. Chang and G. W. Heimbigner, "LAMP: Controllability, observability, and maintenance engineering technique (COMET)," *Bell System Tech. J.* vol. 53, no. 8, pp. 1505–1534, Oct. 1974.

[6] F. Barsi, F. Grandoni, and P. Maestrini, "A theory of diagnosability of digital systems," *IEEE Trans. Comput.*, vol. C-25, pp. 585–593, June 1976.

[7] K. P. Parker and E. J. McCluskey, "Probabilistic treatment of general combinational networks," *IEEE Trans. Comput.*, pp. 668–670, June 1975.

[8] W. L. Keiner and R. P. West, "Testability measures," presented at AUTOTESTCON '77, Nov. 1977.

✦

Lawrence H. Goldstein (S'70–A'77–M'77) was born on January 7, 1952, in New York, NY. He received the B.E. degree from Cooper Union, New York, NY, in 1973, and the M.S.E., M.A., and Ph.D degrees from Princeton University, Princeton, NJ, in 1974, 1975, and 1976, respectively, all in electrical engineering.

Since 1976, he has been a Member of Technical Staff in the Computer-Aided Design Division at Sandia Laboratories, Albuquerque, NM. His work has involved photovoltaic system simulation, automated test sequence generation for LSI circuits, and design for testability concepts.

TESTABILITY ANALYSIS OF MOS VLSI CIRCUITS

David M. Singer

AT&T Bell Laboratories
Murray Hill, New Jersey 07974

ABSTRACT

Modeling problems that are encountered in applying an existing testability measure to MOS circuits are identified. These problems arise primarily because MOS circuits can implement functions that cannot be modeled at the logic gate level. Models for the testability analysis of circuits with memories (RAM and ROM), buses, and transmission gates are developed. In addition, the use of the controllability/observability measures in analyzing the testability of stuck-at-faults, and in defining an overall circuit testability index is discussed.

1. INTRODUCTION

The problem of testing VLSI circuits has found a widely accepted solution in structured design for testability techniques, such as scan design [1,2]. These techniques provide the circuit designer with a deterministic method for adding testability hardware, and for generating test vectors. In chip designs where the addition of testability hardware cannot be justified, because of overhead or yield considerations, *ad-hoc* approaches can be used.

In the ad-hoc approach, testability analysis tools such as SCOAP [3], can be used as an aid to guide the designer in making testability enhancements that are unique to the circuit under consideration. Algorithms for testability analysis require logic gate level circuit models. The application of testability measures to higher level functional blocks has several disadvantages. First, the approximations of the blocks behavior, that are required for the speed of the analysis, further deteriorate accuracy. In addition, no information on the nodes internal to the block can be obtained.

Based on the above considerations, a testability analysis system has been developed for MOS VLSI circuits. This system uses the combinational controllability and observability analysis of SCOAP on gate level circuit models. The basic measures for a node n are, zero controllability $C0(n)$, one controllability $C1(n)$, and observability $B(n)$. The controllability and observability measures are combined to compute more conventional stuck-at fault testability measures that are used to guide the designer in improving circuit testability [4].

Figure 1 illustrates how controllability and observability of a two input AND gate are analyzed. In Figure 1A, the C1 and C0 of the input nodes (X,Y) are assigned directly. The controllability of the output node (Z) can now be expressed in terms of the input node controllabilities. To control the output to logical 1, both inputs must be controlled to 1. Thus, $C1(Z)$ is equal to the sum of $C1(X)$ and $C1(Y)$. To control the output to logical 0, one of the inputs must be set to zero. In the testability algorithm the minimum values are taken, thus $C0(Z)$ is equal to the minimum $[C0(X),C0(Y)]$. In Figure 1B, the observability of the output node (Z) is assigned directly as $B(Z)$. The observability of an input represents the effort of sensitizing a path to the output, and then observing the output. For the two input AND gate, $B(X)$ is the effort to setting the Y input to logical 1 and then observing the output (Z), or $B(X)=C1(Y)+B(Z)$. Similarly, $B(Y)=C1(X)+B(Z)$.

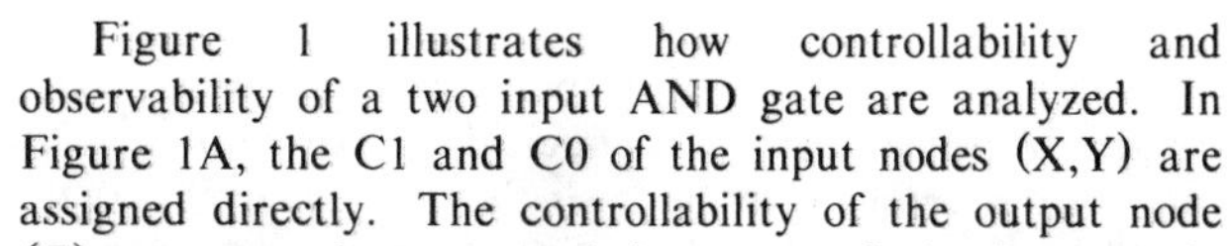

(a) Zero/One controllability equations for nodes X, Y, and Z.

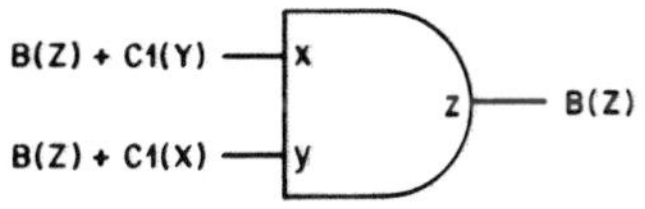

(b) Observability equations for nodes X, Y, and Z.

Figure 1   Controllability and Observability equations for a 2-input AND gate.

Reprinted from *Proceedings of the 1984 International Test Conference,* 1984, pages 690-696. Copyright © 1984 by The Institute of Electrical and Electronics Engineers, Inc. All rights reserved.

2. TESTABILITY MODELS FOR MOS CIRCUITS

It is necessary to adequately model special circuit structures that arise in MOS technologies. These are buses, transmission gates, and memories (RAM and ROM). The philosophy used in the development of these models was to make simplifying assumptions, when possible, about the structure's behavior while retaining the controllability and observability characteristics. This approach seems valid because testability analysis is itself an approximation.

2.1 MOS Bus

A bus is a signal net with more than one source node. Figure 2A shows such a configuration. An MOS bus is functionally represented by a single logic gate. The gate would be OR and AND depending upon the technology as shown in Figure 2B.

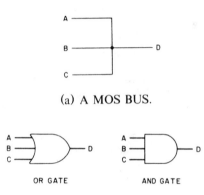

(a) A MOS BUS.

OR GATE   AND GATE

(b) Functional logic equivalent.

Figure 2. An MOS bus and functional equivalents

2.2 MOS Transmission gate

The transmission gate is defined as a unidirectional primitive element. As with other primitives, i.e., logic gates, the controllability and observability equations for the transmission gate are defined in the analysis algorithm. Figure 3 shows the truth table that is used to define the equations.

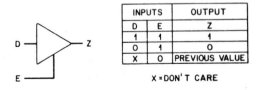

INPUTS		OUTPUT
D	E	Z
1	1	1
0	1	0
X	0	PREVIOUS VALUE

X = DON'T CARE

Figure 3. An MOS transmission gate and its analysis model.

There are four analysis equations for the transmission gate, that determine $C0(Z)$, $C1(Z)$, $B(D)$, and $B(E)$. To control the output to a desired value (1 or 0) the enable input (E) must be set to logical one and the desired value applied to the data input (D). Thus the controllability equations for the output (Z) can be written as

$$C0(Z) = C0(D) + C1(E)$$

$$C1(Z) = C1(D) + C1(E)$$

To observe the data input the enable signal must be made active and the output observed, thus,

$$B(D) = C1(E) + B(Z)$$

A deductive process is used to observe the enable input. This process involves applying a set of input vectors to the element. However, the testability analysis algorithm does not incorporate the concept of multiple operations and thus all operations must be combined into a single equation. The sequence that makes the enable input observable is as follows:

1. Set the output to a known value.

2. Set the data input to the opposite value.

3. Observe the output.

From the above sequence the value on the enable signal can be deduced. If the enable is active then the output will change. If the enable is inactive then the output will show no change. The output can be initially controlled to logical 1 or 0. This results in two equations of which the minimum is taken:

$$B(E) = Min\left[C1(Z)+C0(D)+B(Z), \ C0(Z)+C1(D)+B(Z)\right]$$

2.3 RAM and ROM Models

The main objective of modeling memories for testability analysis is not to analyze the memory itself, but to be able to measure the testability of the logic that is peripheral to the memory. A conventional model constructed from logic gates would meet this objective. However, the size of such a structure would be proportional to the product of the number of words and the number of bits per word, because each bit of each word is modeled. An implementation using this approach would require many analysis steps and a lengthy circuit description.

A more economical model can be devised if one assumes that at most, only one word is selected during any memory operation, and that the logic peripheral to the memory can be tested through the easiest to select word in the memory [5]. The easiest to select word has the select line with the lowest one controllability value.

The above premise allows a memory model that has a size proportional to the sum of the number of words in the memory and the number of bits per word. The analysis of this model includes two steps: word addressing and data bit analysis. Primitive elements have been defined for each step. Word address elements allow testability analysis of the address decoding logic. Similarly, data bit elements form a single word that the data bus can be analyzed through.

2.3.1 Address element
Figure 4 shows the element for address analysis.

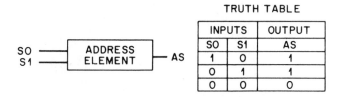

TRUTH TABLE

INPUTS		OUTPUT
S0	S1	AS
1	0	1
0	1	1
0	0	0

Figure 4. Analysis model for address select

The inputs (S0, S1) to this element are select lines coming from the address decoding logic. When either of the inputs is logic one then the output (AS) is logic one. The logic (1,1) input assignment is not defined because it is assumed that only one address is selected at a time.

From the table in figure 4 the four equations, C0(AS), C1(AS), B(S0), and B(S1) can be derived.

By definition, controlling the output to zero requires setting both inputs to zero, thus:

$$C0(AS) = C0(S0) + C0(S1)$$

Setting a logical one on the output, an operation that corresponds to addressing the easiest to select word in the memory, requires setting one of the two inputs to logical one. During analysis the minimum value is taken, thus:

$$C1(AS) = Min\left[C1(S0), C1(S1)\right]$$

Observing either of the address elements inputs (select lines) requires that the other input be set to a logical zero and the elements output be observed. Thus:

$$B(S0) = C0(S1) + B(AS)$$

$$B(S1) = C0(S0) + B(AS)$$

The address elements are used in cascade. For example, figure 5 shows the address element connectivity for a memory with four words.

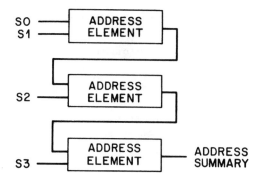

Figure 5. Configuration for address elements of a four word memory

The output of the final element is the address summary line. This line is used as a common input to the data bit elements. The data bit elements form the data word of the memory. There are two types, a RAM bit and a ROM bit element.

2.3.2 RAM element
The RAM element is used to model one bit of the data word for a RAM. Figure 6 shows a RAM element.

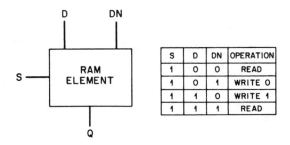

S	D	DN	OPERATION
1	0	0	READ
1	0	1	WRITE 0
1	1	0	WRITE 1
1	1	1	READ

Figure 6. A RAM bit element

This element has three inputs, data (D), complementary data (DN), and select (S). The data output is Q. The read and write conventions for this element are taken from the functional model and are listed in the table in Figure 6. Controlling a zero on the output, C0(Q), requires a sequence that writes a zero to the cell and then reads from it. This sequence is:

1. Select the cell: C1(S)

2. Write a zero to the cell. This requires $D=0, DN=1$: $C0(D)+C1(DN)$

3. Read from the cell. This involves making D and DN equal. The previous write operation left the two inputs at opposite values. Therefore, changing the value of only one will set them equal. This determined by: $Min[C1(D), C0(DN)]$

The resulting equation for the zero controllability of the output Q is:

$$C0(Q) = Min\left[C1(S)+C0(D)+C1(DN)+C1(D),\right.$$

$$\left.C1(S)+C0(D)+C1(DN)+C0(DN)\right]$$

Controlling the output to logic 1, $C1(Q)$, is similiar except that a logic 1 must be written to the cell:

1. Select the cell: $C1(S)$

2. Write a logic 1 to the cell. This requires $D=1, DN=0$: $C1(D)+C0(DN)$

3. Read from the cell. This involves making D and DN equal: $Min[C0(D), C1(DN)]$

The resulting equation for the one controllability of the output is:

$$C1(Q) = Min\left[C1(S)+C1(D)+C0(DN)+C0(D)\right.$$

$$\left.C1(S)+C1(D)+C0(DN)+C1(DN)\right]$$

The method for observing the data (D) and complementary data (DN) inputs is the same for both. The general sequence for observing these inputs is as follows:

1. Select the cell.

2. Write a logic value to the cell.

3. Read from the cell.

4. Observe the output.

The value that is initially written to the cell is dependent on the one and zero controllability values of the inputs. The equation with the smallest calculated value will be chosen. The steps that comprise the subsequent read operation are dependent on the initial value that was written to the cell. Hence, the final observability value will be equal to the minimum of four terms.

For example, if a logic 1 is initially written to the element then two of the terms can be derived from the specific sequence for this operation:

1. Select the cell: $C1(S)$.

2. Write a logic 1 to the cell: $C1(D) + C0(DN)$.

3. Read from the cell. This involves making D equal to DN: $Min[C0(D), C1(DN)]$.

4. Observe the output: $B(Q)$.

The observability equation for initially writing a logic one to the RAM element is

$$B(D) = B(DN) = Min\left[C1(S)+C1(D)+C0(DN)+C0(D)+B(Q),\right.$$

$$\left.C1(S)+C1(D)+C0(DN)+C1(DN)+B(Q)\right]$$

Similarly, if the controllability value of initially writing a zero to the element is smaller, then the specific sequence for observing the data inputs would be:

1. Select the cell: $C1(S)$.

2. Write a logic zero to the cell: $C0(D)+C1(DN)$

3. Read from the cell. Make D equal to DN: $Min[C1(D), C0(DN)]$.

4. Observe the output: $B(Q)$.

Hence, the observability equation for initially writing a logic zero to the RAM element is:

$$B(D) = B(DN)$$

$$= Min\left[C1(S)+C0(D)+C1(DN)+C1(D)+B(Q),\right.$$

$$\left.C1(S)+C0(D)+C1(DN)+C0(DN)+B(Q)\right]$$

Combining the equations for the two possible initial write operations results in the complete equation for the observability of the data inputs:

$$B(D) = B(DN)$$

$$= Min\left[C1(S)+C1(D)+C0(DN)+C0(D)+B(Q),\right.$$

$$C1(S)+C1(D)+C0(DN)+C1(DN)+B(Q),$$

$$C1(S)+C0(D)+C1(DN)+C1(D)+B(Q),$$

$$\left.C1(S)+C0(D)+C1(DN)+C0(DN)+B(Q)\right]$$

The method of observing the select input (S) is similiar to that of the enable input of the transmission gate. It is a process that requires a series of input vectors. The general sequence is as follows:

1. Set the output to a known value.

2. Write the opposite value to the cell.

3. Read the value.

4. Observe the output.

The value of the select input can be deduced from the above sequence. If the element is selected the output will toggle. If the element is not selected the output will remain the same. The initial value of the output depends on the value of the one and zero controllabilities of the output. The minimum of the two controllability equations will be taken as the initial value. This again will result in an observability equation that takes the minimum value of four terms. Two of the terms can be derived if a logic one is chosen as the initial output value. The specific sequence for this is:

1. Set the output to logic 1: $C1(Q)$.

2. Write a logic 0 to the cell:
   $C0(D) + C1(DN)$.

3. Read the value: $Min[C1(D), C0(DN)]$.

4. Observe the output: $B(Q)$.

From the above the first two terms of the observability equation are:

$$C1(Q)+C0(D)+C1(DN)+C1(D)+B(Q)$$

$$C1(Q)+C0(D)+C1(DN)+C0(DN)+B(Q)$$

Similarly, if the output is initially set to logic zero the remaining two terms are:

$$C0(Q)+C1(D)+C0(DN)+C0(D)+B(Q)$$

$$C0(Q)+C1(D)+C0(DN)+C1(DN)+B(Q)$$

Combining all the terms into a single equation for the observability of the select signal results in:

$$B(S) = Min\left[C1(Q)+C0(D)+C1(DN)+C1(D)+B(Q), \right.$$
$$C1(Q)+C0(D)+C1(DN)+C0(DN)+B(Q),$$
$$C0(Q)+C1(D)+C0(DN)+C0(D)+B(Q),$$
$$\left. C0(Q)+C1(D)+C0(DN)+C1(DN)+B(Q) \right]$$

The RAM elements are configured to form the single data word of the memory model. Figure 7 shows the RAM element configuration for a RAM with a four bit word.

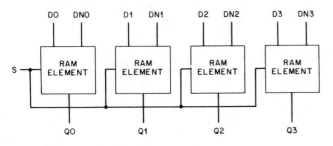

Figure 7. RAM element configuration for
an 4 bit data word.

The common select signal (S) is the address summary line that is the output of the address element chain.

2.3.3 ROM element

The ROM element is used to model one data bit of a ROM. Figure 8 shows that this element has a single input and a single output.

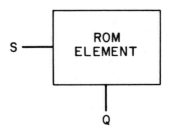

Figure 8. A ROM element

The input (S) is a select signal and the output (Q) is the data output. The three analysis equations for this element are $C0(Q)$, $C1(Q)$, and $B(S)$. Because no information about the contents of the ROM is used in the model, it is assumed that the effort of controlling the output to a logical one or zero is equal. This effort is equivalent to simply selecting the element, thus:

$$C0(Q) = C1(Q) = C1(S)$$

The select input can be observed by selecting the element and observing the output:

$$B(S) = C1(S) + B(Q)$$

The ROM elements are configured similar to the RAM element to form the data word.

2.3.4 Use of the memory model

Figure 9 shows a complete model for a 5 word RAM with a 3 bit data word.

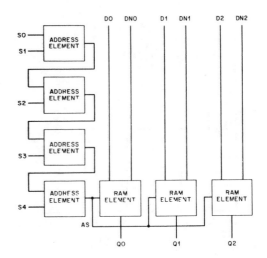

Figure 9. A analysis model of a 5
word RAM with a 3 bit data word.

Lines S0-S4 are address select lines coming from the address decoding logic. The inputs D0-D2 are data inputs to the memory, and the lines Q0-Q2 are data outputs. The description for the 5x3 RAM model is generated internal to the analysis program. Only 7 elements are used to model a memory that has 15 memory cells. The user input description of this memory is as follows:

MEM: RAM =1, COLUMNS = 5, ROWS = 3

Memory functions for set, reset, precharge, and dual rail output are specified in a similiar manner and are modeled by adding conventional logic gates to the appropriate signals.

3. TESTABILITY ANALYSIS FOR MOS CIRCUITS

The testability analysis produces testability measures for each node in the circuit and a single overall testability index. The testability analysis is divided into two steps: Applying the testability analysis algorithm to the circuit description, and post-processing of the testability data. The post-processor is used to display a histogram that shows the distribution of nodes at each value of a selected testability measure. Figure 10 shows a histogram of the observability testability measure for an example circuit. The nodes that appear in the right most region of the histogram have the highest testability values. These nodes can be examined by name, to see if they define local areas of high testability within the circuit. Appropriate modifications can then be made to the circuit and the testability algorithm run again. Positive effects of modifications will be reflected in the histogram by a shift in the distribution of nodes from high testability values to lower values. Three new nodal testability measures and the circuit testability index are defined in the following sections.

3.1 Testability Measures

Controllability and observability values obtained from SCOAP were examined in view of actual fault detection data. From this examination, only the combinational testability measures calculated by the original SCOAP algorithm are used. Three new measures are also used. These new measures allow the designer to analyze the SCOAP data using more conventional testing concepts than the original SCOAP measures [3]. The new measures are called, stuck-at-zero (SA0), stuck-at-one (SA1), and sum (SUM). The SA0 for a node is a measure of the effort required to detect a stuck-at-zero fault at that node. This effort is equivalent to setting the node to logical 1 and then observing it at a primary output. SA0 is expressed as the sum of the one controllability and observability of the node, i.e., $SA0 = C1 + B$. Similiarly, SA1 is a measure of the effort required to detect a stuck-at-one fault at a node and is calculated by adding the C0 and B values for that node [4].

3.2 A testability index

An overall circuit testability index is also calculated. This index is a function of circuit size (number of nodes in the circuit) and circuit complexity (interconnection complexity). This figure is calculated by adding the SUM testability measure of each node in the circuit, and then taking the $\log_{10}$ of the total. Table 1 shows that the typical values of the testability index fall between 4.0 and 10.0 for circuits having 400 to 30,000 nodes.

The data was obtained from circuits in various stages of design. The number of nodes signifies the total number of gate input and output nodes in each circuit. Final fault coverage results are incomplete for some circuits, because the test vector sets had not been fully developed at the time of the testability analysis.

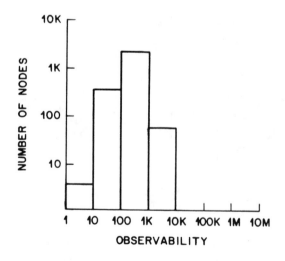

Figure 10   Observability histogram.

CIRCUIT	#NODES	TESTABILITY INDEX	FAULT COVERAGE %	#VECTORS
1	425	4.78	80	114
2	2115	6.59	84	6K
3	2302	5.24	84	340
4	5201	6.55	85	4K
5	5779	6.33	89	8K
6	6157	6.81	71	1.7K
7	6931	6.67	59	390
8	7775	6.10	90	13K
9	7837	6.82	-	-
10	9251	6.18	-	-
11	13000	8.74	-	-
12	26000	9.24	-	-

TABLE 1

Data shows that the index may serve as some indication of the number of test vectors required to achieve a given fault coverage. For circuits of the same size, the number of nodes can be viewed as a constant in the index function. Then, interconnection complexity is a variable that should be proportional to the test generation effort. In table 1, several circuits having similar index, but widely varying sizes, have similar test length. This suggests a strong relation between the testability index and test length. Figure 11 shows a graph of the testability index against the number of test vectors required to achieve a 90% fault coverage. The equation of the number V of vectors obtained by fitting a straight line is: $V \simeq 10^{1.6(index)-5.9}$. This relation may be used for index between 5 and 7, where it is supported by data. In regions of extrapolation, shown by dotted line, more data are needed. For instance, the relation for values of testability index less than 4 may be non-linear.

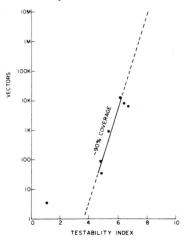

Figure 11. Number of vectors as a function of Testability Index

4. CONCLUSION

The extension of testability analysis to MOS VLSI circuits requires the modeling of special circuit structures. This modeling is preferably done at the gate or primitive level. Primitive models for buses, transmission gates, and memories were developed.

In addition, the SCOAP combinational controllability and observability measures were extended to higher level testability measures that represent the difficulty of detecting stuck-at-faults. A circuit testability index was also defined. Data were presented that showed circuits of different size and similar index had similar test length to achieve a given fault coverage.

5. ACKNOWLEDGMENT

The contributions of V. D. Agrawal and M. R. Mercer to this work are gratefully acknowledged.

REFERENCES

[1] E. B. Eichelberger, T. W. Williams, "A Logic Design Structure for LSI Testability," Proceedings of the 14th Design Automation Conference, New Orleans, LA, June 1977, pp. 462-468.

[2] V. D. Agrawal, S. K. Jain, D. M. Singer "Automation in Design for Testability," Proceedings of the Custom Integration Circuits Conference, Rochester NY, May 1984, pp. 159-163.

[3] L. A. Goldstein, E. J. Thigpen "SCOAP: Sandia Controllability/Observability Analysis Program," Proceedings of the 17th Design Automation Conference, Minneapolis MN, July 1980, pp. 190-196.

[4] V. D. Agrawal, M. R. Mercer "Testability Measures-what do they tell us?," IEEE International Test Conference, Philadelphia, PA, November, 1982, pp. 391-396.

[5] M. R. Mercer "SCOAP Memory Model," Internal Memorandum.

Probabilistic Treatment of General Combinational Networks

KENNETH P. PARKER AND EDWARD J. McCLUSKEY

Abstract—In this correspondence two methods are given for calculating the probability that the output of a general combinational network is 1 given the probabilities for each input being 1. We define the notions of the *probability of a signal* and *signal independence*. Then several proofs are given to show the relationship between Boolean operations and algebraic operations upon probabilities. As a result of these, two simple algorithms are presented for calculating output probabilities. An example of the usefulness of these results is given with respect to the generation of tests for the purpose of fault detection.

Index Terms—General combinational networks, input probability, output probability, probability, test generation.

I. INTRODUCTION

In this correspondence we present two algorithms for general combinational logic circuits which allow the formulation of an *output probability* given a set of *input probabilities*. An output probability is defined as the probability that the output attains a specified value, and similarly, an input probability is the probability that a given input has the specified value. The circuit function (which is independent of circuit structure) effectively provides a transform from input to output probabilities. Here we emphasize that we are treating the signals in a probabilistic sense and not the circuit components or function. Indeed, it will be seen that when all input probabilities are set at either extreme (1 or 0), the probability function of the circuit produces identically the same result as the Boolean function of the circuit.

Previous work in the area is generally based on the classic paper by Von Neuman [6], which treated concepts of reliability, stochastic processing, processing in the presence of noise (error), etc. The derivation of the first algorithm (which we have formalized) has been informally presented in part by other authors [1], [5]. Our second algorithm offers significant improvement over the first, since it allows us to calculate output probabilities directly from the circuit description without need of any Boolean manipulations. This is done for general networks despite the fact that dependencies may exist between gate inputs. Finally, we have been careful to remove all physical interpretation from our concepts of probabilities. This allows us full freedom of application in either time or space.

II. ASSIGNING A PROBABILITY TO A LOGIC SIGNAL

First, we arbitrarily choose a "reference value" about which to define probabilities. We choose "1" and then define the *probability of a logic signal* as follows.

Manuscript received December 10, 1973; revised September 7, 1974. This work was supported in part by the National Science Foundation under Grant GJ-40286.

The authors are with the Digital Systems Laboratory, Departments of Electrical Engineering and Computer Science, Stanford University, Stanford, Calif.

Definition 1: The probability of a (logic) signal, expressed as

$$a = P(A = 1)$$

for signal A, is a real number on the interval $[0, 1]$ which expresses the probability that signal A equals 1. [We use the convention here that upper case letters correspond to signal names (Boolean variables) and lower case letters represent the corresponding probabilities.] Since Boolean algebra is based on two-valued variables, we give the following definition.

Definition 2: The probability that signal $A = 0$ is given as

$$P(A = 0) = 1 - P(A = 1) = 1 - a.$$

III. OPERATIONS ON SIGNAL PROBABILITIES

The following statements relate Boolean operations to corresponding operations on probabilities.

Lemma 1: Boolean negation (NOT) such as in the expression $B = \bar{A}$ corresponds to the probability expression

$$b = 1 - a.$$

Proof: $b = P(B = 1) = P(\bar{A} = 1) = P(A = 0) = 1 - P(A = 1) = 1 - a.$

Before continuing, we must clarify the notion of *independence*. The concept of independence is that given a set of events, these events are individually determined by properties that are in no way interrelated. That is, event A (or subset of events A) in no way affects the outcome of event B (or subset of events B). The mathematical equivalent of the statement "A is independent of B" is

$$P(AB) = P(A)P(B).[1]$$

Independence is a family property, i.e., if events $X_1, X_2, \cdots, X_n$ are independent, $[P(X_1 X_2 \cdots X_n) = P(X_1)P(X_2)\cdots P(X_n)]$ then all possible subsets of events are independent. We continue.

Lemma 2: Boolean conjunction (AND) of two independent signals A, B in the expression $C = AB$ corresponds to the probability expression $c = ab$.

Proof: $C = 1$ iff $A = 1$ AND $B = 1$. It follows from the independence property that;

$$c = P(C = 1) = P(A = 1 \text{ AND } B = 1)$$
$$= P[(A = 1)(B = 1)] = P(A = 1)P(B = 1) = ab.$$

Corollary: $Z = X_1 X_2 X_3 \cdots X_n$ corresponds to the probability expression $z = x_1 x_2 x_3 \cdots x_n$ provided all X_i are independent.

Lemma 3: Boolean disjunction (OR) of two independent signals A, B in the expression $C = A \vee B$ corresponds to the probability expression

$$c = a + b - ab.$$

Proof:

$$C = A \vee B = \overline{\bar{A}\bar{B}}$$
$$c = P(C = 1) = P(\overline{\bar{A}\bar{B}} = 1) = 1 - P(\bar{A}\bar{B} = 1)$$
$$= 1 - P(\bar{A} = 1)P(\bar{B} = 1)$$
$$= 1 - (1 - a)(1 - b) = a + b - ab.$$

[1] Interested readers are invited to pursue the issue of independence and the basic axioms of probability in a basic text such as Papoulis [3].

Corollary: $Z = X_1 \vee X_2 \vee \cdots \vee X_n$ corresponds to

$$z = 1 - \prod_{i=1}^{n} (1 - x_i)$$

provided all X_i are independent.

Lemma 4: Boolean disjunction (OR) in the expression $C = A \vee B$ with the restriction that the inputs A,B are not simultaneously 1 corresponds to the following expression:

$$c = a + b.$$

Proof: Since only 1 input A or B equals 1 at a time, their union is disjoint (i.e., $AB = 0$ and $P(AB = 1) = 0$). A basic axiom [3] of probability is that the probability of the disjoint union of events is the sum of the individual probabilities. Hence, the lemma follows directly from the axiom.

Corollary: $Z = \bigcup_{i=1}^{n} X_i$ where $X_i X_j = 0$ for all $i \neq j$ corresponds to

$$z = \sum_{i=1}^{n} x_i$$

Notice that Lemma 3 can be shown from Lemma 4. Let $C = A \vee B$ with A,B independent. Then $C = AB \vee \bar{A}B \vee A\bar{B}$. But $AB\bar{A}B = 0$ and $ABA\bar{B} = 0$ and $\bar{A}BA\bar{B} = 0$ so Lemma 4 produces

$$c = P(AB = 1) + P(\bar{A}B = 1) + P(A\bar{B} = 1)$$

$$= ab + (1 - a)b + a(1 - b)$$

$$= ab + a - ab + b - ab$$

$$= ab + b - ab, \text{ which is the result of Lemma 3.}$$

The following lemma defines the result of combining two signals that are totally dependent.

Lemma 5: Boolean conjunction (AND) of a signal A with itself in the expression $B = AA$ corresponds to the following probability expression:

$$b = a.$$

Proof: The proof makes use of conditional probability [3].

$$b = P(B = 1) = P(AA = 1)$$

$$= P(A = 1)P(A = 1 \mid A = 1)$$

$$= P(A = 1)1$$

$$= a, \quad \text{(from [3]).}$$

Corollary: The following correspondences follow similarly:

$$P(A\bar{A} = 1) = 0$$

$$P(A \vee A = 1) = a$$

$$P(A \vee \bar{A} = 1) = 1.$$

The immediate consequence of Lemma 5 is that $P(AA = 1) = a$ and not a^2 as one gets from Lemma 2 by assuming independence. Similarly, by Lemma 2 we get $P(A\bar{A} = 1) = a - a^2$, by Lemma 3 we get $P(A \vee A = 1) = 2a - a^2$ and $P(A \vee \bar{A} = 1) = 1 - a + a^2$. Clearly, it is wrong to use Lemmas 2 and 3 in these cases since the operands are not independent. However, we note in each case that suppressing the exponent yields the correct result given by Lemma 5. This observation forms the basis for the second algorithm.

IV. TWO ALGORITHMS FOR PRODUCING PROBABILITY EXPRESSIONS FROM GENERAL NETWORKS

We base the first algorithm on the following facts:

1) Any general combinational network function can be expressed in a sum-of-products form.

2) A sum-of-products expression can be written as a canonical sum [2] of fundamental products Π_i.

3) In a canonical sum of Π_i, at most one $\Pi_i = 1$ for any input, i.e., $\Pi_i \Pi_j = 0$ for all $i \neq j$.

Algorithm One:

Step 1: From the circuit description obtain the canonical sum expression[2]

$$Z = \bigcup_{i=1}^{k} \Pi_i.$$

Step 2: For each Π_i in the canonical sum, produce the appropriate π_i product, where $\pi_i = P(\Pi_i = 1)$.

Step 3: The probability expression is given as

$$z = \sum_{i=1}^{k} \pi_i$$

which may be simplified algebraically.

Since each Boolean function has a unique canonical sum, there is a unique probability expression for each Boolean function.

Example 1: Given the circuit in Fig. 1, find the probability expression.

Step 1:

$$G = A(B \vee C) \vee BC = ABC \vee \bar{A}BC \vee A\bar{B}C \vee AB\bar{C}.$$

Step 2:

$$P(ABC = 1) = abc$$

$$P(\bar{A}BC = 1) = (1 - a)bc = bc - abc$$

$$P(A\bar{B}C = 1) = a(1 - b)c = ac - abc$$

$$P(AB\bar{C} = 1) = ab(1 - c) = ab - abc.$$

Step 3:

$$g = abc + ab - abc + ac - abc + bc - abc$$

$$= ab + ac + bc - 2abc.$$

A quick analysis of algorithm one shows that though it is simple and straightforward, its complexity has an attainable upper bound of order 2^n where n is the number of circuit inputs. Clearly, the Boolean analysis in Step 1 is the cause of the complexity. We now present the second algorithm which overcomes this problem by eliminating all Boolean analysis and derives the output probability expressions directly from the circuit description.

We base the second algorithm on the following facts:

1) Dependencies occur between gate input signals only in circuits containing recombined fanout, only at the site of recombination.

2) The gate function (either AND or OR) at a "recombination site" will in either case require (from Lemmas 2 and 3) the multiplication of input expressions, and these input expressions will contain common variables.

3) Lemma 5 states that we should suppress exponents after multiplying expressions with common terms.

Algorithm Two:

Step 1: For each input signal and gate output in the circuit, assign a unique variable.

Step 2: Starting at the inputs and proceeding to the outputs, write the expression for the output of each gate as a function (using Lemmas 2 and 3) of its input expressions.

Step 3: Suppress all exponents in a given expression to obtain the correct probability expression for that signal.

We note that Step 3 is deliberately somewhat vague about when to suppress exponents. The reader should verify that as long as exponents are suppressed in the output expression the correct

---

[2] We can simplify the process by summing the product expressions for disjoint implicants.

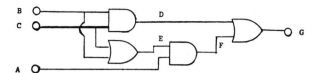

Fig. 1. Circuit realizing $G = A(B \lor C) \lor BC$.

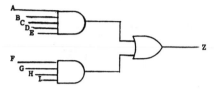

Fig. 2. Circuit realizing $Z = ABCDE \lor FGHI$.

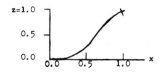

Fig. 3. Graph of $z = x^4 + x^5 - x^9$.

$$z = x^4 + x^5 - x^9$$

which is graphed in Fig. 3. Clearly, the probability of detecting the fault is highly dependent upon the value of x. It can be shown that many methods of producing tests from a list of raondom numbers inherently fixes x at the value of 0.5 and for the previous example, when $x = 0.5$, $z = 0.09$, and we can see in this instance why purely random test generation can be inefficient. As reported in [4], fair increases in testing efficiency can be obtained by controlling the value of x.

VI. CONCLUSION

We have demonstrated two methods for producing probability expressions for general combinational networks which relate the output probability to the set of input probabilities. These formulations are consistent with the requirements of probability theory, (can be easily implemented) and are immediately applicable to the practical problem of fault detection in logic circuits.

REFERENCES

[1] G. Klir, *Introduction to the Methodology of Switching Circuits.* New York: Van Nostrand, 1972.
[2] E. J. McCluskey, *Introduction to the Theory of Switching Circuits.* New York: McGraw-Hill, 1965.
[3] A. Papoulis, *Probability, Random Variables, and Stochastic Processes.* New York: McGraw-Hill, 1965.
[4] K. P. Parker, "Probabilistic test generation," Digital Syst. Lab., Stanford Univ., Stanford, Calif., Tech. Note 18, Aug. 1973.
[5] S. T. Ribeiro, "Random-pulse machines," *IEEE Trans. Electron. Comput.*, vol. EC-16, pp. 261–276, June 1967.
[6] J. Von Neumann, "Probabilistic logics and the synthesis of reliable organisms from unreliable components," C. Shannon and J. McCarthy, Ed. Princeton, N. J.: Princeton Univ. Press, 1956.

result is obtained regardless of whether or not exponents are suppressed for internal signals. This has important implications towards the implementation of algorithm two, one of which being that existing symbolic mathematical processing programs can be used to derive output expressions for circuits with the simple requirement that the final result be "fixed up" by suppressing any exponents.

Example 2: Given the circuit in Fig. 1, find the probability expressions for the output and all internal signals.

Step 1: Assign variables A,B,C,D,E,F,G to the indicated signals.
Step 2: Then

$$d = bc,$$

$$e = b + c - bc,$$

$$f = ae = ab + ac - abc$$

$$g = d + f - df = bc + ab + ac - abc - ab^2c - abc^2 + ab^2c^2.$$

Step 3: Only expression for g needs to be operated on

$$g = ab + bc + ac - abc - abc - abc + abc$$

$$= ab + bc + ac - 2abc.$$

Analysis of algorithm two shows that it is less complex than algorithm one. It can be implemented using existing software with little or no modification. We obtain all internal expressions and we can be completely cavalier about when exponent suppression is done as long as it is done to the desired output expression. We will not discard algorithm one since for some circuits (e.g., circuits that have some regular structure to their prime implicants such as threshold functions and parity generators) it is quite suitable.

V. MOTIVATION

Motivation for this work comes from the observation that test generation for the detection of faults in digital circuitry can be treated probabilistically [4]. Consider the circuit in Fig. 2. We see that in order to detect the failure Z stuck-at-0 we need to provide a $Z = 1$ output. Thus, the probability of detecting Z stuck-at-0 is simply $P(Z = 1)$ when we apply a probabilistic distribution of ones and zeroes to the inputs.

Now

$$z = abcde + fghi - abcdefghi.$$

Let the input test vectors be chosen such that $P(a = 1) = P(B = 1) = \cdots = P(I = 1) = x$, which is the case when tests are created from a large set of random numbers, a popular method. Then

Random Pattern Testability

JACOB SAVIR, MEMBER, IEEE, GARY S. DITLOW, MEMBER, IEEE, AND
PAUL H. BARDELL, SENIOR MEMBER, IEEE

Reprinted from *IEEE Transactions on Computers,* Volume C-33, Number 1,
January 1984, pages 79-90. Copyright © 1984 by The Institute of Electrical
and Electronics Engineers, Inc. All rights reserved.

Abstract—A major problem in self testing with random inputs is
verification of the test quality, i.e., the computation of the fault coverage. The brute-force approach of using full-fault simulation does
not seem attractive because of the logic structure volume, and the CPU
time encountered. A new approach is therefore necessary. This paper
describes a new analytical method of computing the fault coverage that
is fast compared with simulation. If the fault coverage falls below a
certain threshold, it is possible to identify the "random-pattern-resistant" faults, modify the logic to make them easy to detect, and thus,
increase the fault coverage of the random test.

Index Terms—Detection probability, fault coverage, random patterns, self test, signal probability.

INTRODUCTION

THE difficulty of test generation has been known for some
time [1], [2]. Although the process has been shown to be,
in general, NP complete, Goel's [3] experience is that computation time is close to an N^2 curve, where N is the number
of gates in the circuit. Since this kind of time complexity fails
to produce test patterns in a reasonable amount of time in a
VLSI environment, new approaches to the testing problem
have been investigated.

With the introduction of VLSI it has become apparent that
some investment in chip area to ease the testing problem is
more than worthwhile. Design for testability in reference to
self test (or built-in test) has become a prime issue. Simply
speaking, the idea was to have the chip (card, subassembly,
etc.) test itself. Two basic self-test strategies have been proposed, *exhaustive self test* and *random self test*. The class of
exhaustive self test [4]-[8] proposes to partition the logic into
small enough pieces that exhaustive application of inputs could
be practical. Some sort of data compression is used to store the
expected responses on chip. The problem with this approach
is that good partitioning programs are virtually nonexistent,
and unless this problem is successfully solved this solution will
remain an academic exercise. The class of random self test uses
random input stimuli rather than an exhaustive set. As a result,
partitioning is avoided. The number of random inputs applied
during test is closely related to the affordable test time and can
be roughly ten million for high performance circuits. Several
random self-test architectures have been proposed in the literature [9]-[12]. Basically speaking, all these versions use a
linear feedback shift register (LFSR) to generate pseudorandom inputs that are fed to the circuit, and a multiple-input
signature register (MISR) [10] to compress the circuit responses. With level-sensitive scan design (LSSD) principles
followed [13], it is easy to add some gates to have the shift
register latches (SRL's) function as an LFSR or an MISR in
self-test mode. A second implementation of the same basic idea
could be to leave the original SRL's intact, add an LFSR as
input stimulus, a MISR as an output response compressor, and
use the scan-in/scan-out ports to transport data from the input
LFSR to the network's SRL chain, and from the output SRL
chain to the MISR by SRL string loads [9].

Although the random self test has removed the partitioning
burden, it has introduced the problem of test quality verification. In an exhaustive self test this is not an issue since proper
testable design can guarantee that all single faults be covered
[4]. However, application of a random pattern test, which is
far from being exhaustive, may require a quality verification,
especially when high fault coverages are required. For a self
test to replace the traditional test generation/fault simulation
process, it is necessary that its resulting fault coverage be
virtually equivalent. Since simulation of long random patterns
against large logic structures does not seem practical, we have
to seek an analytical solution.

The random pattern testability problem can be spelled out
simply as follows. Given a combinational circuit that has to be
tested with N random patterns, either prove that 100-ϵ percent
of the population's single stuck-faults would be detected with
probability $1 - \delta$, or modify the logic to satisfy this. Typically,
we would like to have $\epsilon < 2$, $\delta < 0.001$.

The object of this paper is to show a cost-effective method
to solve this problem. An attempt is made to identify all the
random pattern-resistant faults, namely, those faults whose
detection probability falls below a given threshold. Then, extra
logic would be used to increase the probability of detecting
those "hard faults" by making them more susceptible to random inputs. The value of this threshold is directly related to
the affordable test time and is roughly 10^{-6} for a random
pattern test of ten million patterns. Details of this issue will be
discussed in a future paper.

To achieve this goal we show that there is a relationship
between signal probability [14], [15] and detection probability.
In fact, a signal probability program can serve as an engine to
compute detection probabilities. Since the signal probability
algorithms reported to date [14]-[18] suffer from an exponential storage problem it was necessary to develop a new algorithm that trades off accuracy in order to decrease the space
complexity. The cutting algorithm reported in this paper
computes signal probability bounds, rather than the exact

Manuscript received November 8, 1982; revised August 15, 1983.

J. Savir is with the IBM Data Systems Division, 265/415, Poughkeepsie,
NY 12602, on leave from the IBM T. J. Watson Research Center, Yorktown
Heights, NY 10598.

G. S. Ditlow is with the IBM T. J. Watson Research Center, Yorktown
Heights, NY 10598.

P. H. Bardell is with the IBM Data Systems Division, 265/938, Poughkeepsie, NY 12602.

figure, with the advantage that both the time and space complexities are practically linear. By using the cutting algorithm it is possible to compute a lower bound of the detection probability. Then, if this lower bound is larger than the threshold it may be marked off as an "easy fault." Otherwise it will be marked as a "hard fault," whose detection probability would have to be upgraded by logic modification.

The cutting algorithm takes advantage of the fact that exact computation of signal probabilities in tree networks can be done in linear time and space complexities. Thus, in order to compute signal probabilities in a general-type combinational circuit, the cutting algorithm "cuts" fan-out branches to turn the circuit into a tree. In the paper we show which probability bounds to assign to the cutpoints so that the signal probability computation in the tree network is compatible with that in the original network. All that is left is to propagate those bounds, on the equivalent tree, to the rest of the lines.

In following sections we describe 1) the relationship between signal probability and detection probability, 2) the cutting algorithm, which is central to our random pattern testability analysis, 3) some heuristics that can be used with the cutting algorithm to make it efficient, 4) the algorithm of computing lower bounds for the detection probability, which is based on the cutting algorithm, 5) some thoughts on how to correct hard faults once they are identified, and 6) some cutting algorithm applications to other disciplines. Finally, we summarize the main ideas and draw conclusions. The fault analysis is restricted to single stuck-at faults.

RELATIONSHIP BETWEEN SIGNAL AND DETECTION PROBABILITIES

The signal probability of line w, $p_s(w)$, is the probability that a randomly selected input vector will yield $w = 1$. The detection probability of a fault w/i (read line w stuck-at-$i \in \{0, 1\}$), $p_d(w/i)$, is the probability that a randomly selected input vector will cause at least one of the primary outputs to assume a wrong value. For simplicity assume the circuit has a single output, F.

Suppose first that there exists only one propagation path from w to F, as shown in Fig. 1. Assume that the fault is $w/0$. Detection of this fault requires having an input vector that will force both inputs of gate G_1 to 1; the input of G_2 that does not lie on the propagation path should be forced to a 0; the input of G_k that does not lie on the propagation path should be forced to 0, etc. This set of conditions can be put together by introducing an auxiliary gate G^0, whose output $F^0 = 1$ if and only if the previous set of sensitizing conditions is satisfied. Thus, a line that has to be forced to a zero (according to the sensitizing pattern) should be complemented when connected to G^0; and a line that has to be forced to a one should be left uninverted. With this arrangement we have turned the detection probability to a signal probability problem:

$$p_d(w/i) = p_s(F^0). \qquad (1)$$

Fig. 1 displays the special case where $i = 0$. Suppose now that there are j paths from line w to F. There may be, in general, $2^j - 1$ propagation patterns between w and F, counting all single and multiple paths.

Suppose further that an auxiliary gate, G^q, is introduced whose output $F^q = 1$ if and only if the fault on w propagates along the qth path (single path) to the output F. Then, obviously,

$$p_d(w/i) \geq p_s(F^q). \qquad (2)$$

Thus, this signal probability is a lower bound to the detection probability of the fault w/i. The cutting algorithm presented here rests on this relationship, namely, that it is possible to compute lower bounds on the detection probabilities by computing signal probabilities of auxiliary gates.

Definition 1: The *prime faults* are the faults on the input lines and on the origin of fan-out branches.

In Fig. 2, the origin of the fan-out branches are lines $\{w_1, w_2, \cdots, w_m\}$.

Definition 2: A fault, w/i, is *random-pattern testable* if $p_d(w/i) > p_{dt}$, where p_{dt} is a given threshold.

The following well-known theorem in deterministic testing is also true in random testing [19].

Theorem 1: A circuit is random-pattern testable if all its prime faults are.

Proof: Since all the prime faults are random-pattern testable, then their detection probability is larger than the threshold, p_{dt}. However, since the prime faults dominate all the other faults in the circuit, the detection probability of all the other faults is at least p_{dt}. Q.E.D

Theorem 1 will be our vehicle to prove random-pattern testability of any given circuit.

It is important to note that since our random-pattern testability analysis rests on examining single path propagation of faults, it may end up giving a zero lower bound for detection of a fault that can only be propagated through multiple paths. In these cases the resulting lower bound will be too pessimistic. To solve this problem we have two options: either simulate the circuit with this fault to get a more realistic figure, or introduce some extra hardware to force an acceptable single-path propagation.

THE CUTTING ALGORITHM

The Full-Range Cutting Algorithm

The cutting algorithm is the work-horse of the signal probability estimation engine. Its objective is to turn the combinational network into a tree, by cutting reconvergent fanout branches, and inserting equivalent bounds at the cut points, which will guarantee that all the signal probability bounds computed on this tree will enclose the true values. The advantage of doing this is the reduction of the computational complexity (time and space); the disadvantage is that the output is not an exact figure but just a bound.

In the full-range cutting algorithm we assign a signal probability range of $[0, 1]$ to all the cut points, and propagate the bounds to all the other lines of the circuit by using tree formulas. Notice that in order to cut an n-way fan-out it is only necessary to cut $n - 1$ of its branches to turn it into a tree. Therefore, the line not cut receives the signal probability of its immediate ancestor. Fig. 3 illustrates this point.

Intuitively, at least, it should be clear that this assignment

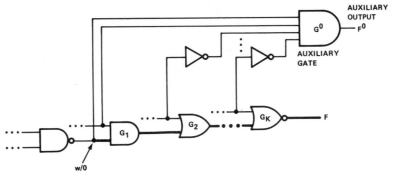

Fig. 1.   An example for which there is only one propagation path from the site of the fault to a primary output.

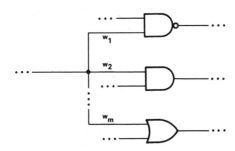

Fig. 2.   An illustration of the origin of fan-out branches, $\{w_1, w_2, \cdots, w_m\}$.

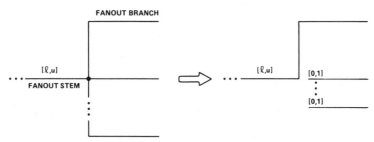

Fig. 3.   The full-range cutting process performed on an n-way reconvergent fan-out point (reconverging gate not shown).

always works, because this covers the full range of the probability spectrum. Before we present a formal proof we define some terms, describe the algorithm, and show an example.

Definition 3: The *cone of influence* of a line w, $c(w)$, is the logic that feeds, directly or indirectly, this line.

Definition 4: A *tree line* is a line, w, for which $c(w)$ is a tree.

The signal probability of all the tree lines can be computed without the cutting algorithm. These values will naturally be exact. The cutting algorithm will enable one to compute signal probability bounds for all the nontree lines as follows.

Procedure 1:

Step 1: Assign signal probability of $\frac{1}{2}$ to all input lines.

Step 2: Compute the signal probability for all the tree-lines.

Step 3: Turn the circuit into a tree by cutting reconvergent fanout branches according to Fig. 3.

Step 4: Propagate the signal probability bounds to all the nontree lines by using tree formulas (Fig. 4).

Fig. 4 displays the formulas of propagating signal probability bounds through an INVERTER, AND, and OR gates. The formulas for NAND and NOR can be easily derived from Fig.

4 by noting that NAND is AND-NOT, and that NOR is OR-NOT.

Example 1: Consider the circuit of Fig. 5. In (a) we compute the signal probabilities of all the tree lines. In (b) we compute the signal probabilities of the nontree lines. The complete set of signal probabilities is shown in (c). The only nontree lines in Fig. 5 are lines $\{w_1, w_2\}$. The Boolean functions realized by these lines are

$$w_1 = x_1(\overline{x}_2 + x_3 x_4) + x_5(\overline{x}_3 + \overline{x}_4), \text{ and}$$

$$w_2 = \overline{x}_5[\overline{x}_1 + x_2(\overline{x}_3 + \overline{x}_4)] + \overline{x}_1 x_3 x_4 + x_6(\overline{x}_3 + \overline{x}_4).$$

Note that the exact signal probabilities for these lines are within the computed bounds.

$$p_s(w_1) = 19/32 \in [1/4, 3/4],$$

$$p_s(w_2) = 41/64 \in [17/32, 27/32].$$

Theorem 2: The full-range cutting algorithm computes true bounds.

Proof: There is a one-to-one correspondence between set operations and logic gates. AND corresponds to intersection; OR to union; NOT to complementation, etc. Let the universe

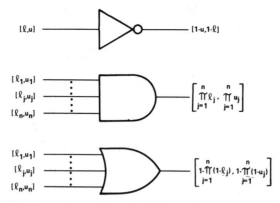

Fig. 4. Tree formulas for propagating signal probability bounds.

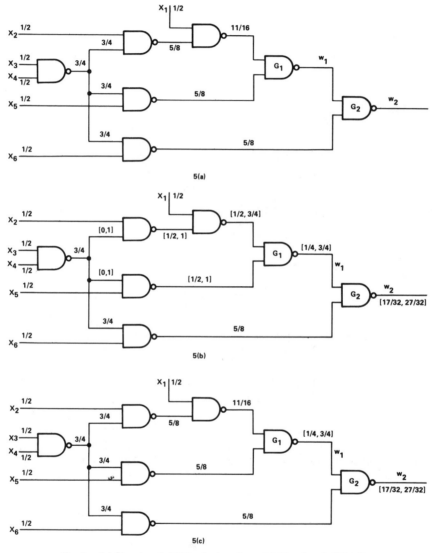

Fig. 5. (a) Signal probabilities for tree-lines. (b) Signal probability for nontree lines. (c) The final set of signal probabilities.

be the set of all possible input vectors. Assume that we assign to each input line the subset of input vectors for which the line assumes the value one (called the on-set) and that we perform the set operations that correspond to the logic gates that the circuit utilizes.

By performing those operations, the resulting set attached to each line in the circuit will be the subset of all input vectors that force that line to have the value one. Thus, the normalized cardinality of each such set is nothing but the signal probability of that line (normalized with respect to the cardinality of the universe).

A cutting of a fan-out branch corresponds to a replacement of the on-set of that line by two sets: the null set and the set universe. Assume that Procedure 1 is followed to completion with the associated sets. Then all the set operations done on the modified circuit (which is a tree) will compute subsets or

284

supersets of the on-sets of all the lines in the circuit. In other words, if the on-set of line w_i is $OS(w_i)$, then the cutting algorithm will compute the set $OS^*(w_i)$ and $OS^{**}(w_i)$ such that $OS^*(w_i) \subseteq OS(w_i) \subseteq OS^{**}(w_i)$. The reason lies in the fact that all gates represent a monotone function and that the on-set relation above holds separately for each gate.　　　Q.E.D.

It is important to note that divergent (nonreconvergent) fanout branches do not have to be cut. These lines will get the signal probability of their ancestor during the computation process.

The Restricted-Range Cutting Algorithm

Here we show how to take advantage of the inversion parity of the reconvergent fan-out branches to compute tighter bounds. We show that in some cases it is possible to assign one of the ranges $[0, g]$ or $[g, 1]$ to the cut fan-out branch, where g is the signal probability of the stem of the fan-out. If g is in itself a range $[l, u]$, then one of the ranges $[0, u]$ or $[l, 1]$ will be assigned.

Theorem 3: Let w be a fan-out stem with signal probability g, from which only one pair of reconverging paths emanates. Let this pair of reconverging paths be the only one in the network. Let H be the gate through which the pair of paths reconverges. Let h be the output of this gate. Then, if a fan-out branch is cut and assigned a range according to the appropriate case of Table I, then all the signal probability ranges computed on the resultant tree will include the true values.

Before we prove Theorem 3, we will show an example.

Example 2: Consider the circuit of Fig. 6. The two paths emanating at w and reconverging at h have unequal inversion parities, and the type of the reconverging gate is a NOR. Suppose we would like to cut the upper path, which has an odd parity between w and h. According to Table I, the assigned range should be $[3/4, 1]$. The signal probability ranges computed for the resultant tree are shown in Fig. 6.

Proof of Theorem 3: For the purpose of this proof, let g be the Boolean function realized by the fan-out stem. We will prove one of the entries of Table I. The proof for the rest is similar. We prove it for the case where both paths have even parity and where the reconverging gate is an AND. We have to show that a range of $[P_s(g), 1]$ for the cut branch will yield true bounds on all other lines in the circuit. Because of the assumptions imposed in the theorem, it is sufficient to prove that the signal probability range computed for line h includes the true value. The Boolean function of h expressed in terms of g can be written as

$$h = (A_1 g + B_1)(A_2 g + B_2)$$

where g is independent of A_1, B_1, A_2, B_2.

If the first fan-out branch is cut and assigned a primary input x, then the function realized by h expressed in terms of x and g is

$$h^* = (A_1 x + B_1)(A_2 g + B_2).$$

The question now is what should $p_s(x)$ be so that

$$p_s(h) = p_s(h^*). \tag{3}$$

The computation of $p_s(h)$ and $p_s(h^*)$ yields

$$p_s(h) = p_s[(A_1 A_2 \overline{B}_1 + A_1 \overline{B}_1 B_2 + A_2 B_1 \overline{B}_2)g]$$
$$+ p_s(B_1 B_2) \tag{4}$$

TABLE I

THE RESTRICTED RANGES ASSIGNED TO A CUT FAN-OUT BRANCH AS A FUNCTION OF TYPE OF RECONVERGING GATE, THE PATH INVERSION PARITY, AND THE SIGNAL PROBABILITY OF THE STEM

		TYPE OF RECONVERGING GATE, H		
		AND/NOR	OR/NAND	
PARITY OF CUT BRANCH BETWEEN w AND h	EVEN	$[g, 1]$	$[0, g]$	INVERSION PARITIES OF RECONVERGING PATHS EQUAL
	ODD	$[0, g]$	$[g, 1]$	
	EVEN	$[0, g]$	$[g, 1]$	INVERSION PARITIES OF RECONVERGING PATHS UNEQUAL
	ODD	$[g, 1]$	$[0, g]$	

$$p_s(h^*) = p_s[A_1 \overline{B}_1(A_2 g + B_2)]p_s(x) + p_s(A_2 B_1 \overline{B}_2 g)$$
$$+ p_s(B_1 B_2). \tag{5}$$

Substitution of (4) and (5) into (3) results in

$$p_s(x) = \frac{p_s[A_1 \overline{B}_1(A_2 + B_2)g]}{p_s[A_1 \overline{B}_1(A_2 g + B_2)]}. \tag{6}$$

Note that $g = 0 \rightarrow p_s(x) = 0$, and $g = 1 \rightarrow p_s(x) = 1$.

Moreover, note that

$$p_s(x) - p_s(g) = \frac{p_s(A_1 A_2 \overline{B}_1 \overline{B}_2 \overline{g})p_s(g)}{p_s[A_1 \overline{B}_1(A_2 g + B_2)]} \geq 0,$$

which completes the proof.　　　Q.E.D.

The restricted range cutting algorithm is described in the following procedure.

Procedure 2:

Step 1: Assign a signal probability of $p_i = 1/2$ to all input lines, and compute the signal probabilities of all the tree lines.

Step 2: Moving from the inputs towards the outputs, cut reconvergent fan-out branches to turn the circuit into a tree. When a fanout branch is cut, assign to it a restricted range, if all reconverging pairs of paths in which this line participates, along with their corresponding reconverging gates, yield the same restricted range according to Table I; otherwise assign a full-range to the cut branch.

Step 3: Propagate the bounds on the resultant tree.

Example 3: Consider the circuit of Fig. 5, redrawn in Fig. 7. The tree line values were computed in Example 1. In Fig. 7(a) we show the computation of $p_s(h_1)$ and $p_s(h_2)$ based on restricted ranges. Suppose we want to cut line w_2. Line w_2 participates in two pairs of reconverging paths: the pair $\{G_1 G_4 G_5, G_2 G_5\}$ with G_5 the reconverging gate; and the pair $\{G_1 G_4 G_5 G_6, G_3 G_6\}$ with G_6 the reconverging gate. In the first pair, w_2 lies on an odd path where the paths have unequal inversion parities. In the second pair, w_2 lies on an even path where the paths have equal inversion parities. According to Table I, in both these two cases, the range to be assigned to line w_2 should be $[0, g]$, where g is the signal probability of the stem, w_1. Thus, in Fig. 7(a), a range of $[0, 3/4]$ is assigned to line w_2. After we cut line w_2, there is only one pair of reconverging paths left, namely, $\{G_2 G_5 G_6, G_3 G_6\}$. Suppose we want to cut line w_4, next. This is the case where the paths have unequal inversion parities, and where w_4 lies on the even path. According to Table I, the range to be assigned to it is $[g, 1] = [3/4, 1]$. Fig. 7(a) shows the propagation of the bounds to the

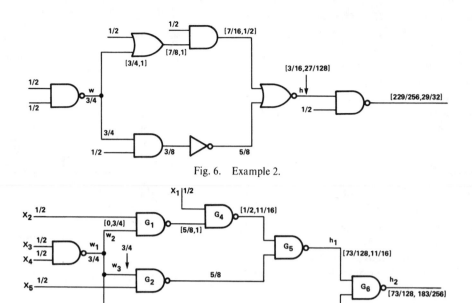

Fig. 6. Example 2.

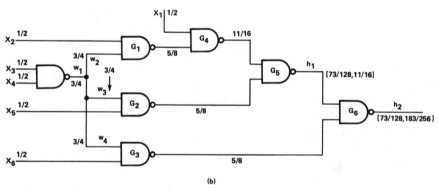

(a)

(b)

Fig. 7. (a) Nontree bounds computed with restricted ranges. (b) The final signal probability bounds.

nontree lines, h_1 and h_2. Fig. 7(b) shows the signal probability bounds for all lines in the circuit.

Note that Procedure 2, Step 2 calls for cutting fan-out branches as you move from inputs to outputs. Thus, when a line w is considered for cutting, there should be no stem of fan-out in $c(w)$. In other words, all fanout lines prior to line w should be resolved by the time line w is considered.

Note also that there is room for optimizing the bounds by properly choosing the cut branches. For example, if a fan-out stem, g, has signal probability larger than $1/2$ and the branches following it are such that if one is cut a bound $[0, g]$ should be assigned; and if the other one is cut, a bound $[g, 1]$ should be assigned, then, at least locally, the second choice would result in a tighter bound. Note also that if we had decided to cut line w_4 before cutting line w_2, we would have had to assign the full range to it. This would have probably resulted in a looser bound for lines h_1 and h_2.

Theorem 4: The restricted-range cutting algorithm computes true bounds.

Proof: As outlined in Procedure 2, fan-out branches are cut starting from the inputs. Thus, when a fan-out branch has to be cut, there is no fan-out stem left in its cone of influence (as required by Theorem 3). If according to all possible pairs of reconverging paths in which this fan-out branch participates, the required restricted range is unique, then such an assignment will result in signal probability bounds that enclose the true value for each and every line in the circuit (if computed). If, however, according to Table I, one pair of paths requires one type of restricted range, while another pair of paths requires the other one, Procedure 2 would assign to that branch the full range, which would also result in true bounds, according to Theorem 2. Therefore, since the network is turned out into a tree sequentially, and since each time a branch is cut its attached range is valid, then the final end result is that the

286

computed bounds will enclose the true signal probability for each and every line in the circuit. Q.E.D.

HEURISTICS

Although the cutting algorithm is our engine for computing signal probabilities, it is worthwhile to also have a number of heuristics that we can switch to when tighter bounds are required. Some insight into the importance of the ordering of the cuts was given in the previous section; this section will continue in that vein. In the following heuristics we show how to improve the signal probability bounds based on multiple runs of the cutting algorithm.

Lemma: If the cutting algorithm is run $k \geq 1$ times and if the signal probability of a wire is computed to be in the range $[l_i, u_i]$ for the ith trial, then the signal probability of the wire is bounded by $[l, u]$ where

$$l = \operatorname*{Max}_{i} \{l_i\}, i = 1, 2, \cdots, k \tag{7}$$

$$u = \operatorname*{Min}_{i} \{u_i\}, i = 1, 2, \cdots, k. \tag{8}$$

Proof: Suppose the cutting algorithm is applied k times, each time recording the computed bounds for each line in the circuit. Let w be a line in the circuit and let the computed bounds for this line be $[l_i, u_i], i = 1, 2, \cdots, k$. Then, since each bound constitutes a true range, the combined bound for this line may be set to $[l, u]$, according to (7) and (8). Q.E.D.

Coin Flipping

Coin flipping is an *a priori* unbiased way of cutting fan-out branches. Suppose w is a fan-out stem of a q-way reconverging fanout. In any assignment of ranges, one fan-out branch will be assigned the signal probability of the stem, $p_s(w)$, while all the rest will be cut and assigned appropriate bounds. Obviously, there are q ways in which the line assigned to $p_s(w)$ can be selected. The coin flipping method would flip a fair q-way coin to decide which line would be selected. Note that if only full ranges are considered, there are q different cutting patterns associated with this q-way fan-out. If, however, restricted ranges are used, more patterns are possible.

Suppose the coin flipping strategy is applied for k times. Then, based on the results of these k trials, a tight bound can be computed for each line in the circuit by using (7) and (8).

Group Exhaustion

In this heuristic we group the fan-out stems in small groups to make it possible to exhaust all cutting patterns within a group and compute tight bounds based on (7) and (8). It is worthwhile to group fan-out stems that appear "close" in terms of circuit connectivity.

Adaptive Cuts

Suppose that after computing the bounds based on some cutting patterns, some lines still have unacceptable ranges. In the next cutting pattern it is possible to orient the cuts in such a way that true values (or tight bounds) would be propagated towards those lines, thus improving the bounds.

Macros

Many regular structures constitute repetitions of a basic macro. A ripple carry adder repeats the basic structure of a full adder. The number of repetitions depends on the width of the memory word. An EXCLUSIVE-OR gate is used regularly in many digital designs. If an input/output signal probability bound relation were established for these macros, considerable CPU time could be gained when they are used in the circuit.

Consider a two-input EXCLUSIVE-OR gate. Let the signal probability bounds on the inputs be $[l_1, u_1]$ and $[l_2, u_2]$. Let the output signal probability bound be $[l, u]$. Based on the full-range assignment, the following input/output relations can be derived.

If the cones of influence of the two inputs to the gate are disjoint, then it can be shown that

$$l = \operatorname*{Min}_{i} \{s_i\} \tag{9}$$

$$u = \operatorname*{Max}_{i} \{s_i\} \tag{10}$$

where
$$\begin{aligned} s_1 &= l_1 + l_2 - 2l_1 l_2 \\ s_2 &= l_1 + u_2 - 2l_1 u_2 \\ s_3 &= u_1 + l_2 - 2u_1 l_2 \\ s_4 &= u_1 + u_2 - 2u_1 u_2. \end{aligned}$$

However, if the cones of influence of the two inputs to the gate are conjoint, then the relationship can be shown to be

$$l = \operatorname{Max}\{l_1(1 - u_2), l_2(1 - u_1)\} \tag{11}$$

$$u = \operatorname{Min}\{1 - l_1 l_2, u_1 + u_2 - u_1 u_2\}. \tag{12}$$

Consider now an iterative network like the one shown in Fig. 8. Assume that all the fan-out stems and reconverging paths are "hidden" within the blocks. In other words, assume that there are no reconverging paths crossing block boundaries. In this case, it is possible to treat each block as a macro and propagate bounds from inputs to internal macro lines, as well as to macro outputs, by using transfer relations.

A ripple carry-adder satisfies the requirement above. In this case each block (except for the first) is a full-adder stage receiving three inputs (two external inputs and a carry from the previous stage) and generating two outputs (the sum bit and the carry to the next stage). A full-adder stage is shown in Fig. 9. Given that the signal probabilities to lines A_i, B_i, and C_{i-1} are respectively $[l_1, u_1]$, $[l_2, u_2]$, and $[l_3, u_3]$, the full-range cutting algorithm yields the following bounds for the other macro lines:

$$l_4 = l_1 l_2, u_4 = u_1 u_2 \tag{13}$$

$$l_5 = l_1 + l_2 - l_1 l_2, u_5 = u_1 + u_2 - u_1 u_2 \tag{14}$$

$$l_6 = l_3(l_1 + l_2 - l_1 l_2), u_6 = u_3(u_1 + u_2 - u_1 u_2) \tag{15}$$

$$l_7 = l_1 l_2 l_3, u_7 = u_1 u_2 u_3 \tag{16}$$

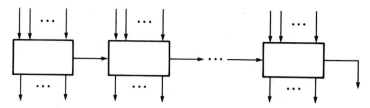

Fig. 8.   An iterative network with no cross-boundary fan-out.

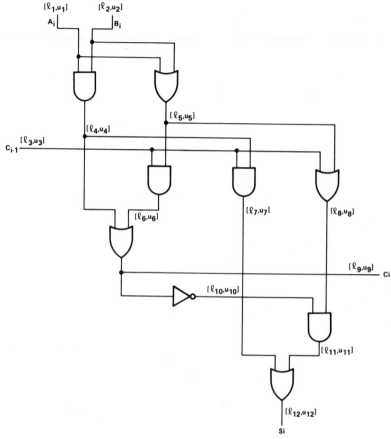

Fig. 9.   A full adder stage.

$$l_8 = 1 - (1 - l_1)(1 - l_2)(1 - l_3),$$

$$u_8 = 1 - (1 - u_1)(1 - u_2)(1 - u_3) \qquad (17)$$

$$l_9 = \text{Max}\{l_1 l_2, l_3(l_1 + l_2 - l_1 l_2)\},$$

$$u_9 = u_3 + u_1 u_2 (1 - u_3) \qquad (18)$$

$$l_{10} = 1 - u_9, u_{10} = 1 - l_9 \qquad (19)$$

$$l_{11} = \text{Max}\{l_1(1 - u_2)(1 - u_3), l_2(1 - u_1)(1 - u_3)\},$$

$$u_{11} = \text{Min}\{1 - l_1 l_2, 1 - l_2 l_3, 1 - l_1 l_3\} \qquad (20)$$

$$l_{12} = l_1 l_2 l_3, u_{12} = \text{Min}\{1 - (1 - u_1)l_2 l_3,$$

$$1 - (1 - u_2)l_1 l_3, 1 - (1 - u_3)l_1 l_2\}. \qquad (21)$$

By placing proper initial conditions on the primary inputs, all the signal probability bounds in the network can be computed very fast (by a computer program).

Expansion

It is possible to use the cutting algorithm jointly with Shannon's expansion to achieve both tighter bounds and gain in CPU time. Suppose a signal probability range is computed for line w_1. Suppose, further, that line w_2, which is reachable from w_1 (namely, $w_1 \in c(w_2)$), does not have an acceptable signal probability range. It is possible to improve the bound on line w_2 by computing the signal probabilities of two special cases. Let $p_s(w_2/w_1 = 0)$ $(p_s(w_2/w_1 = 1))$ be the conditional signal probability for line w_2 given that line w_1 is fixed at zero (fixed at one). Then, the following theorem holds.

Theorem 5: If $p_s(w_2/w_1 = 0) \in [a_0, a_1]$,

$$p_s(w_2/w_1 = 1) \in [b_0, b_1],$$

and $p_s(w_1) \in [c_0, c_1]$, then $p_s(w_2) \in [d_0, d_1]$ where

$$d_0 = a_0(1 - c_1) + b_0 c_0 \qquad (22)$$

$$d_1 = \text{Min}\{a_1(1 - c_0) + b_1 c_1, 1\}. \qquad (23)$$

Proof: By Shannon's expansion we have

$$p_s(w_2) = p_s(w_2/w_1 = 0) \cdot [1 - p_s(w_1)]$$
$$+ p_s(w_2/w_1 = 1) \cdot p_s(w_1).$$

Substituting the ranges in this formula yields

$$[d_0, d_1] = [a_0, a_1] \cdot [1 - c_1, 1 - c_0] + [b_0, b_1] \cdot [c_0, c_1].$$

Equating lower bounds of both sides of the equation yields

$$d_0 = a_0(1 - c_1) + b_0 c_0.$$

Equating upper bounds of both sides of the equation yields

$$d_1 = a_1(1 - c_0) + b_1 c_1.$$

However, since the right-hand side of this equation may be larger than one, in general, and since the left-hand side should always be smaller than one, we have to take

$$d_1 = \text{Min}\{a_1(1 - c_0) + b_1 c_1, 1\}. \qquad \text{Q.E.D.}$$

The following corollary shows a useful application of Theorem 5.

Corollary: Let the gate G_2 have the output w_2. If there is no fan-out stem in $c(w_1)$ whose reconvergent gate is G_2, then $p_s(w_2/w_1 = 0)$ $(p_s(w_2/w_1 = 1))$ can be computed by simply considering the residual circuit resulting after cutting line w_1 and fixing its input counterpart to a fixed 0 (1).

Proof: If the restriction imposed by the corollary holds, then $p_s(w_2/w_1 = 0)$ $(p_s(w_2/w_1 = 1))$ are independent of the primary inputs in $c(w_1)$. Q.E.D.

Example 4: Consider the circuit of Fig. 10(a). In this example we will show how expansion around line w is used to compute the signal probability bound on the output line F. Note that the restriction of the corollary holds for lines w and F. The following bounds have been computed by using the restricted-range cutting algorithm.

$$p_s(w) \in [3/8, 39/64].$$

Forcing w to a zero yields $F = 1$. Thus

$$p_s(F/w = 0) \in [1, 1].$$

Forcing w to a one yields the circuit of Fig. 10(b). The signal probability bound on F is computed to be

$$p_s(F/w = 1) \in [1/8, 15/64].$$

Thus,

$$p_s(F) \in [7/16, 3145/4096].$$

Note that the usefulness of the expansion heuristic rests on the observation that it is easier to compute bounds for the two special cases than for the original circuit. This is because the circuit resulting after forcing w_1 to either zero or to one is simpler than the original circuit.

COMPUTATION OF LOWER BOUNDS FOR DETECTION PROBABILITIES

The algorithm is spelled out in the following procedure:

Procedure 3:

Step 1: Pick a prime fault which has not been considered yet. If all prime faults considered—stop.

Step 2: Choose a single[1] propagation path, that has not yet

---

[1] In the case where all propagation paths from the site of the fault to a primary output have equal inversion parity, this requirement can be relaxed.

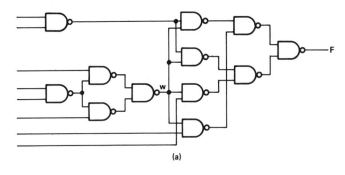

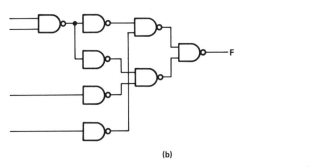

Fig. 10. (a) The circuit of Example 4. (b) The circuit resulting after forcing w to a one.

been considered, from the site of the fault to a primary output. If all single paths have been considered, mark the fault as "hard-fault" and go to Step 1.

Step 3: Introduce the auxiliary AND gate whose signal probability equals the detection probability along the selected path.

Step 4: Compute the lower bound of the signal probability on the output of the auxiliary gate. If the lower bound is acceptable (larger than the threshold), mark it off as an "easy-fault" and go to Step 1. Otherwise, go to Step 2.

Note that only single propagation paths are treated in Procedure 3. A fault that can be detected only along *multiple paths* will be marked as hard.

Example 5: Consider the circuit of Fig. 11. In Fig. 11(b) we show the computation of a lower bound for $x_3/0$. In Fig. 11(c) we show the computation of a lower bound for $x_4/1$. Notice that we propagate the fault $x_3/0$ along a single path, and the fault $x_4/1$ along either a single or a double path. Table II displays the detection probabilities and the computed lower bounds for all the prime faults in the circuit. The exact detection probability figures were computed by the Boolean difference technique, and the lower bounds by the cutting algorithm.

CORRECTION OF HARD FAULTS

Once the hard faults are identified it is necessary to upgrade their detection probabilities so that they will be susceptible to random patterns. Some hard faults are known to be introduced by high fan-in gates. The probability of detecting a stuck-at-zero fault at the input of an n-way AND is 2^{-n}. A similar situation occurs with other high fan-in gates, like OR, NAND, and NOR. Faults at the inputs of a long cascade of alternating AND's and OR's are also hard to detect. Faults in PLA's realizing large product terms are also hard to detect. Hard faults may appear also in an unstructured design. All it takes for a fault to be hard [20] is to have a small cardinality of inter-

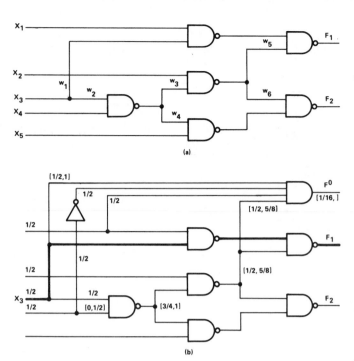

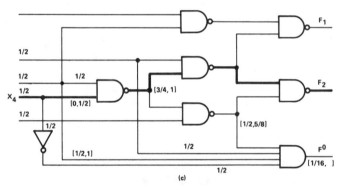

Fig. 11. (a) The circuit of example 5. (b) Computation of the lower bound of the detection probability of $x_3/0$ along the bold face line. (c) The same as (b), but for $x_4/1$.

TABLE II
THE DETECTION PROBABILITY, p_d, AND THE COMPUTED LOWER
BOUND OF THE DETECTION PROBABILITY FOR ALL PRIME FAULTS
IN EXAMPLE 5

Prime Fault	p_d	Lower Bound
$x_1/0$	3/16	5/32
$x_1/1$	3/16	5/32
$x_2/0$	11/32	9/32
$x_2/1$	11/32	9/32
$x_3/0$	9/32	1/16
$x_3/1$	9/32	1/16
$x_4/0$	3/16	5/64
$x_4/1$	3/16	1/16
$x_5/0$	3/16	3/16
$x_5/1$	3/16	3/16
$w_1/0$	3/16	5/32
$w_1/1$	1/8	1/8
$w_2/0$	3/16	5/64
$w_2/1$	3/16	1/16
$w_3/0$	11/32	3/16
$w_3/1$	1/8	5/64
$w_4/0$	3/16	3/16
$w_4/1$	1/8	5/64
$w_5/0$	7/16	3/8
$w_5/1$	5/16	9/32
$w_6/0$	7/16	25/64
$w_6/1$	3/16	3/16

section between the controllability and observability sets. So, in general, hard faults may be randomly spread in a logic design. The cutting algorithm serves as an engine to identify these faults. Some thoughts on random pattern design for testability are reported in [21]. Here we present some of our thoughts on the subject.

The first approach, a unified one, is general enough to be applied to any design. The idea is to use a semirandom rather than a completely random self test. After the hard faults have been identified, compute a set of tests that cover these faults and store them in a read-only memory (ROM) built on chip. All the experiments conducted until now support the conjecture that there is not a large number of hard faults. So, with a relatively small area overhead, all the desired test patterns for hard faults can be stored on chip. The self test therefore would consist of two parts. In the first, all the hard faults would be exercised with the deterministic patterns stored in the ROM, and the signature accumulated in the MISR. In the second part, the input stimulus would be switched to a random mode. Random patterns are continuously applied to the circuit while the signature keeps accumulating in the MISR. The final signature for the chip is the combined signature of the two test

modes, and this is the one to use as signature reference. The advantage of this approach is that it is unified, in the sense that it can be readily applied to any design. The disadvantage is that it uses two test modes.

The second approach is circuit-dependent. Once a hard fault has been identified, it is possible to ease its testing by random inputs by introducing control lines and test points along the propagation path of the fault. It is also possible to introduce new primary outputs to make the fault more observable. Note that in an LSSD environment one can implement these extra inputs and outputs by introducing extra latches in the SRL chains rather than by actual I/O pins, which may be scarce. The advantage of this approach is that the self test will have only one mode—the random mode—rather than both the deterministic and the random that the previous approach had. The disadvantage is that the design for testability is circuit-dependent and has to be treated case by case. It is still to be found which approach leads to smallest hardware overhead. Our belief is that the hardware overhead will not exceed 5 percent of the chip area, including both the hardware modifications necessary for self test due to the MISR's and the overhead penalty due to random pattern resistant faults. For more information on correction of hard faults consult [22].

Application to Other Disciplines

The cutting algorithm could also be used in other disciplines, like design verification, current-switching problems (known as ΔI) [23]–[25], timing analysis, etc.

The problem one faces in design verification is whether a design meets its objective function. Put in different terms, suppose it is necessary to verify that design number 1 is logically equivalent to design number 2. One design may be human-created, the other generated automatically. Or, one design may have been produced by a logic designer; the other, by simulation.

Suppose we take the two designs and EXCLUSIVE-OR their corresponding outputs, namely, output 1 of design 1 with output 1 of design 2, etc. Suppose also that the corresponding inputs of the designs are tied together, namely, input 1 of design 1 to input 1 of design 2, etc. Then obviously, if the two designs are logically equivalent, the signal probability of the outputs of the XOR gates should be zero.

The cutting algorithm, if run, can indicate whether the two designs are different. If the signal probability range is computed for each XOR output, and if at least one of the ranges discovers a nonzero lower bound, then certainly the two designs differ. If all lower bounds are zero, no conclusion can be drawn. Notice that this scheme may help to screen out bad designs, but it will fail, as other methods do also, to tell for certain that the two designs are identical. To confirm that point requires exhaustion of their input space to see whether a specific input results in a different output.

A current-switching problem may occur when more than a specified number of outputs simultaneously change value, due to an input change. To see whether there is a ΔI problem, we construct the network of Fig. 12.

The outputs of two copies of the circuit are XORed respectively. The outputs of the XOR gates feed a threshold detection circuit, whose output is $F = 1$ if and only if more than k, say, inputs are one. The inputs to the two copies of the circuit are considered independent inputs. The input vectors to the two copies should be considered as two contiguous input vectors applied to the original circuit. Then if $F = 1$, we have discovered a ΔI problem due to an input change.

The cutting algorithm can be used to compute a bound on the probability of a ΔI problem with parameter k by computing the signal probability of the output F. This bound will tell how likely it is to have a ΔI problem in the original design.

Notice that this procedure, in fact, underestimates slightly the desired probability. In the computation model of Fig. 12, we have not excluded the possibility that the two input vectors to the two copies are identical. Thus, the cardinality of the input space is 4^n, rather than $4^n - 2^n$, where n is the number of inputs to the circuit. However, even for small values of n (≥ 5), the underestimation error is negligible.

A timing analysis program attempts to identify short paths and long paths of propagation in a logic design. Since the identification of these paths is based on delay equations, there is no guarantee that the paths marked off by the program as either short or long are at all functional (exercisable). Once a potentially long (or short) path is identified, it is possible to test whether it is functional by the cutting algorithm. As in the detection probability calculation method, it is possible to display the conditions necessary to activate the path by an auxiliary AND gate and compute the signal probability at its output. If the lower bound of this signal probability is nonzero, then the path is functional; otherwise, no conclusion can be drawn.

SUMMARY AND CONCLUSIONS

The problem of random pattern testability, in the context of self test, was discussed in this paper. The objective was to determine which faults, if any, manifest resistance to random pattern stimuli. We have shown how the cutting algorithm can be used to identify these hard faults in any design. Once these

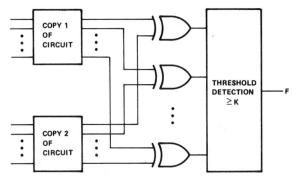

Fig. 12.   Detection of a ΔI problem in a logic design.

hard faults are identified it is possible to make them easy by paying some hardware penalty either in a ROM, or in a close proximity to the site of the hard fault. We have also discussed some heuristics that should make the cutting algorithm efficient and practical.

The question arises as to what the complexity is of this new approach. A careful study is currently being conducted and will be reported in [26]. A rough estimate can be given now. If N is the number of gates in the circuit, then in the worst case the complexities are:

Computing signal probabilities	with full ranges:	$O(N^2)$
	with restricted ranges:	$O(N^3)$
Computing detection probabilities	with full ranges:	$O(N^2)$
	with restricted ranges	$O(N^3)$.

These are worst-case mathematical bounds, and we expect the actuality to be much less.

REFERENCES

[1] O. H. Ibara and S. K. Sahni, "Polynomially complete fault detection problems," *IEEE Trans. Comput.*, vol. C-24, pp. 242–249, Mar. 1975.

[2] H. Fujiwara and S. Toida, "The complexity of fault detection: An approach to design for testability," in *Proc. 12th Annu. Fault-Tolerant Comput. Symp.*, June 1982, pp. 101–108.

[3] P. Goel, "Test generation costs analysis and projections," in *Proc. 17th Design Automat. Conf.*, June 1980, pp. 79–84.

[4] J. Savir, "Syndrome-testable design of combinational circuits," *IEEE Trans. Comput.*, vol. C-29, pp. 442–451, June 1980; and "Correction to 'Syndrome-testable design of combinational circuits,'" *IEEE Trans. Comput.*, vol. C-29, pp. 1012–1013, Nov. 1980.

[5] Z. Barzilai, J. Savir, G. Markowsky, and M. G. Smith, "The weighted syndrome sums approach to VLSI testing," *IEEE Trans. Comput.*, vol. C-30, pp. 996–1000, Dec. 1981.

[6] A. K. Susskind, "Testing by verifying Walsh coefficients," in *Proc. 11th Annu. Fault-Tolerant Comput. Symp.*, June 1981, pp. 206–208.

[7] J. C. Muzio and D. M. Miller, "Spectral techniques for fault detection," in *Proc. 12th Annu. Fault-Tolerant Comput. Symp.*, June 1982, pp. 297–302.

[8] E. J. McCluskey and Bozorgui-Nesbat, "Design for autonomous test," *IEEE Trans. Comput.*, vol. C-30, pp. 866–875, Nov. 1981.

[9] P. H. Bardell and W. H. McAnney, "Self-testing of multichip logic modules," in *Proc. 1982 Int. Test Conf.*, Nov. 1982, pp. 200–204.

[10] B. Konemann, J. Mucha, and G. Zwiehoff, "Built-in logic block observation techniques," in *Proc. 1979 Int. Test Conf.*, Oct. 1979, pp. 37–41.

[11] P. P. Fasang, "BIDCO, built-in digital circuit observer," in *Proc. 1980 Int. Test Conf.*, Nov. 1980, pp. 261–266.

[12] J. Mucha, "Hardware techniques for testing VLSI circuits based on built-in test," in *Proc. COMPCON 81*, Feb. 1981, pp. 366–369.

[13] E. B. Eichelberger and T. W. Williams, "A logic design structure for LSI testability," in *Proc. 14th Design Automat. Conf.*, June 1977, pp. 462–468.

[14] K. P. Parker and E. J. McCluskey, "Analysis of logic circuits with faults

using input signal probabilities," *IEEE Trans. Comput.*, vol. C-24, pp. 573-578, May 1975.

[15] ——, "Probabilistic treatment of general combinational networks," *IEEE Trans. Comput.*, vol. C-24, pp. 668-670, June 1975.

[16] I. Koren, "Analysis of the signal reliability measure and an evaluation procedure," *IEEE Trans. Comput.*, vol. C-28, pp. 244-249, Mar. 1979.

[17] K. K. Aggarwal, "Output probability expression for general combinational networks," *Microelectron. Reliab.*, vol. 17, pp. 601-602, 1978.

[18] P. Agrawal and V. D. Agrawal, "Probabilistic analysis of random test generation method for irredundant combinational logic networks," *IEEE Trans. Comput.*, vol. C-24, pp. 691-695, July 1975.

[19] M. A. Breuer and A. D. Friedman, *Diagnosis and Reliable Design of Digital Systems.* Silver Spring, MD: Computer Science Press, 1976.

[20] J. Savir, "Good controllability and observability do not guarantee good testability," IBM Res. Rep., RC 9432, June 1982.

[21] K. L. Meinert, "Designing for testability with GUEST," *Hewlett-Packard J.*, p. 28, Mar. 1982.

[22] E. B. Eichelberger and E. Lindbloom, "Random-pattern coverage enhancement and diagnosis for LSSD logic self-test," *IBM J. Res. Develop.*, vol. 27, pp. 265-272, May 1983.

[23] E. E. Davidson, "Electrical design of high-speed computer package," *IBM J. Res. Develop.*, vol. 26, pp. 349-361, May 1982.

[24] A. Brown and G. Ditlow, "Delta-I failure detection technique," *IBM Tech. Disclosure Bulletin*, to be published.

[25] G. Ditlow, J. Savir, and A. Brown, "Computing the probability of a Delta-I failure," *IBM Tech. Disclosure Bulletin*, to be published.

[26] T. H. Spencer, "Complexity analysis of the cutting algorithm," in preparation.

FTCS-12, and published numerous papers in the testing field. In the academic area he has taught numerous courses in mathematics, physics, statistics, electrical engineering, and computer science at the Technion—Israel Institute of Technology, in 1967 and from 1972-75, and at Ort Singalovsky, Tel-Aviv, from 1969-1974. Since 1979 he has been an Adjunct Professor at Pace University, New York, teaching undergraduate, and graduate courses, at the Department of Math and Sciences, and the Department of Computer and Information Systems. His research interests include test generation, self-test, design automation, design for testability, data compression for testing purposes, and related topics.

Dr. Savir is a member Sigma Xi.

Gary S. Ditlow (M'82) was born in Lancaster, PA on May 24, 1949. He received the B.S.E.E. degree in 1971 from the University of Maryland and the M.S. in computer science from Rensselaer Polytechnic Institute in 1973.

In 1973 he joined the IBM Poughkeepsie Laboratory where he developed algorithms in the areas of chip placement, package analysis, graphics, design verification, and binary trees for data base design. Later he moved to IBM Fishkill and designed bipolar chips and circuits in the VLSI exploratory circuits area. In 1982, he joined the staff of the IBM T. J. Watson Research Center where his current interests are random pattern testability, circuit analysis using waveform relaxation, and the creation of logic equations for VLSI FET circuits.

Mr. Ditlow is a member of Tau Beta Pi and Eta Kappa Nu.

Jacob Savir (S'76-M'78) received the B.Sc. (cum laude) and M.Sc. degrees in electrical engineering from the Technion—Israel Institute of Technology, Haifa, Israel, in 1968 and 1973, and the M.S. in statistics and Ph.D. in electrical engineering from Stanford University, Stanford, CA, in 1976 and 1977.

Since 1967 he has held several technical and teaching positions. In the technical area he served in the Israel Defense Forces from 1968-72; worked for Israel Ministry of Defense from 1974-75; worked with Prof. E. J. McCluskey, as a research assistant, and as a post doctoral fellow, on intermittent fault problems, and syndrome testing from 1975-78. He joined IBM in 1978 at the T. J. Watson Research Center, as a research staff member, to work on testing problems in VLSI. He is currently on sabbatical at the IBM Data Systems Division in Poughkeepsie, NY. He served on several conference committees, including FTCS-11, and

Paul H. Bardell (S'53-M'57-SM'71) received the B.S.E.E. from the University of Colorado, Boulder, CO, and the M.S.E.E. and Ph.D. from Stanford University, Stanford, CA.

Since joining IBM, he has worked in the areas of superconductors, semiconductor physics and integrated circuit design, especially semiconductor memory, and the test of complex circuit packages. He is currently Advanced Engineering in Manufacturing Manager for DSD, Poughkeepsie. His current interest is the testing of large digital networks.

Dr. Bardell is a member of the American Physical Society, the American Association for the Advancement of Science, the New York Academy of Science, and the Association for Computing Machinery.

ON TESTABILITY ANALYSIS OF COMBINATIONAL NETWORKS

Franc Brglez

Bell-Northern Research
P.O.Box 3511, Station C
Ottawa, Ontario, Canada

ABSTRACT

The complexity and density of digital circuits is straining the capacity of computers when solving two basic aspects of the testing problem: test pattern generation to verify correct operation of the device, and assessment of the test pattern effectiveness with regard to the coverage of the postulated faults. The application of emerging design for testability (DFT) techniques can reduce the testing problem to one of testing large combinational modules. Still, even with a huge number of on-chip generated random patterns, the question of fault coverage remains. This paper examines a testability algorithm that measures both the test pattern generation requirements as well as susceptibility to random pattern testing of large combinational networks.

INTRODUCTION

The techniques that are currently in use to manage the testing problem are outlined in the recent state-of-the-art survey by Williams and Parker [1]. The practice of DFT as we know it at present [1] requires that in test mode, a random sequential circuit be either controllable and observable for a module-specific test, or that all of its memory elements are both controllable and observable, via a scan or an alternate addressing technique. The logic partitioning of the latter approach converts the problem of testing a large random sequential circuit into two smaller problems: that of independently testing the memory elements, and the still difficult one of testing the function and the structure of imbedded combinational modules.

Analyses that would assess network topology for its testability, without the expense of either generating test patterns or grading test patterns via fault simulation (both increase exponentially with circuit complexity), have been an elusive goal of several publications. A recent report by Agrawal and Mercer [2] provides a framework to measure their effectiveness, concluding that more calibration is necessary for these measures to provide the desired impact. Recently, work in this direction has been published by Savir [3],[4]. Concurrently, our work on the subject is discussed in [5]. This contribution summarizes key ideas of the algorithm in [5], it outlines the implementation as a controllability/observability program named COP, and presents a set of results that characterize the performance and large-scale application of COP.

ON CARDINALS IN BINARY SETS

The central problem in test pattern generation is finding specific input patterns that test the digital network for all postulated structural faults. This is a difficult and computationally intensive problem for large combinational networks; no practical solution exists for random sequential networks unless they are restructured into combinational modules while in test mode [1]. The central idea in the proposed testability analysis algorithm is not to find input test patterns themselves, but to determine the existence and specifically, the number of patterns that would test all single stuck-at-1 or -0 faults in an arbitrary combinational network. Intuitively, this appears as a much simpler problem than that of test pattern generation.

The fundamental relationships in the proposed testability algorithm are centered around the evaluation of cardinals in a binary set. Assume an exhaustive n-bit wide binary set of patterns, e.g. generated by a counter, and let n represent the number of all primary inputs to the combinational network under consideration. Then

$$\#(U) = 2**n \qquad (1)$$

where $\#(U)$ designates the cardinal of the binary set on every input. Thus, when normalized to $\#(U)$, cardinals of the subsets of all 1's and all 0's on every primary input line equal to 0.5. As to the network interior, the cardinal of the set of all possible 1's and 0's on every line remains $\#(U)$. However, the cardinal of the subset of all possible 1's on every line depends on the logic operations that take place between the primary input and the line in question. As we are always considering binary sets that are exhaustive, the logic operations of AND, OR and NOT can be replaced with set operations of intersection, union and complement. Consequently, to initiate the proposed testability analysis, we merely enumerate the cardinality of the subsets of all 1's on every line. E.g. if X and Y are independent binary sets with cardinals specified by (1), then

$$\text{for } Z = X \cap Y, \qquad \#(z) = \#(x).\#(y)/\#(U) \qquad (2)$$

where $\#(z)$, $\#(x)$, $\#(y)$ denote the cardinals of all the subsets of 1's in Z, X, and Y; $\cap$ denotes set intersection, while ., / denote arithmetic multiplication and division.

Reprinted from *Proceedings of the International Symposium on Circuits and Systems*, 1984, pages 221-225. Copyright © 1984 by The Institute of Electrical and Electronics Engineers, Inc. All rights reserved.

Similar enumerative procedures apply to the complement and the union of <u>independent</u> binary sets [5]. At this point, the algebra and notation is similar and in principle equivalent to the notion of signal probability, introduced by Parker and McCluskey [6]; however we expect advantages with the proposed approach when enumerating sets that are not always independent.

THE THOUGHT EXPERIMENT

The purpose of this experiment is to clarify the notion of cardinals and to illustrate definitions required in testability analysis formalized in Section 4. Consider the network in Figure 1 and the associated exhaustive pattern evaluation. Straightforward count of 1's and 0's on every line produces the 1-co and 0-co row of numbers; the cardinals of input pattern sets that control the given line to either a 1 or a 0. Both cardinals add to 8, which is the cardinal of the universal input pattern set for this example with 3 primary inputs. As the topology of the network in Figure 1 is a tree, pattern sets (or Boolean signals) on every line are independent, and e.g., the cardinal on the line D can be predicted from cardinals on line A and B alone, using (2):

$$\#(d) = (4 \cdot 4)/8 = 2$$

However, for purpose of testability analysis, a normalized pair of cardinals is defined:

1-controllability of a line, say A, as

$$a = con(A) = \#(a)/\#(U) \qquad (3a)$$

0-controllability of the same line as

$$a' = 1 - a \qquad (3b)$$

where $\#(a)$ is cardinal of all subsets of 1's in A.

The next question to be answered by this experiment is similar: how many 1's and 0's can be observed on each line, one at a time, at the primary output during the exhaustive enumeration. We accomplish this by masking the pattern set in Figure 1 with * and ** in accordance with the topological constraints imposed by the network. For example, while primary output F is completely observable, line D is unobservable at F whenever E=1, and line A is unobservable at F whenever is unobservable, but also whenever B=0 etc. The count of unmasked, i.e. observable 1's and 0's, is listed in the rows 1-ob, 0-ob, and the totals in the row t-ob of Figure 1. The process of masking is equivalent to set intersection and, since the network is a tree, evaluation of cardinals according to (2) exactly supports results in Figure 1; e.g. the cardinal of all observable patterns at output F on line D:

$$\#(F/A) = \#(U).(\#(U) - \#(e))/\#(U) \quad (= 4) \qquad (4a)$$

Similarly, for observable patterns at F on line A:

$$\#(F/A) = \#(F/D).\#(b)/\#(U) \qquad (= 2) \qquad (4b)$$

The actual number of 1's observable at F on line A:

$$\#(F/a) = \#(a).\#(F/A)/\#(U) \qquad (= 1) \qquad (4c)$$

The calculus that follows uses similar notation for two types of related expressions. The notation we adopt is similar to one introduced in [6]: upper case variables and functions refer to Boolean expressions, lower case ones to controllability and observability expressions. Correspondingly, +, ., ', denote the logical AND, OR, NOT in Boolean expressions, while +, -, ., /, denote arithmetic addition, subtraction, multiplication and division in evaluation of controllability and observability measures.

The unmasked 1-0 entries in Figure 1 define a characteristic Boolean function for every line; we term it the "Boolean observability function" and denote it as (F/A), for line A observable at the output F. According to the exhaustive masking procedure described above (a sequential intersection of specific pattern sets), (F/A) itself is an AND function with Boolean inputs that assert the observability at F of line A along a particular sensitized path from F to A:

$$(F/D) = E', \text{ followed by } (F/A) = (F/D).B \qquad (5)$$

The observability function (F/A) is an OR of two functions, the set of all 1's and the set of all 0's on line A observable at output F:

$$(F/A) = A.(F/A) + A'.(F/A) \qquad (6)$$

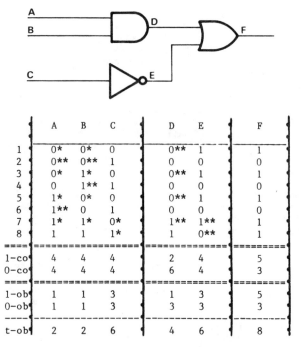

	A	B	C		D	E		F
1	0*	0*	0		0**	1		1
2	0**	0**	1		0	0		0
3	0*	1*	0		0**	1		1
4	0	1**	1		0	0		0
5	1*	0*	0		0**	1		1
6	1**	0	1		0	0		0
7	1*	1*	0*		1**	1**		1
8	1	1	1*		1	0**		1
1-co	4	4	4		2	4		5
0-co	4	4	4		6	4		3
1-ob	1	1	3		1	3		5
0-ob	1	1	3		3	3		3
t-ob	2	2	6		4	6		8

* unobservable since successor output unobservable
** unobservable due to adjacent input conditions

FIGURE 1. Simple logic network example illustrating key points of the thought experiment.

As with controllabilities in (3), observabilities for the purpose of testability analysis are defined in terms of normalized cardinals:

(total) observability of A at F

$$obs(F/A) = \#(F/A)/\#(U) \qquad (7)$$

Combining (2), (3), (6) and (7) defines the two components of the (total) observability:

1-observability of A at F

$$F/a = a.obs(F/A) \qquad (8a)$$

0-observability of A at F

$$F/a' = obs(F/A) - F/a \qquad (8b)$$

Given the above definitions, the following initial conditions apply universally:

for all primary inputs,
1-controllability = 0.5   (9a)

for all primary outputs,
1-observability = 1-controllability
0-observability = 0-controllability
observability   = 1.0   (9b)

Finally, we establish the relationship of controllability and observability to test pattern generation. The set of all patterns that detects at the output F that a line A is stuck-at-0 or stuck-at-1 is defined by the true values of the Boolean functions

$$A/0 = A.(dF/dA) \quad or \quad A/1 = A'.(dF/dA) \qquad (10)$$

where (dF/dA) is defined as the Boolean difference [7]. Whenever the status of the line can be propagated to output along a single sensitized path only (e.g. equations 5a, 5b), the Boolean functions (dF/dA) in (10) and (F/A) in (5) are readily seen as the same. We elaborate on the different approaches to their evaluations in a later paragraph. As to the Boolean functions in (10): the normalized cardinal of A/0 is identical to F/a in (8a); similarly for the normalized cardinal of A/1 versus F/a' in (8b). Thus, the 1-observability of A at F is a measure of how many patterns can detect a single stuck-at-0 fault of A at F, and vice versa for the 0-observability. Consequently, single stuck-at-1 or -0 testability of any line is characterized completely by the pair of 1-observability and 0-observability of the line; these in turn relate simply to the basic pair of 1-controllability and total observability via (8).

To conclude, a note on Boolean differences. Consider the evaluation of observability of a line A at the primary output F in an arbitrary network. By conventional definition [7], this function is evaluated by EXOR-ing the "black-box" outputs of two networks that are identical, except for the value on line A, and is designated as (dF/dA), the Boolean difference. In contrast, evaluation that is based on application of masking and the chain rule as expressed in (5) is correct only if the assert-

ing signals are independent of the signals that are being observed along the particular sensitized path. This may not be the case when a signal fans out and reconverges at or before the primary output. The enumerative process is similar to the one required e.g. in evaluating #(z) in (2) when X and Y are dependent and will thus not be addressed here. In the current proposal and implementation, the exhaustive masking procedure and the respective chain rule is applied to every sensitized path, assuming signal independence. Consequently, the set of all observable patterns at any fanout stem is the union of observable patterns established for each path to the particular stem. Denoting $(F/A)_i$ as the partial Boolean observability function on path i to the fanout stem A, the total Boolean observability function at the fanout stem A is thus an OR of all the partial ones:

$$(F/A) = (F/A)_1 + (F/A)_2 + ... + (F/A)_i + .. \quad (11)$$

Expression in (11) is exact if line signals at the fanout stem A are independent or if the signal dependence is taken into account in evaluating every $(F/A)_i$ as well as the OR function of (11).

PERSONALITY MATRIX AND TESTABILITY ALGORITHM

The notion of the personality matrix [5] is introduced to map the topological description of the logic network and to structure several aspects of computation. An example is shown in Figure 2. The line types are depicted on the main diagonal: primary input lines are marked as "PI", the fanout lines as "=" and the remainder symbolizes the gate function performed on the incident lines to the particular gate, e.g. "*-" represents a NAND gate. The only non-zero entries below the main diagonal are marked by "x" whenever a specific line is incident at the input of a particular gate. As it depends on the sorting algorithm, e.g. the levelizing technique suggested in [7], the personality matrix need not be unique but is always lower triangular. The arrangement shown in Figure 2 implies ordering that clusters every fanout stem with its fanout lines, thereby providing for very efficient sparse mode storage and addressing.

The personality matrix controls the flow of testability analysis; the same flow can be utilized for efficient logic evaluation. Controllabilities are evaluated within a single forward substitution, following initialization in accordance with (9a). Depending on the main diagonal entry in the personality matrix, the following rules for basic primitives apply [5], assuming signal independence:

AND : $c = a.b$ (12a)

NOT : $c = 1 - a$ (12b)

OR : $c = 1 - (1-a).(1-b)$ (12c)

where A, B are line inputs and C the line output.

Observabilities are evaluated within a single backward substitution, following initialization in accordance with (9b). Depending on the main diag-

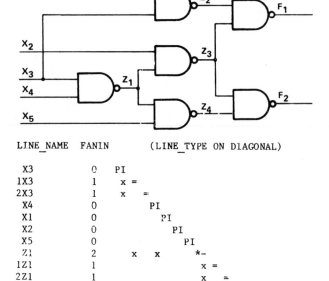

```
LINE_NAME   FANIN        (LINE_TYPE ON DIAGONAL)

X3          0     PI
1X3         1     x =
2X3         1     x      =
X4          0          PI
X1          0             PI
X2          0                PI
X5          0                   PI
Z1          2     x    x        *-
1Z1         1                       x  =
2Z1         1                       x    =
Z2          2     x    x             *-
Z3          2          x     x    x     *-
1Z3         1                             x  =
2Z3         1                             x    =
Z4          2          x     x             *-
F1          2                    x    x     *-
F2          2                           x  x  *-

LINE # ===>      1 2 3 4 5 6 7 8 910111213141516 17

FANOUT ===>      2 1 1 1 1 1 1 2 1 1 1 2 1 1 1 0 0
```

FIGURE 2. A typical logic network example and
the associated personality matrix.

onal entry in the personality matrix and the associated sensitized input(s), the following rules
apply, assuming signal independence:

AND : $obs(F/A) = b.obs(F/C)$ (13a)

OR : $obs(F/A) = (1-b).obs(F/C)$ (13b)

where F designates a primary output line, C the
line output of an interior gate, A and B the gate
input lines, and F/a and F/a' are evaluated according to (8). Sensitizing conditions at the input(s)
of OR and NOR gates are the same, similarly for AND
and NAND gates, while buffers and inverters do not
affect evaluation of observabilities. Observabilities at the fanout stems are evaluated in accordance with (11).

THE CASE OF RECONVERGENT FANOUT

Whenever a logic signal fans out to several destinations and later reconverges on two or more inputs
of a gate, signals at these inputs are no longer
independent, hence the simple algebra based on
cardinals in (2) produces results that can be more
or less in error. In our earlier unpublished work
we have combined the procedure of [6] with the

personality matrix and the proposed definitions to
determine the exact solution for networks with
arbitrary topology; however, for large networks an
alternative approach appears necessary. In an
interesting recent proposal [3], every fanout line
is cut and initialized to a controllability interval rather than a single value; in the worst case
the full [0,1] range may be assigned. The resulting
uncertainties are allowed to propagate and ultimately the lower bound of 1- and 0-observabilities
is retained. We find it instructive to compare our
results, exact and as obtained simply via (12) and
(13), with the ones disclosed in [3].

Consider the network Figure 3. This is a
well-known textbook example [7], since it requires
double path sensitization to detect F/0. Applying
exact testability analysis establishes that 1 out
of 16 patterns detects F/0, and 2 out of 16
patterns detect F/1. Performing the testability
analysis according to (11), (12) and (13) we find
that obs(M/F)=3.3/16 while M/f=0.8/16 and
M/f'=2.5/16, an acceptable approximation to exact
results in this case. Note that obs(M/F) has been
evaluated from partial obs(M/F) , along each path
separately, and then combining results in accordance with (11), (12c).

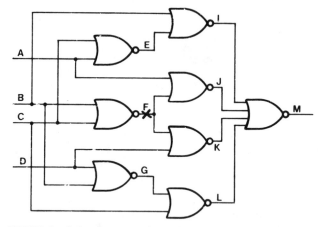

FIGURE 3. A logic network with reconvergent fanout.

Unnormalized 1-obs	0-obs at output F1		Proposed evaluation		Exact evaluation		Lwr bound from [3]	
1) F1/x3	F1/x3'		5	5	6	4	2	2
2) F1/x3	F1/x3'		3	3	2	4	2	2
** F1/x3	F1/x3'		7.1	7.1	8	8	not appl.	

** via multiple path sensitization

FIGURE 4. Comparative evaluations of the network
example in Figure 2.

The next example, based on the network in [3] and
shown in Figure 2, has 4 reconverging paths. We are
comparing lower bounds on detection probabilities
in [3] with the equivalents (according to our definitions) of 1- and 0-observabilities, as evaluated

with the algorithm proposed here. A small sample of the results is shown in Figure 4; an extended table an discussion is presented in [5].

The interesting questions to be resolved next are: how accurately would the proposed algorithm work for typical large networks, and how conservative are the conservative estimates when the algorithm in [3] is applied to the same networks. The first question is briefly addressed below.

APPLICATION AND PERFORMANCE OF COP

The present version of the controllability/observability program COP implements the algorithm as outlined by equations (8-13). Its CPU performance has been benchmarked by executing a set examples that combine 4-bit ALU and LAC macros from a TTL library into combinational modules of increasing complexity, from 4-bit ALU to 64-bit ALU. Not surprisingly, CPU requirements to evaluate controllability/observability of each and every line increase only linearly with increase in circuit complexity, as depicted in Figure 5.

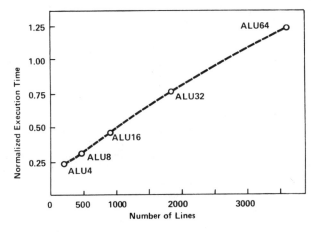

FIGURE 5. Performance evaluation of COP, the controllability/observability program.

Next, a single 4-bit ALU is assessed for random pattern testability in greater detail. Our version of ALU has 206 lines connecting 77 gates and 31 fanout stems, with an average fanin of 2.16 per gate and an average fanout of 3.71 per fanout stem. Significant signal reconvergence can be expected as there are 14 primary inputs and only 8 primary outputs. The testability analysis identified a line with a minimum 0-observability of 0.01718 and a total of 19 lines with 0-, 1-observabilities in the range between minimum and twice the minimum. Assuming for a moment that these values are exact, 0-observability of 0.01718 would imply that there are $0.01718*2^{14} = 281$ patterns from the exhaustive set of 2^{14} that would all detect the stuck-at-1 fault on the particular line. According to statistical arguments proposed by Savir [4], we find that $\ln(1. - 0.999)/(-0.01718) = 402$ random patterns are required in order to detect this "hardest fault" with probability of 0.999.

It is instructive to relate these results to the ones obtained with actual fault simulation of the 4-bit ALU using random patterns. In order to correlate well with the proposed testability analysis, 1-controllability of random patterns on every primary input is expected in the range between 0.45 to 0.55. Executing fault simulation with 100 patterns, and depending on the seeded value of the first random pattern, we find that there are 5 to 9 faults persistently undetected. The undetected fault set is not always the same, but it remains a subset of the 19 "hardest faults" identified above. With 200 patterns, depending on the seed, 1 or 2 faults persist as undetected. However, no faults are left undetected when the number of random patterns increases to 400, irrespective of the seed.

Similar correlations between testability analysis and random pattern fault simulation were obtained for other typical circuits. In contrast with fault simulation, the cost of testability analysis is fixed by the network size. For a 64-bit ALU, testability analysis is 100 times faster than fault simulation, the latter executing only 100 patterns. Such trade-offs and the complexity of VLSI provide strong motivation that the calibration of testability analysis be enhanced and its role expanded.

ACKNOWLEDGEMENT

The discussions with Ray Mercer during ITC'83 provided me with new insights as to the applicability of (11) and broadened my views on testability issues. The encouragement and support by Robert Hum throughout this work made my persistence with the subject worthwhile.

REFERENCES

[1] T.W. Williams, K.P. Parker,"Design for testability - A survey", Proc. IEEE, vol. 71, pp. 98-112, January 1983

[2] V.D. Agrawal, M.R. Mercer, "Testability measures - what do they tell us?", IEEE Proc. 1982 Int. Test Conf., pp. 391-396, Nov. 15-18, 1982

[3] J. Savir et al, "Random pattern testability", Proc. 13th Intl. Fault Tolerant Comp. Symp., pp. 80-89, June 28-30, 1983

[4] J. Savir, P.H. Bardell, "On random pattern test length", Proc. 1983 Intl. Test Conference, pp. 95-106, Oct. 18-20, 1983

[5] F. Brglez, "Testability in VLSI", Proc. 1983 Canadian Conference on VLSI, Univ. of Waterloo, pp. 90-95, Oct. 24-25, 1983

[6] K.P. Parker, E.J. McCluskey, "Probabilistic treatment of general combinational circuits", IEEE Trans. Comp, C-24, pp. 668-670, June 1975

[7] M.A. Breuer, A.D. Friedman, Diagnosis and Reliable Design of Digital Systems, Computer Science Press, 1976

PREDICT — PROBABILISTIC ESTIMATION OF DIGITAL CIRCUIT TESTABILITY

Sharad C. Seth
Lilu Pan
Department of Computer Science
University of Nebraska, Lincoln, NE 68588

Vishwani D. Agrawal
AT&T Bell Laboratories
Murray Hill, NJ 07974

ABSTRACT—This paper presents a technique of Probabilistic Estimation of Digital Circuit Testability (PREDICT). Node controllabilities and observabilities are defined in terms of signal probabilities. A graph approach is used to compute these probabilities exactly using Shannon's expansion. A proposed approximation of this procedure keeps the computational complexity within reasonable bounds while providing a tradeoff between accuracy and computational cost in terms of the value of an easily interpreted parameter. Experimental results are given to demonstrate the effectiveness of PREDICT.

1. INTRODUCTION

Testability analysis is based on circuit topology. It determines parameters like controllability and observability for circuit nodes. This information can be useful in making the circuit design easily testable. The only other method employed for assessing circuit testability is *fault simulation* which evaluates the effectiveness of given test vectors in testing circuit nodes. Since testability analysis does not depend upon a specific set of test vectors, it can be more economical and its results, more widely applicable.

Earliest efforts in testability analysis [1] provided the model for much subsequent work (e.g., see [2]) aimed at producing an analysis with a complexity linear in circuit size. The accuracy of these efforts, however, was far from satisfactory [3]. More recent work in this area has attempted to bring testability analysis closer to fault simulation. Applications to test vector generation [4] and fault coverage analysis [5] are being explored. In spite of this encouraging progress in testability analysis, a panel discussion [6] at a recent conference appeared to favor fault simulation over testability analysis, primarily on account of accuracy.

In this paper we present a technique of Probabilistic Estimation of Digital Circuit Testability (PREDICT). Like some recent papers, (see [5] and [7]), we define node controllabilities as signal probabilities. A graph approach is used to compute these probabilities exactly using Shannon's expansion [8]. The proposed approximations of this procedure keep the computational complexity within reasonable bounds while providing a tradeoff between accuracy and computational cost in terms of the value of an easily interpreted parameter. Experimental results are given to demonstrate the effectiveness of PREDICT. Results from other experiments, currently in progress, are reported elsewhere [9].

2. SUPERGATE DEFINITION

In this section we define the concept of a supergate of a node in terms of a graph model for a combinational circuit. Briefly, a supergate associated with a node is the minimal circuit substructure necessary to compute that node's controllability. The concept is crucial to both the exact and the approximate methods of computation proposed in this paper.

Let us consider a graph representation derived from the circuit in an obvious way: primary inputs, primary outputs, and gates each have a distinct representative node in the graph; the connections ("wires") are represented by edges oriented in the direction of information flow. The following definitions paraphrase for the graph model some well understood terms for a logic circuit. The graph terms used below can be found in any standard text on graph theory, e.g., [10].

A node with an outdegree greater than one is a *fanout stem* whose outgoing edges are called its *fanout branches*. The (boolean) *function of an edge* is the function on its associated line in the circuit. The *function of a node* is the same as the function on an outgoing edge from the node. Two distinct (directed) paths are *reconvergent* if they start at a common node (say A) and terminate at another common node (say B). These paths are said to *fanout* at A and *reconverge* at B. Node B is also called a *reconvergent node*. The *cone of influence* of a node X is a subgraph of the circuit graph that includes the edges and nodes on all the paths that start at a primary input and terminate at X.

The *supergate* of a node X, denoted as SG(X), is a subgraph of the circuit graph defined as follows:

(1) If X is not reconvergent then SG(X) consists of node X and all its incoming edges.

(2) If X is reconvergent then consider each path from a primary input to X. Let this path be denoted by P and have the form $(Y = X_1, X_2, \ldots, X_n = X)$, where Y is a primary input and n is greater than 1. Consider two mutually disjoint cases.

Case A (P includes as a suffix a path reconvergent at X): Include the edges and nodes on the longest such suffix in SG(X). Also include inputs of all the nodes on the path P in SG(X).

Case B (otherwise): Include the edge (X_{n-1}, X_n) in SG(X).

The *input nodes of a supergate* SG(X), denoted as I(X), are the nodes in the subgraph whose indegree is zero. The input nodes can be further partitioned into two classes: 1) fanout inputs IF(X), namely those that either themselves fanout or are included in the cone of influence of an internal fanout stem in

EH0278-2/88/0000/0298$01.00 © 1985 IEEE

SG(X), and 2) all remaining inputs of SG(X). The *output* of a supergate SG(X) is the output of node X.

Example 1: Fig. 1(a) shows a logic network used as an example in [7]. Its graph representation appears in Fig. 1(b). This graph has only non-trivial supergates corresponding to the reconvergent nodes 12 and 13. The supergate SG(12) is shown in Fig. 1(c). It contains 8 nodes of which I = {1, 2, 5, 7} defines the input set. The latter can be further partitioned into the fanout set IF = {7} and the non-fanout set INF = {1, 2, 5}. The supergate SG(13) is shown in Fig. 1(d).

Lemma 1: If Y is an interior node in SG(X), that is, Y ≠ X and Y is not in I(X) then SG(Y) is a proper subgraph of SG(X).

For example, in Fig. 1(d), SG(12) is a subgraph of SG(13). The topological relationship between the supergates of a circuit is an interesting question in its own right but will not be further explored in this paper.

3. EXACT COMPUTATION OF NODE CONTROLLABILITIES

The *1-controllability* of an edge in the circuit graph is defined as the fraction of 1's in the truth table of its function. Its *0-controllability* is defined as one minus its 1-controllability.

The 1-controllability (0-controllability) of an edge represents the probability of a 1 (0) at the line represented by the edge, when an input vector is randomly selected and applied to the circuit. Since the controllabilities of all the fanout branches issuing from a common stem node must be equal, it is possible to define node controllabilities in an unambiguous way where the node is assumed to inherit the controllability values associated with an edge directed away from it. The only exceptional case is a primary output node with no outgoing edges; it will be assumed to inherit the controllabilities from its (unique) incoming edge. We will denote the zero- and one-controllabilities of a node A by C0(A) and C1(A), respectively.

As shown in [7], for any node whose cone of influence contains no reconvergent fanout, the controllability calculation is a straight-forward one-pass process involving only the nodes in the cone of influence. Thus we will only consider calculation of controllability for a reconvergent node X. Let IF(X) = {y_1, y_2, ..., y_n}, where n is greater than 0. We will make the inductive assumption that the controllabilities of all the inputs of SG(X) are known. Consider an assignment of binary values to the fanout inputs, represented by the vector A = (a_1, a_2, ..., a_n). For each such assignment we make a single pass through the nodes of SG(X) from inputs to outputs. First, the controllabilities of the non-fanout input nodes are known by the inductive assumption; for a fanout node y_i we assume its a_i-controllability to be 1. Next, for the nodes connected only to the primary inputs we compute node controllabilities using independence of signals at the node inputs (the formulae for this computation are straight-forward and given in [7] for various kinds of gates.) Proceeding in this manner, we will eventually compute the 1-controllability of X. This is the conditional controllability of X when the assignment A is made to the fanout inputs. We will denote this by C1(X|A).

Lemma 2: The one-controllability of a node X is

$$C1(X) = \sum_{\text{all A}} C1(X|A)\,\text{Prob}(A)$$

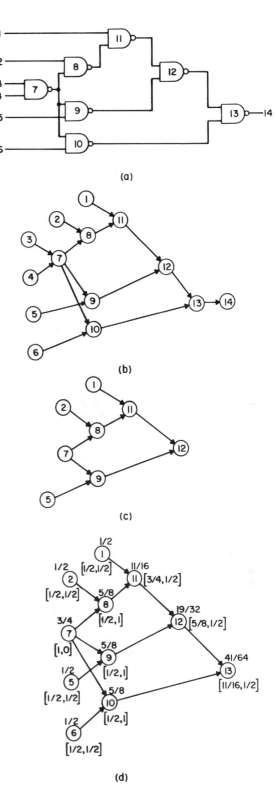

Fig. 1 (Examples 1 and 2). Graph model and supergates. (a) Circuit, (b) Graph model, (c) Supergate SG(12) with input sets IF = {7} and INF = {1, 2, 5}, and (d) Supergate SG(13) with input sets IF = {7} and INF = {1, 2, 5, 6}. The values within square brackets are the conditional controllabilities and the values above the nodes are the exact controllabilities obtained from Lemma 2.

where,

$$\mathrm{Prob}(A) = \mathrm{Prob}(y_1 = a_1)\,\mathrm{Prob}(y_2 = a_2)...\mathrm{Prob}(y_n = a_n)\,,$$

is the product of the known a_i-controllabilities of the fanout inputs assuming independence among y's that would follow from the definition of SG(X). An example illustrating the use of this result appears after our discussion of a computational procedure based on this lemma.

A Computational Procedure

The computational procedure to be discussed essentially requires three major steps: 1) identification of reconvergent nodes, 2) determination of a supergate for each node (this is non-trivial only for reconvergent nodes), and 3) calculation of controllabilities at the supergate outputs. The first two steps become considerably simpler if, in a preprocessing step, each node in the circuit graph is "labeled" by the list of primary inputs occurring in its cone of influence. This can be done in time linearly proportional to the product of circuit size and the number of primary inputs.

For a circuit graph with nodes labeled as above, it is easy to identify reconvergent nodes. To determine if a node X is reconvergent we simply need to check the labels of nodes in pred(X) where, pred(X) consists of all nodes Y such that (Y, X) is an edge in the graph. X is *not* reconvergent if and only if the labels in pred(X) are mutually disjoint.

Identification of supergates from the labeled graph is slightly more involved; it requires a backward sweep of the nodes in the cone of influence of the node X whose supergate is to be identified. The basic idea is to continue to examine a new "frontier" of nodes in the cone of influence and stop as soon as the labels attached to the frontier nodes become disjoint. The time complexity of this algorithm is linear in the size of the supergate being determined.

Finally, the computation of controllabilities of all the nodes in the cone of influence of a node X can be done by a single call to a recursive procedure as suggested by Lemma 1 and the inductive assumption stated before Lemma 2. This is potentially the most expensive computational step since its time complexity, for a supergate, is exponential in the number of fanout inputs to the supergate. As an extreme example, Table 1 provides summary data for running a controllability procedure on the 4-bit ALU (74181) [11]:

Table 1
Supergate data (4-bit ALU)

Supergate Number	Supergate Size	Number of Fanout Inputs
1	68 nodes	14
2	51 nodes	13
3	26 nodes	10

We found that the 4-bit ALU is unusual in its "richness" of fanout structure (see Table 4), thus the data above may be too pessimistic, specially for random logic circuits. However, the example does point out the fact that exact controllability analysis, in general, could be quite expensive.

Example 2: The graph for the circuit in Fig. 1(a) is shown with nodes labelled in Fig. 3(a). Since only the predecessors of nodes 12 and 13 do not have mutually disjoint labels these are the only two nodes of reconvergence. We will consider the computation of one-controllability for the supergate SG(13) shown in

Fig. 1(d). Since node 7 is the only fanout input to this supergate we must consider the conditional controllabilities for the two cases when one and zero are alternately assigned to node 7. Let these two assignments be represented by $A1$ and $A0$ respectively. For each node X in Fig. 1(d) the values $C1(X|A_1)$ and $C1(X|A_0)$ are shown within square parentheses. From these, the exact 1-controllability of each node can be determined by using Lemma 2; we assume that the controllabilities of all the inputs of SG(13) are already determined (inductive assumption) as shown. Thus

$$C1(13) = (3/4)(11/16) + (1/4)(1/2) = 41/64\,.$$

The exact controllability of all the other nodes in SG(13) can be determined in a similar manner and are shown above the nodes in the figure.

4. APPROXIMATE COMPUTATION OF NODE CONTROLLABILITIES

In the worst case the supergate for a node may include all the primary inputs as fanout inputs, e.g., the first supergate for the 4-bit ALU mentioned in the last section. In such cases, the exact controllability procedure outlined above becomes equivalent to an exhaustive true-value simulation of the supergate, that is, the computational time is exponential in the number of primary inputs and linear in the size of the supergate. In this section we will discuss three different ways of reducing the time complexity to manageable proportions while sacrificing some accuracy in the computed results. The first two involve heuristics and the third involves sampling.

Both the heuristics are based on the idea that under certain circumstances correlated signals at node outputs may be treated as being independent without incurring severe loss of accuracy. However, the criteria on which this decision is based are related to different measures of independence of node signals. In both cases, a higher value of this measure will indicate greater independence of the signals involved. A threshold value for the measure will then be used to make a binary decision about whether to treat the signals as independent. The motivation is to establish the threshold value as the basis for a tradeoff between accuracy and computational cost with a higher threshold value generally providing greater accuracy but at a greater cost.

Heuristic 1

For a node Y in a supergate SG(X) we define the distance of Y from X as the shortest distance (measured in terms of number of edges in a path) from Y to X; single input nodes (inverters or non-inverting buffers) will be ignored in computing the shortest distance. The justification for this heuristic is that the farther a node Y is away from X, the more other signals it will "mix with" before arriving at X and thereby the less will be its effect on X.

If an integer T is used as the threshold value for this heuristic, we would trace back all paths upto length T from a reconvergent node and assume the signals at the nodes so arrived at as being independent. The supergate computation is restricted to the resultant subgraph. Intuitively, we will be considering the effect on the controllability of X of all reconvergent fanouts within a distance T from X but ignore others which are more "global" in scope. At one extreme, when the threshold is one, we will be assuming each node to carry independent signal, as is done in Goldstein's analysis [1]. At the other extreme, when the threshold value exceeds the maximum depth of a supergate, all controllability calculations will be exact.

Example 3: Consider again the circuit shown in Fig. 1(a). Fig. 2(a) shows the supergates SG(12) and SG(13) determined for this circuit when the threshold value is either 1 or 2. For either threshold value the reconvergence of node 7 at 12 or 13 is ignored so the supergate in each case includes just the node and all its inputs. The resulting 1-controllability of each node is as shown. However, when the threshold is increased to 3 (Fig. 2(b)) the reconvergence is picked up for node 12 but only partially so for node 13. The controllability values for node 12 will therefore be computed exactly and for node 13 approximately. Finally, for the threshold value of 4 all computations become exact. Fig. 2(c) summarizes these results for nodes 12 and 13 and shows the error in controllability values in each case.

Heuristic 2

In this heuristic we define a distance between a pair of nodes in a supergate in terms of their labels. Let L(V) and L(W) be the labels assigned to nodes V and W (recall that the label of a node corresponds to the set of primary inputs in its cone of influence). The distance between V and W is defined as [12]:

$$d(V, W) = \frac{|L(V) \, \Delta \, L(W)|}{|L(V) \cap L(W)|}$$

where $|x|$ is the cardinality of a set x, $x \, \Delta \, y$ is the symmetric difference of sets x and y, and $x \cap y$ is the intersection of sets x and y. Intuitively, the distance measure can be understood as follows. In the extreme case, when the cones of influences of V and W have no primary inputs in common, the signals V and W are indeed statistically independent. This is properly indicated by an infinite value of the measure. Next assume that the two cones of influence have one or more common primary inputs. In this case, the greater the overlap the larger is the denominator and smaller the value of the measure, again correctly reflecting greater dependence between the two signals. For a given overlap, however, the larger the number of primary inputs that influence V or W (but not both) the less will be the correlation between the two due to common inputs. This justifies the symmetric difference in the numerator.

Example 4: The circuit of Fig. 1(a) will again be considered. Fig. 3(a) shows, within braces, the label set associated with each node in the circuit graph. In order to determine the supergate for node 12 we begin by computing the distance between its predecessor nodes 9 and 11. This is found to be 1.5 so we will stop here if the threshold was 1 (Fig. 3(b)). Otherwise, we determine a new "frontier" by considering predecessors of one of the current frontier nodes, say, node 9. Then the new frontier consists of nodes 5, 7, and 11. Node 5 is at an infinite distance from both 7 and 11. So we need consider only the distance between 7 and 11. This is 1 so a new frontier must be computed by going back from either 7 or 11. Notice that depending on the order in which the choice is made at each step, it is possible to obtain different subgraphs and hence different supergates for the same node. We show in Fig. 3(c) one of the two possible subgraphs for node 12 which leads to exact computation of controllability for this node (the other subgraph does not pick up the reconvergent fanout so the result will be the same as for threshold = 1). The corresponding subgraphs for node 13 are also shown in Figs. 3(b) and 3(c). When the threshold is 3, the computation becomes exact in both cases. The summary of these results is given in the table in Fig. 3(d).

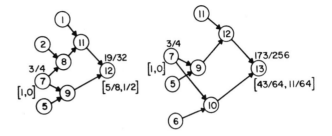

(a)

(b)

Threshold	Controllability		Error	
	C1(12)	C1(13)	C1(12)	C1(13)
1	73/128	659/1024	−3/128	3/1024
2	73/128	659/1024	−3/128	3/1024
3	19/32	173/256	0	9/256
4	19/32	41/64	0	0

(c)

Fig. 2 (Example 3). Supergates for the nodes 12 and 13 with restricted depth threshold (Heuristic 1). (a) Threshold = 1 or 2, (b) Threshold = 3, and (c) Computed controllabilities.

It is worth noting that while progressively more and more nodes assume their exact controllability values as the threshold is increased, the convergence to the exact value for an individual node is not monotonic in either heuristic (see, for example, the increase in error magnitude for C1(13) in Figs. 2(c) and 3(d)). The experimental results, reported in Section 6, however, show that the root-mean-square error for the whole circuit does converge monotonically to zero.

A Sampling Technique

Our third alternative to exact computation involves sampling of the space defined by fanout inputs to a supergate. As before, we assume that the input controllabilities are known beforehand so it is possible to generate a sample of fanout inputs where each bit is randomly selected to be one with its known 1-controllability. Only a small sample of assignments indicated in Lemma 2 is tried. The weighted sum in the lemma must, however, be normalized by dividing the sample probability into the result. Sampling may be restricted only to cases where the number of fanout inputs of a supergate exceeds a certain threshold value. Results of sampling for the ALU circuit are discussed in Section 6.

5. COMPUTATION OF OBSERVABILITIES

We will follow the definition of observabilities given in [13], reproduced here for completeness:

The *1-observability (0-observability)* of an edge representing line ℓ in the circuit is the conditional probability of sensitizing a

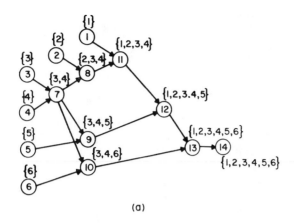

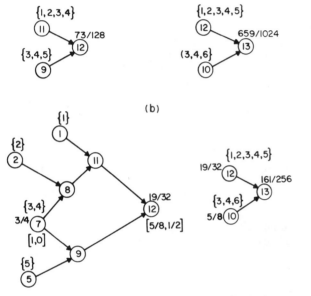

Threshold	Controllability		Error	
	C1(12)	C1(13)	C1(12)	C1(13)
1	73/128	659/1024	−3/128	3/1024
2	19/32	161/256	0	−3/256
3	19/32	41/64	0	0

(d)

Fig. 3 (Example 4). Supergates for nodes 12 and 13 determined by Heuristic 2. (a) Circuit graph with node labels, (b) Supergates with Threshold = 1, (c) Supergates with Threshold = 2, and (d) Computed controllabilities.

path from line ℓ to a primary output, given that the value of line ℓ is 1 (0). By definition, the 1- and 0-observabilities of a primary output are 1. We will denote the 1- and 0-observabilities of edge "e" as B1(e) and B0(e), respectively.

Unlike controllabilities, the observabilities of fanout branches with a common stem are not always equal. Thus there is no direct way of associating fanout stem observabilities with

observabilities of fanout branches. For a node which is not a fanout stem we can still assume that it inherits the observability values from its (unique) outgoing edge. For a fanout stem the node observability will be derived by an approximation discussed below.

The observability calculations proceed from primary outputs to primary inputs in a recursive fashion as detailed in [13]. We will consider two representative cases. In the first case we compute the observability of an edge (say ℓ) connected as an input to a node G representing a logic gate (say AND). Let $i, j,$ and k be the other edges connected as inputs to G. We assume that the observabilities of G are known, as are the controllabilities of all the nodes in the circuit graph. Then the observabilities of edge ℓ are given by the following expressions:

$$B1(\ell) = B1(G)C1(G)/C1(\ell) \text{ and}$$

$$B0(\ell) = B0(G)[S(\ell) - C1(G)]/C0(\ell)$$

where, $S(\ell)$ represents the sensitization probability of ℓ given by Prob$\{i = 1, j = 1, k = 1\}$. Similar expressions for other gate types can be found in [13].

In the second representative case to be considered, we compute the observabilities of a fanout stem. In this case we assume that the observabilities of all the fanout branches issuing from this stem are already known. In general, the relationship between the observabilities of the stem and its branches is quite complex if the fanout is reconvergent since one must consider the possibility of correlated sensitizations through different paths to the reconvergent node. However, empirical evidence [13] suggests that the maximum observability of a branch used as the observability of the stem is quite accurate hence we will use this approximation.

It follows from the above discussion that once all the controllabilities are known, the observability calculations depend only on the knowledge of line sensitization probabilities. In Stafan [13] this is achieved by maintaining counters for each line during a true-value simulation of the circuit. Here, we propose an analytical approach, based on an extension of the controllability computation described earlier.

Consider the computation of node controllabilities for a given assignment A to the fanout inputs of a supergate SG(X) (refer to the discussion preceding Lemma 2). Let a node G in SG(X) represent an AND gate with four input edges: $i = (I, G)$, $j = (J, G)$, $k = (K, G)$, and $\ell = (L, G)$. We define $S(\ell|A)$ as the conditional sensitization of line ℓ when the fanout inputs of the supergate are assigned the values in A. For the AND gate G, $S(\ell|A) = C1(I|A)C1(J|A)C1(K|A)$ (similar expressions for conditional line sensitization are easily derived for other gate types). Then the following lemma (which parallels Lemma 2) can be proved:

Lemma 3: The line sensitization

$$S(\ell) = \sum_{\text{all A}} S(\ell|A)\text{Prob}(A)$$

where Prob(A) is as defined in Lemma 2.

This lemma and the approximation discussed above for fanout stems form the basis for our observability calculations. Notice that both exact and approximate methods discussed in the previous sections can be extended for observability calculations, thus the same tradeoff between speed and accuracy are available.

6. EXPERIMENTAL RESULTS

In order to validate the computational approach proposed in this paper, a Pascal implementation of PREDICT on VAX/11-780 was instrumented to run several experiments. In one experiment exact controllability values were compared against those obtained using a heuristic based on the label of a node. The results are summarized in Table 2 which shows the root-mean-square error, maximum error, and standard deviation (taken over all the nodes in the circuit graph) for increasing values of the threshold until computations become exact.

Table 2
Computational Error vs. Threshold for Label Heuristic (4-bit ALU)

Threshold:	1	2	3	4	5	6	7	8	9
r.m.s. error	0.047	0.047	0.044	0.042	0.042	0.028	0.028	0.028	0
max. error	0.172	0.172	0.133	0.125	0.125	0.141	0.141	0.141	0
std. dev.	0.041	0.041	0.039	0.038	0.038	0.027	0.027	0.027	0

While the maximum error fluctuates, we notice that both the root-mean square error and the standard deviation decrease monotonically with increasing threshold values.

In another experiment the sampling technique was used to compute the controllability values. The effect of sample size on the accuracy of computation can be seen in Table 3.

Table 3
Computational Error vs. Sample Size in Sampling Heuristic (4-bit ALU)

Sample Size:	10	50	100	1000	Exact
r.m.s. error	0.103	0.052	0.046	0.011	0
max. error	0.300	0.140	0.145	0.036	0
std. dev.	0.073	0.035	0.030	0.007	0

We note that a sample of as small as 50 patterns on the fanout inputs can provide quite accurate results.

In the last experiment a program implementing the distance heuristic was modified to observe the effect of the distance threshold on computational error, number, average depth, and average size of supergate, and computational time. The results for an 880-line circuit, C880 in [14], appear in Table 4. The much smaller average size of a supergate compared to the 4-bit ALU (Table 1) is worth noting, as also the shallowness of supergates represented by relatively small average depth. The average error settles down to a stable value after a distance threshold of 3. On the other hand, the computation cost rises exponentially with the distance threshold.

Table 4
Distance Heuristic (Circuit C880)

| Threshold Distance | Supergates | | | Controllability | | |
	Number of Supergates	Average Depth	Average no. of nodes	Average error	Max. error	Computation time (Normalized)
1	383	1.00	2.90	0.03	0.47	1.00
2	264	1.26	3.64	0.06	0.65	2.50
3	163	1.32	5.51	0.02	0.29	7.38
4	141	1.45	6.88	0.02	0.29	23.47
5	134	1.63	8.19	0.02	0.17	45.67
6	127	1.63	8.99	0.02	0.25	78.54

7. CONCLUSION

We have proposed a new method of determining the random-pattern testability of a combinational circuit. A distinct feature of our approach is that both the exact and approximate analyses are possible within a common framework, with time complexities ranging from the exponential to the linear in circuit size. Experimental results show that reasonable accuracy may be achievable even by linear algorithms.

We have used Stafan's formulation [13] of line observability but, unlike Stafan, our approach does not require simulation of any kind. It appears that using supergate as a basis, it is possible to carry out more accurate observability analysis than Stafan. We are currently exploring this further. Extensions of the reported results to sequential circuits are also being considered.

Acknowledgment — Authors thank M. Abramovici for useful comments on the manuscript.

REFERENCES

[1] L. H. Goldstein, "Controllability/observability analysis of digital circuits," *IEEE Trans. Circuits and Systems,* vol. CAS-26, No. 9, Sept. 1979, pp. 685-693.

[2] R. G. Bennetts, *Design of Testable Logic Circuits*, Reading, MA: Addison-Wesley, 1984.

[3] V. D. Agrawal and M. R. Mercer, "Testability measures — What do they tell us?" Int. Test Conf., Philadelphia, PA, Nov. 16-18, 1982, *Digest of Papers,* pp. 391-396.

[4] A. C. Hung and F. C. Wang, "Test generation directly from testability analysis," to be published.

[5] F. Brglez, P. Pownall, and R. Hum, "Applications of testability analysis: From ATPG to critical delay path tracing," *Proceedings of Int. Test Conf.,* Philadelphia, PA, Oct. 16-18, 1984, pp. 705-712.

[6] "Will testability analysis replace fault simulation?" Panel discussion, *Proceedings of Int. Test Conf.,* Philadelphia, PA, Oct. 16-18, 1984, pp. 718-728.

[7] J. Savir, G. S. Ditlow, and P. H. Bardell, "Random pattern testability," *IEEE Trans. Computers,* Vol. C-33, Jan. 1984, pp. 79-90.

[8] Z. Kohavi, *Switching and Finite Automata Theory,* Second Edition, New York: McGraw-Hill, 1978, p. 53.

[9] V. D. Agrawal, S. C. Seth, and C. C. Chuang, "Probabilistically Guided Test Generation," *Int. Symp. on Circuits and Systems,* Kyoto, Japan, June 5-7, 1985.

[10] F. Harary, *Graph Theory*, Reading, MA: Addison-Wesley, 1969.

[11] Eng. Staff of Texas Instruments, Inc., Semiconductor Group, *The TTL Data Book for Engineers,* 2nd. ed., Texas Instruments, Inc. 1981.

[12] S. MacLane and G. Birkhoff, *Algebra,* New York: Macmillan, (3rd printing) 1968, p. 19.

[13] S. K. Jain and V. D. Agrawal, "Statistical Fault Analysis," *IEEE Design and Test,* Vol. 2, pp. 38-44, February 1985.

[14] F. Brglez, P. Pownall, and R. Hum, "Accelerated ATPG and Fault Grading Via Testability Analysis," Int. Symp. on Circuits and Systems, Kyoto, Japan, June 5-7, 1985.

Chapter VI: Design for Testability

Design for testability (DFT) affects test generation only in an indirect way. However, we believe with the growing use of DFT techniques some knowledge and understanding of the basic DFT concepts and terminology has become essential to the test engineer. Several good survey articles and recent books have appeared on this topic. The discussion here is intended to provide the reader with a very quick introduction to the field.

In Chapter V, we defined testability and discussed methods of evaluating it for a given circuit. In this chapter, we will describe techniques of designing or modifying circuits so that they have good testability.

To understand the role of DFT consider an analogy with data communication through a noisy channel. Shannon's theorem [Shan49] shows that each such channel has an associated "channel capacity" which specifies the maximum rate at which data can be transmitted with absolute accuracy. This result only hints at the possibility of error-free transmission without explicitly providing practical techniques for achieving this aim. In data communications, this gap is filled by encoding/decoding techniques which are matched to signal and noise characteristics of the channel (Figure 6.1).

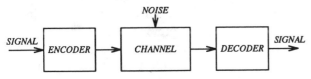

Figure 6.1: Signal Transmission in presence of noise.

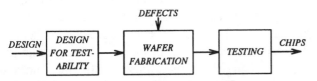

Figure 6.2: Chip manufacturing in presence of defects.

Just as data must be transmitted through a noisy channel with a fixed capacity, so must a chip design go through a defect-prone fabrication line with a fixed maximum yield realizable from it. An arbitrary design is unlikely to achieve this maximum yield, specially for very large scale integration (VLSI) chips. The analog of encoding/decoding functions here are a DFT technique and a corresponding test method, a pair designed to match the defect characteristics of a fabrication line (Figure 6.2).

1: Sequential vs. Combinational Testing

Even before large scale integration (LSI) circuits became available, it was recognized that test generation, evaluation, and application were significantly more complex for a sequential circuit than a combinational circuit of comparable size. To be observable at a primary output, the effect of a fault may have to be cycled through internal latches by applying a *sequence* of inputs to the sequential circuit. Further, to excite the fault it may be necessary to precede the above sequence by an intialization sequence. Thus a test for a fault becomes a sequence of input vectors compared to a single vector for combinational circuits. For any finite length n of the input sequence, the response of a sequential circuit can be determined from a combinational model which is $n-fold$ replication of the combinational part in the sequential circuit (Figure 6.3). Unfortunately, good *a priori* bounds on the lengths of a test sequence for a given fault are not available; hence, the iterative model of Figure 6.3 must be extended to larger and larger value of n until a test is found. Further, if asynchronous latches are used in a circuit, the iterative model does not represent the circuit behavior accurately. In such cases, the derived test sequence must be validated by fault simulation.

Theoretical approaches to the sequential circuit test generation problem have followed a functional

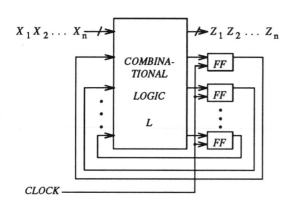

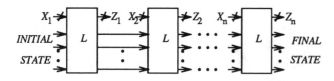

Figure 6.3: Iterative expansion of sequential logic.

approach. The circuit is modeled as a black box enclosing a *sequential machine,* which is described by its state transition table. A *checking experiment* [Henn68] can be designed for such a machine to isolate it from any other machine with the same or fewer number of states. A checking experiment verifies that each transition represented by an entry in the state table is correctly made by the machine being tested.

Even when the state table description of a circuit is available and the number of states is not unreasonably large, the checking-experiment approach may not be practical. The bound on the length of a checking experiment given by Hennie [Henn64] for a machine with m inputs and n states is $mn^4(n+1)!$. As an example, with 4 inputs and 8 states (encoded, respectively, by two binary input lines and 3 latches), the bound is 566,231,040.

The reason for such a large bound is to be found in the way a checking sequence is automatically generated for a sequential machine using *transfer* sequences to navigate between states and *distinguishing* sequences to identify the state resulting from transitions. These sequences have relatively large bounds themselves. Moreover, they are used repeatedly in a checking experiment. Thus from the point of view of checking experiments, a circuit becomes easier to test (has shorter checking sequence) if it could be modified to minimize the

lengths of its transfer and distinguishing sequences. While DFT techniques are rarely viewed in this light, most have the effect of reducing the lengths of transfer and distinguishing sequences. This is certainly true of the most successful class of such techniques, collectively known as the *scan designs* as we shall show in the following section.

2: Scan Design

Scan design methods [Eich78] require that all memory elements in the circuit be especially designed clocked flip-flops which can derive their inputs from different sources in the *normal* and *scan* modes. One commonly used design for a D-type flip-flop is shown in Figure 6.4a. The multiplexer at the input selects either D or the *SCAN-IN* input depending on the mode bit. The selected signal is connected to the input of a standard master-slave D flip-flop. Figure 6.4b shows how flip-flops are connected in a scan design. In the normal mode, the flip-flop inputs, connected as in Figure 6.3 to provide feedback, are inaccessible. However, in the scan mode, they are chained together in the form of a shift register, the input and output of which are connected, respectively, to *SCAN-IN* and scan-out pads, which must be added to the circuit for testing. During the scan mode, any arbitrary bit sequence can be applied to the scan-in line, thereby setting each latch to the desired value. The circuit can then be switched to its normal mode and tested with these values on the latches and any arbitrary pattern on the primary inputs. After switching back to the scan mode the resulting values of the latches can be shifted out and observed at the scan-out line. Obviously, the scanning-in of the values for the next test pattern can be combined with the scanning-out of the results of the previous test in a single step. In general, scan requires three extra pins: scan-in, scan-out, and mode control. In practice, very long chains of flip-flops may be broken into two or more pieces and all the pieces scanned concurrently to gain speed. Multiple scan chains will require extra scan-in and scan-out pins. In cases where extra pins are not available, the pin overhead could be kept to just one (the *mode* control pin) by multiplexing the scan-in and scan-out lines with the normal input/output lines of the circuit.

From a functional viewpoint, a scan design can be thought to add an extra input column (scan-in)

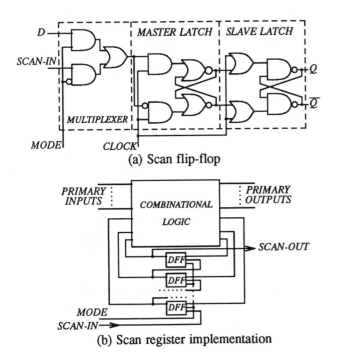

(a) Scan flip-flop

(b) Scan register implementation

Figure 6.4: Scan design.

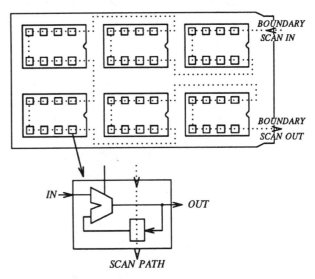

Figure 6.5: Design with boundary-scan chips.

at the chip and the board levels [Lee83].

and an extra output (scan-out) to the state transition table. These modifications guarantee transfer and distinguishing sequences of length $\log_2 n$. Since navigation between two states and identification of a state after a transition is possible by sequences of this length, the complexity of the checking experiment is reduced to $O(mn \log_2 n)$. Test generation, based on circuit structure, can further reduce verification of transitions to a fraction of the entries in the state-transition table.

A recent proposal, called *boundary scan* [vanE86] extends the idea of scan design to the board level. It is aimed at solving the problems in board testing resulting from the combined effects of rising test-equipment costs and difficulties in dealing with the surface-mount technology. The technique involves the inclusion of a shift register latch adjacent to each component pin so that signals between chips can be controlled and observed using the scan method described above (see Figure 6.5). The access to component pins is equivalent to that provided by in-circuit testers but without the need for extensive bed-of-nails fixtures and expensive test equipment.

On-chip *shadow registers* have been suggested as another method of serial scan to improve testability

3: Testing Complex Combinational Circuits

For combinational circuits, the biggest stumbling block in automation of test generation, evaluation, and application is that their costs grow at a faster than linear rate with the size of the circuit. We have seen that the computation time of available methods for test generation and evaluation grows at least as the square of the number of gates in the circuit. The test volume, reflecting the cost of test application, is also shown to grow proportional to the square of the number of gates. The term *testable design* is used loosely to refer to a collection of techniques proposed to combat this nonlinear growth in any of these phases of testing.

A common element in most such techniques is the concept of 'divide and conquer.' A complex circuit is designed as an interconnection of modules which, in turn, may be further partitioned into sub-modules, and so on. Acknowledging the similar approach used earlier in software design, the term 'structured design' is used to refer to methods espousing rules constraining the designed structures.

Logic partitioning by itself is not enough to reduce the complexity of test problems. The divide and conquer is fruitful only if the subproblems resulting from the division are independently solvable and there is a simple way of marrying the resultant solutions. This implies that before logic partitioning becomes useful in testing, a way must be found to make the internal signals more easily controllable and observable from inputs and outputs.

4: Built-In Self Test

In the built-in self test (BIST) approach [Kone80] one way is to carry out the partitioning to a level where each partitioned block can be tested exhaustively by a built-in pattern generator. Another way, useful when the partitions are too large for exahustive testing, is to ensure high testability of the circuit, so that it can be tested by random patterns. The response, which may run into millions of bits, is compressed into a *signature* of a small number of bits. A multiple-input linear feedback shift register is used for this purpose. An external control signal is introduced to reconfigure the circuit for testing and start pattern generation. At the end, the contents of all the signature registers may be scanned out serially (as in scan designs) and compared with reference values stored externally. Alternatively, the comparison may be done internally against signatures in a read-only memory (ROM) with only the results of the comparison made available off-chip.

In another proposal involving partitioning [McCl81] circuit reconfiguration in the test mode makes inputs and outputs of any block available externally at the pins. The selection of a block is made by applying signals to certain other pins which control a network of multiplexers. By time-multiplexing different functions on the same pins in the normal and test modes the need for additional pins can be avoided.

The scan and BIST design methods can nicely complement each other, the first solving test problems arising from the sequential nature and the second avoiding the problem of test generation for complex combinational blocks.

Designers not conversant with testability requirements often question the use of scan and BIST methods with attendant penalties of higher design and fabrication costs and lower yield. Indeed, it is not unreasonable to demand that *any* DFT method be shown to be economically viable before it becomes acceptable. Note that in the case of BIST, offsetting the above disadvantages are reduced testing costs at all stages of a device because of reduced test times and automatic test equipment (ATE) costs. In a recent study [Ambl86], the total life-cycle test costs were included in the cost model.

The results refer to a particular method of BIST but may be assumed to be generally applicable to other similar methods. They show that BIST is economically viable and that the cost advantage over unmodified designs increases with increasing production quantities.

5: Random Testing

For the cases where logic partitioning is not feasible (e.g., gate arrays or unstructured designs), exhaustive testing may not be practical because of the large number of circuit inputs. A combinational logic circuit implementing, say, 32-bit multiplication, may fall into such a category. Non-exhaustive *random testing* is an attractive alternative in such cases. Recent analyses show that very high fault coverage can be attained by test patterns generated by setting each input line to zero or one with equal probability. Further, computational algorithms [Savi84, Seth86] can be used to identify those faults that are not likely to be covered. Such random-pattern-resistant faults can be eliminated by a redesign. Alternatively, additional test patterns may be generated and stored in a read only memory to catch such faults.

6: Recent Trends

It would appear that because of their superior ability to simplify testing of sequential circuits, scan design methods should be the rule for complex chips. In practice, they have been accepted only begrudgingly by the designers because of their perceived high overhead. Acceptance could be higher if not *all* the latches were required to be placed in the scan chain. Such *partial scan* schemes, if properly developed, would not only overcome objections of unacceptable overhead but also extend the range of scan designs to circuits containing (1) asynchronous latches or (2) latches on a longest-delay path from input to output. A recent paper [Agra88] contains proposals for partial scan. Owing to the obvious attractiveness of this idea we are likely to see further developments in partial scan.

Going back to our analogy between encoding and DFT, we note that data transmission codes are applied at a very low (alphabet) level which has almost no semantic content in a message. The equivalent in DFT would be schemes that aim at improving the testability at the small- or medium-scale component levels. Several suggestions for such *structural level* DFT have appeared in the literature [Merc86, Redd86, Fuji86] even though none of these had yet gained commercial acceptance.

For a complex chip no single DFT method may be appropriate for all parts of the chip. Rule-based systems [Laht86, Abad85] can help in evaluating testability, partitioning the logic, and deciding on the proper technique to use for each part. For a DFT design, these systems must also check for conformance to DFT guidelines.

7: Conclusion

For a VLSI designer, who gets involved in test generation, it is impossible not to feel the need for design for testability. In this chapter we have provided only the introductory information because this is not the focus of this tutorial. For a serious reader, we recommend a more detailed study.

8: Selected Reading

Abundant literature exists on design for testability (see Chapter VIII.) A volume of reprints has appeared [Timo84] and a recently published book is entirely devoted to built-in self-test [Bard87]. In order not to burden our reader presently interested in test generation, we have reprinted only one 1983 survey paper by Williams and Parker [Will83] in this chapter. A list of other survey papers, books, and noteworthy contributions since the publication of the reprinted survey appears in Chapter VIII. As a starting point, the reader may also want to refer to two classical papers in this area. The first is a description of the IBM's version of scan design known as LSSD [Eich78]. The second is a proposal for the built-in test method known as BILBO (Built-in Logic Block Observation) [Kone80].

9: References

[Abad85] M. S. Abadir and M. A. Breuer, "A Knowledge-Based System for Designing Testable VLSI Chips," *IEEE Design & Test of Computers*, Vol. 2, pp. 56-68, August 1985.

[Agra88] V. D. Agrawal, K. T. Cheng, D. D. Johnson, and T. Lin, "Designing Circuits with Partial Scan," *IEEE Design & Test of Computers*, Vol. 5, pp. 8-15, April 1988.

[Ambl86] A. P. Ambler, M. Paraskeva, D. F. Burrows, W. L. Knight, and I. D. Dear, "Economically Viable Automatic Insertion of Self-Test Features for Custom VLSI," *Proc. Int. Test Conf.*, Washington, D.C., pp. 232-243, September 1986.

[Bard87] P. H. Bardell, W. H. McAnney, and J. Savir, *Built-In Test for VLSI: Pseudorandom Techniques*, Wiley, Somerset, NJ, 1987.

[Eich78] E. B. Eichelberger and T. W. Williams, "A Logic Design Structure for LSI Testability," *J. Des. Aut. and Fault. Tol. Comp.*, Vol. 2, pp. 165-178, May 1978.

[Fuji86] R. Fujii and J. A. Abraham, "Approaches to Circuit Level Design for Testability," *Proc. Int. Test Conf.*, pp. 480-483, September 1986.

[Henn64] F. C. Hennie, "Fault Detecting Experiments for Sequential Circuits," *Proc. 5th Ann. Symp. Sw. Cir. Theory and Logical Des.*," pp. 95-110, November 1964.

[Henn68] F. C. Hennie, in *Finite-State Models for Logical Machines*, John Wiley, 1968.

[Kone80] B. Konemann, J. Mucha, and G. Zweihoff, "Built-In Test for Complex Digital Integrated Circuits," *IEEE J. Solid-State Circuits*, Vol. SC-15, pp. 315-319, June 1980.

[Laht86] D. O. Lahti and G. C. Chen-Ellis, "PROSPECT: A Production System for Partitioning and Evaluating Chip Testability," *Proc. Int. Test Conf.*, Washington, D.C., pp. 360-367, September 1986.

[Lee83] F. Lee, V. Coli, and W. Miller, "On-Chip Circuitry Reveals System Logic States," *Electronic Design*, April 14, 1983.

[McCl81] E. J. McCluskey and S. Bozorgui-Nesbat, "Design for Autonomous Test," *IEEE Trans. Comp.*, Vol. C-30, pp. 860-875, Nov. 1981.

[Merc86] M. R. Mercer, "Logic Elements for Universally Testable Circuits," *Proc. Int. Test Conf.*, Washington, D.C., pp. 493-497, September 1986.

[Redd86] M. K. Reddy and S. M. Reddy, "Detecting FET Stuck-Open Faults in CMOS Latches and Flip-Flops," *IEEE Design & Test of Computers*, pp. 17-26, October 1986.

[Savi84] J. Savir, G. S. Ditlow, and P. H. Bardell, "Random Pattern Testability," *IEEE Trans. Computers*, Vol. C-33, pp. 79-90, January 1984.

[Seth86] S. C. Seth, B. B. Bhattacharya, and V. D. Agrawal, "An Exact Analysis for Efficient Computation of Random-Pattern Testability in Combinational Circuits," *Fault-Tolerant Computing Symp. (FTCS-16) Digest of Papers*, Vienna, Austria, pp. 318-323, July 1986.

[Shan49] C. E. Shannon, "Communication in the Presence of Noise," *Proc. IRE*, Vol. 37, pp. 10-21, Jan. 1949.

[Timo84] C. C. Timoc, *Selected Reprints on Logic Design for Testability,* Computer Society Press, Washington, D.C., 1984.

[vanE86] K. J. E. vanEerdewijk and F. P. M. Beenker, *A Modular Boundary Scan Implementation,* Philips Research Labs Report, Eindhoven, The Netherlands, 1986.

[Will83] T. W. Williams and K. P. Parker, "Design for Testability – A Survey," *Proc. IEEE*, Vol. 71, pp. 98-112, Jan. 1983, **see reprint in this chapter.**

Design for Testability—A Survey

THOMAS W. WILLIAMS, MEMBER, IEEE, AND KENNETH P. PARKER, MEMBER, IEEE

Reprinted from *Proceedings of the IEEE*, Volume 71, Number 1, January 1983, pages 98-112.

Abstract—This paper discusses the basics of design for testability. A short review of testing is given along with some reasons why one should test. The different techniques of design for testability are discussed in detail. These include techniques which can be applied to today's technologies and techniques which have been recently introduced and will soon appear in new designs.

I. INTRODUCTION

INTEGRATED Circuit Technology is now moving from Large-Scale Integration (LSI) to Very-Large-Scale Integration (VLSI). This increase in gate count, which now can be as much as factors of three to five times, has also brought a decrease in gate costs, along with improvements in performance. All these attributes of VLSI are welcomed by the industry. However, a problem never adequately solved by LSI is still with us and is getting much worse: the problem of determining, in a cost-effective way, whether a component, module, or board has been manufactured correctly [1]–[3], [52]–[68].

The testing problem has two major facets:

1) test generation [74]–[99]
2) test verification [100]–[114].

Test generation is the process of enumerating stimuli for a circuit which will demonstrate its correct operation. Test verification is the process of proving that a set of tests are effective towards this end. To date, formal proof has been impossible in practice. Fault simulation has been our best alternative, yielding a quantitative measure of test effectiveness. With the vast increase in circuit density, the ability to generate test patterns automatically and conduct fault simulation with these patterns has drastically waned. As a result, some manufacturers are foregoing these more rigorous approaches and are accepting the risks of shipping a defective product. One general approach to addressing this problem is embodied in a collection of techniques known as "Design for Testability" [12]–[35].

Design for Testability initially attracted interest in connection with LSI designs. Today, in the context of VLSI, the phrase is gaining even more currency. The collection of techniques that comprise Design for Testability are, in some cases, general guidelines; in other cases, they are hard and fast design rules. Together, they can be regarded essentially as a menu of techniques, each with its associated cost of implementation and return on investment. The purpose of this paper is to present the basic concepts in testing, beginning with the fault models and carrying through to the different techniques associated with Design for Testability which are known today in

the public sector. The design for testability techniques are divided into two categories [10]. The first category is that of the ad hoc technique for solving the testing problem. These techniques solve a problem for a given design and are not generally applicable to all designs. This is contrasted with the second category of structured approaches. These techniques are generally applicable and usually involve a set of design rules by which designs are implemented. The objective of a structured approach is to reduce the sequential complexity of a network to aid test generation and test verification.

The first ad hoc approach is partitioning [13], [17], [23], [26]. Partitioning is the ability to disconnect one portion of a network from another portion of a network in order to make testing easier. The next approach which is used at the board level is that of adding extra test points [23], [24]. The third ad hoc approach is that of Bus Architecture Systems [12], [27]. This is similar to the partitioning approach and allows one to divide and conquer—that is, to be able to reduce the network to smaller subnetworks which are much more manageable. These subnetworks are not necessarily designed with any design for testability in mind. The forth technique which bridges both the structured approach and the ad hoc approach is that of Signature Analysis [12], [27], [33], [55]. Signature Analysis requires some design rules at the board level, but is not directed at the same objective as the structure approaches are—that is, the ability to observe and control the state variables of a sequential machine.

For structured approaches, there are essentially four categories which will be discussed—the first of which is a multiplexer technique [14], [21], Random Access Scan, that has been recently published and has been used, to some extent, by others before. The next techniques are those of the Level-Sensitive Scan Design (LSSD) [16], [18]–[20], [34], [35] approach and the Scan Path approach which will be discussed in detail. These techniques allow the test generation problem to be completely reduced to one of generating tests for combinational logic. Another approach which will be discussed is that of the Scan/Set Logic [31]. This is similar to the LSSD approach and the Scan Path approach since shift registers are used to load and unload data. However, these shift registers are not part of the system data path and all system latches are not necessarily controllable and observable via the shift register. The fourth approach which will be discussed is that of Built-In Logic Block Observation (BILBO) [25] which has just recently been proposed. This technique has the attributes of both the LSSD network and Scan Path network, the ability to separate the network into combinational and sequential parts, and has the attribute of Signature Analysis—that is, employing linear feedback shift registers.

For each of the techniques described under the structured approach, the constraints, as well as various ways in which

Manuscript received June 14, 1982; revised September 15, 1982.
T. W. Williams is with IBM, General Technology Division, Boulder, CO 80302.
K. P. Parker is with Hewlett-Packard, Loveland Instrument Division, Loveland, CO 80537.

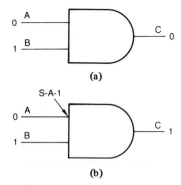

Fig. 1. Test for input stuck at fault. (a) Fault-free AND gate (good machine). (b) Faulty AND gate (faulty machine).

they can be exploited in design, manufacturing, testing, and field servicing will be described. The basic storage devices and the general logic structure resulting from the design constraints will be described in detail. The important question of how much it costs in logic gates and operating speed will be discussed qualitatively. All the structured approaches essentially allow the controllability and observability of the state variables in the sequential machine. In essence, then, test generation and fault simulation can be directed more at a combinational network, rather than at a sequential network.

A. Definitions and Assumptions

A model of faults which is used throughout the industry that does not take into account all possible defects, but is a more global type of model, is the Stuck-At model. The Stuck-At model [1]–[3], [9], [11] assumes that a logic gate input or output is fixed to either a logic 0 or a logic 1. Fig. 1(a) shows an AND gate which is fault-free. Fig. 1(b) shows an AND gate with input "A," Stuck-At-1 (S-A-1).

The faulty AND gate perceives the "A" input as 1, irrespective of the logic value placed on the input. The pattern applied to the fault-free AND gates in Fig. 1 has an output value of 0 since the input is 0 on the "A" input and 1 on the "B" input, and the AND'ing of those two leads to a 0 on the output. The pattern in Fig. 1(b) shows an output of 1, since the "A" input is perceived as a 1 even though a 0 is applied to that input. The 1 on the "B" input is perceived as a 1, and the results are AND'ed together to give a 1 output. Therefore, the pattern shown in Fig. 1(a) and (b) is a test for the "A" input, S-A-1, since there is a difference between the faulty gate (faulty machine) and the good gate (good machine). This pattern 01 on the "A" and "B" inputs, respectively, is considered a test because the good machine responds differently from the faulty machine. If they had the same response then that pattern would not have constituted a test for that fault.

If a network contained N nets, any net may be good, Stuck-At 1 or Stuck-At 0; thus all possible network state combinations would be 3^N. A network with 100 nets, then, would contain 5×10^{47} different combinations of faults. This would be far too many faults to assume. The run time of any program trying to generate tests or fault simulate tests for this kind of design would be impractical.

Therefore, the industry, for many years, has clung to the single Stuck-At fault assumption. That is, a good machine will have no faults. The faulty machines that are assumed will have one, and only one, of the stuck faults. In other words, all faults taken two at a time are not assumed, nor are all faults taken three at a time, etc. History has proven that the single

Stuck-At fault assumption, in prior technologies, has been adequate. However, there could be some problems in LSI—particularly with CMOS using the single Stuck-At fault assumption.

The problem with CMOS is that there are a number of faults which could change a combinational network into a sequential network. Therefore, the combinational patterns are no longer effective in testing the network in all cases. It still remains to be seen whether, in fact, the single Stuck-At fault assumption will survive the CMOS problems.

Also, the single Stuck-At fault assumption does not, in general, cover the bridging faults [43] that may occur. Historically again, bridging faults have been detected by having a high level—that is, in the high 90 percent—single Stuck-At fault coverage, where the single Stuck-At fault coverage is defined to be the number of faults that are tested divided by the number of faults that are assumed.

B. The VLSI Testing Problem

The VLSI testing problem is the sum of a number of problems. All the problems, in the final analysis, relate to the cost of doing business (dealt with in the following section). There are two basic problem areas:

1) test generation
2) test verification via fault simulation.

With respect to test generation, the problem is that as logic networks get larger, the ability to generate tests automatically is becoming more and more difficult.

The second facet of the VLSI testing problem is the difficulty in fault simulating the test patterns. Fault simulation is that process by which the fault coverage is determined for a specific set of input test patterns. In particular, at the conclusion of the fault simulation, every fault that is detected by the given pattern set is listed. For a given logic network with 1000 two-input logic gates, the maximum number of single Stuck-At faults which can be assumed is 6000. Some reduction in the number of single Stuck-At faults can be achieved by fault equivalencing [36], [38], [41], [42], [47]. However, the number of single Stuck-At faults needed to be assumed is about 3000. Fault simulation, then, is the process of applying every given test pattern to a fault-free machine and to each of the 3000 copies of the good machine containing one, and only one, of the single Stuck-At faults. Thus fault simulation, with respect to run time, is similar to doing 3001 good machine simulations.

Techniques are available to reduce the complexity of fault simulation, however, it still is a very time-consuming, and hence, expensive task [96], [104], [105], [107], [110], [112]–[114].

It has been observed that the computer run time to do test [80] generation and fault simulation is approximately proportional to the number of logic gates to the power of 3;[1] hence, small increases in gate count will yield quickly increasing run times. Equation (1)

---

[1] The value of the exponent given here (3) is perhaps pessimistic in some cases. Other analyses have used the value 2 instead. A quick rationale goes as follows: with a linear increase k in circuit size comes an attendant linear increase in the number of failure mechanisms (now yielding k squared increase in work). Also, as circuits become larger, they tend to become more strongly connected such that a given block is effected by more blocks and even itself. This causes more work to be done in a range we feel to be k cubed. This fairly nebulous concept of connectivity seems to be the cause for debate on whether the exponent should be 3 or some other value.

$$T = KN^3 \qquad (1)$$

shows this relationship, where T is computer run time, N is the number of gates, and K is the proportionality constant. The relationship does not take into account the falloff in automatic test generation capability due to sequential complexity of the network. It has been observed that computer run time just for fault simulation is proportional to N^2 without even considering the test generation phase.

When one talks about testing, the topic of functional testing always comes up as a feasible way to test a network. Theoretically, to do a complete functional test ("exhaustive" testing) seems to imply that all entries in a Karnaugh map (or excitation table) must be tested for a 1 or a 0. This means that if a network has N inputs and is purely combinational, then 2^N patterns are required to do a complete functional test. Furthermore, if a network has N inputs with M latches, at a minimum it takes 2^{N+M} patterns to do a complete functional test. Rarely is that minimum ever obtainable; and in fact, the number of tests required to do a complete functional test is very much higher than that. With LSI, this may be a network with $N = 25$ and $M = 50$, or 2^{75} patterns, which is approximately 3.8×10^{22} Assuming one had the patterns and applied them at an application rate of 1 μs per pattern, the test time would be over a billion years (10^9).

C. Cost of Testing

One might ask why so much attention is now being given to the level of testability at chip and board levels. The bottom line is the cost of doing business. A standard among people familiar with the testing process is: If it costs $0.30 to detect a fault at the chip level, then it would cost $3 to detect that same fault when it was embedded at the board level; $30 when it is embedded at the system level; and $300 when it is embedded at the system level but has to be found in the field. Thus if a fault can be detected at a chip or board level, then significantly larger costs per fault can be avoided at subsequent levels of packaging.

With VLSI and the inadequacy of automatic test generation and fault simulation, there is considerable difficulty in obtaining a level of testability required to achieve acceptable defect levels. If the defect level of boards is too high, the cost of field repairs is also too high. These costs, and in some cases, the inability to obtain a sufficient test, have led to the need to have "Design for Testability."

II. DESIGN FOR TESTABILITY

There are two key concepts in Design for Testability: controllability and observability. Control and observation of a network are central to implementing its test procedure. For example, consider the case of the simple AND block in Fig. 1. In order to be able to test the "A" input Stuck-At 1, it was necessary to control the "A" input to 0 and the "B" input to 1 and be able to observe the "C" output to determine whether a 0 was observed or a 1 was observed. The 0 is the result of the good machine, and the 1 would be the result, if you had a faulty machine. If this AND block is embedded into a much larger sequential network, the requirement of being able to control the "A" and "B" inputs to 0 and 1, respectively, and being able to observe the output "C," be it through some other logic blocks, still remains. Therein lies part of the problem of being able to generate tests for a network.

Because of the need to determine if a network has the attributes of controllability and observability that are desired, a number of programs have been written which essentially give analytic measures of controllability and observability for different nets in a given sequential network [69]–[73].

After observing the results of one of these programs in a given network, the logic designer can then determine whether some of the techniques, which will be described later, can be applied to this network to ease the testing problem. For example, test points may be added at critical points which are not observable or which are not controllable, or some of the techniques of Scan Path or LSSD can be used to initialize certain latches in the machine to avoid the difficulties of controllability associated with sequential machines. The popularity of such tools is continuing to grow, and a number of companies are now embarking upon their own controllability/observability measures.

III. AD HOC DESIGN FOR TESTABILITY [10]

Testing has moved from the afterthought position that it used to occupy to part of the design environment in LSI and VLSI. When testing was part of the afterthought, it was a very expensive process. Products were discarded because there was no adequate way to test them in production quantities.

There are two basic approaches which are prevalent today in the industry to help solve the testing problem. The first approach categorized here is Ad Hoc, and the second approach is categorized as a Structured Approach. The Ad Hoc techniques are those techniques which can be applied to a given product, but are not directed at solving the general sequential problem. They usually do offer relief, and their cost is probably lower than the cost of the Structured Approaches. The Structured Approaches, on the other hand, are trying to solve the general problem with a design methodology, such that when the designer has completed his design from one of these particular approaches, the results will be test generation and fault simulation at acceptable costs. Structured Approaches lend themselves more easily to design automation. Again, the main difference between the two approaches is probably the cost of implementation and hence, the return on investment for this extra cost. In the Ad Hoc approaches, the job of doing test generation and fault simulation are usually not as simple or as straightforward as they would be with the Structured Approaches, as we shall see shortly.

A number of techniques have evolved from MSI to LSI and now into VLSI that fall under the category of the ad hoc approaches of "Design for Testability." These techniques are usually solved at the board level and do not necessarily require changes in the logic design in order to accomplish them.

A. Partitioning

Because the task of test pattern generation and fault simulation is proportional to the number of logic gates to the third power, a significant amount of effort has been directed at approaches called "Divide and Conquer."

There are a number of ways in which the partitioning approach to Design for Testability can be implemented. The first is to mechanical partition by dividing a network in half. In essence, this would reduce the test generation and fault simulation tasks by 8 for two boards. Unfortunately, having two boards rather than one board can be a significant cost disadvantage and defeats the purpose of integration.

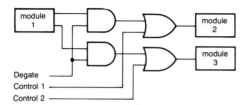

Fig. 2. Use of degating logic for logical partioning.

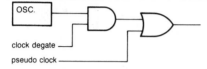

Fig. 3. Degating lines for oscillator.

Another approach that helps the partitioning problem, as well as helping one to "Divide and Conquer" is to use jumper wires. These wires would go off the board and then back on the board, so that the tester and the test generator can control and observe these nets directly. However, this could mean a significant number of I/O contacts at the board level which could also get very costly.

Degating is another technique for separating modules on a board. For example, in Fig. 2, a degating line goes to two AND blocks that are driven from Module 1. The results of those two AND blocks go to two independent OR blocks—one controlled by Control Line 1, the other with Control Line 2. The output of the OR block from Control Line 1 goes into Module 2, and the output of Control Line 2 goes into Module 3. When the degate line is at the 0 value, the two Control Lines, 1 and 2, can be used to drive directly into Modules 2 and 3. Therefore, complete controllability of the inputs to Modules 2 and 3 can be obtained by using these control lines. If those two nets happen to be very difficult nets to control, as pointed out, say, by a testability measure program, then this would be a very cost-effective way of controlling those two nets and hence, being able to derive the tests at a very reasonable cost.

A classical example of degating logic is that associated with an oscillator, as shown in Fig. 3. In general, if an oscillator is free-running on a board, driving logic, it is very difficult, and sometimes impossible, to synchronize the tester with the activity of the logic board. As a result, degating logic can be used here to block the oscillator and have a pseudo-clock line which can be controlled by the tester, so that the dc testing of all the logic on that board can be synchronized. All of these techniques require a number of extra primary inputs and primary outputs and possibly extra modules to perform the degating.

B. Test Points

Another approach to help the controllability and observability of a sequential network is to use test points [23], [24]. If a test point is used as a primary input to the network, then that can function to enhance controllability. If a test point is used as a primary output, then that is used to enhance the observability of a network. In some cases, a single pin can be used as both an input and an output.

For example, in Fig. 4, Module 1 has a degate function, so that the output of those two pins on the module could go to noncontrolling values. Thus the external pins which are dotted into those nets could control those nets and drive Module 2.

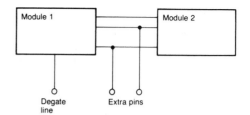

Fig. 4. Test points used as both inputs and outputs.

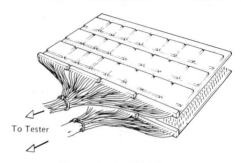

Fig. 5. "Bed of Nails" test.

On the other hand, if the degate function is at the opposite value, then the output of Module 1 can be observed on these external pins. Thus the enhancement of controllability and observability can be accommodated by adding pins which can act as both inputs and outputs under certain degating conditions.

Another technique which can be used for controllability is to have a pin which, in one mode, implies system operation, and in another mode takes N inputs and gates them to a decoder. The 2^N outputs of the decoder are used to control certain nets to values which otherwise would be difficult to obtain. By so doing, the controllability of the network is enhanced.

As mentioned before, predictability is an issue which is as important as controllability and observability. Again, test points can be used here. For example, a CLEAR or PRESET function for all memory elements can be used. Thus the sequential machine can be put into a known state with very few patterns.

Another technique which falls into the category of test points and is very widely used is that of the "Bed of Nails" [31] tester, Fig. 5. The Bed of Nails tester probes the underside of a board to give a larger number of points for observability and controllability. This is in addition to the normal tester contact to the board under test. The drawback of this technique is that the tester must have enough test points to be able to control and observe each one of these nails on the Bed of Nails tester. Also, there are extra loads which are placed on the nets and this can cause some drive and receive problems. Furthermore, the mechanical fixture which will hold the Bed of Nails has to be constructed, so that the normal forces on the probes are sufficient to guarantee reliable contacts. Another application for the Bed of Nails testing is to do "drive/sense nails" [31] or "*in situ*" or "in-circuit" testing, which, effectively, is the technique of testing each chip on the board independently of the other chips on the board. For each chip, the appropriate nails and/or primary inputs are driven so as to prevent one chip from being driven by the other chips on the board. Once this state has been established, the isolated chip on the board can now be tested. In this case, the resolution to the failing

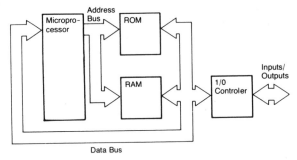

Fig. 6. Bus structured microcomputer.

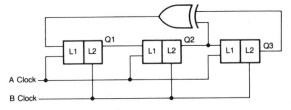

Fig. 7. Counting capabilities of a linear feedback shift register.

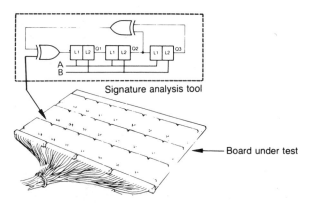

Fig. 8. Use of signature analysis tool.

chip is much better than edge connector tests, however, there is some exposure to incomplete testing of interconnections and care must be taken not to damage the circuit when over-driving it. Design for testability in a Bed of Nails environment must take the issues of contact reliability, multiplicity, and electrical loading into account.

C. Bus Architecture

An approach that has been used very successfully to attack the partitioning problem by the microcomputer designers is to use a bus structured architecture. This architecture allows access to critical buses which go to many different modules on the computer board. For example, in Fig. 6, you can see that the data bus is involved with both the microprocessor module, the ROM module, the RAM module, and the I/O Controller module. If there is external access to the data bus and three of the four modules can be turned off the data bus—that is, their outputs can be put into a high-impedence state (three-state driver)—then the data bus could be used to drive the fourth module, as if it were a primary input (or primary output) to that particular module. Similarly, with the address bus, access again must be controlled externally to the board, and thus the address bus can be very useful to controlling test patterns to the microcomputer board. These buses, in essence, partition the board in a unique way, so that testing of subunits can be accomplished. A drawback of bus-structured designs comes with faults on the bus itself. If a bus wire is stuck, any module or the bus trace itself may be the culprit. Normal testing is done by deducing the location of a fault from voltage information. Isolating a bus failure may require current measurements, which are much more difficult to do.

D. Signature Analysis

This technique for testing, introduced in 1977 [27], [33], [55] is heavily reliant on planning done in the design stage. That is why this technique falls between the Ad Hoc and the Structured Approaches for Design for Testability, since some care must be taken at the board level in order to ensure proper operation of this Signature Analysis of the board [12]. Signature Analysis is well-suited to bus structure architectures, as previously mentioned and in particular, those associated with microcomputers. This will become more apparent shortly.

The integral part of the Signature Analysis approach is that of a linear feedback shift register [8]. Fig. 7 shows an example of a 3-bit linear feedback shift register. This linear feedback shift register is made up of three shift register latches. Each one is represented by a combination of an $L1$ latch and an $L2$ latch. These can be thought of as the master latch being the $L1$ latch and the slave latch being the $L2$ latch. An "A" clock clocks all the $L1$ latches, and a "B" clock clocks all the $L2$ latches, so that turning the "A" and "B" clocks on and off independently will shift the shift register 1-bit position to the right. Furthermore, this linear shift register has an EXCLUSIVE-OR gate which takes the output, $Q2$, the second bit in the shift register, and EXCLUSIVE-OR's it with the third bit in the shift register, $Q3$. The result of that EXCLUSIVE-OR is the input to the first shift register. A single clock could be used for this shift register, which is generally the case, however, this concept will be used shortly when some of the structured design approaches are discussed which use two nonoverlapping clocks. Fig. 7 shows how this linear feedback shift register will count for different initial values.

For longer shift registers, the maximal length linear feedback configurations can be obtained by consulting tables [8] to determine where to tap off the linear feedback shift register to perform the EXCLUSIVE-OR function. Of course, only EXCLUSIVE-OR blocks can be used, otherwise, the linearity would not be preserved.

The key to Signature Analysis is to design a network which can stimulate itself. A good example of such a network would be microprocessor-based boards, since they can stimulate themselves using the intelligence of the processor driven by the memory on the board.

The Signature Analysis procedure is one which has the shift register in the Signature Analysis tool, which is external to the board and not part of the board in any way, synchronized with the clocking that occurs on the board, see Fig. 8. A probe is used to probe a particular net on the board. The result of that probe is EXCLUSIVE-OR'ed into the linear feedback shift register. Of course, it is important that the linear feedback shift register be initialized to the same starting place every time, and that the clocking sequence be a fixed number, so that the tests can be repeated. The board must also have some initialization, so that its response will be repeated as well.

After a fixed number of clock periods—let's assume 50—a particular value will be stored in $Q1$, $Q2$, and $Q3$. It is not necessarily the value that would have occurred if the linear feedback shift register was just counted 50 times—Modulo 7.

The value will be changed, because the values coming from the board via the probe will not necessarily be a continuous string of 1's; there will be 1's intermixed with 0's.

The place where the shift register stops on the Signature Analysis Tool—that is, the values for $Q1$, $Q2$, and $Q3$ is the Signature for that particular node for the good machine. The question is: If there were errors present at one or more points in the string of 50 observations of that particular net of the board, would the value stored in the shift register for $Q1$, $Q2$, and $Q3$ be different than the one for the good machine? It has been shown that with a 16-bit linear feedback shift register, the probability of detecting one or more errors is extremely high [55]. In essence, the signature, or "residue," is the remainder of the data stream after division by an irreduceable polynomial. There is considerable data compression—that is, after the results of a number of shifting operations, the test data are reduced to 16 bits, or, in the case of Fig. 8, 3 bits. Thus the result of the Signature Analysis tool is basically a Go/No-Go for the output for that particular module.

If the bad output for that module were allowed to cycle around through a number of other modules on the board and then feed back into this particular module, it would not be clear after examining all the nodes in the loop which module was defective—whether it was the module whose output was being observed, or whether it was another module upstream in the path. This gives rise to two requirements for Signature Analysis. First of all, closed-loop paths must be broken at the board level. Second, the best place to start probing with Signature Analysis is with a "kernel" of logic. In other words, on a microprocessor-based board, one would start with the outputs of the microprocessor itself and then build up from that particular point, once it has been determined that the microprocessor is good.

This breaking of closed loops is a tenant of Design for Testability and for Signature Analysis. There is a little overhead for implementing Signature Analysis. Some ROM space would be required (to stimulate the self-test), as well as extra jumpers, in order to break closed loops on the board. Once this is done, however, the test can be obtained for very little cost. The only question that remains is about the quality of the tests—that is, how good are the tests that are being generated, do they cover all the faults, etc.

Unfortunately, the logic models—for example, microprocessors—are not readily available to the board user. Even if a microprocessor logic model were available, they would not be able to do a complete fault simulation of the patterns because it would be too large. Hence, Signature Analysis may be the best that could be done for this particular board with the given inputs which the designer has. Presently, large numbers of users are currently using the Signature Analysis technique to test boards containing LSI and VLSI components.

IV. STRUCTURED DESIGN FOR TESTABILITY

Today, with the utilization of LSI and VLSI technology, it has become apparent that even more care will have to be taken in the design stage in order to ensure testability and produceability of digital networks. This has led to rigorous and highly structured design practices. These efforts are being spearheaded not by the makers of LSI/VLSI devices but by electronics firms which possess captive IC facilities and the manufacturers of large main-frame computers.

Most structured design practices [14]–[16], [18]–[21], [25], [31], [32], [34], [35] are built upon the concept that if the

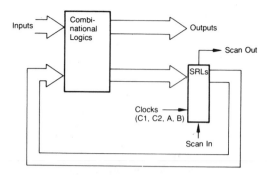

Fig. 9. Classical model of a sequential network utilizing a shift register for storage.

values in all the latches can be controlled to any specific value, and if they can be observed with a very straightforward operation then the test generation, and possibly, the fault task, can be reduced to that of doing test generation and fault simulation for a combinational logic network. A control signal can switch the memory elements from their normal mode of operation to a mode that makes them controllable and observable.

It appears from the literature that several companies, such as IBM, Fujitsu Ltd., Sperry-Univac, and Nippon Electric Co., Ltd. [14]–[16], [18]–[21], [31], [32], [35] have been dedicating formidable amounts of resources toward Structured Design for Testability. One notes simply by scanning the literature on testing, that many of the practical concepts and tools for testing were developed by main-frame manufacturers who do not lack for processor power. It is significant, then, that these companies, with their resources, have recognized that unstructured designs lead to unacceptable testing problems. Presently, IBM has extensively documented its efforts in Structured Design for Testability, and these are reviewed first.

A. Level-Sensitive Scan Design (LSSD)

With the concept that the memory elements in an IC can be threaded together into a shift register, the memory elements values can be both controlled and observed. Fig. 9 shows the familiar generalized sequential circuit model modified to use a shift register. This technique enhances both controllability and observability, allowing us to augment testing by controlling inputs and internal states, and easily examining internal state behavior. An apparent disadvantage is the serialization of the test, potentially costing more time for actually running a test.

LSSD is IBM's discipline for structural design for testability. "Scan" refers to the ability to shift into or out of any state of the network. "Level-sensitive" refers to constraints on circuit excitation, logic depth, and the handling of clocked circuitry. A key element in the design is the "shift register latch" (SRL) such as can be implemented in Fig. 10. Such a circuit is immune to most anomalies in the ac characteristics of the clock, requiring only that it remain high (sample) at least long enough to stabilize the feedback loop, before being returned to the low (hold) state [18], [19]. The lines D and C form the normal mode memory function while lines I, A, B, and $L2$ comprise additional circuitry for the shift register function.

The shift registers are threaded by connecting I to $L2$ and operated by clocking lines A and B in two-phase fashion. Fig. 11 shows four modules threaded for shift register action. Now note in Fig. 11 that each module could be an SRL or, one level up, a board containing threaded IC's, etc. Each level of pack-

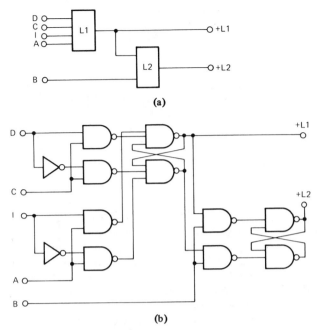

(a)

(b)

Fig. 10. Shift register latch (SRL). (a) Symbolic representation. (b) Implementation in AND-INVERT gates.

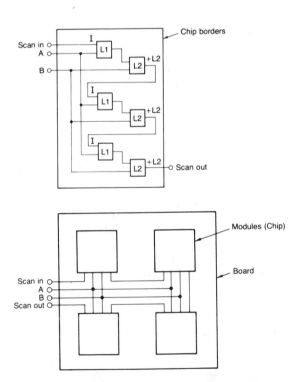

Fig. 11. Interconnection of SRL's on an integrated circuit and board.

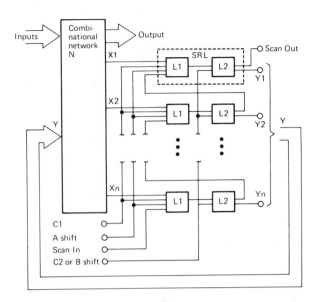

Fig. 12. General structure of an LSSD subsystem with two system clocks.

aging requires the same four additional lines to implement the shift register scan feature. Fig. 12 depicts a general structure for an LSSD subsystem with a two-phase system clock. Additional rules concerning the gating of clocks, etc., are given by Williams and Eichelberger [18], [19]. Also, it is not practical to implement RAM with SRL memory, so additional procedures are required to handle embedded RAM circuitry [20].

Given that an LSSD structure is achieved, what are the rewards? It turns out that the network can now be thought of as purely combinational, where tests are applied via primary inputs and shift register outputs. The testing of combinational circuits is a well understood and (barely) tractable problem. Now techniques such as the D-Algorithm [93] compiled code Boolean simulation [2], [74], [106], [107], and adaptive random test generation [87], [95], [98] are again viable approaches to the testing problem. Further, as small subsystems are tested, their aggregates into larger systems are also testable by cataloging the position of each testable subsystem in the shift register chain. System tests become (ideally) simple concatenations of subsystem tests. Though ideals are rarely achieved, the potential for solving otherwise hopeless testing problems is very encouraging.

In considering the cost performance impacts, there are a number of negative impacts associated with the LSSD design philosophy. First of all, the shift register latches in the shift register are, logically, two or three times as complex as simple latches. Up to four additional primary inputs/outputs are required at each package level for control of the shift registers. External asynchronous input signals must not change more than once every clock cycle. Finally, all timing within the subsystem is controlled by externally generated clock signals.

In terms of additional complexity of the shift register hold latches, the overhead from experience has been in the range of 4 to 20 percent. The difference is due to the extent to which the system designer made use of the $L2$ latches for system function. It has been reported in the IBM System 38 literature that 85 percent of the $L2$ latches were used for system function. This drastically reduces the overhead associated with this design technique.

With respect to the primary inputs/outputs that are required to operate the shift register, this can be reduced significantly by making functional use of some of the pins. For example, the scan-out pin could be a functional output of an SRL for that particular chip. Also, overall performance of the subsystem may be degraded by the clocking requirement, but the effect should be small.

The LSSD structured design approach for Design for Testability eliminates or alleviates some of the problems in designing, manufacturing and maintaining LSI systems at a reasonable cost.

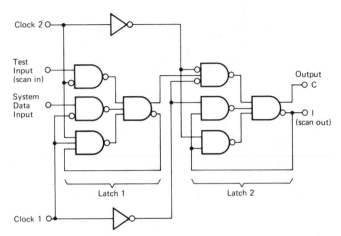

Fig. 13. Raceless D-type flip-flop with Scan Path.

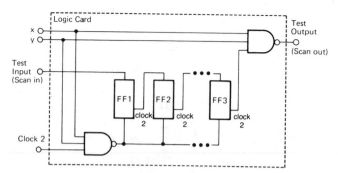

Fig. 14. Configuration of Scan Path on Card.

B. Scan Path

In 1975, a survey paper of test generation systems in Japan was presented by members of Nippon Electric Co., Ltd. [21]. In that survey paper, a technique they described as Scan Path was presented. The Scan Path technique has the same objectives as the LSSD approach which has just been described. The Scan Path technique similarities and differences to the LSSD approach will be presented.

The memory elements that are used in the Scan Path approach are shown in Fig. 13. This memory element is called a raceless D-type flip-flop with Scan Path.

In system operation, Clock 2 is at a logic value of 1 for the entire period. This, in essence, blocks the test or scan input from affecting the values in the first latch. This D-type flip-flop really contains two latches. Also, by having Clock 2 at a logic value of 1, the values in Latch 2 are not disturbed.

Clock 1 is the sole clock in system operation for this D-type flip-flop. When Clock 1 is at a value of 0, the System Data Input can be loaded into Latch 1. As long as Clock 1 is 0 for sufficient time to latch up the data, it can then turn off. As it turns off, it then will make Latch 2 sensitive to the data output of Latch 1. As long as Clock 1 is equal to a 1 so that data can be latched up into Latch 2, reliable operation will occur. This assumes that as long as the output of Latch 2 does not come around and feed the system data input to Latch 1 and change it during the time that the inputs to both Latch 1 and Latch 2 are active. The period of time that this can occur is related to the delay of the inverter block for Clock 1. A similar phenomenon will occur with Clock 2 and its associated inverter block. This race condition is the exposure to the use of only one system clock.

This points out a significant difference between the Scan Path approach and the LSSD approach. One of the basic principles of the LSSD approach is level-sensitive operation—the ability to operate the clocks in such a fashion that no races will exist. In the LSSD approach, a separate clock is required for Latch 1 from the clock that operates Latch 2.

In terms of the scanning function, the D-type flip-flop with Scan Path has its own scan input called test input. This is clocked into the L1 latch by Clock 2 when Clock 2 is a 0, and the results of the L1 latch are clocked into Latch 2 when Clock 2 is a 1. Again, this applies to master/slave operation of Latch 1 and Latch 2 with its associated race with proper attention to delays this race will not be a problem.

Another feature of the Scan Path approach is the configuration used at the logic card level. Modules on the logic card are all connected up into a serial scan path, such that for each card, there is one scan path. In addition, there are gates for selecting a particular card in a subsystem. In Fig. 14, when X and Y are both equal to 1—that is the selection mechanism—Clock 2 will then be allowed to shift data through the scan path. Any other time, Clock 2 will be blocked, and its output will be blocked. The reason for blocking the output is that a number of card outputs can then be put together; thus the blocking function will put their output to noncontrolling values, so that a particular card can have unique control of the unique test output for that system.

It has been reported by the Nippon Electric Company that they have used the Scan Path approach, plus partitioning which will be described next, for systems with 100 000 blocks or more. This was for the FLT-700 System, which is a large processor system.

The partitioning technique is one which automatically separates the combinational network into smaller subnetworks, so that the test generator can do test generation for the small subnetworks, rather than the larger networks. A partition is automatically generated by backtracing from the D-type flip-flops, through the combinational logic, until it encounters a D-type flip-flop in the backtrace (or primary input). Some care must be taken so that the partitions do not get too large.

To that end, the Nippon Electric Company approach has used a controlled D-type flip-flop to block the backtracing of certain partitions when they become too high. This is another facet of Design for Testability—that is, the introduction of extra flip-flops totally independent of function, in order to control the partitioning algorithm.

Other than the lack of the level sensitive attribute to the Scan Path approach, the technique is very similar to the LSSD approach. The introduction of the Scan Path approach was the first practical implementation of shift registers for testing which was incorporated in a total system.

C. Scan/Set Logic

A technique similar to Scan Path and LSSD, but not exactly the same, is the Scan/Set technique put forth by Sperry-Univac [31]. The basic concept of this technique is to have shift registers, as in Scan Path or in LSSD, but these shift registers are not in the data path. That is, they are not in the system data path; they are independent of all the system latches. Fig. 15 shows an example of the Scan/Set Logic, referred to as bit serial logic.

The basic concept is that the sequential network can be

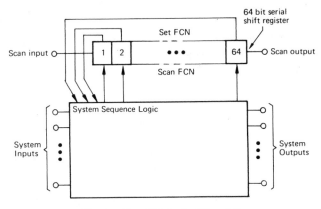

Fig. 15. Scan/Set Logic (bit-serial).

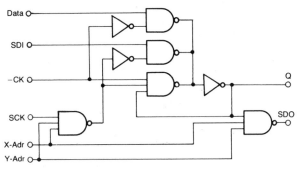

Fig. 16. Polarity-hold-type addressable latch.

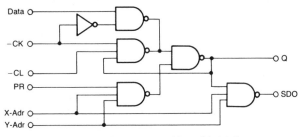

Fig. 17. Set/Reset type addressable latch.

sampled at up to 64 points. These points can be loaded into the 64-bit shift register with a single clock. Once the 64 bits are loaded, a shifting process will occur, and the data will be scanned out through the scan-out pin. In the case of the set function, the 64 bits can be funneled into the system logic, and then the appropriate clocking structure required to load data into the system latches is required in this system logic. Furthermore, the set function could also be used to control different paths to ease the testing function.

In general, this serial Scan/Set Logic would be integrated onto the same chip that contrains sequential system logic. However, some applications have been put forth where the bit serial Scan/Set Logic was off-chip, and the bit-serial Scan/Set Logic only sampled outputs or drove inputs to facilitate in-circuit testing.

Recently, Motorola has come forth with a chip which is T^2L and which has I^2L logic integrated on that same chip. This has the Scan/Set Logic bit serial shift registers built in I^2L. The T^2L portion of the chip is a gate array, and the I^2L is on the chip, whether the customer wants it or not. It is up to the customer to use the bit-serial logic if he chooses.

At this point, it should be explained that if all the latches within the system sequential network are not both scanned and set, then the test generation function is not necessarily reduced to a total combinational test generation function and fault simulation function. However, this technique will greatly reduce the task of test generation and fault simulation.

Again, the Scan/Set technique has the same objectives as Scan Path and LSSD—that is, controllability and observability. However, in terms of its implementation, it is not required that the set function set all system latches, or that the scan function scan all system latches. This design flexibility would have a reflection in the software support required to implement such a technique.

Another advantage of this technique is that the scan function can occur during system operation—that is, the sampling pulse to the 64-bit serial shift register can occur while system clocks are being applied to the system sequential logic, so that a snapshot of the sequential machine can be obtained and off-loaded without any degradation in system performance.

D. Random-Access Scan

Another technique similar to the Scan Path technique and LSSD is the Random-Access Scan technique put forth by Fujitsu [14]. This technique has the same objective as Scan Path and LSSD—that is, to have complete controllability and observability of all internal latches. Thus the test generation func-

tion can be reduced to that of combinational test generation and combinational fault simulation as well.

Random-Access Scan differs from the other two techniques in that shift registers are not employed. What is employed is an addressing scheme which allows each latch to be uniquely selected, so that it can be either controlled or observed. The mechanism for addressing is very similar to that of a Random-Access Memory, and hence, its name.

Figs. 16 and 17 show the two basic latch configurations that are required for the Random-Access Scan approach. Fig. 16 is a single latch which has added to it an extra data port which is a Scan Data In port (SDI). These data are clocked into the latch by the SCK clock. The SCK clock can only affect this latch, if both the X and Y addresses are one. Furthermore, when the X address and Y address are one, then the Scan Data Out (SDO) point can be observed. System data labeled Data in Figs. 16 and 17 are loaded into this latch by the system clock labeled CK.

The set/reset-type addressable latch in Fig. 17 does not have a scan clock to load data into the system latch. This latch is first cleared by the CL line, and the CL line is connected to other latches that are also set/reset-type addressable latches. This, then, places the output value Q to a 0 value. A preset is directed at those latches that are required to be set to a 1 for that particular test. This preset is directed by addressing each one of those latches and applying the preset pulse labeled PR. The output of the latch Q will then go to a 1. The observability mechanism for Scan Data Out is exactly the same as for the latch shown in Fig. 16.

Fig. 18 gives an overall view of the system configuration of the Random-Access Scan approach. Notice that, basically, there is a Y address, an X address, a decoder, the addressable storage elements, which are the memory elements or latches, and the sequential machine, system clocks, and CLEAR function. There is also an SDI which is the input for a given latch, an SDO which is the output data for that given latch, and a scan clock. There is also one logic gate necessary to create the preset function.

319

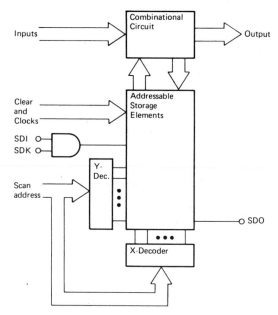

Fig. 18. Random-Access Scan network.

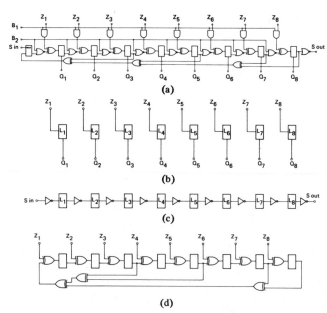

(a)

(b)

(c)

(d)

Fig. 19. BILBO and its different modes. (a) General form of BILBO register. (b) $B_1 B_2 = 11$ system orientation mode. (c) $B_1 B_2 = 00$ linear shift register mode. (d) $B_1 B_2 = 10$ signature analysis register with m multiple inputs ($Z_1, Z_2, \cdots, Z_8$).

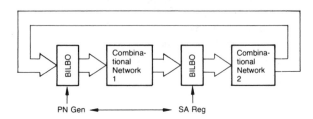

Fig. 20. Use of BILBO registers to test combinational Network 1.

The Random-Access Scan technique allows the observability and controllability of all system latches. In addition, any point in the combinational network can be observed with the addition of one gate per observation point, as well as one address in the address gate, per observation point.

While the Scan Path approach and the LSSD approach require two latches for every point which needs to be observed, the overhead for Random-Access Scan is about three to four gates per storage element. In terms of primary inputs/outputs, the overhead is between 10 and 20. This pin overhead can be diminished by using the serial scan approach for the X and Y address counter, which would lead to 6 primary inputs/outputs.

V. Self-Testing and Built-In Tests

As a natural outgrowth of the Structured Design approach for "Design for Testability," Self-Tests and Built-In Tests have been getting considerably more attention. Four techniques will be discussed, which fall into this category, BILBO, Syndrome Testing, Testing by Verifying Walsh Testing Coefficients, and Autonomous Testing. Each of these techniques will be described.

A. Built-In Logic Block Observation, BILBO

A technique recently presented takes the Scan Path and LSSD concept and integrates it with the Signature Analysis concept. The end result is a technique for Built-In Logic Block Observation, BILBO [25].

Fig. 19 gives the form of an 8-bit BILBO register. The block labeled L_i ($i = 1, 2, \cdots, 8$) are the system latches. B_1 and B_2 are control values for controlling the different functions that the BILBO register can perform. S_{IN} is the scan-in input to the 8-bit register, and S_{OUT} is the scan-out for the 8-bit register. Q_i ($i = 1, 2, \cdots, 8$) are the output values for the eight system latches. Z_i ($i = 1, 2, \cdots, 8$) are the inputs from the combinational logic. The structure that this network will be embedded into will be discussed shortly.

There are three primary modes of operation for this register, as well as one secondary mode of operation for this register. The first is shown in Fig. 19(b)—that is, with B_1 and B_2 equal to 11. This is a Basic System Operation mode, in which the

Z_i values are loaded into the L_i, and the outputs are available on Q_i for system operation. This would be your normal register function.

When $B_1 B_2$ equals 00, the BILBO register takes on the form of a linear shift register, as shown in Fig. 19(c). Scan-in input to the left, through some inverters, and basically lining up the eight registers into a single scan path, until the scan-out is reached. This is similar to Scan Path and LSSD.

The third mode is when $B_1 B_2$ equals 10. In this mode, the BILBO register takes on the attributes of a linear feedback shift register of maximal length with multiple linear inputs. This is very similar to a Signature Analysis register, except that there is more than one input. In this situation, there are eight unique inputs. Thus after a certain number of shift clocks, say, 100, there would be a unique signature left in the BILBO register for the good machine. This good machine signature could be off-loaded from the register by changing from Mode $B_1 B_2 = 10$ to Mode $B_1 B_2 = 00$, in which case a shift register operation would exist, and the signature then could be observed from the scan-out primary output.

The fourth function that the BILBO register can perform is $B_1 B_2$ equal to 01, which would force a reset on the register. (This is not depicted in Fig. 19.)

The BILBO registers are used in the system operation, as shown in Fig. 20. Basically, a BILBO register with combinational logic and another BILBO register with combinational logic, as well as the output of the second combinational logic network can feed back into the input of the first BILBO regis-

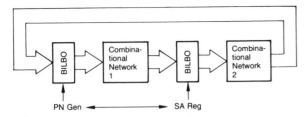

Fig. 21. Use of BILBO registers to test combinational Network 2.

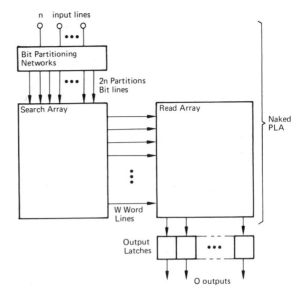

Fig. 22. PLA model.

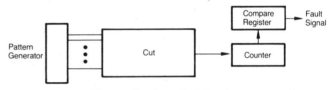

Fig. 23. Syndrome test structure.

ter. The BILBO approach takes one other fact into account, and that is that, in general, combinational logic is highly susceptible to random patterns. Thus if the inputs to the BILBO register, $Z_1, Z_2, \cdots, Z_8$, can be controlled to fixed values, such that the BILBO register is in the maximal length linear feedback shift register mode (Signature Analysis) it will output a sequence of patterns which are very close to random patterns. Thus random patterns can be generated quite readily from this register. These sequences are called Pseudo Random Patterns (PN).

If, in the first operation, this BILBO register on the left in Fig. 20 is used as the PN generator—that is, its data inputs are held to fixed values—then the output of that BILBO register will be random patterns. This will then do a reasonable test, if sufficient numbers of patterns are applied, of the Combinational Logic Network 1. The results of this test can be stored in a Signature Analysis register approach with multiple inputs to the BILBO register on the right. After a fixed number of patterns have been applied, the signature is scanned out of the BILBO register on the right for good machine compliance. If that is successfully completed, then the roles are reversed, and the BILBO register on the right will be used as a PN sequence generator; the BILBO register on the left will then be used as a Signature Analysis register with multiple inputs from Combinational Logic Network 2, see Fig. 21. In this mode, the Combinational Logic Network 2 will have random patterns applied to its inputs and its outputs stored in the BILBO register on the far left. Thus the testing of the combinational logic networks 1 and 2 can be completed at very high speeds by only applying the shift clocks, while the two BILBO registers are in the Signature Analysis mode. At the conclusion of the tests, off-loading of patterns can occur, and determination of good machine operation can be made.

This technique solves the problem of test generation and fault simulation if the combinational networks are susceptible to random patterns. There are some known networks which are not susceptible to random patterns. They are Programmable Logic Arrays (PLA's), see Fig. 22. The reason for this is that the fan-in in PLA's is too large. If an AND gate in the search array had 20 inputs, then each random pattern would have $1/2^{20}$ probability of coming up with the correct input pattern. On the other hand, random combinational logic networks with maximum fan-in of 4 can do quite well with random patterns.

The BILBO technique solves another problem and that is of test data volume. In LSSD, Scan Path, Scan/Set, or Random-Access Scan, a considerable amount of test data volume is involved with the shifting in and out. With BIBLO, if 100 patterns are run between scan-outs, the test data volume may be reduced by a factor of 100. The overhead for this technique is higher than for LSSD since about two EXCLUSIVE-OR's must be used per latch position. Also, there is more delay in the system data path (one or two gate delays). If VLSI has the huge number of logic gates available than this may be a very efficient way to use them.

Recently, a technique was shown which could be used to test a network with fairly minor changes to the network. The technique is Syndrome Testing. The technique requires that all 2^n patterns be applied to the input of the network and then the number of 1's on the output be counted [115], [116].

Testing is done by comparing the number of 1's for the good machine to the number of 1's for the faulty machine. If there is a difference, the fault(s) in the faulty machine are detected (or Syndrome testable). To be more formal the Syndrome is:

Definition 1: The *Syndrome S* of a Boolean function is defined as

$$S = \frac{K}{2^n}$$

where K is the number of minterns realized by the function, and n is the number of binary input lines to the Boolean function.

Not all Boolean functions are totally Syndrome testable for all the single stuck-at-faults. Procedures are given in [115] with a minimal or near minimal number of primary inputs to make the networks Syndrome testable. In a number of "real networks" (i.e., SN74181, etc.) the numbers of extra primary inputs needed was at most one (<5 percent) and not more than two gates (<4 percent) were needed. An extension [116] to this work was published which showed a way of making a network Syndrome testable by adding extra inputs. This resulted in a somewhat longer test sequence. This is accomplished by holding some input constant while applying all 2^k inputs ($k < n$) then holding others constant and applying 2^l input patterns to l inputs. Whether the network is modified or not, the test data volume for a Syndrome testable design is extremely low. The general test setup is shown in Fig. 23.

The structure requires a pattern generator which applies all possible patterns once, a counter to count the 1's, and a com-

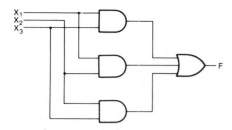

Fig. 24. Function to be tested with Walsh coefficients.

TABLE I
Examples of Walsh Functions and Walsh Coefficients

$X_1X_2X_3$	W_2	$W_{1,3}$	F	W_2F	$W_{1,3}F$	W_{ALL}	$W_{ALL}F$
0 0 0	−1	+1	0	+1	−1	+1	+1
0 0 1	−1	−1	0	+1	+1	−1	−1
0 1 0	+1	+1	0	−1	−1	−1	−1
0 1 1	+1	−1	1	+1	−1	+1	−1
1 0 0	−1	−1	0	+1	+1	−1	−1
1 0 1	−1	+1	1	−1	+1	+1	−1
1 1 0	+1	−1	1	+1	−1	+1	−1
1 1 1	+1	+1	1	+1	+1	−1	+1

$$C_{ALL} = 4$$

pare network. The overhead quoted is necessary to make the CUT Syndrome testable and does not include the pattern generator, counter, or compare register.

C. Testing by Verifying Walsh Coefficients

A technique which is similar to Syndrome Testing, in that it requires all possible input patterns be applied to the combinational network, is testing by verifying Walsh coefficients [117]. This technique only checks two of the Walsh coefficients and then makes conclusions about the network with respect to stuck-at-faults.

In order to calculate the Walsh coefficients, the logical value 0 (1) is associated with the arithmetic value −1(+1). There are 2^n Walsh functions. W_0 is defined to be 1, W_i is derived from all possible (arithmetic) products of the subject of independent input variables selected for that Walsh function. Table I shows the Walsh function for W_2, $W_{1,3}$, then W_2F, $W_{1,3}F$, finally W_{all} and $W_{all}F$. These values are calculated for the network in Fig. 24. If the values are summed for $W_{all}F$, the Walsh coefficient C_{all} is calculated. The Walsh coefficient C_0 is just W_0F summed. This is equivalent to the Syndrome in magnitude times 2^n. If $C_{all} \neq 0$ then all stuck-at-faults on primary inputs will be detected by measuring C_{all}. If the fault is present $C_{all} = 0$. If the network has $C_{all} = 0$ it can be easily modified such that $C_{all} \neq 0$. If the network has reconvergent fan-out then further checks need to be made (the number of inverters in each path has a certain property); see [117]. If these are successful, then by checking C_{all} and C_0, all the single stuck-at-faults can be detected. Some design constraints maybe needed to make sure that the network is testable by measuring C_{all} and C_0. Fig. 25 shows the network needed to determine C_{all} and C_0. The value p is the parity of the driving counter and the response counter is an up/down counter. Note, two passes must be made of the driving counter, one for C_{all} and one for C_0.

D. Autonomous Testing

The fourth technique which will be discussed in the area of self-test/built-in-test is Autonomous Testing [118]. Autonomous Testing like Syndrome Testing and testing Walsh coefficients requires all possible patterns be applied to the network inputs. However, with Autonomous Testing the outputs of

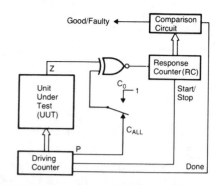

Fig. 25. Tester for veryfying C_0 and C_{all} Walsh coefficients.

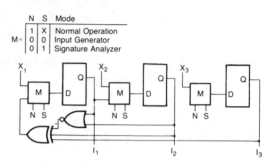

Fig. 26. Reconfigurable 3-bit LFSR module.

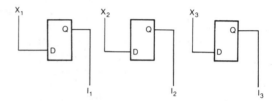

N = 1: Normal Operation

Fig. 27. Reconfigurable 3-bit LFSR module.

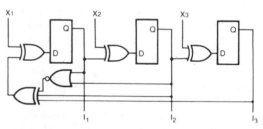

N = 0, S = 1: Signature Analyzer

Fig. 28. Reconfigurable 3-bit LFSR module.

the network must be checked for each pattern against the value for the good machine. The results is that irrespective of the fault model Autonomous Testing will detect the faults (assuming the faulty machine does not turn into a sequential machine from a combinational machine). In order to help the network apply its own patterns and accumulate the results of the tests rather than observing every pattern for 2^n input patterns, a structure similar to BILBO register is used. This register has some unique attributes and is shown in Figs. 26–29. If a combinational network has 100 inputs, the network must be modified such that the subnetwork can be verified and, thus, the whole network will be tested.

Two approaches to partitioning are presented in the paper "Design for Autonomous Test" [118]. The first is to use

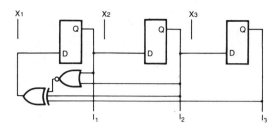

N = 0, S = 0: Input Generator

Fig. 29. Reconfigurable 3-bit LFSR module.

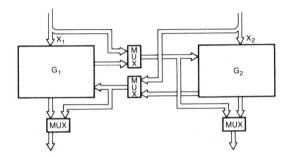

Fig. 30. Autonomous Testing—general network.

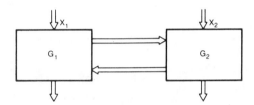

Fig. 31. Autonomous Testing—functional mode.

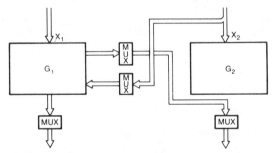

Fig. 32. Autonomous Testing—configuration to test network G_1.

multiplexers to separate the network and the second is a Sensitized Partitioning to separate the network. Fig. 30 shows the general network with multiplexers, Fig. 31 shows the network in functional mode, and Fig. 32 shows the network in a mode to test subnetwork G_1. This approach could involve a significant gate overhead to implement in some networks. Thus the Sensitized Partitioning approach is put forth. For example, the 74181 ALU/Function Generator is partitioned using the Sensitized Partitioning. By inspecting the network, two types of subnetworks can be partitioned out, four subnetworks N_1, one subnetwork N_2 (Figs. 33 and 34). By further inspection, all the L_i outputs of network N_1 can be tested by holding $S_2 = S_3 = $ low. Further, all the H_i outputs of network N_1 can be tested by holding $S_0 = S_1 = $ high, since sensitized paths exist through the subnetwork N_2. Thus far fewer than 2^n input patterns can be applied to the network to test it.

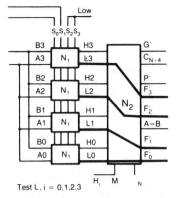

Test L, i = 0,1,2,3

Fig. 33. Autonomous Testing with sensitized partitioning.

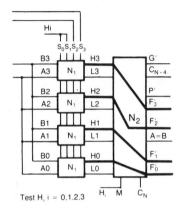

Test H, i = 0.1.2.3

Fig. 34. Autonomous Testing with sensitized partitioning.

VI. Conclusion

The area of Design for Testability is becoming a popular topic by necessity. Those users of LSI/VLSI which do not have their own captive IC facilities are at the mercy of the vendors for information. And, until the vendor information is drastically changed, the Ad Hoc approaches to design for testability will be the only answer.

In that segment of the industry which can afford to implement the Structured Design for Testability approach, there is considerable hope of getting quality test patterns at a very modest cost. Furthermore, many innovative techniques are appearing in the Structured Approach and probably will continue as we meander through VLSI and into more dense technologies.

There is a new opportunity arriving in the form of gate arrays that allow low volume users access to VLSI technology. If they choose, structured design disciplines can be utilized. Perhaps "Silicon Foundries" of the future will offer a combined package of structured, testable modules and support software to automatically provide the user with finished parts AND tests.

Acknowledgment

The authors wish to thank D. J. Brown for his helpful comments and suggestions. The assistance of Ms. B. Fletcher, Ms. C. Mendoza, Ms. L. Clark, Ms. J. Allen, and J. Smith in preparing this manuscript for publication was invaluable.

References

General References and Surveys

[1] M. A. Breuer, Ed., *Diagnosis and Reliable Design of Digital Systems.* Rockville, MD: Computer Science Press, 1976.
[2] H. Y. Chang, E. G. Manning, and G. Metze, *Fault Diagnosis of*

Digital Systems. New York: Wiley-Interscience, 1970.

[3] A. D. Friedman and P. R. Menon, *Fault Detection in Digital Circuits.* Englewood Cliffs, NJ: Prentice-Hall, 1971.

[4] F. C. Hennie, *Finite State Models for Logical Machines.* New York: Wiley, 1968.

[5] P. G. Kovijanic, in "A new look at test generation and verification," in *Proc. 14th Design Automation Conf.,* IEEE Pub. 77CH1216-1C, pp. 58–63, June 1977.

[6] E. I. Muehldorf, "Designing LSI logic for testability," in *Dig. Papers, 1976 Ann. Semiconductor Test Symp.,* IEEE Pub. 76CH1179-1C, pp. 45–49, Oct. 1976.

[7] E. I. Muehldorf and A. D. Savkar, "LSI logic testing—An overview," *IEEE Trans. Comput.,* vol. C-30, no. 1, pp. 1–17, Jan. 1981.

[8] W. W. Peterson and E. J. Weldon, *Error Correcting Codes.* Cambridge, MA: MIT Press, 1972.

[9] A. K. Susskind, "Diagnostics for logic networks," *IEEE Spectrum,* vol. 10, pp. 40–47, Oct. 1973.

[10] T. W. Williams and K. P. Parker, "Testing logic networks and design for testability," *Computer,* pp. 9–21, Oct. 1979.

[11] IEEE, Inc., *IEEE Standard Dictionary of Electrical and Electronics Terms.* New York: Wiley-Interscience, 1972.

Designing for Testability

[12] "A designer's guide to signature analysis," Hewlett-Packard Application Note 222, Hewlett Packard, 5301 Stevens Creek Blvd., Santa Clara, CA 95050.

[13] S. B. Akers, "Partitioning for testability," *J. Des. Automat. Fault-Tolerant Comput.,* vol. 1, no. 2, Feb. 1977.

[14] H. Ando, "Testing VLSI with random access scan," in *Dig. Papers Compcon 80,* IEEE Pub. 80CH1491-OC, pp. 50–52, Feb. 1980.

[15] P. Bottorff and E. I. Muehldorf, "Impact of LSI on complex digital circuit board testing," *Electro 77,* New York, NY, Apr. 1977.

[16] S. DasGupta, E. B. Eichelberger, and T. W. Williams, "LSI chip design for testability," in *Dig. Tech. Papers, 1978 Int. Solid-State Circuits Conf.* (San Francisco, CA, Feb. 1978), pp. 216–217.

[17] "Designing digital circuits for testability," Hewlett-Packard Application Note 210-4, Hewlett Packard, Loveland, CO 80537.

[18] E. B. Eichelberger and T. W. Williams, "A logic design structure for LSI testability," *J. Des. Automat. Fault-Tolerant Comput.,* vol. 2, no. 2, pp. 165–178, May 1978.

[19] ——, "A logic design structure for LSI testing," in *Proc. 14th Design Automation Conf.,* IEEE Pub. 77CH1216-1C, pp. 462–468, June 1977.

[20] E. B. Eichelberger, E. J. Muehldorf, R. G. Walter, and T. W. Williams, "A logic design structure for testing internal arrays," in *Proc. 3rd USA-Japan Computer Conf.* (San Francisco, CA, Oct. 1978), pp. 266–272.

[21] S. Funatsu, N. Wakatsuki, and T. Arima, "Test generation systems in Japan," in *Proc. 12th Design Automation Symp.,* pp. 114–122, June 1975.

[22] H. C. Godoy, G. B. Franklin, and P. S. Bottoroff, "Automatic checking of logic design structure for compliance with testability groundrules," in *Proc. 14th Design Automation Conf.,* IEEE Pub. 77CH1216-1C, pp. 469–478, June 1977.

[23] J. P. Hayes, "On modifying logic networks to improve their diagnosability," *IEEE Trans. Comput.,* vol. C-23, pp. 56–62, Jan. 1974.

[24] J. P. Hayes and A. D. Friedman, "Test point placement to simplify fault detection," in *FTC-3, Dig. Papers, 1973 Symp. on Fault-Tolerant Computing,* pp. 73–78, June 1973.

[25] B. Koenemann, J. Mucha, and G. Zwiehoff, "Built-in logic block observation techniques," in *Dig. Papers, 1979 Test Conf.,* IEEE Pub. 79CH1509-9C, pp. 37–41, Oct. 1979.

[26] M. D. Lippman and E. S. Donn, "Design forethought promotes easier testing of microcomputer boards," *Electronics,* pp. 113–119, Jan. 18, 1979.

[27] H. J. Nadig, "Signature analysis-concepts, examples, and guidelines," *Hewlett-Packard J.,* pp. 15–21, May 1977.

[28] M. Neil and R. Goodner, "Designing a serviceman's needs into microprocessor based systems," *Electronics,* pp. 122–128, Mar. 1, 1979.

[29] S. M. Reddy, "Easily testable realization for logic functions," *IEETC Trans. Comput.,* vol. C-21, pp. 1183–1188, Nov. 1972.

[30] K. K. Saliya and S. M. Reddy, "On minimally testable logic networks," *IEEE Trans. Comput.,* vol. C-23, pp. 1204–1207, Nov. 1974.

[31] J. H. Stewart, "Future testing of large LSI circuit cards," in *Dig. Papers 1977 Semiconductor Test Symp.,* IEEE Pub. 77CH1261-7C, pp. 6–17, Oct. 1977.

[32] A. Toth and C. Holt, "Automated data base-driven digital testing," *Computer,* pp. 13–19, Jan. 1974.

[33] E. White, "Signature analysis, enhancing the serviceability of microprocessor-based industrial products," in *Proc. 4th IECI Annual Conf.,* IEEE Pub. 78CH1312-8, pp. 68–76, Mar. 1978.

[34] M.J.Y. Williams and J. B. Angell, "Enhancing testability of large scale integrated circuits via test points and additional logic," *IEEE Trans. Comput.,* vol. C-22, pp. 46–60, Jan. 1973.

[35] T. W. Williams, "Utilization of a structured design for reliability and serviceability," in *Dig., Government Microcircuits Applications Conf.* (Monterey, CA, Nov. 1978), pp. 441–444.

Faults and Fault Modeling

[36] R. Boute and E. J. McCluskey, "Fault equivalence in sequential machines," in *Proc. Symp. on Computers and Automata* (Polytech. Inst. Brooklyn, Apr. 13–15, 1971), pp. 483–507.

[37] R. T. Boute, "Optimal and near-optimal checking experiments for output faults in sequential machines," *IEEE Trans. Comput.,* vol. C-23, no. 11, pp. 1207–1213, Nov. 1974.

[38] ——, "Equivalence and dominance relations between output faults in sequential machines," Tech. Rep. 38, SU-SEL-72-052, Stanford Univ., Stanford, CA, Nov. 1972.

[39] F.J.O. Dias, "Fault masking in combinational logic circuits," *IEEE Trans. Comput.,* vol. C-24, pp. 476–482, May 1975.

[40] J. P. Hayes, "A NAND model for fault diagnosis in combinational logic networks," *IEEE Trans. Comput.,* vol. C-20, pp. 1496–1506, Dec. 1971.

[41] E. J. McCluskey and F. W. Clegg, "Fault equivalence in combinational logic networks," *IEEE Trans. Comput.,* vol. C-20, pp. 1286–1293, Nov. 1971.

[42] K.C.Y. Mei, "Fault dominance in combinational circuits," Tech. Note 2, Digital Systems Lab., Stanford Univ., Aug. 1970.

[43] ——, "Bridging and stuck-at faults," *IEEE Trans. Comput.,* vol. C-23, no. 7, pp. 720–727, July 1974.

[44] R. C. Ogus, "The probability of a correct output from a combinational circuit," *IEEE Trans. Comput.,* vol. C-24, no. 5, pp. 534–544, May 1975.

[45] K. P. Parker and E. J. McCluskey, "Analysis of logic circuits with faults using input signal probabilities," *IEEE Trans. Comput.,* vol. C-24, no. 5, pp. 573–578, May 1975.

[46] K. K. Saliya and S. M. Reddy, "Fault detecting test sets for Reed-Muller canonic networks," *IEEE Trans. Comput.,* pp. 995–998, Oct. 1975.

[47] D. R. Schertz and G. Metze, "A new representation for faults in combinational digital circuits," *IEEE Trans. Comput.,* vol. C-21, no. 8, pp. 858–866, Aug. 1972.

[48] J. J. Shedletsky and E. J. McCluskey, "The error latency of a fault in a sequential digital circuit," *IEEE Trans. Comput.,* vol. C-25, no. 6, pp. 655–659, June 1976.

[49] ——, "The error latency of a fault in a combinational digital circuit," in *FTCS-5, Dig. Papers, 5th Int. Symp. on Fault Tolerant Computing* (Paris, France, June 1975), pp. 210–214.

[50] K. To, "Fault folding for irredundant and redundant combinational circuits," *IEEE Trans. Comput.,* vol. C-22, no. 11, pp. 1008–1015, Nov. 1973.

[51] D. T. Wang, "Properties of faults and criticalities of values under tests for combinational networks," *IEEE Trans. Comput.,* vol. C-24, no. 7, pp. 746–750, July 1975.

Testing and Fault Location

[52] R. P. Batni and C. R. Kime, "A module level testing approach for combinational networks," *IEEE Trans. Comput.,* vol. C-25, no. 6, pp. 594–604, June 1976.

[53] S. Bisset, "Exhaustive testing of microprocessors and related devices: A practical solution," in *Dig. Papers, 1977 Semiconductor Test Symp.,* pp. 38–41, Oct. 1977.

[54] R. J. Czepiel, S. H. Foreman, and R. J. Prilik, "System for logic, parametric and analog testing," in *Dig. Papers, 1976 Semiconductor Test Symp.,* pp. 54–69, Oct. 1976.

[55] R. A. Frohwerk, "Signature analysis: A new digital field service method," *Hewlett-Packard J.,* pp. 2–8, May 1977.

[56] B. A. Grimmer, "Test techniques for circuit boards containing large memories and microprocessors," in *Dig. Papers, 1976 Semiconductor Test Symp.,* pp. 16–21, Oct. 1976.

[57] W. A. Groves, "Rapid digital fault isolation with FASTRACE," *Hewlett-Packard J.,* pp. 8–13, Mar. 1979.

[58] J. P. Hayes, "Rapid count testing for combinational logic circuits," *IEEE Trans. Comput.,* vol. C-25, no. 6, pp. 613–620, June 1976.

[59] ——, "Detection of pattern sensitive faults in random access memories," *IEEE Trans. Comput.,* vol. C-24, no. 2, Feb. 1975, pp. 150–160.

[60] ——, "Testing logic circuits by transition counting," in *FTC-5, Dig. Papers, 5th Int. Symp. on Fault Tolerant Computing* (Paris, France, June 1975), pp. 215–219.

[61] J. T. Healy, "Economic realities of testing microprocessors," in *Dig. Papers, 1977 Semiconductor Test Symp.,* pp. 47–52, Oct. 1977.

[62] E. C. Lee, "A simple concept in microprocessor testing," in *Dig.*

Papers, 1976 Semiconductor Test Symp., IEEE Pub. 76CH1179-1C, pp. 13–15, Oct. 1976.

[63] J. Losq, "Referenceless random testing," in *FTCS-6, Dig. Papers, 6th Int. Symp. on Fault-Tolerant Computing* (Pittsburgh, PA, June 21–23, 1976), pp. 81–86.

[64] S. Palmquist and D. Chapman, "Expanding the boundaries of LSI testing with an advanced pattern controller," in *Dig. Papers, 1976 Semicondctor Test Symp.*, pp. 70–75, Oct. 1976.

[65] K. P. Parker, "Compact testing: Testing with compressed data," in *FTCS-6, Dig. Papers, 6th Int. Symp. on Fault-Tolerant Computing* (Pittsburgh, PA, June 21–23, 1976).

[66] J. J. Shedletsky, "A rationale for the random testing of combinational digital circuits," in *Dig. Papers, Compcon 75 Fall Meet.* (Washington, DC, Sept. 9–11, 1975), pp. 5–9.

[67] V. P. Strini, "Fault location in a semiconductor random access memory unit," *IEEE Trans. Comput.*, vol. C-27, no. 4, pp. 379–385, Apr. 1978.

[68] C. W. Weller, in "An engineering approach to IC test system maintenance," in *Dig. Papers, 1977 Semiconductor Test Symp.*, pp. 144–145, Oct. 1977.

Testability Measures

[69] W. J. Dejka, "Measure of testability in device and system design," in *Proc. 20th Midwest Symp. Circuits Syst.*, pp. 39–52, Aug. 1977.

[70] L. H. Goldstein, "Controllability/observability analysis of digital circuits," *IEEE Trans. Circuits Syst.*, vol. CAS-26, no. 9, pp. 685–693, Sept. 1979.

[71] W. L. Keiner and R. P. West, "Testability measures," presented at AUTOTESTCON '77, Nov. 1977.

[72] P. G. Kovijanic, "testability analysis," in *Dig. Papers, 1979 Test Conf.*, IEEE Pub. 79CH1509-9C, pp. 310–316, Oct. 1979.

[73] J. E. Stephenson and J. Grason, "A testability measure for register transfer level digital circuits," in *Proc. 6th Fault Tolerant Computing Symp.*, pp. 101–107, June 1976.

Test Generation

[74] V. Agrawal and P. Agrawal, "An automatic test generation system for ILLIAC IV logic boards," *IEEE Trans. Comput.*, vol. C-C-21, no. 9, pp. 1015–1017, Sept. 1972.

[75] D. B. Armstrong, "On finding a nearly minimal set of fault detection tests for combinational logic nets," *IEEE Trans. Electron. Comput.*, vol. EC-15, no. 1, pp. 66–73, Feb. 1966.

[76] R. Betancourt, "Derivation of minimum test sets for unate logical circuits," *IEEE Trans. Comput.*, vol. C-20, no. 11, pp. 1264–1269, Nov. 1973.

[77] D. C. Bossen and S. J. Hong, "Cause and effect analysis for multiple fault detection in combinational networks," *IEEE Trans. Comput.*, vol. C-20, no. 11, pp. 1252–1257, Nov. 1971.

[78] P. S. Bottorff et al., "Test generation for large networks," in *Proc. 14th Design Automation Conf.*, IEEE Pub. 77CH1216-1C, pp. 479–485, June 1977.

[79] R. D. Edlred, "Test routines based on symbolic logic statements," *J. Assoc. Comput. Mach.*, vol. 6, no. 1, pp. 33–36, 1959.

[80] P. Goel, "Test generation costs analysis and projections," presented at the 17th Design Automation Conf., Minneapolis, MN, 1980.

[81] E. P. Hsieh et al., "Delay test generation," in *Proc. 14th Design Automation Conf.*, IEEE Pub. 77CH1216-1C, pp. 486–491, June 1977.

[82] C. T. Ku and G. M. Masson, "The Boolean difference and multiple fault analysis," *IEEE Trans. Comput.*, vol. C-24, no. 7, pp. 691–695, July 1975.

[83] E. I. Muehldorf, "Test pattern generation as a part of the total design process," in *LSI and Boards: Dig. Papers, 1978 Ann. Semiconductor Test Symp.*, pp. 4–7, Oct. 1978.

[84] E. I. Muehldorf and T. W. Williams, "Optimized stuck fault test patterns for PLA macros," in *Dig. Papers, 1977 Semiconductor Test Symp.*, IEEE Pub. 77CH1216-7C, pp. 89–101, Oct. 1977.

[85] M. R. Page, "Generation of diagnostic tests using prime implicants," Coordinated Science Lab. Rep. R-414, University of Illinois, Urbana, May 1969.

[86] S. G. Papaioannou, "Optimal test generation in combinational networks by pseudo Boolean programming," *IEEE Trans. Comput.*, vol. C-26, no. 6, pp. 553–560, June 1977.

[87] K. P. Parker, "Adaptive random test generation," *J. Des. Automat. Fault Tolerant Comput.*, vol. 1, no. 1, pp. 62–83, Oct. 1976.

[88] ——, "Probabilistic test generation," Tech. Note 18, Digital Systems Laboratory, Stanford University, Stanford, CA, Jan. 1973.

[89] J. F. Poage and E. J. McCluskey, "Derivation of optimum tests for sequential machines," in *Proc. 5th Ann. Symp. on Switching Circuit Theory and Logic Design*, pp. 95–110, 1964.

[90] ——, "Derivation of optimum tests to detect faults in combinational circuits," in *Mathematical Theory of Automation.* New

York: Polytechnic Press, 1963.

[91] G. R. Putzolu and J. P. Roth, "A heuristic algorithm for testing of asynchronous circuits," *IEEE Trans. Comput.*, vol. C-20, no. 6, pp. 639–647, June 1971.

[92] J. P. Roth, W. G. Bouricius, and P. R. Schneider, "Programmed algorithms to compute tests to detect and distinguish between failures in logic circuits," *IEEE Trans. Electron. Comput.*, vol. EC-16, pp. 567–580, Oct. 1967.

[93] J. P. Roth, "Diagnosis of automata failures: A calculus and a method," *IBM J. Res. Devel.*, no. 10, pp. 278–281, Oct. 1966.

[94] P. R. Schneider, "On the necessity to examine D-chairs in diagnostic test generation—An example," *IBM J. Res. Develop.*, no. 11, p. 114, Nov. 1967.

[95] H. D. Schnurmann, E. Lindbloom, R. G. Carpenter, "The weighted random test pattern generation," *IEEE Trans. Comput.*, vol. C-24, no. 7, pp. 695–700, July 1975.

[96] E. F. Sellers, M. Y. Hsiao, and L. W. Bearnson, "Analyzing errors with the Boolean difference," *IEEE Trans. Comput.*, vol. C-17, no. 7, pp. 676–683, July 1968.

[97] D. T. Wang, "An algorithm for the detection of tests sets for combinational logic networks," *IEEE Trans. Comput.*, vol. C-25, no. 7, pp. 742–746, July 1975.

[98] T. W. Williams and E. E. Eichelberger, "Random patterns within a structured sequential logic design," in *Dig. Papers, 1977 Semiconductor Test Symp.*, IEEE Pub. 77CH1261-7C, pp. 19–27, Oct. 1977.

[99] S. S. Yau and S. C. Yang, "Multiple fault detection for combinational logic circuits," *IEEE Trans. Comput.*, vol. C-24, no. 5, pp. 233–242, May 1975.

Simulation

[100] D. B. Armstrong, "A deductive method for simulating faults in logic circuits," *IEEE Trans. Comput.*, vol. C-22, no. 5, pp. 464–471, May 1972.

[101] M. A. Breuer, "Functional partitioning and simulation of digital circuits," *IEEE Trans. Comput.*, vol. C-19, no. 11, pp. 1038–1046, Nov. 1970.

[102] H.Y.P. Chiang et al., "Comparison of parallel and deductive fault simulation," *IEEE Trans. Comput.*, vol. C-23, no. 11, pp. 1132–1138, Nov. 1974.

[103] E. B. Eichelberger, "Hazard detection in combinational and sequential switching circuits," *IBM J. Res. Devel.*, Mar. 1965.

[104] E. Manning and H. Y. Chang, "Functional technique for efficient digital fault simulation," in *IEEE Int. Conv. Dig.*, p. 194, 1968.

[105] K. P. Parker, "Software simulator speeds digital board test generation," *Hewlett-Packard J.*, pp. 13–19, Mar. 1979.

[106] S. Seshu, "On an improved diagnosis program," *IEEE Trans. Electron. Comput.*, vol. EC-12, no. 1, pp. 76–79, Feb. 1965.

[107] S. Seshu and D. N. Freeman, "The diagnosis of asynchronous sequential switching systems," *IRE Trans, Electron. Compat.*, vol. EC-11, no. 8, pp. 459–465, Aug. 1962.

[108] T. M. Storey and J. W. Barry, "Delay test simulation," in *Proc. 14th Design Automation Conf.*, IEEE Pub. 77CH1216-1C, pp. 491–494, June 1977.

[109] S. A. Szygenda and E. W. Thompson, "Modeling and digital simulation for design verification diagnosis," *IEEE Trans. Comput.*, vol. C-25, no. 12, pp. 1242–1253, Dec. 1976.

[110] S. A. Szygenda, "TEGAS2—Anatomy of a general purpose test generation and simulation system for digital logic," in *Proc. 9th Design Automation Workshop*, pp. 116–127, 1972.

[111] S. A. Szygenda, D. M. Rouse, and E. W. Thompson, "A model for implementation of a universal time delay simulation for large digital networks," in *AFIPS Conf. Proc.*, vol. 36, pp. 207–216, 1970.

[112] E. G. Ulrich and T. Baker, "Concurrent simulation of nearly identical digital networks," *Computer*, vol. 7, no. 4, pp. 39–44, Apr. 1974.

[113] ——, "The concurrent simulation of nearly identical digital networks," in *Proc. 10th Design Automation Workshop*, pp. 145–150, June 1973.

[114] E. G. Ulrich, T. Baker, and L. R. Williams, "Fault test analysis techniques based on simulation," in *Proc. 9th Design Automation Workshop*, pp. 111–115, 1972.

[115] J. Savir, "Syndrome—Testable design of combinational circuits," *IEEE Trans. Comput.*, vol. C-29, pp. 442–451, June 1980 (corrections: Nov. 1980).

[116] ——, "Syndrome—Testing of 'syndrome-untestable' combinational circuits," *IEEE Trans. Comput.*, vol. C-30, pp. 606–608, Aug. 1981.

[117] A. K. Susskind, "Testing by verifying Walsh coefficients," in *Proc. 11th Ann. Symp. on Fault-Tolerant Computing* (Portland, MA), pp. 206–208, June 1981.

[118] E. J. McCluskey and S. Bozorgui-Nesbat, "Design for autonomous test," *IEEE Trans. Comput.*, vol. C-30, pp. 866–875, Nov. 1981.

Chapter VII: Automatic Test Application

Figure 7.1 illustrates the basic principle of digital testing. Binary patterns (or test vectors) are applied to the inputs of the circuit. The response of the circuit is compared with the expected response. The circuit is considered good if the responses match. Obviously, the quality of the tested circuit will depend upon the thoroughness of the test vectors. Generation and evaluation of test vectors is the main subject of this tutorial and has been discussed in the preceding chapters. In this chapter, we describe the mechanics of very large scale integration (VLSI) chip testing, which is an important part of the manufacturing process.

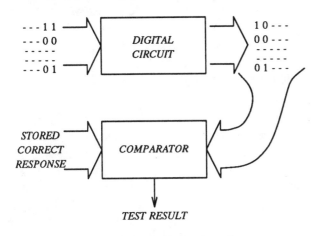

Figure 7.1: Principle of testing.

Our discussion on test application is rather brief and introductory. It is included because we consider some basic familiarity with this material essential for engineers involved in design and testing of VLSI. Sources of more detailed information are provided in the last section of this chapter.

1: The Testing Scenario

While Figure 7.1 illustrates the basics, it does not tell the full story. VLSI devices are tested by automatic test equipment (ATE) that performs a variety of tests [Stov84]. Modern ATE is a powerful computer operating under the control of a *test program* written in a high level language.

1.1: Types of Testing

VLSI testing can be classified into four types depending upon the specific purpose it accomplishes [Stev86].

Characterization: Also known as *design debug* or *verification testing,* this form of testing is performed on a new design before it is sent to production. The purpose is to verify that the design is correct and the device will meet all specifications. Functional tests are run and comprehensive AC and DC measurements are made. Probing of internal nodes of the chip, commonly not done in production testing, may also be required during characterization. Use of specialized tools like scanning electron microscope (SEM) and electron beam testers, and techniques like artificial intelligence (AI) and expert systems, can be effective. Design errors are diagnosed and corrected, chip characteristics are measured for setting final specifications, and a production test program is developed. A somewhat less comprehensive characterization testing is often continued throughout the production life of the device for possible improvements in the design and the process yield. This may be done on the chips rejected during the production test or in the field.

Production: Every fabricated chip is subjected to production test. These tests are less comprehensive than the characterization tests, yet they must enforce the quality requirements. For example, the vectors may not cover all possible functions and data patterns but must have a high coverage of modeled faults. At the chip level, fault diagnosis is generally not attempted and only a *go/no-go* decision is made. Production tests are typically short but verify all relevant specifications of the device.

Burn-in: All devices that pass production tests are

not identical. When put to actual use, some will fail very quickly while others will function for a long time. Burn-in ensures reliability of tested devices by testing, either continuously or periodically, over a long period and causing the bad devices to actually fail. According to correlation studies, the occurrence of potential failures can be accelerated at elevated temperatures. For a detailed theory of the burn-in process, the reader is referred to a book by Jensen and Petersen [Jens82]. Briefly, two types of failures are isolated by burn-in: *Infant mortality failures,* often caused by a combination of sensitive design and process variation, may be screened out by a short-term burn-in (10-30 hours) in a normal or slightly accelerated working environment. *Freak failures* (i.e., the devices having the same failure mechanisms as the reliable devices) require long burn-in time (100-1,000 hours) in an accelerated environment. In practice, a manufacturer must balance economic considerations against the device reliability. In any case, the elimination of infant mortality failures is considered essential.

Incoming Inspection: System manufacturers perform incoming inspection on the purchased devices before integrating them into the system. Depending upon the context, this testing can be either similar to production testing or more comprehensive than production testing or even tuned to the specific systems application. Also, the incoming inspection may be done for a random sample with the sample size depending on the device quality and the system requirement. The most important purpose of this testing is to reduce the chance of allowing a defective device in a system assembly where the cost of diagnosis may far exceed the cost of the incoming inspection.

1.2: Types of Tests

Actual selection of tests may depend upon the manufacturing level (processing, wafer, or package) at which testing is performed. Although some testing is done during device fabrication to assess the integrity of the process itself, most device testing is performed after the wafers have been fabricated. The first test, known as *wafer sort* or *probe,* differentiates potentially good devices from the defective ones [Eins85, Stev86]. After this, the wafer is scribed and cut, and the potentially good devices are packaged.

Also, during wafer sort, a *test site character-* *ization* is performed. Specially designed tests are applied to certain test sites on the wafer containing specific test structures. The tests and the site structures are designed to characterize the processing technology through measurement of parameters such as gate threshold, poly field threshold, bypass, metal field threshold, poly and metal sheet resistances, and contact resistance [Stev86].

In general, each chip is subjected to two types of tests:

1. Parametric tests: DC parametric tests include shorts test, opens test, maximum current test, leakage test, output drive current test, and threshold levels test. AC parametric tests include propagation delay test, setup and hold test, functional speed test, access time test, refresh and pause time test, and rise and fall time test. These tests are usually technology dependent. For example, voltage output measurements are done with no load in complementary metal oxide semiconductor (CMOS) devices while, bipolar devices require current load.

2. Functional Tests: These consist of the input vectors and the corresponding responses. They check for proper operation of a verified design by testing the internal nodes of the chip. Functional tests cover a very high percentage of modeled (e.g., stuck type) faults and their generation is the main topic of this tutorial.

Functional tests are used for several purposes. They may be applied at an elevated temperature to guarantee specifications. For example, testing may be done at 85 degree C to guarantee 70 degree operation. This is called *guardbanding.* Another application is in *speed binning* to grade the chips according to performance. This may be done by applying the tests at several voltages and at varying timing conditions (e.g., clock frequency).

The scenario described above represents a generality. The actual test plan for a VLSI device may vary depending upon factors such as the specific application it is intended for, manufacturer's test philosophy, available test equipment, and test economics.

While the general testing methodology is applicable to memory chips as well, there are some notable differences. Memory tests are *functional;* no stuck-type fault coverage is evaluated for these tests. The tests are designed to check functional attributes like address uniqueness, address decoder speed, cell coupling, column and row coupling, data sensitivity, write recovery, and refresh. Elaborate testing may require long vector sequences. To increase throughput, memory testers sometimes have parallel testing capability. Specialized testers may even provide a capability to repair redundant cells used in large memories (256K and 1M bits) to enhance yield.

VLSI chip testing, in many ways, resembles the testing of other digital equipment such as circuit boards [Park87]. But there are differences. Circuit boards consist of components that have already been tested. A primary objective of board testing is to check the printed wiring and the contacts between wires and components. It is possible to perform a bare-board testing of interconnections before the components are inserted. After the components (such as chips) are in place, *in-circuit testing* [Bate85] (through a *bed-of-nails* fixture) is often used to verify the performance of individual components. Finally, functional testing determines whether or not individual components, possibly designed with different technologies, function as a system and produce the expected response. The ATE employed for boards is different from that used for chips.

2: Test Specifications and Test Plan

Device specification, normally a document, initiates the development activity. This document contains the following information:

- Functional characteristics – Algorithms to be implemented,input-output signal characteristics (timing waveforms, signal levels, etc.), data and control signal behavior, clock rate.

- Type of device – Logic, microprocessor, memory, analog, etc.

- Physical characteristics – Package, pin assignments, etc.

- Technology – CMOS or bipolar gate array, full-custom or standard cell, etc.

- Environmental characteristics – Operating temperature range, supply voltage, humidity, etc.

- Reliability – Acceptance quality level (defective parts per million), failure rate per 1,000 hours, noise characteristics, etc.

Test specifications, if not given explicitly, are derived from the above data. On the basis of these test specifications, a test plan is generated. In the test plan, the type of test equipment and the type of tests are specified. Selection of a tester depends on such parameters as throughput, clock rate, timing accuracy, test sequence length, tester availability, and cost. The types of test may include parametric, functional, burn-in, margin, and speed sorting. Fault coverage requirement should also be specified.

3: Testers

The basic purpose of a tester is to drive the inputs and to monitor the outputs of a device under test. Testers are popularly known as ATE. Fast-changing VLSI technology has driven the development of modern ATE [Garc84, Kaza85, Poni85]. Selection of ATE for a VLSI device must consider the specifications of the device. Major factors are speed (clock rate of the device), timing (strobe) accuracy, number of input/output pins, etc. Other considerations in selecting a tester are cost, reliability, serviceability, ease of programming, etc. Detailed description of testers may be found in references cited in the last section.

4: Test Programming

Once the device under test has been mounted in the tester, *test program* and *test vectors* are needed to conduct the test. Earlier manual methods of test program development have given way to computer-aided design (CAD) tools [Ahre84, Teis86].

As shown in Figure 7.2, the device specifications spawn several activities. The results of these activities are required for the test program. An automatic test program generation system (often called TPG) requires three types of inputs:

1. Tester specification and the information on the types of tests is obtained from the test plan.

2. Physical data on the device (pin locations, wafer map, etc.) are obtained from the layout.

3. Timing information on signals and test vectors (inputs and expected responses) are obtained from simulators.

The test program contains the sequence of instructions that a tester would follow to conduct

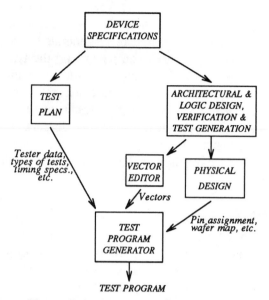

Figure 7.2: Test program generation.

testing. For example, a simple sequence of events will be apply power, apply clocks and vectors to input pins, strobe output pins, and compare output signals with stored expected response. Modern testers provide choice of input signal waveforms, masking of output signals, sensing of high impedance state, and a variety of sophisticated capabilities. Since testers differ in their capabilities and programming languages, TPGs commonly generate a *tester-independent* program which can be customized to any specific ATE [Hick83].

Also, since software simulators used in design verification differ from the ATE in their handling of signal format (logic values, timing, etc.), vector editors [Alle82, Gelm82] are useful tools during test programming.

5: Test Data Analysis

The test data obtained from the ATE serves three purposes. First, it helps to accept or reject the device under test. Second, it provides useful information about the fabrication process. Third, it provides information about weaknesses in the design.

Failing tests quickly point to faulty devices; however, the devices that do not fail during test can be considered *good* only if the tests covered 100 percent of faults. Analysis of test data provides information on device quality [Seth84]. Owing to the random variations in the fabrication process speed characteristics of devices vary. Test data analysis

allows sorting of chips for higher than the nominal performance.

Failure mode analysis (FMA) of the failed devices provides further information for improving the VLSI processing [Flow86]. Also, failing devices often show patterns of repeated failures. Probing into causes of these failures can point to weaknesses (sensitivity to process variations) in the design. Such information is used in improving logic and layout design rules [Liu78, Farn85].

6: Test Economics

Testing is responsible for the quality of VLSI devices. Several tradeoffs are often necessary to obtain the required quality level at minimal cost. Costs include the cost of ATE (initial and running costs), the cost of test development (CAD tools, test vector generation, test programming), and the cost of design for testability [Pitt84, Ambl86]. In the future, design for testability (DFT) will be a dominating factor in the equation of test economics. For instance, the scan design technique can significantly reduce the cost of test generation and the built-in self test (BIST) method can additionally lower the complexity and cost of ATE. DFT techniques should, therefore, be included in the device specification and the test plan.

7: Conclusion

Although test equipment, test programming, test data analysis, and test economics are topics with which most VLSI designers do not have direct involvement, each influences the overall device realization. This chapter has provided only a very brief introduction to these topics. We strongly encourage design engineers to become familiar with this material and follow up on the references when necessary. They will find the information useful in making decisions related to testing and quality.

8: Selected Reading

There are several excellent references on the topics mentioned in this chapter. Hardware aspects and application of ATE are discussed in detail by Stover [Stov84]. A very readable account of general concepts in testing, types of testing, test programming, and specifics of logic and memory testing is given by Stevens [Stev86]. Healy [Heal81] discusses these topics in more details. His book also includes test data analysis, test economics, test specifications, and discussions on tester selection and maintenance, and the future trends in ATE technology. The topic of burn-in is covered in detail by Jensen and Petersen [Jens82]. For more modern topics in test technology such as electron beam testing [Wolf88], artificial intelligence techniques and expert systems for diagnostics, we recommend that the reader review the bibliography given in Chapter VIII, Section 4.7.

9: References

[Ahre84] D. P. Ahrens, P. J. Bednarczyk, D. L. Denburg, and R. M. Robertson, "TPG2 – An Automatic Test Program Generator for Custom ICs," *Proc. Int. Test Conf.*, Philadelphia, PA, pp. 762-767, October 1984.

[Alle82] R. W. Allen, M. M. Ervin-Willis, and R. E. Tulloss, "DORA: CAD Interface to Automatic Diagnostics," *Proc. 19th Des. Auto. Conf.*, Las Vegas, Nevada, pp. 559-565, June 1982.

[Ambl86] A. P. Ambler, M. Paraskeva, D. F. Burrows, W. L. Knight, and I. D. Dear, "Economically Viable Automatic Insertion of Self-Test Features for Custom VLSI," *Proc. Int. Test Conf.*, Washington, D.C., pp. 232-243, September 1986.

[Bate85] J. Bateson, *In-Circuit Testing*, Van Nostrand Reinhold Company, New York, 1985.

[Eins85] N. G. Einspruch, *VLSI Handbook*, Academic Press, Orlando, FL, 1985.

[Farn85] D. F. Farnholtz, "Operational Life Testing of Electronic Components," *IEEE Design & Test of Computers*, Vol. 2, pp. 50-56, Dec., 1985.

[Flow86] A. D. Flowers, K. Mathur, and J. Isakson, "Statistical Process Control Using the Parametric Tester," *Proc. Int. Test Conf.*, Washington, D.C., pp. 422-427, September 1986.

[Garc84] R. Garcia, "The Fairchild Sentry 50 Tester: Establishing New Performance Limits," *IEEE Design & Test of Computers*, Vol. 1, pp. 101-109, May 1984.

[Gelm82] S. J. Gelman, "VEEP – A Vector Editor and Preparer," *Proc. 19th Des. Auto. Conf.*, Las Vegas, Nevada, pp. 771-776, June 1982.

[Heal81] J. T. Healy, *Automatic Testing and Evaluation of Digital Integrated Circuits*, Reston Publishing Company, Inc., Reston, VA, 1981.

[Hick83] R. L. Hickling, "Tester Independent Problem Representation and Tester Dependent Program Generation," *Proc. Int. Test Conf.*, Philadelphia, PA, pp. 476-482, October 1983.

[Jens82] F. Jensen and N. E. Petersen, *Burn-In*, John Wiley & Sons, Chichester, U.K., 1982.

[Kaza85] T. Kazamaki, "Milestones of New-Generation ATE," *IEEE Design & Test of Computers*, Vol. 2, pp. 83-89, October 1985.

[Liu78] B. C. S. Liu, "Automated Characterization Program for Microprocessors," *Semiconductor Test Conf., Digest of Papers*, Cherry Hill, NJ, pp. 209-217, October 1978.

[Park87] K. P. Parker, *Integrating Design and Test: Using CAE Tools for ATE Programming*, Computer Society Press, Washington, DC, 1987.

[Pitt84] J. S. Pittman and W. C. Bruce, "Test Logic Economic Considerations in a Commercial VLSI Chip Environment," *Proc. Int. Test Conf.*, Philadelphia, PA, pp. 31-39, October 1984.

[Poni85] W. Ponik, "Teradyne's J967 VLSI Test System: Getting VLSI to Market on Time," *IEEE Design & Test of Computers*, Vol. 2, pp. 57-62, December 1985.

[Seth84] S. C. Seth and V. D. Agrawal, "Characterizing the LSI Yield from Wafer Test Data," *IEEE Trans. on CAD*, Vol. CAD-3, pp. 123-126, April 1984, Also in *Proc. Int. Conf. Circ. Comp. (ICCC'82)*, New York, September 1982, pp. 556-559.

[Stev86] A. K. Stevens, *Introduction to Component Testing*, Addison-Wesley, Reading, MA, 1986.

[Stov84] A. C. Stover, *ATE: Automatic Test Equipment*, McGraw-Hill, New York, 1984.

[Teis86] J. Teisher, "Improved Workstation/Tester Interface is the Key to the Quality of Test-Program Generation," *Proc. Int. Test Conf.*, Washington, D.C., pp. 626-630, September 1986.

[Wolf88] E. Wolfgang, "Elecectron Beam Testing," in *Handbook of Advanced Semiconductor Technology and Computer Technology*, ed. G. Rabbat, Van Norstrand Reinhold, New York, 1988.

Chapter VIII: Sources of Information

In this information age, sometimes it is all too easy to get information. One is then faced with the task of sifting through this information to find the relevant pieces. In this chapter, we list various sources of information on VLSI testing.

1: Books

[1] E. A. Amersekera and D. S. Campbell, *Failure Mechanisms in Semiconductor Devices*, Wiley, Somerset, NJ, 1987.

[2] P. H. Bardell, W. H. McAnney, and J. Savir, *Built-In Test for VLSI: Pseudorandom Techniques*, Wiley, Somerset, NJ, 1987.

[3] J. Bateson, *In-Circuit Testing*, Van Nostrand Reinhold, New York, 1985.

[4] R. G. Bennetts, *Introduction to Digital Board Testing*, Crane Russak, New York, 1982.

[5] R. G. Bennetts, *Design of Testable Logic Circuits*, Addison-Wesley, Reading, MA, 1984.

[6] M. A. Breuer and A. D. Friedman, *Diagnosis & Reliable Design of Digital Systems*, Computer Science Press, Rockville, MD, 1976.

[7] H. Y. Chang, E. G. Manning, and G. Metze, *Fault Diagnosis of Digital Systems*, Wiley-Interscience, New York, 1970.

[8] J. M. Cortner, *Digital Test Engineering*, Wiley, Somerset, NJ, 1987.

[9] B. Davis, *The Economics of Automatic Testing*, McGraw-Hill, London, UK, 1982.

[10] N. G. Einspruch, *VLSI Handbook*, Academic Press, Orlando, FL, 1985.

[11] W. G. Fee, *Tutorial − LSI Testing*, Computer Society Press, Washington, D.C., 1978.

[12] R. J. Feugate and S. M. McIntyre, *Introduction to VLSI Testing*, Prentice-Hall, Englewood Cliffs, NJ, 1988.

[13] A. D. Friedman and P. R. Menon, *Fault Detection in Digital Circuits*, Prentice-Hall, Englewood Cliffs, NJ, 1971.

[14] H. Fujiwara, *Logic Testing and Design for Testability*, MIT Press, Cambridge, MA, 1985.

[15] W. D. Greason, *Electrostatic Damage in Electronics*, Wiley, Somerset, NJ, 1987.

[16] J. T. Healy, *Automatic Testing and Evaluation of Digital Integrated Circuits*, Reston Publishing Company, Inc., Reston, VA, 1981.

[17] F. Jensen and N. E. Petersen, *Burn-In*, John Wiley & Sons, Chichester, U.K., 1982.

[18] K. Kinoshita, K. Asada, and O. Karatsu, *Design of VLSI*, Iwanami-Shoten, 1985. In Japanese.

[19] Z. Kohavi, *Switching and Automata Theory*, McGraw-Hill, New York, 1978. Second Edition.

[20] P. K. Lala, *Fault Tolerant & Fault Testable Hardware Design*, Prentice-Hall International, London, UK, 1985.

[21] M. Mahoney, *DSP-Based Testing of Analog and Mixed-Signal Circuits (tutorial)*, Computer Society Press, Washington, DC, 1987.

[22] E. J. McCluskey, *Logic Design Principles, With Emphasis on Testable Semicustom Circuits*, Prentice-Hall, Englewood Cliffs, NJ, 1986.

[23] A. Miczo, *Digital Logic Testing and Simulation*, Harper & Row, New York, 1986.

[24] D. M. Miller, Ed., *Developments in Integrated Circuit Testing*, Academic Press, San Diego, CA, 1987.

[25] K. P. Parker, *Integrating Design and Test: Using CAE Tools for ATE Programming*, Computer

Society Press, Washington, DC, 1987.

[26] D. K. Pradhan, Ed., *Fault-Tolerant Computing Theory and Techniques*, I and II, Prentice-Hall, Englewood Cliffs, NJ, 1986.

[27] C. Pynn, *Strategies for Electronics Test*, McGraw-Hill, New York, 1986.

[28] H. K. Reghbati, *Tutorial: VLSI Testing & Validation Techniques*, Computer Society Press, Washington, D.C., 1985.

[29] C. Ronse, *Feedback Shift Registers*, Springer-Verlag, Berlin, 1984.

[30] J. P. Roth, *Computer Logic, Testing, and Verification*, Computer Science Press, Rockville, MD, 1980.

[31] N. Singh, *An Artificial Intelligence Approach to Test Generation*, Kluwer Academic Publishers, Norwell, MA, 1987.

[32] A. K. Stevens, *Introduction to Component Testing*, Addison-Wesley, Reading, MA, 1986.

[33] A. C. Stover, *ATE: Automatic Test Equipment*, McGraw-Hill, New York, 1984.

[34] C. C. Timoc, *Selected Reprints on Logic Design for Testability*, Computer Society Press, Washington, D.C., 1984.

[35] F. F. Tsui, *LSI-VLSI Testability Design*, McGraw-Hill, New York, 1986.

[36] B. R. Wilkins, *Testing Digital Circuits, An Introduction*, Van Nostrand Reinhold, Berkshire, UK, 1986.

[37] T. W. Williams, Ed., *VLSI Testing*, North-Holland, Amsterdam, The Netherlands, 1986.

2: Periodicals

- **IEEE Design & Test of Computers,** bimonthly, published by The Computer Society, Los Vaqueros Circle, Los Alamitos, CA carries articles on digital design and testing that are largely of practical interest.

- **IEEE Transactions on Computers,** published monthly by The Computer Society, is an excellent source of information on computers (including testing).

- **IEEE Transactions on Computer-Aided Design,** bimonthly, published by the IEEE Circuits and Systems Society, prints articles on CAD theory and practice.

- **Electronics Test,** a monthly publication by Morgan-Grampian Publishing Company (1050 Commonwealth Avenue, Boston, MA 02215) carries articles on test software and ATE.

- **Test & Measurement World,** published monthly by Cahners Publishing (275 Washington Street, Newton, MA 02158-1630) contains articles on or related to ATE products.

- **VLSI Systems Design,** published monthly by CMP Publications, Inc. (600 Community Drive, Manhasset, NY 11030) also contains articles on VLSI testing.

3: Conferences and Workshops

The major conference on testing is the **International Test Conference,** held annually. It is sponsored by the Test Technology Technical Committee (TTTC) of the Computer Society. The TTTC also sponsors **Built-In Self-Test Workshop** in Kiawah Island, South Carolina, the **Design for Testability Workshop** in Colorado, the **IEEE VLSI Test Workshop** in Atlantic City, New Jersey, and the **IEEE Test Programming Workshop** in Napa Valley, California. Any member of the IEEE or the Computer Society can join the TTTC at no additional cost. Information on their current activities is published in their Newsletter included in the IEEE Design & Test magazine, three times a year in the April, August, and December issues.

Four major conferences, the **Fault-Tolerant Computing Symposium (FTCS),** the **Design Automation Conference (DAC), International Conference on Computer Design (ICCD),** and **International Conference on Computer-Aided Design (ICCAD),** all held annually, devote a significant portion of their technical program to testing. Two other annual conferences, the **Custom Integrated Circuits Conference (CICC)** and the **International Symposium on Circuits and Systems (ISCAS)** also contain papers on VLSI testing.

4: Bibliography

Our bibliography is divided into seven sections corresponding to the chapters of this book. These sections are 4.1: General and Tutorial, 4.2: Fault Modeling, 4.3: Test Generation, 4.4: Test Evaluation, 4.5: Testability Analysis, 4.6: Design for

Testability, and 4.7: ATE, Test Programming, and other Production Testing Topics. To restrict the volume, we have included the papers published mostly during the 1980-1987 period. To an interested reader, this bibliography should provide a link to the earlier work on testing.

4.1: General and Tutorial

[1] V. D. Agrawal, "Computer-Aids in VLSI Design," *Int. Conf. on Computers, Systems & Signal Processing*, Bangalore, India, Dec. 1984, pp. 1273-1277.

[2] V. D. Agrawal and S. H. C. Poon, "VLSI design process," *1985 ACM Computer Science Conference*, New Orleans, Louisiana, March 1985, pp. 74-78.

[3] H. Amini, S. Hunt, R. Rebello, and M. Schuelein, "ASIC Design with Microcontrollers in Intel's iCEL [tm] Design System," *Proc. Custom Integrated Circ. Conf.*, Portland, OR, May 1985, pp. 442-446.

[4] R. E. Anderson, "Guest Editor's Introduction: Linking Design and Test," *IEEE Design & Test of Computers*, Vol. 1, pp. 27-31, May 1984.

[5] F. C. Bergsten, "Computer-Aided Design, Manufacturing, Assembly and Test (CAD-MAT)," *Proc. 18th Des. Auto. Conf.*, Nashville, TN, June 1981, pp. 873-880.

[6] P. S. Bottorff, "Computer Aids to Testing – An Overview," in *Computer Design Aids for VLSI Circuits*, P. Antognetti, D. O. Pederson, and H. deMan, Eds., Sijthoff & Noordhoff, Rockville, MD, 1981, pp. 417-463.

[7] J. M. Cortner, "Test Strategy for the 1990s," *Proc. Int. Test Conf.*, Washington, DC, September 1987, pp. 532-537.

[8] S. H. Cravens and R. D. Weir, "The Semi-Custom Design System Design Process," *Proc. Custom Integrated Circ. Conf.*, Portland, OR, May 1985, pp. 460-463.

[9] R. Dunn, "IC Quality Control by the User," *Proc. Int. Test Conf.*, Philadelphia, PA, October 1983, pp. 784-789.

[10] E. H. Frank and R. F. Sproull, "Testing and Debugging Custom Integrated Circuits," *ACM Computing Surveys*, Vol. 13, pp. 425-451, December 1981.

[11] H. Fujiwara, *Logic Testing and Design for Testability*, MIT Press, Cambridge, MA, 1985.

[12] S. Goshima, T. Kozawa, Y. Oka, T. Mori, Y. Takeguchi, and Y. Ohno, "Diagnostic System for Large Scale Logic Cards and LSI's," *Proc. 18th Des. Auto. Conf.*, Nashville, TN, June 1981, pp. 256-259.

[13] J. R. Haberer and M. S. Karlovic, "Military Specification, Qualification and Testing of VLSI," *Proc. Custom Integrated Circ. Conf.*, Rochester, NY, May 1984, pp. 295-299.

[14] "International Test Conference Roundtable: College Training of the Test Engineer," *IEEE Design & Test of Computers*, Vol. 3, pp. 74-78, April 1986.

[15] P. K. Lala, *Fault Tolerant & Fault Testable Hardware Design*, Prentice-Hall International, London, UK, 1985.

[16] W. K. Mann, "Microelectronic Device Test Strategies – A Manufacturer's Approach," *Test Conference Digest of Papers*, Philadelphia, PA, November 1980, pp. 195-202.

[17] A. Miczo, *Digital Logic Testing and Simulation*, Harper & Row, New York, 1986.

[18] E. I. Muehldorf and A. D. Savkar, "LSI Logic Testing – An Overview," *IEEE Trans. Computers*, Vol. C-30, pp. 1-17, January 1981.

[19] E. H. Potter, "Testability Considerations in a VLSI Design Automation System," *Test Conference Digest of Papers*, Philadelphia, PA, November 1980, pp. 26-28.

[20] R. A. Rasmussen, "Automated Testing of LSI," *Computer*, Vol. 15, pp. 69-78, March 1982.

[21] H. K. Reghbati, *Tutorial: VLSI Testing & Validation Techniques*, Computer Society Press, Washington, D.C., 1985.

[22] C. Robach, P. Malecha, and G. Michel, "CATA: A Computer-Aided Test Analysis System," *IEEE Design & Test of Computers*, Vol. 1, pp. 68-79, May 1984.

[23] G. D. Robinson, "Artificial Intelligence and Testing," *Proc. Int. Test Conf.*, Philadelphia, PA, October 1984, pp. 200-203.

[24] S. C. Seth and V. D. Agrawal, "A Review of Testing of Digital VLSI Devices," *IETE Technical Review*, Vol. 2, pp. 363-374, November 1985.

[25] S. C. Seth and V. D. Agrawal, "Cutting Chip

Testing Costs," *IEEE Spectrum*, Vol. 22, pp. 38-45, April 1985.

[26] D. P. Siewiorek and L. K. W. Lai, "Testing of Digital Systems," *Proc. IEEE*, Vol. 69, October 1981, pp. 1321-1333.

[27] A. K. Susskind, "Overview of Microprocessor Testing," *Proc. Int. Conf. Comp. Des. (ICCD'83)*, Port Chester, NY, October 1983, pp. 45-48.

[28] A. K. Susskind, "Survey of VLSI Test Strategies," *Proc. Custom Integrated Circ. Conf.*, Rochester, NY, May 1984, pp. 276-280.

[29] H. G. Thonemann, M. Kolonko, and H. Severloh, "VENUS® − An Advanced VLSI Design Environment for Custom Integrated Circuits with Macro Cells, Standard Cells and Gate Arrays," *Proc. Custom Integrated Circ. Conf.*, Portland, OR, May 1987, pp. 492-497.

[30] T. W. Williams, "VLSI Testing," *Computer*, Vol. 17, pp. 126-136, October 1984.

4.2: Fault Modeling

[1] M. S. Abadir and H. K. Reghbati, "Functional Testing of Semiconductor Random Access Memories," *ACM Computing Surveys*, Vol. 15, pp. 175-198, September 1983.

[2] M. Abramovici, P. R. Menon, and D. T. Miller, "Checkpoint Faults Are Not Sufficient Target Faults for Test Generation," *IEEE Trans. Computers*, Vol. C-35, pp. 769-771, August 1986.

[3] J. M. Acken and M. Horowitz, "A Static RAM as a Fault Model Evaluator," *Proc. Custom Integrated Circ. Conf.*, Portland, OR, May 1987, pp. 590-593.

[4] V. K. Agarwal and A. S. Fung, "Predictions of Multiple Fault Coverage Capability," *Fault-Tolerant Comp. Symp. (FTCS-10) Digest of Papers*, pp. 307-312, October 1980.

[5] V. K. Agarwal and A. S. F. Fung, "Multiple Fault Testing of Large Circuits by Single Fault Test Sets," *IEEE Trans. Computers*, Vol. C-30, pp. 855-865, November 1981.

[6] V. K. Agarwal and G. M. Masson, "Generic Fault Characterizations for Table Look-up Coverage Bounding," *IEEE Trans. Computers*, Vol. C-29, pp. 288-299, April 1980.

[7] V. D. Agrawal and D. D. Johnson, "Logic Modeling of PLA Faults," *Proc. Int. Conf. on Computer Design (ICCD-86)*, Port Chester, NY, October 1986, pp. 86-88.

[8] S. A. Al-Arian and D. P. Agrawal, "CMOS Fault Testing: Multiple Faults in Combinational Circuits Single Fault in Sequential Circuits," *Proc. Int. Test Conf.*, Philadelphia, PA, October 1984, pp. 218-223.

[9] S. A. Al-Arian and D. P. Agrawal, "Modeling and Testing of CMOS Circuits," *Proc. Int. Conf. Comp. Des. (ICCD'84)*, Port Chester, NY, October 1984, pp. 763-769.

[10] S. A. Al-Arian and D. P. Agrawal, "Physical Failures and Fault Models of CMOS Circuits," *IEEE Trans. Circ. and Syst.*, Vol. CAS-34, pp. 269-279, March 1987.

[11] E. A. Amersekera and D. S. Campbell, *Failure Mechanisms in Semiconductor Devices*, Wiley, Somerset, NJ, 1987.

[12] P. Banerjee and J. A. Abraham, "Fault Characterization of VLSI MOS Circuits," *Proc. Int. Conf. Circuits and Computers (ICCC'82)*, New York, NY, September 1982, pp. 564-568.

[13] P. Banerjee and J. A. Abraham, "Generating Tests for Physical Failures in MOS Logic Circuits," *Proc. Int. Test Conf.*, Philadelphia, PA, October 1983, pp. 554-559.

[14] P. Banerjee and J. A. Abraham, "Murphy − A Logic Simulator for NMOS and CMOS VLSI Circuits," *Proc. Int. Conf. CAD (ICCAD-83)*, Santa Clara, CA, September 1983, pp. 94-95.

[15] P. Banerjee and J. A. Abraham, "Characterization and Testing of Physical Failures in MOS Logic Circuits," *IEEE Design & Test of Computers*, Vol. 1, pp. 76-86, August 1984.

[16] P. Banerjee and J. A. Abraham, "A Multivalued Algebra for Modeling Physical Failures in MOS VLSI Circuits," *IEEE Trans. on CAD*, Vol. CAD-4, pp. 312-321, July 1985.

[17] Z. Barzilai, V. S. Iyengar, B. K. Rosen, and G. M. Silberman, "Accurate Fault Modeling and Efficient Simulation of Differential CVS Circuits," *Proc. Int. Test Conf.*, Philadelphia, PA, November 1985, pp. 722-729.

[18] D. Baschiera and B. Courtois, "Testing CMOS: A Challenge," *VLSI Design*, Vol. V, p. 58, October 1984.

[19] D. Baschiera and B. Courtois, "Advances in Fault Modelling and Test Pattern Generation for

CMOS," *Proc. Int. Conf. Comp. Des. (ICCD)*, Port Chester, NY, October 1986, pp. 82-85.

[20] C. C. Beh, K. H. Arya, C. E. Radke, and K. E. Torku, "Do Stuck Fault Models Reflect Manufacturing Defects?," *Int. Test Conf. Digest of Papers*, Philadelphia, PA, November 1982, pp. 35-42.

[21] C. Bellon, G. Saucier, and J. M. Gobbi, "Hardware Description Levels and Test for Complex Circuits," *Proc. 18th Des. Auto. Conf.*, Nashville, TN, June 1981, pp. 213-219.

[22] P. Bose and J. A. Abraham, "Test Generation for Programmable Logic Arrays," *Proc. ACM/ IEEE Design Automation Conf.*, Las Vegas, Nevada, June 1982, pp. 574-580.

[23] D. C. Bossen and S. J. Hong, "Cause-Effect Analysis for Multiple Fault Detection in Combinational Networks," *IEEE Trans. Computers*, Vol. C-20, pp. 1252-1257, November 1971. Also Comments by W. Coy, ibid, Vol. C-29, pp. 757-759, Aug. 1980.

[24] R. E. Bryant, "A Switch-Level Model and Simulator for MOS Digital Systems," *IEEE Trans. Computers*, Vol. C-33, pp. 160-177, Feb. 1984.

[25] R. E. Bryant, "A Survey of Switch-Level Algorithms," *IEEE Design & Test of Computers*, Vol. 4, pp. 26-40, August 1987.

[26] K. B. Cameron and J. C. Shovic, "Calculating Minimum Logic State Requirements for Multi-Strength Multi-Value MOS Logic Simulators," *Proc. Int. Conf. Comp. Des. (ICCD-87)*, Rye Brook, NY, October 1987, pp. 672-675.

[27] R. Chandramouli, "On Testing Stuck-Open Faults," *13th Int. Symp. Fault Tolerant Computing (FTCS-13) Digest of Papers*, pp. 258-265, June 1983.

[28] R. Chandramouli and H. Sucar, "Defect Analysis and Fault Modeling in MOS Technology," *Proc. Int. Test Conf.*, Philadelphia, PA, November 1985, pp. 313-321.

[29] S. J. Chang and M. A. Breuer, "A Fault-Collapsing Analysis in Sequential Logic Networks," *Bell Syst. Tech. Jour.*, Vol. 60, pp. 2259-2271, Nov. 1981.

[30] W. T. Cheng and J. H. Patel, "Multiple-Fault Detection in Iterative Logic Arrays," *Proc. Int. Test Conf.*, Philadelphia, PA, November 1985, pp. 493-499.

[31] K. W. Chiang and Z. G. Vranesic, "A Tree Representation of Combinational Networks," *IEEE Trans. Computers*, Vol. C-32, pp. 315-319, March 1983.

[32] M. L. Cortes and E. J. McCluskey, "An Experiment on Intermittent-Failure Mechanism," *Proc. Int. Test Conf.*, Washington, D.C., September 1986, pp. 435-442.

[33] B. T. Cunningham, W. K. Fuchs, and P. Banerjee, "Fault Characterization and Delay Fault Testing of GaAs Logic Circuits," *Proc. Int. Test Conf.*, Washington, DC, September 1987, pp. 836-842.

[34] D. G. Edwards, "Testing for MOS Integrated Circuit Failure Modes," *Test Conference Digest of Papers*, Philadelphia, PA, November 1980, pp. 407-416.

[35] Y. M. El-ziq and S. Y. H. Su, "Fault Diagnosis of MOS Combinational Networks," *IEEE Trans. Computers*, Vol. C-31, pp. 129-139, February 1982.

[36] Y. M. Elziq, "Classifying, Testing, and Eliminating VLSI MOS Failures," *VLSI Design*, Vol. IV, p. 30, September 1983.

[37] F. J. Ferguson and J. P. Shen, "Multiple-Fault Test Sets for MOS Complex Gates," *Proc. Int. Conf. on CAD (ICCAD)*, Santa Clara, CA, November 1985, pp. 36-38.

[38] J. Galiay, Y. Crouzet, and M. Vergniault, "Physical Versus Logical Fault Models MOS LSI Circuits: Impact on Their Testability," *IEEE Trans. Computers*, Vol. C-29, pp. 527-531, June 1980.

[39] A. Goundan and J. P. Hayes, "Identification of Equivalent Faults in Logic Networks," *IEEE Trans. Computers*, Vol. C-29, pp. 978-985, November 1980.

[40] W. D. Greason, *Electrostatic Damage in Electronics*, Wiley, Somerset, NJ, 1987.

[41] A. K. Gupta and J. R. Armstrong, "Functional Fault Modeling and Simulation for VLSI Devices," *Proc. 22nd Des. Auto. Conf.*, Las Vegas, Nevada, June 1985, pp. 720-726.

[42] I. N. Hajj and D. Saab, "Fault Modeling and Logic Simulation of MOS VLSI Circuits based on Logic Expression Extraction," *Proc. Int. Conf. CAD (ICCAD-83)*, Santa Clara, CA, September 1983, pp. 99-100.

[43] C. F. Hawkins and J. M. Soden, "Electrical Characteristics and Testing Considerations for Gate Oxide Shorts in CMOS ICs," *Proc. Int. Test Conf.*, Philadelphia, PA, November 1985, pp. 544-555.

[44] J. P. Hayes, "Fault Modeling of Digital MOS Integrated Circuits," *IEEE Trans. on CAD*, Vol. CAD-3, pp. 200-208, July 1984.

[45] J. P. Hayes, "Fault Modeling," *IEEE Design & Test of Computers*, Vol. 2, pp. 88-95, April 1985.

[46] J. P. Hayes, "An Introduction to Switch-Level Modeling," *IEEE Design & Test of Computers*, Vol. 4, pp. 18-25, August 1987.

[47] J. L. A. Hughes and E. J. McCluskey, "An Analysis of the Multiple Fault Detection Capabilities of Single Stuck-At Fault Test Sets," *Proc. Int. Test Conf.*, Philadelphia, PA, October 1984, pp. 52-58.

[48] J. L. A. Hughes and E. J. McCluskey, "Multiple Stuck-at Fault Coverage of Single Stuck-at Fault Test Sets," *Proc. Int. Test Conf.*, Washington, D.C., September 1986, pp. 368-374.

[49] J. Jacob and N. N. Biswas, "GTBD Faults and Lower Bounds on Multiple Fault Coverage of Single Fault Test Sets," *Proc. Int. Test Conf.*, Washington, D.C., September 1987, pp. 849-855.

[50] S. K. Jain and V. D. Agrawal, "Test Generation for MOS Circuits Using D-Algorithm," *Proc. ACM/IEEE 20th Design Automation Conf.*, Miami Beach, FL, June 1983, pp. 64-70.

[51] S. K. Jain and V. D. Agrawal, "Modeling and Test Generation Algorithms for MOS Circuits," *IEEE Trans. Computers*, Vol. C-34, pp. 426-433, May 1985. Also see, Correction, in *IEEE Trans. Computers*, Vol. C-34, p. 680, July 1985.

[52] N. K. Jha, "Detecting Multiple Faults in CMOS Circuits," *Proc. Int. Test Conf.*, Washington, D.C., September 1986, pp. 514-519.

[53] N. K. Jha, "Multiple Stuck-Open Fault Detection in CMOS Logic Circuits," *IEEE Trans. Computers*, Vol. 37, pp. 426-432, April 1988.

[54] K. L. Kodandapani and D. K. Pradhan, "Undetectability of Bridging Faults and Validity of Stuck-at Fault Test Sets," *IEEE Trans. Computers*, Vol. C-29, pp. 55-59, January 1980.

[55] S. Koeppe, "Modeling and Simulation of Delay Faults in CMOS Logic Circuits," *Proc. Int. Test Conf.*, Washington, D.C., September 1986, pp. 530-536.

[56] I. Kohavi and Z. Kohavi, "Detection of Multiple Faults in Combinational Logic Networks," *IEEE Trans. Computers*, Vol. C-21, pp. 556-573, June 1972.

[57] F. Kremla, "General Criterion for Essential Nonfault Locatability of Logical Functions," *IEEE Trans. Computers*, Vol. C-36, pp. 623-629, May 1987.

[58] M. W. Levi, "CMOS is Most Testable," *Int. Test Conf. Digest of Papers*, Philadelphia, PA, October 1981, pp. 217-220.

[59] C. C. Liaw, S. Y. H. Su, and Y. K. Malaiya, "Test-Experiments for Detection and Location of Intermittent Faults in Sequential Circuits," *IEEE Trans. Computers*, Vol. C-30, pp. 989-995, December 1981. also *Fault-Tolerant Comp. Symp. (FTCS-11) Digest of Papers*, June 1981, pp. 244-246.

[60] C. J. Lin and S. M. Reddy, "On Delay Fault Testing in Logic Circuits," *IEEE Trans. CAD*, Vol. CAD-6, pp. 694-703, September 1987. Also *Proc. Int. Conf. CAD (ICCAD-86)*, November 1986, pp. 148-151.

[61] F. C. H. Lin and S. Y. H. Su, "Single Feedback Bridging Fault in General Combinational Networks," *Test Conference Digest of Papers*, Philadelphia, PA, November 1980, pp. 185-191.

[62] B. Liu, "Soft Failure Detection and Correction in Microprocessor Characterization," *Int. Test Conf. Digest of Papers*, Philadelphia, PA, November 1982, pp. 458-460.

[63] S. L. Lusky and T. Sridhar, "Detectable CMOS Faults in Switch-Level Simulation," *Proc. Int. Test Conf.*, Philadelphia, PA, November 1985, pp. 875-883.

[64] Y. K. Malaiya, "Testing Stuck-On Faults in CMOS Integrated Circuits," *Proc. Int. Conf. CAD (ICCAD-84)*, Santa Clara, CA, November 1984, pp. 248-250.

[65] Y. K. Malaiya, A. P. Jayasumana, and R. Rajsuman, "A Detailed Examination of Bridging Faults," *Proc. Int. Conf. Comp. Des. (ICCD)*, Port Chester, NY, October 1986, pp. 78-81.

[66] Y. K. Malaiya and R. Narayanaswamy, "Modeling and Testing for Timing Faults in Synchronous Sequential Circuits," *IEEE Design & Test*

of Computers, Vol. 1, pp. 62-74, November 1984. Also *Proc. Int. Test Conf.*, Philadelphia, PA, October 1983, pp. 560-571.

[67] Y. K. Malaiya and S. Y. H. Su, "A New Fault Model and Testing Technique for CMOS Devices," *Int. Test Conf. Digest of Papers*, Philadelphia, PA, November 1982, pp. 25-34.

[68] W. Maly, "Fault Models for the NMOS Programmable Logic Array," *Proc. Custom Integrated Circ. Conf.*, Rochester, NY, May 1986, pp. 467-470.

[69] W. Maly, "Realistic Fault Modeling for VLSI Testing," *Proc. 24th Des. Auto. Conf.*, Miami Beach, FL, June 1987, pp. 173-180.

[70] W. Maly, F. J. Ferguson, and J. P. Shen, "Systematic Characterization of Physical Defects for Fault Analysis of MOS IC Cells," *Proc. Int. Test Conf.*, Philadelphia, PA, October 1984, pp. 390-399.

[71] T. E. Mangir and A. Avizienis, "Failure Modes for VLSI and Their Effect on Chip Design," *Proc. Int. Conf. Circ. Computers (ICCC-80)*, Port Chester, NY, October 1980, pp. 685-688.

[72] P. Marchal, "Updating Functional Fault Model for Microprocessor Internal Buses," *Fault-Tolerant Comp. Symp. (FTCS-15) Digest of Papers*, pp. 58-64, June 1985.

[73] P. Marchal and B. Courtois, "On Detecting the Hardware Failures Disrupting Programs in Microprocessors," *Fault-Tolerant Comp. Symp. (FTCS-12) Digest of Papers*, pp. 249-256, June 1982.

[74] V. Masurkar, "An Algorithmic Pretest Development for Fault Identification in Analog Networks," *Proc. 18th Des. Auto. Conf.*, Nashville, TN, June 1981, pp. 204-212.

[75] K. D. Mendl, "CMOS VLSI Challenges to Test," *Proc. Int. Test Conf.*, Philadelphia, PA, October 1984, pp. 642-648.

[76] A. Miczo, "Fault Modelling for Functional Primitives," *Int. Test Conf. Digest of Papers*, Philadelphia, PA, November 1982, pp. 43-49.

[77] Y. Min and S. Y. H. Su, "Testing Functional Faults in VLSI," *Proc. 19th Des. Auto. Conf.*, Las Vegas, Nevada, June 1982, pp. 384-392.

[78] P. S. Moritz and L. M. Thorsen, "CMOS Circuit Testability," *IEEE J. Solid State Circ.*, Vol. SC-21, pp. 306-309, April 1986. also *Proc.*

Custom Integrated Circ. Conf., May 1985, pp. 311-314.

[79] V. V. Nickel, "VLSI – The Inadequacy of the Stuck at Fault Model," *Test Conference Digest of Papers*, Philadelphia, PA, November 1980, pp. 378-381.

[80] M. Nicolaidis, "Shorts in Self-Checking Circuits," *Proc. Int. Test Conf.*, Washington, DC, September 1987, pp. 408-417.

[81] A. Noore, R. S. Nutter, and R. E. Swartwout, "Creating a Test Knowledge Base for VLSI Testing," *Proc. Int. Conf. Comp. Des. (ICCD-87)*, Rye Brook, NY, October 1987, pp. 288-291.

[82] P. Odryna and A. J. Strojwas, "PROD: A VLSI Fault Diagnosis System," *IEEE Design & Test of Computers*, Vol. 2, pp. 27-35, December 1985.

[83] K. N. Oikonomou, "Abstractions of Finite-State Machines Optimal with Respect to Single Undetectable Output Faults," *IEEE Trans. Computers*, Vol. C-36, pp. 185-200, February 1987.

[84] V. G. Oklobdzija and P. G. Kovijanic, "On Testability of CMOS-Domino Logic," *Fault-Tolerant Comput. Symp. (FTCS-14), Digest of Papers*, pp. 50-55, June 1984.

[85] D. K. Pradhan, Ed., *Fault-Tolerant Computing Theory and Techniques*, I and II, Prentice-Hall, Englewood Cliffs, NJ, 1986.

[86] D. K. Pradhan and K. Son, "The Effect of Untestable Faults in PLAs and a Design for Testability," *Test Conference Digest of Papers*, Philadelphia, PA, November 1980, pp. 359-367.

[87] R. Rajsuman, Y. K. Malaiya, and A. P. Jayasumana, "On Accuracy of Switch-Level Modeling of Bridging Faults in Complex Gates," *Proc. 24th Des. Auto. Conf.*, Miami Beach, FL, June 1987, pp. 244-250.

[88] S. M. Reddy, V. D. Agrawal, and S. K. Jain, "A Gate Level Model for CMOS Combinational Logic Circuits with Application to Fault Detection," *Proc. 21st Des. Auto. Conf.*, Albuquerque, NM, June 1984, pp. 504-509.

[89] M. Renovell, G. Cambon, and D. Auvergne, "FSPICE: A Tool for Fault Modeling in MOS Circuits," *Integration, the VLSI Journal*, Vol. 3, pp. 245-255, September 1985.

[90] D. R. Schertz and G. Metze, "A New

Representation for Faults in Combinational Digital Circuits," *IEEE Trans. Computers*, Vol. C-21, pp. 858-866, August 1972.

[91] S. C. Seth and K. Narayanaswamy, "A Graph Model for Pattern-sensitive Faults in Random Access Memories," *IEEE Trans. Computers*, Vol. C-30, pp. 973-977, December 1981.

[92] J. P. Shen, W. Maly, and F. J. Ferguson, "Inductive Fault Analysis of MOS Integrated Circuits," *IEEE Design & Test of Computers*, Vol. 2, pp. 13-26, December 1985.

[93] F. M. Smith, "A Simulation Model for Functional Fault Injection Written in ISP," *Proc. Int. Conf. Circ. Computers (ICCC-80)*, Port Chester, NY, October 1980, pp. 742-745.

[94] G. L. Smith, "Model for Delay Faults Based upon Paths," *Proc. Int. Test Conf.*, Philadelphia, PA, November 1985, pp. 342-349.

[95] L. J. Sobotka, "The Effect of Backdriving Digital Integrated Circuits During In-Circuit Testing," *Int. Test Conf. Digest of Papers*, Philadelphia, PA, November 1982, pp. 269-286.

[96] J. M. Soden and C. E. Hawkins, "Test Considerations for Gate Oxide Shorts in CMOS ICs," *IEEE Design & Test of Computers*, Vol. 3, pp. 56-64, August 1986.

[97] K. Son and D. K. Pradhan, "Testing for Delay Faults in a PLA," *Proc. Int. Conf. Circ. Computers (ICCC'82)*, New York, NY, September 1982, pp. 346-349.

[98] C. H. Stapper, "Modeling of Defects in Integrated Circuit Photolithographic Patterns," *IBM J. Res. Develop.*, Vol. 28, pp. 461-475, July 1984.

[99] S. Y. H. Su and Y. I. Hsieh, "Testing Functional Faults in Digital Systems Described by Register Transfer Language," *Int. Test Conf. Digest of Papers*, Philadelphia, PA, October 1981, pp. 447-457.

[100] D. S. Suk and S. M. Reddy, "A March Test for Functional Faults in Semiconductor Random Access Memories," *IEEE Trans. Computers*, Vol. C-30, pp. 982-985, December 1981.

[101] F. L. Swern, S. J. Bavuso, A. L. Martensen, and P. S. Miner, "The Effect of Latent Faults on Highly Reliable Computer Systems," *IEEE Trans. Computers*, Vol. C-36, pp. 1000-1005, August 1987.

[102] M. Syrzycki, "Modelling of Spot Defects in MOS Transistors," *Proc. Int. Test. Conf.*, Washington, DC, September 1987, pp. 148-157.

[103] S. A. Szygenda and E. W. Thompson, "Fault Insertion Techniques and Models for Digital Logic Simulation," *Fall Joint Comp. Conf.*, 1972, pp. 875-884.

[104] N. N. Tendolkar, "Analysis of Timing Failures Due to Random AC Defects in VLSI Modules," *Proc. 22nd Des. Auto. Conf.*, Las Vegas, Nevada, June 1985, pp. 709-714.

[105] S. M. Thatte and J. A. Abraham, "Test Generation for Microprocessors," *IEEE Trans. Computers*, Vol. C-29, pp. 429-441, June 1980.

[106] P. Thevenod-Fosse and R. David, "Random Testing of the Control Section of a Microprocessor," *Fault-Tolerant Comp. Symp. (FTCS-13) Digest of Papers*, pp. 366-373, June 1983.

[107] C. Timoc, M. Buehler, T. Griswold, C. Pina, F. Stott, and L. Hess, "Logical Models of Physical Faults," *Proc. Int. Test Conf.*, Philadelphia, PA, October 1983, pp. 546-553.

[108] C. Vivier and G. Fournie, "Automatic Modeling of MOS Transistor Networks for Test Pattern Generation," *Proc. Int. Test Conf.*, Washington, DC, September 1986, pp. 340-349.

[109] R. L. Wadsack, "Fault Modeling and Logic Simulation of CMOS and MOS Integrated Circuits," *Bell Syst. Tech. Jour.*, Vol. 57, pp. 1449-1474, May-June 1978.

[110] K. D. Wagner, "The Error Latency of Delay Faults in Combinational and Sequential Circuits," *Proc. Int. Test Conf.*, Philadelphia, PA, November 1985, pp. 334-341.

[111] K. D. Wagner and E. J. McCluskey, "Effect of Supply Voltage on Circuit Propagation Delay and Test Applications," *Proc. Int. Conf. on CAD (ICCAD)*, Snata Clara, CA, November 1985, pp. 42-44.

[112] B. W. Woodhall, B. D. Newman, and A. G. Sammuli, "Empirical Results on Undetected CMOS Stuck-Open Failures," *Proc. Int. Test. Conf.*, Washington, DC, September 1987, pp. 166-170.

[113] H. J. Wunderlich and W. Rosenstiel, "On Fault Modeling for Dynamic MOS Circuits," *Proc. Des. Aut. Conf.*, Las Vegas, Nevada, June 1986, pp. 540-546.

[114] S. Xu and S. Y. H. Su, "Testing Feedback Bridging Faults Among Internal, Input and Output Lines by Two Patterns," *Proc. Int. Conf. Circ. Computers (ICCC'82)*, New York, NY, September 1982, pp. 214-217.

[115] S. Xu and S. Y. H. Su, "Detecting I/O and Internal Feedback Bridging Faults," *IEEE Trans. Computers*, Vol. C-34, pp. 553-557, June 1985.

[116] T. Yamada and T. Nanya, "Stuck-At Fault Tests in the Presence of Undetectable Bridging Faults," *IEEE Trans. Computers*, Vol. C-33, pp. 758-761, August 1984.

[117] Y. Yuan and T. Chen, "The Dynamic Testing of Combinational Logic Networks," *Fault-Tolerant Comp. Symp. (FTCS-12) Digest of Papers*, pp. 173-180, June 1982.

4.3: Test Generation

[1] J. Abadir and Y. Deswarte, "Run-Time Program for Self-Checking Single Board Computer," *Int. Test Conf. Digest of Papers*, Philadelphia, PA, November 1982, pp. 205-213.

[2] M. S. Abadir and H. K. Reghbati, "Functional Testing of Semiconductor Random Access Memories," *ACM Computing Surveys*, Vol. 15, pp. 175-198, September 1983.

[3] M. S. Abadir and H. K. Reghbati, "LSI Testing Techniques," *IEEE Micro*, Vol. 3, pp. 34-50, Feb. 1983.

[4] M. S. Abadir and H. K. Reghbati, "Functional Test Generation for LSI Circuits Described by Binary Decision Diagrams," *Proc. Int. Test Conf.*, Philadelphia, PA, November 1985, pp. 483-492.

[5] M. S. Abadir and H. K. Reghbati, "Functional Test Generation for Digital Circuits Described Using Binary Decision Diagrams," *IEEE Trans. Computers*, Vol. C-35, pp. 375-379, April 1986.

[6] M. S. Abadir and H. K. Reghbati, "Functional Test Generation Using Binary Decision Diagrams," *Comput. Math. Applic.*, Vol. 13, No. 5/6, pp. 413-430, 1987.

[7] Z. Abazi and P. Thevenod-Fosse, "Markov Models for the Random Testing Analysis of Cards," *Fault-Tolerant Comp. Symp. (FTCS-16) Digest of Papers*, pp. 272-277, July 1986.

[8] E. M. Aboulhamid, "Efficient Testing and Truth Table Verification of Unilateral Combinational Iterative Arrays," *Proc. Int. Conf. on CAD (ICCAD)*, Santa Clara, CA, November 1985, pp. 68-70.

[9] M. Abramovici and M. A. Breuer, "Multiple Fault Diagnosis in Combinational Circuits Based on an Effect-Cause Analysis," *IEEE Trans. Computers*, Vol. C-29, pp. 451-460, June 1980.

[10] M. Abramovici and M. A. Breuer, "Fault Diagnosis in Synchronous Sequential Circuits Based on an Effect-Cause Analysis," *IEEE Trans. Computers*, Vol. C-31, pp. 1165-1172, December 1982. Also *Fault-Tolerant Comp. Symp. (FTCS-10) Digest of Papers*, Kyoto, Japan, October 1980, pp. 313-315.

[11] M. Abramovici, J. J. Kulikowski, P. R. Menon, and D. T. Miller, "SMART and FAST: Test Generation for VLSI Scan-Design Circuits," *IEEE Design & Test of Computers*, Vol. 3, pp. 43-54, Aug., 1986. Also *Proc. Int. Test Conf.*, Philadelphia, PA, Nov., 1985, pp. 45-56.

[12] M. Abramovici and P. R. Menon, "A Practical Approach to Fault Simulation and Test Generation for Bridging Faults," *IEEE Trans. Computers*, Vol. C-34, pp. 658-663, July 1985. Also *Proc. Int. Test Conf.*, Philadelphia, PA, October 1983, pp. 138-142.

[13] C. F. Acken, "Automatic Test Generating Using a Matrix Model of Digital Systems," *Proc. Int. Conf. Circ. Computers (ICCC'82)*, New York, NY, September 1982, pp. 464-467.

[14] M. Adiletta, E. Cooper, and K. Gutfreund, "Automatic Test Generation for Generic Scan Designs," *Proc. Int. Test Conf.*, Philadelphia, PA, November 1985, pp. 40-44.

[15] V. K. Agarwal, "Multiple Fault Detection in Programmable Logic Arrays," *IEEE Trans. Computers*, Vol. C-29, pp. 518-522, June 1980.

[16] P. Agrawal, "Test Generation at Switch Level," *Int. Conf. Computer-Aided Design (ICCAD-84)*, Santa Clara, CA, Nov. 1984, pp. 128-130.

[17] P. Agrawal and V. D. Agrawal, "Probabilistic Analysis of Random Test Generation Method of Irredundant Combinational Logic Networks," *IEEE Transaction on Computers*, Vol. C-24, pp. 691-695, July, 1975.

[18] P. Agrawal and V. D. Agrawal, "On Monte Carlo Testing of Logic Tree Networks," *IEEE Trans. Computers*, Vol. C-15, pp. 664-667, June 1976.

[19] P. Agrawal and S. M. Reddy, "Test Generation at MOS Level," *Int. Conf. on Computer, Systems & Signal Processing*, Bangalore, India, Dec. 1984, pp. 1116-1119.

[20] V. D. Agrawal, "When to Use Random Testing," *IEEE Trans. Computers*, Vol. C-27, pp. 1054-1055, Nov. 1978. Also see comments by P. B. Schneck and the author's reply in *IEEE Trans. Comp.*, Vol. C-28, pp. 580-581, August 1979.

[21] V. D. Agrawal, "Information Theory in Digital Testing – A New Approach to Functional Test Pattern Generation," *Proc. Int. Conf. Circ. Computers (ICCC-80)*, Port Chester, NY, October 1980, pp. 928-931.

[22] V. D. Agrawal, "An Information Theoretic Approach to Digital Fault Testing," *IEEE Transaction on Computers*, Vol. C-30, pp. 582-587, August 1981.

[23] V. D. Agrawal and P. Agrawal, "An Automatic Test Generation System for Illiac IV Logic Boards," *IEEE Trans. Computers*, Vol. C-21, pp. 1015-1017, September 1972.

[24] V. D. Agrawal and D. D. Johnson, "Logic Modeling of PLA Faults," *Proc. Int. Conf. on Computer Design (ICCD-86)*, Port Chester, NY, October 1986, pp. 86-88.

[25] V. D. Agrawal, S. C. Seth, and C. C. Chuang, "Probabilistically Guided Test Generation," *Proc. of Int. Symp. Circuits and Systems (ISCAS)*, May 1985, pp. 687-689.

[26] A. N. Airapetian and J. F. McDonald, "Improved Test Set Generation Algorithm for Combinational Circuit Control," *Fault-Tolerant Computing Symp. (FTCS-9) Digest of Papers*, pp. 133-136, Jun. 1979.

[27] S. B. Akers, C. Joseph, and B. Krishnamurthy, "On the Role of Independent Fault Sets in the Generation of Minimal Test Sets," *Proc. Int. Test Conf.*, Washington, DC, September 1987, pp. 1100-1107.

[28] M. A. Annaratone and M. G. Sami, "An Approach to Functional Testing of Microprocessors," *Fault-Tolerant Comp. Symp. (FTCS-12) Digest of Papers*, pp. 158-164, June 1982.

[29] D. B. Armstrong, "On Finding a Nearly Minimal Set of Fault Detection Tests for Combinational Logic Nets," *IEEE Trans. Electronic Computers*, pp. 66-74, October 1965.

[30] D. S. Barclay and J. R. Armstrong, "A Heuristic Chip-Level Test Generation Algorithm," *Proc. 23rd Des. Auto. Conf.*, Las Vegas, Nevada, June 1986, pp. 257-262.

[31] L. Basto, P. Harrod, and W. Bruce, "Testing the MC68030 Caches," *Proc. Int. Test Conf.*, Washington, DC, September 1987, pp. 826-833.

[32] C. Bellon, A. Liothin, S. Sadier, G. Saucier, R. Velazco, F. Grillot, and M. Issenman, "Automatic Generation of microprocessor Test Programs," *Proc. 19th Des. Auto. Conf.*, Las Vegas, Nevada, June 1982, pp. 566-573.

[33] C. Bellon, C. Robach, and G. Saucier, "An Intelligent Assistant for Test Program Generation: The Supercat System," *Proc. Int. Conf. CAD (ICCAD-83)*, Santa Clara, CA, September 1983, pp. 32-33.

[34] C. Bellon, C. Robach, and G. Saucier, "VLSI Test Program Generation: A System for Intelligent Assistance," *Proc. Int. Conf. Comp. Des. (ICCD'83)*, Port Chester, NY, October 1983, pp. 49-52.

[35] C. Bellon and R. Velazco, "Hardware and Software Tools for Microprocessor Functional Test," *Proc. Int. Test Conf.*, Philadelphia, PA, October 1984, pp. 804-810.

[36] M. J. Bending, "Hitest: A Knowledge-Based Test Generation System," *IEEE Design & Test of Computers*, Vol. 1, pp. 83-92, May 1984.

[37] C. Benmehrez and J. F. McDonald, "Measured Performance of a Programmed Implementation of the Subscripted D-Algorithm," *Proc. 20th Des. Auto. Conf.*, Miami Beach, FL, June 1983, pp. 308-315.

[38] C. Benmehrez and J. F. McDonald, "The Subscripted D-Algorithm – ATPG With Multiple Independent Control Paths," *ATPG Workshop Proceedings*, 1983, pp. 71-80.

[39] N. Benowitz, D. F. Calhoun, G. E. Anderson, J. E. Bauer, and C. T. Joeckel, "An Advanced Fault Isolation System for Digital Logic," *IEEE Trans. Comp.*, Vol. C-24, pp. 489-497, May 1975.

[40] R. Beresford, "Gate-array and Standard-cell Design Methods, Part 3: Test Generation," *VLSI Design*, Vol. V, p. 46, July 1984.

[41] W. E. D. Beste, "Using a Software Emulator to

Generate and Edit VLSI Test Patterns," *Electronics Test*, pp. 42-52, March 1984.

[42] D. Bhattacharya and J. P. Hayes, "High-Level Test Generation Using Bus Faults," *Fault-Tolerant Comp. Symp. (FTCS-15) Digest of Papers*, pp. 65-70, June 1985.

[43] P. Bose, "DEPLOMAT: A Design Expert for PLA Optimization, Maintenance and Test," *Proc. Int. Conf. Comp. Des. (ICCD-87)*, Rye Brook, NY, October 1987, pp. 292-296.

[44] P. Bose and J. A. Abraham, "Test Generation for Programmable Logic Arrays," *Proc. ACM/ IEEE Design Automation Conf.*, Las Vegas, Nevada, June 1982, pp. 574-580.

[45] D. Brahme and J. A. Abraham, "Functional Testing of Microprocessors," *IEEE Trans. Comp.*, Vol. C-33, pp. 475-485, June 1984.

[46] M. Brashler, D. Coleman, and R. Dubois, "An Integrated IC Test Development System," *Proc. Custom Integrated Circuits Conf.*, Rochester, NY, May 1984, pp. 169-171.

[47] R. D. Braun and D. T. Givone, "A Generalized Algorithm for Constructing Checking Sequences," *IEEE Trans. Computers*, Vol. C-30, pp. 141-144, February 1981.

[48] M. A. Breuer and M. Abramovici, "Fault Diagnosis Based on Effect-Cause Analysis," *Proc. 17th Des. Auto. Conf.*, Minneapolis, MN, June 1980, pp. 69-76.

[49] M. A. Breuer and R. L. Harrison, "Procedures for Eliminating Static and Dynamic Hazards in Test Generation," *IEEE Trans. Computers*, Vol. C-23, pp. 1069-1092, October 1974.

[50] R. E. Bryant, "Graph-Based Algorithms for Boolean Function Manipulation," *IEEE Trans. Comp.*, Vol. C-35, August 1986.

[51] J. L. Carter, S. F. Dennis, V. S. Iyengar, and B. K. Rosen, "ATPG via Random Pattern Simulation," *Proc. Int. Symp. Circuits and Systems (ISCAS)*, Tokyo, Japan, May 1985, pp. 683-686.

[52] E. Cerny, D. Mange, and E. Sanchez, "Synthesis of Minimal Binary Decision Trees," *IEEE Trans. Computers*, Vol. C-28, pp. 472-482, 1979.

[53] S. J. Chandra and J. H. Patel, "A Hierarchical Approach to Test Vector Generation," *Proc. 24th Des. Auto. Conf.*, Miami Beach, FL, June 1987, pp. 495-501.

[54] R. Chandramouli, "On Testing Stuck-Open Faults," *13th Int. Symp. Fault Tolerant Computing (FTCS-13) Digest of Papers*, pp. 258-265, June 1983.

[55] H. P. Chang, W. A. Rogers, and J. A. Abraham, "Structured Functional Level Test Generation Using Binary Decision Diagrams," *Proc. Int. Test Conf.*, Washington, DC, September 1986, pp. 97-104.

[56] S. G. Chappell, "Automatic Test Generation for Asynchronous Digital Circuits," *The Bell System Technical J.*, Vol. 53, pp. 1477-1503, Feb. 1974.

[57] A. Chatterjee and J. A. Abraham, "Test Generation for Arithmetic Units by Graph Labelling," *Fault-Tolerant Computing Symp. (FTCS-17) Digest of Papers*, pp. 284-289, July 1987.

[58] C. L. Chen and M. W. Du, "Multiple Stuck-Fault Detection and Location in Multivalued Linear Circuits," *IEEE Trans. Computers*, Vol. C-35, pp. 1068-1071, December 1986.

[59] H. H. Chen, R. G. Mathews, and J. A. Newkirk, "Test Generation for MOS Circuits," *International Test Conference*, Philadelphia, PA, Oct. 1984, pp. 70-79.

[60] H. H. Chen, R. G. Mathews, and J. A. Newkirk, "An Algorithm to Generate Tests for MOS Circuits at the Switch Level," *Proc. Int. Test Conf.*, Philadelphia, PA, November 1985, pp. 304-312.

[61] K. T. Cheng and V. D. Agrawal, "A Simulation-Based Directed-Search Method for Test Generation," *Proc. Int. Conf. Comp. Des. (ICCD-87)*, Rye Brook, NY, October 1987, pp. 48-51.

[62] W. T. Cheng and J. H. Patel, "A Minimum Test Set for Multiple-Fault Detection in Ripple Carry Adders," *Proc. Int. Conf. Comp. Des. (ICCD)*, Port Chester, NY, October 1985, pp. 435-438.

[63] W. T. Cheng and J. H. Patel, "A Shortest Length Test Sequence for Sequential-Fault Detection in Ripple Carry Adders," *Proc. Int. Conf. on CAD (ICCAD)*, Santa Clara, CA, November 1985, pp. 71-73.

[64] W. T. Cheng and J. H. Patel, "Testing in Two-dimensional Iterative Logic Arrays," *Fault-Tolerant Comp. Symp. (FTCS-16) Digest of Papers*, pp. 76-81, July 1986.

[65] W. T. Cheng and J. H. Patel, "A Minimum Test Set for Multiple Fault Detection in Ripple Carry Adders," *IEEE Trans. Computers*, Vol. C-36,

pp. 891-895, July 1987.

[66] W. T. Cheng and J. H. Patel, "Testing in Two-Dimensional Iterative Logic Arrays," *Comput. Math. Applic.*, Vol. 13, No. 5/6, 1987.

[67] K. W. Chiang and Z. G. Vranesic, "Test Generation for MOS Complex Gate Networks," *Fault-Tolerant Comp. Symp. (FTCS-12) Digest of Papers*, pp. 149-157, June 1982.

[68] K. W. Chiang and Z. G. Vranesic, "On Fault Detection in CMOS Logic Networks," *Proc. 20th Des. Auto. Conf.*, Miami Beach, FL, June 1983, pp. 50-56.

[69] R. J. Clarke, P. Arya, R. J. Potter, G. J. Smith, and I. D. Smith, "Hierarchical Design Verification and Incremental Test of a 100,000 Transistor Integrated Circuit," *Proc. Custom Integrated Circuit Conf.*, Rochester, NY, May 1984, pp. 601-605.

[70] B. Courtois, "Analytical Testing of Data Processing Sections of Integrated CPUs," *Int. Test Conf. Digest of Papers*, Philadelphia, PA, October 1981, pp. 21-28.

[71] M. Cutler, S. Y. H. Su, and M. Wang, "Test Generation by Critical Backtracing with Time Reducing Heuristics," *Proc. Int. Test Conf.*, Washington, DC, September 1987, pp. 1035-1042.

[72] W. Daehn, "A Unified Treatment of PLA Faults by Boolean Differences," *Proc. 23rd Des. Auto. Conf.*, Las Vegas, Nevada, June 1986, pp. 334-338.

[73] R. I. Damper and N. Burgess, "MOS Test Pattern Generation Using Path Algebras," *IEEE Trans. Computers*, Vol. C-36, pp. 1123-1128, September 1987.

[74] S. R. Das, W. B. Jones, Z. Chen, A. K. Nath, and T. T. Lee, "Fault Location in Combinational Logic Networks by Multistage Binary Tree Classifier," *Proc. Int. Conf. Circ. Computers (ICCC'82)*, New York, NY, September 1982, pp. 624-628.

[75] R. David and P. Thevenod-Fosse, "Minimal Detecting Transition Sequences: Application to Random Testing," *IEEE Trans. Computers*, Vol. C-29, pp. 514-518, June 1980.

[76] R. David and P. Thevenod-Fosse, "Random Testing of Intermittent Faults in Digital Circuits," *Fault-Tolerant Comp. Symp. (FTCS-10) Digest of Papers*, pp. 182-184, October 1980.

[77] T. A. Davis, R. P. Kunda, and W. K. Fuchs, "Testing of Bit-Serial Multipliers," *Proc. Int. Conf. Comp. Des. (ICCD)*, Port Chester, NY, October 1985, pp. 430-434.

[78] C. Delorme, P. Roux, L. D. D'Archimbaud, N. Giambiasi, R. L'Bath, B. MacGee, and R. Charroppin, "A Functional Partitioning Expert System for Test Sequences Generation," *Proc. 22nd Des. Auto. Conf.*, Las Vegas, Nevada, June 1985, pp. 820-824.

[79] F. Distante and V. Piuri, "Optimum Behavioral Test Procedure for VLSI Devices: A Simulated Annealing Approach," *Proc. Int. Conf. Comp. Des. (ICCD)*, Port Chester, NY, October 1986, pp. 31-35.

[80] M. El-Lithy and R. Husson, "Bit-Sliced Microprocessors Testing – A Case Study," *Fault-Tolerant Comp. Symp. (FTCS-10) Digest of Papers*, pp. 126-128, October 1980.

[81] Y. M. El-ziq, H. H. Butt, and A. K. Bhatt, "An Automatic Test Pattern Generation Machine," *Proc. Int. Conf. CAD (ICCAD-84)*, Santa Clara, CA, November 1984, pp. 257-259.

[82] Y. M. El-ziq and R. J. Cloutier, "Functional-Level Test Generation for Stuck-Open Faults in CMOS VLSI," *Int. Test Conference Digest of Papers*, Oct. 1981, pp. 536-546.

[83] Y. M. El-ziq and S. Y. H. Su, "Fault Diagnosis of MOS Combinational Networks," *IEEE Trans. Computers*, Vol. C-31, pp. 129-139, February 1982.

[84] Y. M. Elziq, "A New Test Pattern Generation System," *Proc. 17th Des. Auto. Conf.*, Minneapolis, MN, June 1980, pp. 62-68.

[85] Y. M. Elziq, "Automatic Test Generation for Stuck-Open Faults in CMOS VLSI," *Proc. 18th Des. Auto. Conf.*, Nashville, TN, June 1981, pp. 347-354.

[86] P. P. Fasang, "A Fault Detection and Isolation Technique for Microcomputers," *Int. Test Conf., Digest of Papers*, Nov. 1982, pp. 214-219.

[87] X. Fedi and R. David, "Experimental Results from Random Testing of Microprocessors," *Fault-Tolerant Comp. Symp. (FTCS-14) Digest of Papers*, pp. 225-230, June 1984.

[88] A. Feizi and D. Radhakrishnan, "Multiple Output Pass Networks: Design and Testing," *Proc. Int. Test Conf.*, Philadelphia, PA, November 1985, pp. 907-911.

[89] F. J. Ferguson and J. P. Shen, "Multiple-Fault Test Sets for MOS Complex Gates," *Proc. Int. Conf. on CAD (ICCAD)*, Santa Clara, CA, November 1985, pp. 36-38.

[90] D. Florcik and D. Low, "Simulation Pattern Capturing System for Design Verification Using a Dynamic High Speed Functional Tester," *Proc. Int. Test Conf.*, Philadelphia, PA, October 1983, pp. 122-127.

[91] S. Freeman, "The F-Path Method of Test Generation for Datapath Logic," *Proc. Custom Integrated Circ. Conf.*, Portland, OR, May 1987, pp. 72-77.

[92] J. F. Frenzel and P. N. Marinos, "Functional Testing of Microprocessors in a User Environment," *Fault-Tolerant Comput. Symp. (FTCS-14), Digest of Papers*, pp. 219-224, June 1984.

[93] A. Fuentes, R. David, and B. Courtois, "Random Testing Versus Deterministic Testing of RAMs," *Fault-Tolerant Comp. Symp. (FTCS-16) Digest of Papers*, pp. 266-271, July 1986.

[94] T. Fujieda and N. Arai, "Considerations of the Testing of RAMs with Dual Ports," *Proc. Int. Test Conf.*, Philadelphia, PA, November 1985, pp. 456-461.

[95] H. Fujiwara, "On Closedness and Test Complexity of Logic Circuits," *IEEE Trans. Computers*, Vol. C-30, pp. 556-562, August 1981.

[96] H. Fujiwara, K. Kinoshita, and H. Ozaki, "Universal Test Sets for Programmable Logic Arrays," *Fault-Tolerant Comp. Symp. (FTCS-10) Digest of Papers*, pp. 137-142, October 1980.

[97] H. Fujiwara and T. Shimono, "On the acceleration of test generation algorithms," *IEEE Trans. Comp.*, Vol. C-32, pp. 1137-1144, Dec. 1983.

[98] H. Fujiwara and S. Toida, "The Complexity of Fault Detection Problem for Combinational Logic Circuits," *IEEE Trans. Computers*, Vol. C-31, pp. 555-560, June 1982.

[99] S. Funatsu and H. Terai, "An Automatic Test-Generation System for Large Digital Circuits," *IEEE Design & Test of Computers*, Vol. 2, pp. 54-60, October 1985.

[100] N. Giambiasi, L'Bath, B. MacGee, C. Delorme, P. Roux, and L. D. D'Archimbaud, "An Adaptive and Evolutive Tool for Test Generation Process Based on Frames and Demons," *Fault-Tolerant Comp. Symp. (FTCS-15) Digest of Papers*, pp. 50-57, June 1985.

[101] G. Giles and C. Hunter, "A Methodology for Testing Content Addressable Memories," *Proc. Int. Test Conf.*, Philadelphia, PA, November 1985, pp. 471-474.

[102] P. Goel, "Test Generation Costs Analysis and Projections," *Proc. 17th Design Automation Conference*, Minneapolis, MN, June 1980, pp. 77-84.

[103] P. Goel, "An Implicit Enumeration Algorithm to Generate Tests for Combinational Logic Circuits," *IEEE Trans. Computers*, Vol. C-30, pp. 215-222, March 1981. Also *ault-Tolerant Comp. Symp. (FTCS-10) Digest of Papers*, Kyoto, Japan, October 1980, pp. 145-151.

[104] P. Goel and B. C. Rosales, "PODEM-X: An Automatic Test Generation System for VLSI Logic Structures," *Proc. 18th Des. Auto. Conf.*, Nashville, TN, June 1981, pp. 260-268.

[105] A. V. Goldberg and K. J. Lieberherr, "Efficient Test Generation Algorithms," *Proc. Int. Test Conf.*, Philadelphia, PA, November 1985, pp. 508-516.

[106] J. Grason and A. W. Nagle, "Digital Test Generation and Design for Testability," *Proc. 17th Design Auto. Conf.*, Minneapolis, MN, June 1980, pp. 175-189.

[107] N. L. Gunther and W. C. Carter, "Remarks on the Probability of Detecting Faults," *Fault-Tolerant Comp. Symp. (FTCS-10) Digest of Papers*, pp. 213-215, October 1980.

[108] I. S. Gupta, "Index Vector Testing of Combinational Circuits," *Proc. Int. Test Conf.*, Washington, DC, September 1987, pp. 1108-1112.

[109] T. Hayashi, K. Hatayama, K. Sato, and T. Natabe, "A Delay Test Generator for Logic LSI," *Fault-Tolerant Comput. Symp. (FTCS-14), Digest of Papers*, pp. 146-149, June 1984.

[110] J. P. Hayes, "Testing Memories for Single-Cell Pattern-Sensitive Faults," *IEEE Trans. Computers*, Vol. C-29, pp. 249-254, March 1980.

[111] B. J. Heard, R. N. Sheshadri, R. B. David, and A. G. Sammuli, "Automatic Test Pattern Generation for Asynchronous Networks," *Proc. Int. Test Conf.*, Philadelphia, PA, October 1984, pp. 63-69.

[112] F. C. Hennie, "Fault Detecting Experiments for Sequential Circuits," *Proc. 5th Ann. Symp. Sw.*

Cir. Theory and Logical Des.,", November 1964, pp. 95-110.

[113] F. J. Hill and B. Huey, "A Design Language Based Approach to Test Sequence Generation," *Computer*, pp. 28-33, June 1977.

[114] C. Hinchcliff, "Simplified Microprocessor Test Generation," *Int. Test Conf. Digest of Papers*, Philadelphia, PA, November 1982, pp. 176-180.

[115] H. Hofestadt and M. Gerner, "Qualitative Testability Analysis and Hierarchical Test Pattern Generation − A New Approach to Design for Testability," *Proc. Int. Test Conf.*, Washington, DC, September 1987, pp. 538-546.

[116] S. J. Hong, "Existence Algorithms for Synchronizing/Distinguishing Sequences," *IEEE Trans. Computers*, Vol. C-30, pp. 234-237, March 1981.

[117] S. J. Hong and D. L. Ostapko, "A Simple Procedure to Generate Optimum Test Patterns for Parity Logic Networks," *IEEE Trans. Computers*, Vol. C-30, pp. 356-358, May 1981.

[118] E. P. Hsieh, G. R. Putzolu, and C. J. Tan, "A Test Pattern Generation System for Sequential Logic Circuits," *Fault-Tolerant Comp. Symp. (FTCS-11) Digest of Papers*, pp. 230-232, June 1981.

[119] L. M. Huisman, "Random Pattern Testing of Logic Surrounding Embedded RAMS using Perturbation Analysis," *Proc. Int. Conf. Comp. Des. (ICCD)*, Port Chester, NY, October 1986, pp. 20-23.

[120] A. C. Hung and F. C. Wang, "A Method for Test Generation Directly from Testability Analysis," *Proc. Int. Test Conf.*, Philadelphia, PA, November 1985, pp. 62-78.

[121] A. Hunger and A. Gaertner, "Functional Characterization of Microprocessors," *Proc. Int. Test Conf.*, Philadelphia, PA, October 1984, pp. 794-803.

[122] K. S. Hwang and M. R. Mercer, "Derivation and Refinement of Fan-out Constraints to Generate Tests in Combinational Logic Circuits," *IEEE Trans. on CAD*, Vol. CAD-5, pp. 564-572, October 1986. Also *Proc. Int. Conf. on CAD (ICCAD)*, Santa Clara, CA, November 1985, pp. 10-12.

[123] K. S. Hwang and M. R. Mercer, "Informed Test Generation Guidance Using Partially Specified Fanout Constraints," *Proc. Int. Test Conf.*,

Washington, DC, September 1986, pp. 113-120.

[124] O. H. Ibarra and S. K. Sahni, "Polynomially Complete Fault Detection Problems," *IEEE Trans. Comp.*, Vol. C-24, pp. 242-249, March 1975.

[125] K. Itazaki and K. Kinishita, "Test Pattern Generation for Circuits with Three-State Modules by Improved Z-Algorithm," *Proc. Int. Test Conf.*, Washington, DC, September 1986, pp. 105-112.

[126] N. Itazaki and K. Kinoshita, "Algorithmic Generation of Test Patterns for Circuits with Tristate Modules," *Fault-Tolerant Comp. Symp. (FTCS-16) Digest of Papers*, pp. 64-69, July 1986.

[127] D. M. Jacobson, "A Fast, Probabilistic Algorithm for Functional Testing of Random Access Memory Systems," *Proc. Int. Test Conf.*, Philadelphia, PA, November 1985, pp. 169-177.

[128] S. K. Jain and V. D. Agrawal, "Test Generation for MOS Circuits Using D-Algorithm," *Proc. ACM/IEEE 20th Design Automation Conf.*, Miami Beach, FL, June 1983, pp. 64-70.

[129] S. K. Jain and V. D. Agrawal, "Modeling and Test Generation Algorithms for MOS Circuits," *IEEE Trans. Computers*, Vol. C-34, pp. 426-433, May 1985. Also see, Correction, in *IEEE Trans. Computers*, Vol. C-34, p. 680, July 1985.

[130] S. K. Jain and A. K. Susskind, "Test Strategy for Microprocessors," *Proc. 20th Des. Auto. Conf.*, Miami Beach, FL, June 1983, pp. 703-708.

[131] M. Johansson, "The GENESYS − Algorithm for ATPG without Fault Simulation," *Proc. Int. Test Conf.*, Philadelphia, PA, October 1983, pp. 333-337.

[132] M. Karpovsky, "Universal Tests Detecting Input/Output Faults in Almost All Devices," *Int. Test Conf. Digest of Papers*, Philadelphia, PA, November 1982, pp. 52-57.

[133] M. Karpovsky, "Universal Tests for Detection of Input/Output Stuck-at and Bridging Faults," *IEEE Trans. Computers*, Vol. C-32, pp. 1194-1198, Dec. 1983.

[134] M. Karpovsky and L. Levitin, "Detection and Identification of Input/Output Stuck-at and Bridging Faults in Combinational and Sequential VLSI Networks by Universal Tests," *Integration, the VLSI Journal*, Vol. 1, pp. 211-232, October 1983.

[135] M. Karpovsky and S. Y. H. Su, "Detection and Location of Input and Feedback Bridging Faults among Input and Output Lines," *IEEE Trans. Computers*, Vol. C-29, pp. 523-527, June 1980. Also see correction in *IEEE Trans. Comp.*, Vol. C-30, p. 86, Jan. 1981.

[136] M. Kawai, H. Shibano, S. Funatsu, S. Kato, T. Kurobe, K. Ookawa, and T. Sasaki, "A High Level Test Pattern Generation Algorithm," *Proc. Int. Test Conf.*, Philadelphia, PA, October 1983, pp. 346-352.

[137] R. Khorram, "Functional Test Pattern Generation for Integrated Circuits," *Proc. Int. Test Conf.*, Philadelphia, PA, October 1984, pp. 246-249.

[138] G. Kildiran and P. N. Marinos, "Functional Testing of Microprocessor-Like Architectures," *Proc. Int. Test Conf.*, Washington, D.C., September 1986, pp. 913-920.

[139] T. Kirkland and M. R. Mercer, "A Topological Search Algorithm for ATPG," *Proc. 24th Des. Auto. Conf.*, Miami Beach, FL, June 1987, pp. 502-508.

[140] T. J. Knips and D. J. Malone, "Designing Characterization Tests for Bipolar Array Performance Verification," *Proc. Int. Test Conf.*, Washington, D.C., September 1986, pp. 840-845.

[141] K. Kobayashi, "Functional Test Data Generation for Hardware Design Verification," *Proc. Int. Test Conf.*, Washington, DC, September 1987, pp. 547-552.

[142] B. Koenemann, J. Ducklow, N. Lanners, and T. Vriezen, "Computer Aided Test for VLSI," *Proc. Custom Integrated Circuits Conf.*, Rochester, NY, May 1984, pp. 172-175.

[143] G. A. Kramer, "Employing Massive Parallelism in Digital ATPG Algorithms," *Proc. Int. Test Conf.*, Philadelphia, PA, October 1983, pp. 108-114.

[144] B. Krishnamurthy, "Hierarchical Test Generation: Can AI Help?," *Proc. Int. Test Conf.*, Washington, DC, September 1987, pp. 694-700.

[145] B. Krishnamurthy and S. B. Akers, "On the Complexity of Estimating the Size of a Test Set," *IEEE Trans. Comput.*, Vol. C-33, pp. 750-753, Aug. 1984.

[146] G. Krueger, "Automatic Generation of Self-Test Programs – A New Feature of the MIMOLA Design System," *Proc. 23rd Des. Auto. Conf.*, Las Vegas, Nevada, June 1986, pp. 378-384.

[147] J. R. Kuban and J. E. Salick, "Testing Approaches in the MC68020," *VLSI Design*, Vol. V, p. 22, November 1984.

[148] H. Kubo, "A Procedure for Generating Test Sequences to Detect Sequential Circuit Failures," *NEC Res. & Dev.*, No. 12, pp. 69-78, October 1968.

[149] M. Ladjadj and J. F. McDonald, "Benchmark Runs of the Subscripted D-Algorithm with Observation Path Mergers on the Brglez-Fujiwara Circuits," *Proc. 24th Des. Auto. Conf.*, Miami Beach, FL, June 1987, pp. 509-515.

[150] M. Ladjadj, J. F. McDonald, D. H. Ho, and W. Murray Jr., "Use of the Subscripted DALG in Submodule Testing with Applications in Cellular Arrays," *Proc. 23rd Des. Auto. Conf.*, Las Vegas, Nevada, June 1986, pp. 346-353.

[151] K. W. Lai, "Test Program Compiler – A High Level Test Program Specification Language," *Proc. Int. Conf. CAD (ICCAD-83)*, Santa Clara, CA, September 1983, pp. 30-31.

[152] K. W. Lai and D. P. Siewiorek, "Functional Testing of Digital Systems," *Proc. 20th Des. Auto. Conf.*, Miami Beach, FL, June 1983, pp. 207-213.

[153] P. Lamoureux and V. K. Agarwal, "Non-Stuck-At Fault Detection in nMOS Circuits by Region Analysis," *Proc. Int. Test Conf.*, Philadelphia, PA, October 1983, pp. 129-137.

[154] J. D. Lesser and J. J. Shedletsky, "An Experimental Delay Test Generator for LSI Logic," *IEEE Trans. Computers*, Vol. C-29, pp. 235-248, March 1980.

[155] Y. Levendel and P. R. Menon, "The *-Algorithm: Critical Traces for Functions and CHDL Constructs," *Fault-Tolerant Comp. Symp. (FTCS-13) Digest of Papers*, pp. 90-97, June 1983.

[156] Y. H. Levendel and P. R. Menon, "Test Generation Algorithms for Nonprocedural Computer Hardware Description Languages," *Fault-Tolerant Comp. Symp. (FTCS-11) Digest of Papers*, pp. 200-205, June 1981.

[157] M. W. Levi, "Opens Tests for CMOS," *IEEE J. Solid State Circ.*, Vol. SC-22, p. 129, February 1987.

[158] C. Liaw, S. Y. H. Su, and Y. K. Malaiya, "Test

Generation for Delay Faults Using Stuck-at-Fault Test Set," *Test Conference Digest of Papers*, Philadelphia, PA, November 1980, pp. 167-175.

[159] C. C. Liaw, S. Y. H. Su, and Y. K. Malaiya, "State Diagram Approach for Functional Testing of Control Section," *Int. Test Conf. Digest of Papers*, Philadelphia, PA, October 1981, pp. 433-446.

[160] G. K. Lin and P. R. Menon, "Totally Preset Checking Experiments for Sequential Machines," *IEEE Trans. Computers*, Vol. C-32, pp. 101-108, February 1983.

[161] M. G. Lin and K. Rose, "Applying Test Theory to VLSI Testing," *Int. Test Conf. Digest of Papers*, Philadelphia, PA, November 1982, pp. 580-586.

[162] T. Lin and S. Y. H. Su, "Functional Test Generation of Digital LSI/VLSI Systems Using Machine Symbolic Execution Technique," *Proc. Int. Test Conf.*, Philadelphia, PA, October 1984, pp. 660-668.

[163] T. Lin and S. Y. H. Su, "The S-Algorithm: A Promising Solution for Systematic Functional Test Generation," *IEEE Trans. on CAD*, Vol. CAD-4, pp. 250-263 Also *Proc. Int. Conf. CAD (ICCAD-84)*, Santa Clara, CA, Nov. 1984, pp. 134-136, July 1985.

[164] T. Lin and S. Y. H. Su, "VLSI Functional Test Pattern Generation – A Design and Implementation," *Proc. Int. Test Conf.*, Philadelphia, PA, November 1985, pp. 922-929.

[165] R. Lisanke, F. Brglez, A. deGeus, and D. Gregory, "Testability-Driven Random Pattern Generation," *IEEE Trans. CAD*, Vol. CAD-6, pp. 1082-1087, November 1987. Also *Proc. Int. Conf. CAD (ICCAD-86)*, Santa Clara, CA, Nov., 1986, pp. 144-147.

[166] P. K. Lui and J. C. Muzio, "Spectral Signature Testing of Multiple Stuck-at Faults in Irredundant Combinational Networks," *IEEE Trans. Computers*, Vol. C-35, pp. 1088-1092, December 1986.

[167] R. H. Macmillan and M. R. Bentley, "An Efficient Test Vector Generation and Reduction Method for an LSI Digital Filter Circuit Using an Adaptive Search Technique," *Int. Test Conf. Digest of Papers*, Philadelphia, PA, November 1982, pp. 601-605.

[168] S. Mallela and S. Wu, "A Sequential Circuit Test Generation System," *Proc. Int. Test Conf.*, Philadelphia, PA, November 1985, pp. 57-61.

[169] M. Mannan, "Instability – A CAD Dilemma," *Proc. Int. Test Conf.*, Washington, D.C., September 1986, pp. 637-643.

[170] W. Mao and X. Ling, "Robust Test Generation Algorithm for Stuck-Open Fault in CMOS Circuits," *Proc. 23rd Des. Aut. Conf.*, Las Vegas, Nevada, June 1986, pp. 236-242.

[171] M. Marinescu, "Simple and Efficient Algorithms for Functional RAM Testing," *Int. Test Conf. Digest of Papers*, Philadelphia, PA, November 1982, pp. 236-239.

[172] R. Marlett, "An Effective Test Generation System for Sequential Circuits," *23rd Des. Aut. Conf.*, Las Vegas, Nevada, June 1986, pp. 250-256.

[173] R. Marlett, "Automated Test Generation for Integrated Circuits," *VLSI Systems Design*, Vol. VII, pp. 68-73, July 1986.

[174] W. P. Marnane, W. R. Moore, H. M. Yassine, E. Gautrin, N. Burgess, and A. P. H. McCabe, "Testing Bit-Level Systolic Arrays," *Proc. Int. Test Conf.*, Washington, DC, September 1987, pp. 906-914.

[175] C. Maunder, "HITEST Test Generation System – Interfaces," *Proc. Int. Test Conf.*, Philadelphia, PA, October 1983, pp. 324-332.

[176] P. Mazumder, J. H. Patel, and W. K. Fuchs, "Design and Algorithms for Parallel Testing of Random Access and Content Addressable Memories," *Proc. 24th Des. Auto. Conf.*, Miami Beach, FL, June 1987, pp. 688-694.

[177] W. H. McAnney, J. Savir, and S. R. Vecchio, "Random Pattern Testing for Address-line Faults in an Embedded Multiport Memory," *Proc. Int. Test Conf.*, Philadelphia, PA, November 1985, pp. 106-114.

[178] W. H. McAnney, J. Savir, and S. R. Vecchio, "Random Pattern Testing for Data-line Faults in an Embedded Multiport Memory," *Proc. Int. Test Conf.*, Philadelphia, PA, November 1985, pp. 100-105.

[179] E. J. McCluskey, "Verification Testing," *Proc. 19th Des. Auto. Conf.*, Las Vegas, Nevada, June 1982, pp. 495-500.

[180] J. F. McDonald and C. Benmehrez, "Test Set

Reduction Using Subscripted D-Algorithm," *Proc. Int. Test Conf.*, Philadelphia, PA, October 1983, pp. 115-121.

[181] J. F. McDonald and C. Benmehrez, "Test Set Reduction Using the Subscripted D-Algorithm," *Proc. International Test Conference*, Philadelphia, PA, October 1983, pp. 115-121.

[182] M. R. Mercer, V. D. Agrawal, and C. M. Roman, "Test Generation for Highly Sequential Scan-Testable Circuits Through Logic Transformation," *Int. Test Conference Digest of Papers*, Philadelphia, PA, Oct. 1981, pp. 561-565.

[183] A. Miczo, "The Sequential ATPG: A Theoretical Limit," *Proc. Int. Test Conf.*, Philadelphia, PA, October 1983, pp. 143-147.

[184] T. Middleton, "Functional Test Vector Generation for Digital LSI/VLSI Devices," *Proc. Int. Test Conf.*, Philadelphia, PA, October 1983, pp. 682-691.

[185] P. J. Miller and G. E. Taylor, "Automatic Test Generation for VLSI," *Proc. Int. Conf. Circ. Computers (ICCC'82)*, New York, NY, September 1982, pp. 452-455.

[186] H. Miyamoto, K. Mashiko, Y. Morooka, K. Arimoto, M. Yamada, and T. Nakano, "Test Pattern Considerations for Fault Tolerant High Density DRAM," *Proc. Int. Test Conf.*, Philadelphia, PA, November 1985, pp. 451-455.

[187] A. Motohara, K. Nishimura, H. Fujiwara, and I. Shirakawa, "A Parallel Scheme for Test-Pattern Generation," *Proc. Int. Conf. CAD (ICCAD-86)*, Santa Clara, CA, November 1986, pp. 156-159.

[188] S. Mourad, "An Optimized ATPG," *Proc. 17th Des. Auto. Conf.*, Minneapolis, MN, June 1980, pp. 381-385.

[189] E. I. Muehldorf, "Test Pattern Generation as a Part of the Total Design Process," *Semiconductor Test Conf., Digest of Papers*, Cherry Hill, NJ, October, 1978, pp. 4-7.

[190] E. I. Muehldorf, G. P. Papp, and T. W. Williams, "Efficient Test Pattern Generation for Embedded PLAs," *Test Conference Digest of Papers*, Philadelphia, PA, November 1980, pp. 349-358.

[191] E. I. Muehldorf and T. W. Williams, "Analysis of the Switching Behavior of Combinatorial Logic Networks," *Int. Test Conf. Digest of Papers*, Philadelphia, PA, November 1982, pp. 379-390.

[192] M. Murakami, N. Shiraki, and K. Hirakawa, "Logic Verification and Test Generation for LSI Circuits," *Test Conference Digest of Papers*, Philadelphia, PA, November 1980, pp. 467-472.

[193] P. Muth, "A Nine-Valued Circuit Model for Test Generation," *IEEE Trans. Computers*, Vol. C-25, pp. 630-636, June 1976.

[194] J. C. Muzio and D. M. Miller, "Spectral Techniques for Fault Detection," *Fault-Tolerant Comp. Symp. (FTCS-12) Digest of Papers*, pp. 297-302, June 1982.

[195] S. Naito and M. Tsunoyama, "Fault Detection for Sequential Machines by Transition Tours," *Fault-Tolerant Comp. Symp. (FTCS-11) Digest of Papers*, pp. 238-243, June 1981.

[196] A. S. Nale and S. Y. H. Su, "Testing a PLA without Augmentation," *Proc. Int. Test Conf.*, Washington, DC, September 1987, pp. 111-118.

[197] S. Nitta, K. Kawamura, and K. Hirabayashi, "Test Generation by Activation and Defect-Drive (TEGAD)," *Integration, The VLSI Journal*, Vol. 3, pp. 3-12, March 1985.

[198] S. E. Noujaim, R. T. Jerdonek, and S. J. Hong, "A Structured Approach to Test Vector Generation," *Proc. Int. Conf. Comp. Des. (ICCD'84)*, Port Chester, NY, October 1984, pp. 757-762.

[199] T. Ogihara, S. Murai, Y. Takamatsu, and K. Kinoshita, "Test Generation for Scan Design Circuits with Tri-State Modules and Bidirectional Terminals," *Proc. 20th Des. Auto. Conf.*, Miami Beach, FL, June 1983, pp. 71-78.

[200] T. Ogihara, S. Saruyama, and S. Murai, "PATEGE: An Automatic DC Parameter Test Generation System for Series Gated ECL Circuits," *Proc. 22nd Des. Auto. Conf.*, Las Vegas, Nevada, June 1985, pp. 212-218.

[201] C. A. Papachristou and N. B. Sahagal, "An Improved Method for Detecting Functional Faults in Semiconductor Random Access Memories," *IEEE Trans. Computers*, Vol. C-34, pp. 110-116, February 1985.

[202] E. S. Park and M. R. Mercer, "Robust and Nonrobust Tests for Path Delay Faults in a Combinational Circuit," *Proc. Int. Test Conf.*, Washington, DC, September 1987, pp. 1027-1034.

[203] K. P. Parker, "Adaptive Random Test Generation," *J. Des. Auto. and Fault-Tolerant Computing*, Vol. 1, pp. 62-83, October 1976.

[204] S. Patel and J. Patel, "Effectiveness of Heuristics Measures for Automatic Test Pattern Generation," *Proc. Des. Auto. Conf.*, Las Vegas, Nevada, June 1986, pp. 547-552.

[205] C. Paulson, "Classes of Diagnostic Tests," *Proc. 20th Des. Auto. Conf.*, Miami Beach, FL, June 1983, pp. 316-322.

[206] V. Pitchumani and S. Soman, "An Application of Unate Function Theory to Functional Testing," *Fault-Tolerant Comp. Symp. (FTCS-16) Digest of Papers*, pp. 70-75, July 1986.

[207] D. K. Pradhan, Ed., *Fault-Tolerant Computing Theory and Techniques*, I and II, Prentice-Hall, Englewood Cliffs, NJ, 1986.

[208] G. R. Putzolu and J. P. Roth, "A Heuristic Algorithm for the Testing of Asynchronous Circuits," *IEEE Trans. Computers*, Vol. C-20, pp. 639-647, June 1971.

[209] J. Rajski and H. Cox, "Stuck-Open Fault Testing in Large CMOS Networks by Dynamic Path Tracing," *Proc. Int. Conf. Comp. Des. (ICCD)*, Port Chester, NY, October 1986, pp. 252-255.

[210] J. Rajski and H. Cox, "A Method of Test Generation and Fault Diagnosis in Very Large Combinational Circuits," *Proc. Int. Test Conf.*, Washington, DC, September 1987, pp. 932-943.

[211] J. Rajski and J. Tyszer, "Combinatorial Approach to Multiple Contact Faults Coverage in Programmable Logic Arrays," *IEEE Trans. Computers*, Vol. C-34, pp. 549-553, June 1985.

[212] M. K. Reddy, S. M. Reddy, and P. Agrawal, "Transistor Level Test Generation for MOS Circuits," *Proc. 22nd Des. Auto. Conf.*, Las Vegas, Nevada, June 1985, pp. 825-828.

[213] S. M. Reddy, "Complete Test Sets for Logic Functions," *IEEE Trans. Comp.*, Vol. C-22, pp. 1016-1020, Nov. 1973.

[214] S. M. Reddy, M. K. Reddy, and V. D. Agrawal, "Robust Tests for Stuck-Open Faults in CMOS Combinational Circuits," *Fault-Tolerant Comput. Symp. (FTCS-14) Digest of Papers*, pp. 44-49, June 1984.

[215] E. Regener, "A Transition Sequence Generator for RAM Fault Detection," *IEEE Trans. Computers*, Vol. 37, pp. 362-368, March 1988.

[216] C. Robach, P. Malecha, and G. Michel, "Computer Aided Testability Evaluation and Test Generation," *Proc. Int. Test Conf.*, Philadelphia, PA, October 1983, pp. 338-345.

[217] C. Robach and G. Saucier, "Application Oriented Microprocessor Test Method," *Fault-Tolerant Comp. Symp. (FTCS-10) Digest of Papers*, pp. 121-125, October 1980.

[218] C. Robach and G. Saucier, "Microprocessor Functional Testing," *Test Conference Digest of Papers*, Philadelphia, PA, November 1980, pp. 433-443.

[219] G. D. Robinson, "HITEST − Intelligent Test Generation," *Proc. Int. Test Conf.*, Philadelphia, PA, October 1983, pp. 311-323.

[220] S. H. Robinson and J. P. Shen, "Towards a Switch-Level Test Pattern Generation Program," *Proc. Int. Conf. on CAD (ICCAD)*, Santa Clara, CA, November 1985, pp. 39-41.

[221] B. C. Rosales and P. Goel, "Results from Application of a Commercial ATG System to Large-Scale Combinational Circuits," *Proc. Int. Symp. Circ. Syst. (ISCAS-85)*, Kyoto, Japan, June 1985, pp. 667-670.

[222] J. P. Roth, W. G. Bouricius, and P. R. Schneider, "Programmed Algorithms to Compute Tests and to Detect and Distinguish Between Failures in Logic Circuits," *IEEE Trans. Electronic Computers*, Vol. EC-16, pp. 567-580, October 1967.

[223] J. P. Roth, V. G. Oklobdzija, and J. F. Beetem, "Test Generation for FET Switching Circuits," *Proc. Int. Test Conf.*, Philadelphia, PA, October 1984, pp. 59-62.

[224] J. Salick, B. Underwood, J. Kuban, and M. R. Mercer, "An Automatic Test Pattern Generation Algorithm for PLAs," *Proc. Int. Conf. CAD (ICCAD-86)*, Santa Clara, CA, November 1986, pp. 152-155.

[225] K. K. Saluja and K. Kinoshita, "Test Pattern Generation For API Faults In RAM," *IEEE Transaction On Computers*, Vol. C-34, pp. 284-287, March 1985.

[226] K. K. Saluja, L. Shen, and S. Y. H. Su, "A Simplified Algorithm for Testing Microprocessors," *Proc. Int. Test Conf.*, Philadelphia, PA, October 1983, pp. 668-675.

[227] K. K. Saluja, L. Shen, and S. Y. H. Su, "A Simplified Algorithm for Testing Microprocessors," *Comput. Math. Applic.*, Vol. 13, No. 5/6, pp. 431-441, 1987.

[228] E. F. Sarkany and W. S. Hart, "Minimal Set of Patterns to Test RAM Components," *Proc. Int. Test Conf.*, Washington, DC, September 1987, pp. 759-764.

[229] T. Sasaki, S. Kato, N. Nomizu, and H. Tanaka, "Logic Design Verification Using Automated Test Generation," *Proc. Int. Test Conf.*, Philadelphia, PA, October 1984, pp. 88-94.

[230] G. Saucier and C. Bellon, "CADOC : A System for Computed Aided Functional Test," *Proc. Int. Test Conf.*, Philadelphia, PA, October 1984, pp. 680-687.

[231] J. Savir, "Detection of Single Intermittent Faults in Sequential Circuits," *IEEE Trans. Computers*, Vol. C-29, pp. 673-678, July 1980.

[232] J. Savir, "Testing for Single Intermittent Failures in Combinational Circuits by Maximizing the Probability of Fault Detection," *IEEE Trans. Computers*, Vol. C-29, pp. 410-416, May 1980.

[233] J. Savir and P. H. Bardell, "On Random Pattern Test Length," *Proc. Int. Test Conf.*, Philadelphia, PA, October 1983, pp. 95-106.

[234] J. Savir, W. H. McAnney, and S. R. Vecchio, "Fault Propagation through Embedded Multiport Memories," *IEEE Trans. Computers*, Vol. C-36, pp. 592-602, May 1987.

[235] J. T. Scanlon and W. K. Fuchs, "A Testing Strategy for Bit-Serial Arrays," *Proc. Int. Conf. CAD (ICCAD-86)*, Santa Clara, CA, November 1986, pp. 284-287.

[236] P. R. Schneider, "On the Necessity to Examine D-Chains in Diagnostic Test Generation," *IBM J. Res. and Dev.*, Vol. 11, p. 114, January 1967.

[237] D. M. Schuler, E. G. Ulrich, T. E. Baker, and S. P. Bryant, "Random Test Generation Using Concurrent Logic Simulation," *Proc. 12th Des. Auto. Conf.*, 1975, pp. 261-267.

[238] M. H. Schulz, E. Trischler, and T. M. Sarfert, "SOCRATES: A Highly Efficient Automatic Test Pattern Generation System," *Proc. Int. Test Conf.*, Washington, DC, September 1987, pp. 1016-1026.

[239] P. Seetharamaiah and V. R. Murthy, "Tabular Mechanism for Flexible Testing of Microprocessors," *Proc. Int. Test Conf.*, Washington, DC, September 1986, pp. 394-407.

[240] F. F. Sellers, M. Y. Hsiao, and L. W. Bearnson, "Analyzing Errors with Boolean Difference," *IEEE Trans. Computers*, Vol. C-17, pp. 676-683, July 1968.

[241] S. C. Seth and V. D. Agrawal, "Statistical Design Verification," *Fault-Tolerant Comp. Symp. (FTCS-12) Digest of Papers*, pp. 393-399, June 1982.

[242] S. Shalem, "Functional Testing of the NS32332 Microprocessor," *Proc. Int. Test Conf.*, Washington, D.C., September 1986, pp. 552-560.

[243] R. Sharma and D. Radhakrishnan, "Test Derivation for CMOS Iterative Logic Arrays," *Proc. Custom Integrated Circ. Conf.*, Portland, OR, May 1985, pp. 315-318.

[244] L. Shen and S. Y. H. Su, "A Functional Testing Method for Microprocessors," *Fault-Tolerant Comput. Symp. (FTCS-14), Digest of Papers*, pp. 212-218, June 1984.

[245] M. Shepherd and D. Rodgers, "Asynchronous FIFO's Require Special Attention," *Proc. Int. Test Conf.*, Philadelphia, PA, November 1985, pp. 445-450.

[246] S. D. Sherlekar and P. S. Subramanian, "Conditionally Robust Two-Pattern Tests and CMOS Design for Testability," *IEEE Trans. CAD*, Vol. 7, pp. 325-332, March 1988.

[247] H. C. Shih and J. A. Abraham, "Transistor-Level Test Generation for Physical Failures in CMOS Circuits," *23rd Des. Aut. Conf.*, June 1986, pp. 243-249.

[248] T. Shimono, K. Oozeki, M. Takahashi, M. Kawai, and S. Funatsu, "An AC/DC Test Generation System for Gate Array LSIs," *Proc. Int. Test Conf.*, Philadelphia, PA, November 1985, pp. 329-333.

[249] M. Shirley, P. Wu, R. Davis, and G. Robinson, "A Synergistic Combination of Test Generation and Design for Testability," *Proc. Int. Test Conf.*, Washington, DC, September 1987, pp. 701-711.

[250] S. Shteingart, A. W. Nagle, and J. Grason, "RTG: Automatic Register Level Test Generator," *Proc. 22nd Des. Auto. Conf.*, Las Vegas, Nevada, June 1985, pp. 803-807.

[251] G. M. Silberman and I. Spillinger, "An Approach to Test Generation of VLSI Designs using Their Functional Level Description," *Proc. Int. Conf. Comp. Des. (ICCD-87)*, Rye Brook, NY, October 1987, pp. 52-55.

[252] G. M. Silberman and I. Spillinger, "Test Generation Using Functional Fault Simulation and the Difference Fault Model," *Proc. Int. Test Conf.*, Washington, DC, September 1987, pp. 400-407.

[253] N. Singh, *An Artificial Intelligence Approach to Test Generation*, Kluwer Academic Publishers, Norwell, MA, 1987.

[254] T. J. Snethen, "Simulator-Oriented Fault Test Generator," *Proc. 14th Des. Auto. Conf.*, 1977, pp. 88-93.

[255] F. Somenzi, S. Gai, M. Mezzalama, and P. Prinetto, "A New Integrated System for PLA Testing and Verification," *Proc. 20th Des. Auto. Conf.*, Miami Beach, FL, June 1983, pp. 57-63.

[256] F. Somenzi, S. Gai, M. Mezzalama, and P. Prinetto, "PART: Programmable Array Testing Based on a PARTitioning Algorithm," *IEEE Trans. on CAD*, Vol. CAD-3, pp. 142-149, April 1984. Also *Fault-Tolerant Comp. Symp. (FTCS-13) Digest of Papers,* Milan, Italy, June 1983, pp. 430-433.

[257] K. Son, "Rule Based Testability Checker and Test Generator," *Proc. Int. Test Conf.*, Philadelphia, PA, November 1985, pp. 884-889.

[258] K. Son and J. Y. O. Fong, "Automatic Behavioral Test Generation," *Int. Test Conf. Digest of Papers*, Philadelphia, PA, November 1982, pp. 161-165.

[259] V. P. Srini, "Test Generation from MacPitts Designs," *Proc. Int. Conf. Comp. Des. (ICCD'83)*, October 1983, pp. 53-56.

[260] N. C. E. Srinivas, A. S. Wojcik, and Y. H. Levendel, "An Artificial Intelligence Based Implementation of the P-Algorithm for Test Generation," *Proc. International Test Conference*, Washington, D.C., Sept. 1986, pp. 732-739.

[261] I. Stamelos, M. Melgara, M. Paolini, S. Morpurgo, and C. Segre, "A Multi-Level Test Pattern Generation and Validation Environment," *Proc. Int. Test Conf.*, Washington, DC, September 1986, pp. 90-96.

[262] K. E. Stoffers, "Test Sets for Combinational Logic – The Edge tracing Approach," *IEEE Trans. Computers*, Vol. C-29, pp. 741-746, August 1980.

[263] D. S. Suk and S. M. Reddy, "Test Procedures for a Class of Pattern-Sensitive Faults in Semiconductor Random-Access Memories," *IEEE Trans. Computers*, Vol. C-29, pp. 419-429, June 1980.

[264] D. S. Suk and S. M. Reddy, "A March Test for Functional Faults in Semiconductor Random Access Memories," *IEEE Trans. Computers*, Vol. C-30, pp. 982-985, December 1981.

[265] A. K. Susskind, "Testing by Verifying Walsh Coefficients," *IEEE Trans. Computers*, Vol. C-32, pp. 198-201, February 1983. Also *Fault-Tolerant Comp. Symp. (FTCS-11) Digest of Papers,* Portland, Maine, June 1981, pp. 206-208.

[266] D. Svanaes and E. J. Aas, "Test Generation through Logic Programming," *Integration, the VLSI Journal*, Vol. 2, pp. 49-67, March 1984.

[267] S. A. Szygenda, "A Software System for Diagnostic Test Generation and Simulation of Large Digital Systems," *Proc. 1969 National Electronics Conference*, 1969, pp. 657-662.

[268] S. A. Szygenda, "TEGAS – A Diagnostic Test Generation And Simulation System for Digital Computers," *Third Hawaii International Conference On System for Digital Computers*, Hawaii, 1970, pp. 163-166.

[269] S. A. Szygenda, "TEGAS2 – Anatomy of a General Purpose Test Generation and Simulation System for Digital Logic," *Proc. 9th Des. Auto. Conf.*, 1972, pp. 116-127.

[270] S. A. Szygenda and R. J. Smith, "A Processor for Software Diagnosis and Simulation of Digital Systems," *Second Annual Houston Conference On Circuits, Systems and Computers*, April 1970.

[271] Y. Takamatsu and K. Kinoshita, "CONT: A Concurrent Test Generation Algorithm," *Fault-Tolerant Computing Symp. (FTCS-17) Digest of Papers*, pp. 22-27, July 1987.

[272] D. T. Tang and L. S. Woo, "Exhaustive Test Pattern Generation with Constant Weight Vectors," *IEEE Trans. Computers*, Vol. C-32, pp. 1145-1150, Dec. 1983.

[273] S. M. Thatte and J. A. Abraham, "Test Generation for Microprocessors," *IEEE Trans. Computers*, Vol. C-29, pp. 429-441, June 1980.

[274] P. Thevenod-Fosse and R. David, "Random Testing of the Data Processing Section of a Microprocessor," *Fault-Tolerant Comp. Symp. (FTCS-11) Digest of Papers*, pp. 275-280, June

1981.

[275] P. Thevenod-Fosse and R. David, "Random Testing of the Control Section of a Microprocessor," *Fault-Tolerant Comp. Symp. (FTCS-13) Digest of Papers*, pp. 366-373, June 1983.

[276] J. J. Thomas, "Automated Diagnostic Test Program for Digital Networks," *Computer Design*, pp. 63-67, August 1971.

[277] C. Timoc, F. Scott, K. Wickman, and L. Hess, "Adaptive Probabilistic Testing of a Microprocessor," *Proc. Int. Conf. CAD (ICCAD-83)*, Santa Clara, CA, September 1983, pp. 71-72.

[278] K. E. Torku and B. M. Huey, "Petry Net Based Search Directing Heuristics for Test Generation," *Proc. 20th Des. Auto. Conf.*, Miami Beach, FL, June 1983, pp. 323-330.

[279] E. Trischler, "Guided inconsistent Path Sensitization: Method and Experimental Results," *Proc. Int. Test Conf.*, Philadelphia, PA, November 1985, pp. 79-86.

[280] M. E. Turner, D. G. Leet, R. J. Prilik, and D. J. McLean, "Testing CMOS VLSI: Tools, Concepts, and Experimental Results," *Proc. Int. Test Conf.*, Philadelphia, PA, November 1985, pp. 322-328.

[281] A. Tzidon, I. Berger, and M. Yoeli, "A Practical Approach to Fault Detection in Combinational Networks," *IEEE Trans. Computers*, Vol. C-27, pp. 968-971, Oct. 1978.

[282] R. Ubar, "Test Pattern Generation for Digital Systems on the Vector Alternative Graph Model," *13th Int. Symp. Fault Tolerant Computing (FTCS-13) Digest of Papers*, pp. 374-377, June 1983.

[283] J. G. Udell Jr., "Test Set Generation for Pseudo-Exhaustive BIST," *Proc. Int. Conf. CAD (ICCAD-86)*, Santa Clara, CA, November 1986, pp. 52-55.

[284] P. Varma and Y. Tohma, "PROTEAN – A Knowledge Based Test Generator," *Proc. Custom Integrated Circ. Conf.*, Portland, OR, May 1987, pp. 78-81.

[285] P. K. Varshney, C. R. P. Hartman, and J. M. De Faria Jr., "Application of Information Theory to Sequential Fault Diagnosis," *IEEE Trans. Computers*, Vol. C-31, pp. 164-170, February 1982.

[286] S. Varszegi, "An Interactive Method for the Generation of Tests Detecting Faults in Logic Netwroks," *Int. J. Electronics*, Vol. 64, pp. 239-253, February 1988.

[287] R. Velazco, H. Ziade, and E. Kolokithas, "A Microprocessor Test Approach Allowing Fault Localisation," *Proc. Int. Test Conf.*, Philadelphia, PA, November 1985, pp. 737-743.

[288] C. S. Venkatraman and K. K. Saluja, "Transition Count Testing of Sequential Machines," *Fault-Tolerant Comp. Symp. (FTCS-10) Digest of Papers*, pp. 167-172, October 1980.

[289] A. R. Virupakshia and V. C. V. P. Reddy, "A Simple Random Test Procedure for Detection of Single Intermittent Fault in Combinational Circuits," *IEEE Trans. Computers*, Vol. C-32, pp. 594-597, Jun. 1983.

[290] K. Walczak and E. Sapiecha, "Multiple Fault Detection and Location in Large Combinational Circuits," *Fault-Tolerant Comput. Symp. (FTCS-14), Digest of Papers*, pp. 134-140, June 1984.

[291] L. Y. Wei and J. Wei, "Comments on Detection of Faults in Programmable Logic Arrays," *IEEE Trans. Computers*, Vol. C-35, pp. 930-931, October 1986.

[292] R. S. Wei and A. Sangiovanni-Vincentelli, "PLATYPUS: A PLA Test Pattern Generation Tool," *IEEE Trans. on CAD*, Vol. CAD-5, pp. 633-644, October 1986.

[293] R. S. Wei and A. L. Sangiovanni-Vincentelli, "New Front-End and Line Justification Algorithm for Automatic Test Generation," *Proc. Int. Test Conf.*, Washington, DC, September 1986, pp. 121-128.

[294] D. J. Wharton, "The HITEST Test Generation System – Overview," *Proc. Int. Test Conf.*, Philadelphia, PA, October 1983, pp. 302-310.

[295] W. Williams, "An Automatic Test Generator for Programmable Logic Devices," *Proc. Int. Test Conf.*, Washington, DC, September 1987, pp. 658-667.

[296] S. Winegarden and D. Pannell, "Paragons for Memory Test," *Int. Test Conf. Digest of Papers*, Philadelphia, PA, October 1981, pp. 44-48.

[297] H. J. Wunderlich, "On Computing Optimized Input Probabilities for Random Tests," *Proc. 24th Des. Auto. Conf.*, Miami Beach, FL, June 1987, pp. 392-398.

[298] S. Xu and S. Y. H. Su, "A Systematic

Technique for Detecting and Locating Bridging and Stuck-At Faults in I/O Pins of LSI/VLSI Chips," *Comput. Math. Applic.*, Vol. 13, No. 5/6, pp. 461-474, 1987.

[299] X. Xu and E. J. McCluskey, "Test Generation and Fault Diagnosis for Multiple Faults in Combinational Circuits," *13th Int. Symp. Fault Tolerant Computing (FTCS-13) Digest of Papers*, pp. 110-115, June 1983.

[300] C. W. Yau, "Concurrent Test Generation Using AI Techniques," *Proc. Int. Test Conf.*, Washington, D.C., September 1986, pp. 722-731.

[301] Z. Zhi-min and C. Ting-huai, "A Near Optimal Algorithm for Test Generation in Sequential Circuit − Star Algorithm," *Fault-Tolerant Comp. Symp. (FTCS-11) Digest of Papers*, pp. 233-237, June 1981.

4.4: Test Evaluation

[1] M. Aboulhamid, Y. Karkouri, E. Cerny, and J. Rajski, "Fault Analysis in Switch-Level Networks by Implicit Enumeration," *Fault-Tolerant Computing Symp. (FTCS-17) Digest of Papers*, pp. 34-39, July 1987.

[2] J. A. Abraham and W. A. Rogers, "HAT: A Heuristic Adviser for Testability," *Proc. Int. Conf. Comp. Des. (ICCD)*, Port Chester, NY, October 1985, pp. 566-569.

[3] M. Abramovici, V. D. Agrawal, F. Brglez, P. Goel, C. L. Huang, and S. C. Seth, "Fault Coverage Tools: Case Studies (Panel Discussion)," *Proc. Int. Test Conf.*, Philadelphia, PA, November 1985, pp. 795-805.

[4] M. Abramovici and P. R. Menon, "A Machine for Design Verification and Testing Problems," *Proc. Int. Conf. CAD (ICCAD-83)*, Santa Clara, CA, September 1983, pp. 27-28.

[5] M. Abramovici and P. R. Menon, "A Practical Approach to Fault Simulation and Test Generation for Bridging Faults," *IEEE Trans. Computers*, Vol. C-34, pp. 658-663, July 1985. Also *Proc. Int. Test Conf.*, Philadelphia, PA, October 1983, pp. 138-142.

[6] M. Abramovici, P. R. Menon, and D. T. Miller, "Critical Path Tracing: An Alternative to Critical Path Tracing," *IEEE Design & Test of Computers*, Vol. 1, pp. 83-93, February 1984.

[7] J. M. Acken, "Testing for Bridging Faults (Shorts) in CMOS Circuits," *Proc. 20th Des.*

Auto. Conf., Miami Beach, FL, June 1983, pp. 717-718.

[8] V. D. Agrawal, "Sampling Techniques for Determining Fault Coverage in LSI Circuits," *Journal of Digital Systems*, Vol. 5, pp. 189-202, 1981.

[9] V. D. Agrawal and S. C. Seth, "Probabilistic Testability," *Int. Conf. on Computer Design (ICCD-85)*, Port Chester, NY, October 1985, pp. 562-565.

[10] V. D. Agrawal, S. C. Seth, and P. Agrawal, "LSI Product Quality and Fault Coverage," *ACM IEEE Eighteenth Design Automation Conference*, Nashville, TN, June 1981, pp. 196-203.

[11] V. D. Agrawal, S. C. Seth, and P. Agrawal, "Fault Coverage Requirement in Production Testing of LSI Circuits," *IEEE Journal of Solid-State Circuits*, Vol. SC-27, pp. 57-61, Feb. 1982.

[12] K. J. Antreich and M. H. Schulz, "Accelerated Fault Simulation and Fault Grading in Combinational Circuits," *IEEE Trans. CAD*, Vol. CAD-6, pp. 704-712, September 1987. Also *Proc. Int. Conf. CAD (ICCAD-86)*, November 1986, pp. 330-333.

[13] E. C. Archambeau and E. J. McCluskey, "Fault Coverage of Pseudo-Exhaustive Testing," *Int. Fault-Tolerant Computing Symp. (FTCS-14), Digest of Papers*, pp. 141-145, June 1984.

[14] D. B. Armstrong, "A Deductive Method for Simulating Faults in Logic Circuits," *IEEE Trans. Computers*, Vol. C-21, pp. 464-471, May 1972.

[15] A. Babitz and K. Lender, "Using Simulation in the Design Process -- A Case Study," *Proc. Int. Test Conf.*, Philadelphia, PA, October 1984, pp. 229-236.

[16] J. P. Barlow, "A New Software Tool for Detecting Problems Caused by Inductively-Generated Switching Noise," *Int. Test Conf. Digest of Papers*, Philadelphia, PA, November 1982, pp. 166-169.

[17] Z. Barzilai, D. K. Beece, L. M. Huisman, V. S. Iyengar, and G. M. Silberman, "SLS − A Fast Switch Level Simulator for Verification and Fault Coverage Analysis," *Proc. 23rd Des. Auto. Conf.*, Las Vegas, Nevada, June 1986, pp. 164-170.

[18] Z. Barzilai, J. L. Carter, V. S. Iyengar, I. Nair, B. K. Rosen, J. Rutledge, and G. M. Silberman, "Efficient Fault Simulation of CMOS Circuits with Accurate Models," *Proc. Int. Test Conf.*, Washington, D.C., September 1986, pp. 520-529.

[19] A. K. Bose, P. Kozak, C. Y. Lo, H. N. Nham, E. Pacas-Skewes, and K. Wu, "A Fault Simulator for MOS LSI Circuits," *Proc. 19th Design Automation Conference*, Las Vegas, Nevada, 1982, pp. 400-409.

[20] K. R. Bowden, "Design Goals and Implementation Techniques for Time-Based Digital Simulation and Hazard Detection," *Int. Test Conf. Digest of Papers*, Philadelphia, PA, November 1982, pp. 147-152.

[21] F. Brglez, "A Fast Fault Grader : Analysis and Applications," *Proc. Int. Test Conf. (ITC-85)*, Philadelphia, PA, Nov. 1985, pp. 785-794.

[22] F. Brglez and K. Kozminski, "Fast Fault Grading of Sequential Logic," *Proc. Custom Integrated Circ. Conf.*, Rochester, NY, May 1986, pp. 319-324.

[23] R. E. Bryant and M. D. Schuster, "Fault simulation of MOS digital circuits," *VLSI Design*, Vol. IV, pp. 24-30, October 1983.

[24] R. E. Bryant and M. D. Schuster, "Performance Evaluation of FMOSSIM, a Concurrent Switch-Level Fault Simulator," *Proc. 22nd Des. Auto. Conf.*, Las Vegas, Nevada, June 1985, pp. 715-719.

[25] F. Buelow and E. Porter, "The Need for Fault Simulation," *VLSI Systems Design*, Vol. VII, pp. 84-86, October 1986.

[26] J. L. Carter, V. S. Iyengar, and B. K. Rosen, "Efficient Test Coverage Determination for Delay Faults," *Proc. Int. Test Conf.*, Washington, DC, September 1987, pp. 418-427.

[27] T. Chan and E. Law, "MegaFault: A Mixed-Mode, Hardware Accelerated Concurrent Fault Simulator," *Proc. Int. Conf. CAD (ICCAD-86)*, Santa Clara, CA, November 1986, pp. 394-397.

[28] H. P. Chang and J. A. Abraham, "Use of High Level Descriptions for Speedup of Fault Simulation," *Proc. Int. Test Conf.*, Washington, DC, September 1987, pp. 278-285.

[29] H. Y. Chang, S. C. Chappell, C. H. Elmendorf, and L. D. Schmidt, "Comparison of parallel and deductive fault simulation methods," *IEEE Trans. Comput.*, Vol. C-23, pp. 1132-1138, Nov. 1974.

[30] S. G. Chappell, C. H. Elmendorf, and L. D. Schmidt, "Logic-circuit simulators," *Bell Syst. Tech. Jour.*, Vol. 53, pp. 1451-1476, Oct. 1974.

[31] C. K. Chin and E. J. McCluskey, "Test Length for Pseudorandom Testing," *IEEE Trans. Computers*, Vol. C-36, pp. 252-256, February 1987. Also *Proc. Int. Test Conf.*, November 1985, pp. 94-99.

[32] R. A. Cliff, "Acceptable Testing of VLSI Components which Contain Error Correctors," *IEEE Trans. Computers*, Vol. C-29, pp. 125-134, February 1980.

[33] M. A. D'Abreu and E. W. Thompson, "An Accurate Functional Level Concurrent Fault Simulator," *Proc. 17th Des. Auto. Conf.*, Minneapolis, MN, June 1980, pp. 210-217.

[34] W. Daehn and M. Geilert, "Fast Fault Simulation for Combinational Circuits by Compiler Driven Single Fault Propagation," *Proc. Int. Test. Conf.*, Washington, DC, September 1987, pp. 286-292.

[35] S. Davidson, "Fault Simulation at the Architectural Level," *Proc. Int. Test Conf.*, Philadelphia, PA, October 1984, pp. 669-679.

[36] S. Davidson and J. L. Lewandowski, "ESIM/AFS − A Concurrent Architectural Level Fault Simulator," *Proc. Int. Test Conf.*, Washington, DC, September 1986, pp. 375-383.

[37] D. B. Day and K. W. Warren, "The Integration of Design and Test, Part 1: Fault Simulation for Design Verification," *VLSI Design*, Vol. VI, p. 46, March 1985.

[38] I. I. Eldumiati and R. N. Gadenz, "Logic and Fault Simulation of the DSP, A VLSI Digital Signal Processor," *Proc. Int. Conf. Circ. Computers (ICCC-80)*, port Chester, NY, October 1980, pp. 948-952.

[39] K. Fukuoka, K. Ohga, A. Sugiyama, and S. Takemura, "DVTS: Design Verification Techniques for Functional Simulation," *Proc. Int. Test Conf.*, Washington, D.C., September 1986, pp. 710-716.

[40] S. Funatsu, M. Takahashi, and A. Yamada, "Digital Fault Simulation in Bidirectional Bus Circuit Environment," *Fault-Tolerant Comp. Symp. (FTCS-10) Digest of Papers*, pp. 155-157, October 1980.

[41] S. Gai, F. Somenzi, and E. Ulrich, "Advanced Techniques for Concurrent Multilevel Simulation," *Proc. Int. Conf. CAD (ICCAD-86)*, Santa Clara, CA, November 1986, pp. 334-337.

[42] S. Ghosh and W. VanCleemput, "Functional Fault Simulation Using Adlib-Sable," *Proc. Int. Conf. CAD (ICCAD-83)*, Santa Clara, CA, September 1983, pp. 103-104.

[43] N. Giambiasi, D. Muriach, and S. Miara, "Methods for Generalized Deductive Fault Simulation," *Proc. 17th Des. Auto. Conf.*, Minneapolis, MN, June 1980, pp. 386-393.

[44] N. Giambiasi, M. Sigal, and J. C. Rault, "A Deductive Method for Non Classical Logic Fault Simulation," *Proc. Int. Conf. Circ. Computers (ICCC'82)*, New York, NY, September 1982, pp. 468-470.

[45] D. Giles, C. Berking, and K. Wacks, "Integrated Functional/Structural Timing for Digital Simulation," *Int. Test Conf. Digest of Papers*, Philadelphia, PA, November 1982, pp. 153-160.

[46] P. Goel, "Test Generation Costs Analysis and Projections," *Proc. 17th Design Automation Conference*, Minneapolis, MN, June 1980, pp. 77-84.

[47] P. Goel, H. Lichaa, T. E. Rosser, T. J. Stroh, and E. B. Eichelberger, "LSSD Fault Simulation Using Conjunctive Combinational and Sequential Methods," *Test Conference Digest of Papers*, Philadelphia, PA, November 1980, pp. 371-376.

[48] P. Goel and P. R. Moorby, "Fault Simulation Techniques for VLSI Circuits," *VLSI Design*, Vol. V, p. 22, July 1984.

[49] L. H. Goldstein, "Computational Complexity/ Confidence Level Tradeoffs in LSI Testing," *Semiconductor Test Conf., Digest of Papers*, Cherry Hill, NJ, October 1978, pp. 50-58.

[50] A. K. Gupta and J. R. Armstrong, "Functional Fault Modeling and Simulation for VLSI Devices," *Proc. 22nd Des. Auto. Conf.*, Las Vegas, Nevada, June 1985, pp. 720-726.

[51] J. Hallauer and R. D. Hess, "Transistor Level Fault Simulation Using Probabilistic Techniques," *Proc. Custom Integrated Circ. Conf.*, Rochester, NY, May 1986, pp. 325-328.

[52] D. Harel and B. Krishnamurthy, "Is There Hope for Linear Time Fault Simulation?," *Fault-Tolerant Computing Symp. (FTCS-17) Digest of Papers*, pp. 28-33, July 1987.

[53] J. P. Hayes, "A Fault Simulation Methodology for VLSI," *Proc. 19th Des. Auto. Conf.*, Las Vegas, Nevada, June 1982, pp. 393-399.

[54] L. P. Henckels, K. M. Brown, and C. Lo, "Functional Level, Concurrent Fault Simulation," *Test Conference Digest of Papers*, Philadelphia, PA, November 1980, pp. 479-485.

[55] R. Hess and W. C. Berg, "Probabilistic Software Quickly Grades Test Vectors for Total Fault Coverage," *Electronic Design*, pp. 161-166, Oct. 1985.

[56] R. D. Hess and W. C. Berg Jr., "Performance of Probabilistic Fault Grading," *VLSI Systems Design*, pp. 40-45, Jan. 1986.

[57] S. Hirschhorn, "Fault Propagation Techniques in a Functional Level Concurrent Fault Simulator," *Proc. Int. Conf. CAD (ICCAD-83)*, Santa Clara, CA, September 1983, pp. 96-98.

[58] W. K. Huang, M. Lightner, and F. Lombardi, "Predicting Fault Coverage for Random Testing of Combinational Circuits," *Proc. Int. Test Conf.*, Washington, DC, September 1987, pp. 843-848.

[59] S. K. Jain and V. D. Agrawal, "STAFAN: An Alternative to Fault Simulation," *Proc. 21st Des. Auto. Conf.*, Albuquerque, NM, June 1984, pp. 18-23.

[60] S. K. Jain and V. D. Agrawal, "Statistical Fault Analysis," *IEEE Design & Test of Computers*, Vol. 2, pp. 38-44, Feb. 1985.

[61] S. K. Jain and D. M. Singer, "Characteristics of Statistical Fault Analysis," *Proc. Int. Conf. Comp. Des. (ICCD)*, Port Chester, NY, October 1986, pp. 24-30.

[62] R. Joobbani, "Functional-Level Fault Simulation," *Proc. Int. Conf. Circ. Computers (ICCC-80)*, Port Chester, NY, October 1980, pp. 1120-1124.

[63] M. Kawai and J. P. Hayes, "An experimental MOS fault simulation program CSASIM," *21st Des. Aut. Conf.*, Albuquerque, NM, June 1984, pp. 2-9.

[64] M. Kawamura and K. Hirabayashi, "AFS: An Approximate Fault Simulator," *Proc. Int. Test Conf.*, Philadelphia, PA, November 1985, pp. 717-721.

[65] Y. H. Levendel and P. R. Menon, "Fault

Simulation Methods – Extensions and Comparison,'' *Bell Sys. Tech. Jour.*, Vol. 60, pp. 2235-2258, November 1981.

[66] Y. H. Levendel, P. R. Menon, and S. H. Patel, ''Parallel Fault Simulation Using Distributed Processing,'' *Bell System Technical Journal*, Vol. 62, p. 3107, Dec 1983.

[67] C. Y. Lo, H. N. Nham, and A. K. Bose, ''Algorithms for an Advanced Fault Simulation System in MOTIS,'' *IEEE Trans. CAD*, Vol. CAD-6, pp. 232-240, March 1987.

[68] S. L. Lusky and T. Sridhar, ''Detectable CMOS Faults in Switch-Level Simulation,'' *Proc. Int. Test Conf.*, Philadelphia, PA, November 1985, pp. 875-883.

[69] H. K. Ma and A. Sangiovanni-Vincentelli, ''Mixed-Level Fault Coverage Estimation,'' *Proc. 23rd Des. Auto. Conf.*, Las Vegas, Nevada, June 1986, pp. 553-559.

[70] A. Mahmood and E. J. McCluskey, ''Watchdog Processors: Error Coverage and Overhead,'' *Fault-Tolerant Comp. Symp. (FTCS-15) Digest of Papers*, pp. 214-219, June 1985.

[71] Y. K. Malaiya and S. Yang, ''The Coverage Problem for Random Testing,'' *Proc. Int. Test Conf.*, Philadelphia, PA, October 1984, pp. 237-245.

[72] P. C. Maxwell, ''Fast Fault Coverage Estimation at the Transistor Level,'' *Microelectronics Conference VLSI 1987 Preprints of Papers*, Melbourne, Australia, April 8-10, 1987, pp. 120-123.

[73] W. H. McAnney, P. H. Bardell, and V. P. Gupta, ''Random Testing for Stuck-At Storage Cells in an Embedded Memory,'' *Proc. Int. Test Conf.*, Philadelphia, PA, October 1984, pp. 157-166.

[74] R. M. McDermott, ''Random Fault Analysis,'' *Proc. 18th Des. Auto. Conf.*, Nashville, TN, June 1981, pp. 360-364.

[75] M. Melgara, M. Paolini, R. Roncella, and S. Morpurgo, ''CVT-FERT: Automatic Generator of Analytical Faults at RT-Level from Electrical and Topological Descriptions,'' *Proc. Int. Test Conf.*, Philadelphia, PA, October 1984, pp. 250-256.

[76] P. R. Menon and S. G. Chappell, ''Deductive Fault Simulation with Functional Blocks,'' *IEEE Trans. Computers*, Vol. C-27, pp. 689-695, Aug.

1978.

[77] P. R. Moorby, ''Fault Simulation Using Parallel Value Lists,'' *Proc. Int. Conf. CAD (ICCAD-83)*, Santa Clara, CA, September 1983, pp. 101-102.

[78] G. Mott and J. Newkirk, ''Eliminating Failures in the Field,'' *VLSI Systems Design*, Vol. VII, pp. 88-90, October 1986.

[79] S. Mourad, J. L. A. Hughes, and E. J. McCluskey, ''Effectiveness of Single Fault Tests to Detect Multiple Faults in Parity Trees,'' *Comput. Math. Applic.*, Vol. 13, No. 5/6, pp. 455-459, 1987.

[80] T. Nishida, S. Miyamoto, T. Kozawa, and K. Sato, ''RFSIM: Reduced Fault Simulator,'' *Proc. Int. Conf. on CAD (ICCAD)*, Santa Clara, CA, November 1985, pp. 13-15.

[81] S. Nitta, K. Kawamura, and K. Hirabayashi, ''Test Generation by Activation and Defect-Drive (TEGAD),'' *Integration, The VLSI Journal*, Vol. 3, pp. 3-12, March 1985.

[82] J. D. Northcutt, ''The Design and Implementation of Fault Insertion Capabilities for ISPS,'' *Proc. 17th Des. Auto. Conf.*, Minneapolis, MN, June 1980, pp. 197-209.

[83] K. Okazaki and T. Yahara, ''Efficient Logic Verification and Test Validation for MOS LSI Circuits,'' *Int. Test Conf. Digest of Papers*, Philadelphia, PA, October 1981, pp. 530-535.

[84] F. Ozguner, ''Deductive Fault Simulation of Internal Faults of Inverter-Free Circuits and PLA,'' *IEEE Trans. Comp*, Vol. C-35, pp. 70-73, Jan. 1986.

[85] D. K. Pradhan, Ed., *Fault-Tolerant Computing Theory and Techniques*, I and II, Prentice-Hall, Englewood Cliffs, NJ, 1986.

[86] B. A. Prasad, ''Model for VLSI Test Optimization Using the Interrelationship of Fault Coverage Yield and Test Quality,'' *Fault-Tolerant Comp. Symp. (FTCS-12) Digest of Papers*, pp. 400-405, June 1982.

[87] M. Renovell, G. Cambon, and D. Auvergn, ''FSPICE: A Tool for Fault Modelling in MOS Circuits,'' *Integration, The VLSI Journal*, Vol. 3, pp. 245-255, September 1985.

[88] W. A. Rogers and J. A. Abraham, ''CHIEFS: A Concurrent, Hierarchical and Extensible Fault Simulator,'' *Proc. Int. Test Conf.*, Philadelphia,

PA, Nov. 1985, pp. 710-716.

[89] W. A. Rogers and J. A. Abraham, "High-Level Hierarchical Fault Simulation Techniques," *Proc. ACM Computer Science Conf.*, New Orleans, Louisiana, March 1985, pp. 89-97.

[90] W. A. Rogers and J. A. Abraham, "A Performance Model for Concurrent Hierarchical Fault Simulation," *Proc. Int. Conf. CAD (ICCAD-86)*, Santa Clara, CA, November 1986, pp. 342-345.

[91] D. Saab and I. Hajj, "Parallel and Concurrent Fault Simulation of MOS Circuits," *Proc. Int. Conf. Comp. Des. (ICCD'84)*, Port Chester, NY, October 1984, pp. 752-756.

[92] J. Savir and J. P. Roth, "Testing for, and Distinguishing Between Failures," *Fault-Tolerant Comp. Symp. (FTCS-12) Digest of Papers*, pp. 165-172, June 1982.

[93] M. H. Schulz and F. Brglez, "Accelerated Transition Fault Simulation," *Proc. 24th Des. Auto. Conf.*, Miami Beach, FL, June 1987, pp. 237-243.

[94] M. D. Schuster and R. E. Bryant, "Concurrent Fault Simulation of MOS Digital Circuits," *Proc. Conf. Adv. Res. in VLSI*, Cambridge, MA, January 1984, pp. 129-138.

[95] S. C. Seth and V. D. Agrawal, "Forecasting Reject Rate of Tested LSI Chips," *IEEE Electron Device Letters*, Vol. EDL-2, p. 286, Nov. 1981.

[96] S. C. Seth and V. D. Agrawal, "Characterizing the LSI Yield from Wafer Test Data," *IEEE Trans. on CAD*, Vol. CAD-3, pp. 123-126, April 1984. Also in *Proc. Int. Conf. Circ. Comp. (ICCC'82)*, New York, September 1982, pp. 556-559.

[97] H. C. Shih, J. T. Rameh, and J. A. Abraham, "AN MOS Fault Simulator with Timing Information," *Proc. Int. Conf. on CAD (ICCAD)*, Santa Clara, CA, November 1985, pp. 45-47.

[98] H. C. Shih, J. T. Rameh, and J. A. Abraham, "FAUST: An MOS Fault Simulator with Timing Information," *IEEE Trans. on CAD*, Vol. CAD-5, pp. 557-563, October 1986.

[99] G. M. Silberman and I. Spillinger, "The Difference Fault Model − Using Functional Fault Simulation to Obtain Implementation Fault Coverage," *Proc. Int. Test Conf.*, Washington, DC, September 1986, pp. 332-339.

[100] D. Smith, "Finding Fault: An Update on Fault Simulation," *VLSI Systems Design*, Vol. VIII, p. 28, October 1987.

[101] L. T. Smith and R. R. Rezac, "A Simulation Engine in the Design Environment, Part 2: Fault Simulation Methodology and Results," *VLSI Design*, Vol. V, p. 74, December 1984.

[102] L. T. Smith and R. R. Rezac, "Methodology for & Results from the Use of a Hardware Logic Simulation Engine for Fault Simulation," *Proc. Int. Test Conf.*, Philadelphia, PA, October 1984, pp. 224-228.

[103] K. Son, "Fault Simulation with the Parallel Value List Algorithm," *VLSI Systems Design*, pp. 36-43, December 1985.

[104] T. Sridhar, D. S. Ho, T. J. Powell, and S. M. Thatte, "Analysis and Simulation of Parallel Signature Analyzers," *Comput. Math. Applic.*, Vol. 13, No. 5/6, pp. 537-545, 1987.

[105] C. H. Staelin and A. Albicki, "Evaluation of Monitor Complexity for Concurrently Testing Microprogrammed Control Units," *Proc. Int. Test Conf.*, Philadelphia, PA, November 1985, pp. 733-736.

[106] C. H. Stapper, F. M. Armstrong, and K. Saji, "Integrated Circuit Yield Statistics," *Proceedings of The IEEE*, Vol. 71, April 1983, pp. 453-470.

[107] A. J. Stein, D. G. Saab, and I. N. Hajj, "A Special-Purpose Architecture for Concurrent Fault Simulation," *Proc. Int. Conf. Comp. Des. (ICCD)*, Port Chester, NY, October 1986, pp. 243-246.

[108] H. R. Sucar and P. Gelsinger, "Functional Test Grading as Applied to the 80386," *Proc. Int. Conf. Comp. Des. (ICCD)*, Port Chester, NY, October 1986, pp. 393-396.

[109] S. A. Szygenda, "A Software System for Diagnostic Test Generation and Simulation of Large Digital Systems," *Proc. 1969 National Electronics Conference*, 1969, pp. 657-662.

[110] S. A. Szygenda, "TEGAS − A Diagnostic Test Generation And Simulation System for Digital Computers," *Third Hawaii International Conference On System for Digital Computers*, Hawaii, 1970, pp. 163-166.

[111] S. A. Szygenda, "TEGAS2 − Anatomy of a General Purpose Test Generation and Simulation System for Digital Logic," *Proc. 9th Des. Auto.*

Conf., 1972, pp. 116-127.

[112] S. A. Szygenda, D. M. Rouse, and E. W. Thompson, "A Model and Implementation of a Universal Time Delay Simulator for Large Digital Nets," *Spring Joint Computer Conference*, 1970, pp. 207-216.

[113] S. A. Szygenda and R. J. Smith, "A Processor for Software Diagnosis and Simulation of Digital Systems," *Second Annual Houston Conference On Circuits, Systems and Computers*, April 1970.

[114] S. A. Szygenda and E. W. Thompson, "Fault Insertion Techniques and Models for Digital Logic Simulation," *Fall Joint Comp. Conf.*, 1972, pp. 875-884.

[115] A. Thakar, H. Sucar, and P. Gelsinger, "Intel's Test Quality System," *Proc. Int. Test Conf.*, Washington, DC, September 1987, pp. 1094-1097.

[116] E. W. Thompson, P. Karger, W. Read, D. Ross, J. Smith, and R. vonBlucher, "The Incorporation of Functional Level Element Routines into an Existing Digital Simulation System," *Proc. 17th Des. Auto. Conf.*, Minneapolis, MN, June 1980, pp. 394-401.

[117] E. W. Thompson and S. A. Szygenda, "Digital Logic Simulation in a Time-Based, Table-Driven Environment, Part 2, Parallel Fault Simulation," *Computer*, Vol. 8, pp. 38-44, March 1975.

[118] E. W. Thompson, S. A. Szygenda, N. Billawala, and R. Pierce, "Timing Analysis for Digital Fault Simulation," *Proc. Design Aut. Conf.*, 1974.

[119] K. E. Torku and C. E. Radke, "Quality Level and Fault Tolerance for Multichip Modules," *Proc. 20th Des. Auto. Conf.*, Miami Beach, FL, June 1983, pp. 201-206.

[120] E. Ulrich, "Concurrent Simulation at the Switch, Gate, and Register Levels," *Proc. Int. Test Conf.*, Philadelphia, PA, November 1985, pp. 703-709.

[121] E. Ulrich, D. Lacy, N. Phillips, J. Tellier, M. Kearney, T. Elkind, and R. Beaven, "High Speed Concurrent Fault Simulation with Vectors and Scalars," *Proc. 17th Des. Auto. Conf.*, Minneapolis, MN, June 1980, pp. 374-380.

[122] E. Ulrich and I. Suetsugu, "Techniques for Logic and Fault Simulation," *VLSI Systems Design*, Vol. VII, pp. 68-81, October 1986.

[123] E. G. Ulrich, "Exclusive Simulation of Activity in Digital Networks," *Communications of ACM*, 12, no. 2, pp. 102-110, Feb. 1969.

[124] E. G. Ulrich and T. Baker, "The Concurrent Simulation of Nearly Identical Digital Networks," *Computer*, pp. 39-44, April 1974.

[125] R. L. Wadsack, "VLSI: How Much Fault Coverage is Enough?," *Int. Test Conf. Digest of Papers*, Philadelphia, PA, October 1981, pp. 547-554.

[126] R. L. Wadsack, "Design Verification and Testing of the WE 32100 CPUs," *IEEE Design & Test of Computers*, Vol. 1, pp. 66-75, August 1984.

[127] K. Wagner, C. Chin, and E. J. McCluskey, "Fault Coverage of Pseudorandom Testing," *Proc. Int. Conf. CAD (ICCAD-86)*, Santa Clara, CA, November 1986, pp. 48-51.

[128] J. A. Waicukauski, E. B. Eichelberger, D. O. Forlenza, E. Lindbloom, and T. McCarthy, "Fault Simulation for Structured VLSI," *VLSI Systems Design*, Vol. VI, pp. 20-32, December 1985.

[129] J. A. Waicukauski, E. Lindbloom, B. Rosen, and V. S. Iyengar, "Transition Fault Simulation," *IEEE Design & Test of Computers*, Vol. 4, pp. 32-38, April 1987. Also *Proc. Int. Test Conf.*, Sept. 1986, pp. 542-549.

[130] K. Walczak, "Deductive Fault Simulation for Sequential Module Circuits," *IEEE Trans. Computers*, Vol. 37, pp. 237-239, February 1988.

[131] T. W. Williams, "Sufficient Testing in a Self-Test Environment," *Proc. Int. Test Conf.*, Philadelphia, PA, October 1984, pp. 167-172.

[132] T. W. Williams, "Test Length in a Self-Testing Environment," *IEEE Design & Test of Computers*, Vol. 2, pp. 59-63, April 1985.

[133] T. W. Williams and N. C. Brown, "Defect Level as a Function of Fault Coverage," *IEEE Trans. Computers*, Vol. C-30, pp. 987-988, December 1981.

[134] D. M. Wu, C. E. Radke, and J. P. Roth, "Statistical AC Test Coverage," *Proc. Int. Test Conf.*, Washington, D.C., September 1986, pp. 538-541.

[135] P. S. Yu, C. M. Krishna, and Y. H. Lee, "VLSI Circuit Testing Using an Adaptive Optimization Model," *Proc. 24th Des. Auto. Conf.*, Miami

Beach, FL, June 1987, pp. 399-406.

4.5: Testability Analysis

[1] E. J. Aas and M. R. Mercer, "Algebraic and Structural Computation of Signal Probability and Fault Detectability in Combinational Circuits," *Fault-Tolerant Computing Symp. (FTCS-17) Digest of Papers*, pp. 72-77, July 1987.

[2] J. A. Abraham and W. A. Rogers, "HAT: A Heuristic Adviser for Testability," *Proc. Int. Conf. Comp. Des. (ICCD)*, Port Chester, NY, October 1985, pp. 566-569.

[3] V. D. Agrawal, J. L. Carter, P. Goel, F. C. Wang, and R. Willoner, "Will Testability Analysis Replace Fault Simulation? (Panel Discussion)," *Proc. Int. Test Conf.*, Philadelphia, PA, October 1984, pp. 718-728.

[4] V. D. Agrawal and M. R. Mercer, "Testability Measures -- What Do They Tell Us?," *International Test Conf. Digest of Papers*, Philadelphia, PA, November 1982, pp. 391-396.

[5] V. D. Agrawal and S. C. Seth, "Probabilistic Testability," *Int. Conf. on Computer Design (ICCD-85)*, Port Chester, NY, October 1985, pp. 562-565.

[6] V. D. Agrawal, S. C. Seth, and C. C. Chuang, "Probabilistically Guided Test Generation," *Proc. of Int. Symp. Circuits and Systems (ISCAS)*, May 1985, pp. 687-689.

[7] S. B. Akers, "On the use of Linear Sums in Exhaustive Testing," *Fault-Tolerant Comp. Symp. (FTCS-15) Digest of Papers*, pp. 148-153, June 1985.

[8] S. B. Akers, "A Parity Bit Signature for Exhaustive Testing," *Proc. Int. Test Conf.*, Washington, DC, September 1986, pp. 48-53.

[9] S. B. Akers and B. Krishnamurthy, "On the Application of Test Counting to VLSI Testing," *Chapel Hill Conference on Very Large Scale Integration*, 1985, pp. 343-362. (Conf. Proc. published by Computer Science Press).

[10] E. Archambeau, "Testability Analysis Techniques: A Critical Survey," *VLSI Systems Design*, Vol. VI, pp. 46-52, December 1985.

[11] S. C. Bass, "The Application of Probabilistic Modeling to the Design and Fault Analysis of Digital Networks," *Proc. Int. Symp. on Circ. Syst. (ISCAS)*, Houston, Texas, April 1980, pp. 753-756.

[12] S. C. Bass and J. W. Grundmann, "Expected Value Analysis of Combinational Logic Networks," *IEEE Trans. on Circ. Syst.*, Vol. CAS-28, pp. 367-382, May 1981.

[13] R. G. Bennetts, C. M. Maunder, and G. D. Robinson, "CAMELOT: A Computer-Aided Measure for Logic Testability," *IEE Proc.*, 128, Pt. E, September 1981, pp. 177-189.

[14] W. C. Berg and R. D. Hess, "COMET: A Testability Analysis and Design Modification Package," *Int. Test Conf. Digest of Papers*, Philadelphia, PA, November 1982, pp. 364-378.

[15] F. Brglez, "On Testability Analysis Of Combinational Networks," *Proc. Int. Symp. Circuits and Systems (ISCAS)*, Montreal, Canada, May 1984, pp. 221-225.

[16] F. Brglez, "A Fast Fault Grader : Analysis and Applications," *Proc. Int. Test Conf. (ITC-85)*, Philadelphia, PA, Nov. 1985, pp. 785-794.

[17] F. Brglez, P. Pownall, and R. Hum, "Application of Testability Analysis from ATPG to Critical Delay Path Tracing," *Proc. Int. Test Conf.*, Philadelphia, PA, October 1984, pp. 705-712.

[18] H. Y. Chang and G. W. Heimbigner, "Controllability, Observability, and Maintenance Engineering Technique (COMET)," *Bell Syst. Tech. J.*, Vol. 53, pp. 1505-1534, October 1974.

[19] T. H. Chen and M. A. Breuer, "Automatic Design for Testability Via Testability Measures," *IEEE Trans. Computer-Aided Design*, Vol. CAD-4, pp. 3-11, January 1985.

[20] F. G. Danner, "System Test Visibility – Or Why Can't You Test Your Electronics?," *Proc. Int. Test Conf.*, Philadelphia, PA, October 1983, pp. 635-639.

[21] J. Dussault, "A Testability Measure," *Int. Test Conf., Digest of Papers*, Cherry Hill, NJ, October 1978, pp. 113-116.

[22] J. L. Fike, "Predicting Fault Detectability in Combinational Circuits – A New Design Tool?," *Proc. 12th Des. Auto. Conf.*, 1975, pp. 290-295.

[23] J. Y. O. Fong, "On Functional Controllability and Observability Analysis," *Int. Test Conf. Digest of Papers*, Philadelphia, PA, November 1982, pp. 170-175.

[24] H. S. Fung and J. Y. O. Fong, "An Information Flow Approach to Functional Testability

Measures," *Proc. Int. Conf. Circ. Computers (ICCC'82)*, New York, NY, September 1982, pp. 460-463.

[25] D. K. Goel and R. M. McDermott, "An Interactive Testability Analysis Program — ITTAP," *Proc. 19th Des. Auto. Conf.*, Las Vegas, Nevada, June 1982, pp. 581-586.

[26] L. H. Goldstein, "Controllability / Observability Analysis of Digital Circuits," *IEEE Trans. on Circuits and Systems*, Vol. CAS-26, pp. 685-693, Sept 1979.

[27] L. H. Goldstein and E. L. Thigpen, "SCOAP: Sandia Controllability/Observability Analysis Program," *Proc. 17th Des. Auto. Conf.*, Minneapolis, MN, June 1980, pp. 190-196.

[28] J. Grason, "TMEAS, A Testability Measure Program," *Proc. 16th Des. Auto. Conf.*, San Diego, CA, June 1979, pp. 156-161.

[29] J. Grason and A. W. Nagle, "Digital Test Generation and Design for Testability," *Proc. 17th Design Auto. Conf.*, Minneapolis, MN, June 1980, pp. 175-189.

[30] R. D. Hess, "Testability Analysis: An Alternative to Structured Design for Testability," *VLSI Design*, Vol. III, p. 22, March/April 1982.

[31] A. Ivanov and V. K. Agarwal, "Testability Measures — What Do They Do for ATPG?," *Proc. Int. Test Conf.*, Washington, DC, September 1986, pp. 129-138.

[32] W. Jian-Chao and W. Dao-Zheng, "A New Testability Measure for Digital Circuits," *Proc. Int. Test Conf.*, Washington, DC, September 1986, pp. 506-512.

[33] P. G. Kovijanic, "Single Testability Figure of Merit," *Int. Test Conf., Digest of Papers*, Philadelphia, PA, October 1981, pp. 521-529.

[34] P. G. Kovijanic and R. G. Kulkarni, "Testability Analysis of Programmable Array Logic," *Proc. Int. Test Conf.*, Philadelphia, PA, November 1985, pp. 760-768.

[35] B. Krishnamurthy and R. L. C. Sheng, "A New Approach to the Use of Testability Analysis in Test Generation," *Proc. Int. Test Conf.*, Philadelphia, PA, November 1985, pp. 769-778.

[36] B. Krishnamurthy and I. Tollis, "Improved Techniques for Estimating Signal Probabilities," *Proc. Int. Test Conf.*, Washington, DC, September 1986, pp. 244-251.

[37] R. Lisanke, F. Brglez, A. deGeus, and D. Gregory, "Testability-Driven Random Pattern Generation," *IEEE Trans. CAD*, Vol. CAD-6, pp. 1082-1087, November 1987. Also *Proc. Int. Conf. CAD (ICCAD-86)*, Santa Clara, CA, Nov., 1986, pp. 144-147.

[38] D. J. Lu and E. J. McCluskey, "Quantitative Evaluation of Self-Checking Circuits," *IEEE Trans. on CAD*, Vol. CAD-3, pp. 150-155, April 1984.

[39] B. Magnhagen, "Practical Experiments from Signal Probability Simulation of Digital Designs," *Proc. 14th Des. Auto. Conf.*, New Orleans, Louisiana, June 1977, pp. 216-219.

[40] G. Markowsky, "Bounding Signal Probabilities in Combinational Circuits," *IEEE Trans. Computers*, Vol. C-36, pp. 1247-1251, October 1987.

[41] M. R. Mercer and B. Underwood, "Correlating Testability with Fault Detection," *Proc. Int. Test Conf.*, Philadelphia, PA, October 1984, pp. 697-704.

[42] R. C. Ogus, "The Probability of a Correct Output from a Combinational Circuit," *IEEE Trans. Computers*, Vol. C-24, pp. 534-544, May 1975.

[43] K. P. Parker and E. J. McCluskey, "Analysis of Logic Circuits with Faults Using Input Signal Probabilities," *IEEE Trans. Computers*, Vol. C-24, pp. 573-578, May 1975.

[44] K. P. Parker and E. J. McCluskey, "Probabilistic Treatment of General Combinational Networks," *IEEE Trans. Computers*, Vol. C-24, pp. 668-670, June 1975.

[45] S. Patel and J. Patel, "Effectiveness of Heuristics Measures for Automatic Test Pattern Generation," *Proc. Des. Auto. Conf.*, Las Vegas, Nevada, June 1986, pp. 547-552.

[46] R. W. Preister and J. B. Cleary, "New Measures of Testability and Test Complexity for Linear Analog Failure Analysis," *IEEE Trans. Computers*, Vol. C-30, pp. 884-889, November 1981.

[47] I. M. Ratiu, "VICTOR: A Fast VLSI Testability Analysis Program," *Int. Test Conf. Digest of Papers*, Philadelphia, PA, November 1982, pp. 397-401.

[48] G. R. Redinbo and A. Brown, "The Boolean Partial Derivative and the Probability of Undetected Errors in Checked Logic," *Proc. Int. Conf. Comp. Des. (ICCD)*, Port Chester, NY, October 1985, pp. 421-425.

[49] C. Robach, P. Malecha, and G. Michel, "Computer Aided Testability Evaluation and Test Generation," *Proc. Int. Test Conf.*, Philadelphia, PA, October 1983, pp. 338-345.

[50] J. Savir, "Good Controllability and Good Observability do not Guarantee Good Testability," *IEEE Trans. Computers*, Vol. C-32, pp. 1198-1200, December 1983.

[51] J. Savir, G. S. Ditlow, and P. H. Bardell, "Random Pattern Testability," *IEEE Trans. Computers*, Vol. C-33, pp. 79-90, January 1984.

[52] J. Savir and W. H. McAnney, "On the Masking Probability with One's Count and Transition Count," *Proc. Int. Conf. on CAD (ICCAD)*, Santa Clara, CA, November 1985, pp. 111-113.

[53] J. Savir and W. H. McAnney, "Random Pattern Testability of Delay Faults," *IEEE Trans. Computers*, Vol. 37, pp. 291-300, March 1988.

[54] A. Sengupta, S. D. Durham, A. Sen, and S. Bandyopadhyay, "On a New Measure of System Diagnosability in Presence of Hybrid Faults," *IEEE Trans. Circ. and Syst.*, Vol. CAS-34, pp. 1053-1058, September 1987.

[55] S. C. Seth, B. B. Bhattacharya, and V. D. Agrawal, "An Exact Analysis for Efficient Computation of Random-Pattern Testability in Combinational Circuits," *Fault-Tolerant Computing Symp. (FTCS-16) Digest of Papers*, pp. 318-323, July 1986.

[56] S. C. Seth, L. Pan, and V. D. Agrawal, "PREDICT – Probabilistic Estimation of Digital Circuit Testability," *Fault-Tolerant Comp. Symp. (FTCS-15) Digest of Papers*, pp. 220-225, June 1985.

[57] J. J. Shedletsky and E. J. McCluskey, "The Error Latency of a Fault in a Combinational Digital Circuit," *Fault-Tolerant Computing Symp. (FTCS-5) Digest of Papers*, pp. 210-214, June 1975.

[58] D. M. Singer, "Testability Analysis of MOS VLSI Circuits," *Proc. Int. Test Conf.*, Philadelphia, PA, Oct. 1984, pp. 690-696.

[59] K. Son, "Rule Based Testability Checker and Test Generator," *Proc. Int. Test Conf.*, Philadelphia, PA, November 1985, pp. 884-889.

[60] T. H. Spencer, "Calculating Fault Detection Probabilities from Signal Probabilities," *IBM Report TR 00.3240*, p. 18, April 1984.

[61] T. H. Spencer and J. Savir, "Layout Influences Testability," *Proc. Int. Conf. Comp. Des. (ICCD'84)*, Port Chester, NY, October 1984, pp. 291-295. Also *IEEE Trans. Comp.* Vol. C-34, pp. 287-290, March 1985.

[62] R. Spillman, N. Glaser, and D. Peterson, "Development of a General Testability Figure-of-Merit," *Proc. Int. Conf. CAD (ICCAD-83)*, Santa Clara, CA, September 1983, pp. 34-35.

[63] J. E. Stephenson and J. Grason, "A Testability Measure for Register Transfer Level Digital Circuits," *Fault-Tolerant Computing Symp. (FTCS-6) Digest of Papers*, pp. 101-107, June 1976.

[64] S. Takasaki, M. Kawai, S. Funatsu, and A. Yamada, "A Calculus of Testability Measure at the Functional Level," *Int. Test Conf. Digest of Papers*, Philadelphia, PA, October 1981, pp. 95-101.

[65] E. Trischler, "Incomplete Scan Path with an Automatic Test Generation Methodology," *Int. Test Conf. (ITC-80), Digest of Papers*, November 1980, pp. 153-162.

[66] E. Trischler, "ATWIG, An Automatic Test Pattern Generator with Inherent Guidance," *Proc. Int. Test Conf.*, Philadelphia, PA, October 1984, pp. 80-87.

[67] A. Vergis and K. Steiglitz, "Testability Conditions for Bilateral Arrays of Combinational Cells," *Proc. Int. Conf. Comp. Des. (ICCD'83)*, Port Chester, NY, October 1980, pp. 40-44.

[68] J. A. Waicukauski, E. B. Eichelberger, D. O. Forlenza, E. Lindbloom, and T. McCarthy, "A Statistical Calculation of Fault Detection Probabilities by Fast Fault Simulation," *Proc. Int. Test Conf.*, Philadelphia, PA, November 1985, pp. 779-784.

[69] L. T. Wang and E. Law, "DTA: Daisy Testability Analyzer," *Proc. Int. Conf. CAD (ICCAD-84)*, Santa Clara, CA, November 1984, pp. 143-145.

[70] H. J. Wunderlich, "PROTEST : A Tool For Probabilistic Testability Analysis," *Proc. Design Automation Conference*, Las Vegas, Nevada, June 1985, pp. 204-211.

[71] H. J. Wunderlich, "The Random Pattern Testability of Programmable Logic Arrays," *Proc. Int. Conf. Comp. Des. (ICCD-87)*, Rye Brook, NY, October 1987, pp. 682-685.

[1] D. R. Aadsen and S. K. Jain, "Automation of BIST for Embedded RAM," *Proc. Custom Integrated Circ. Conf.*, Portland, OR, May 1987, pp. 66-67.

[2] M. S. Abadir and M. A. Breuer, "A Knowledge-Based System for Designing Testable VLSI Chips," *IEEE Design & Test of Computers*, Vol. 2, pp. 56-68, August 1985.

[3] M. S. Abadir and M. A. Breuer, "Scan Path with Look Ahead Shifting (SPLASH)," *Proc. Int. Test Conf.*, Washington, D.C., September 1986, pp. 696-704.

[4] M. S. Abadir and M. A. Breuer, "Test Schedules for VLSI Circuits Having Built-in Test Hardware," *IEEE Trans. Computers*, Vol. C-35, pp. 361-367, April 1986.

[5] M. S. Abadir and M. A. Breuer, "Test Schedules for VLSI Circuits having Built-In Test Hardware," *Comput. Math. Applic.*, Vol. 13, No. 5/6, pp. 519-536, 1987.

[6] E. M. Aboulhamid and E. Cerny, "A Class of Test Generators for Built-in-Testing," *Proc. Int. Conf. Circ. Computers (ICCC'82)*, New York, NY, September 1982, pp. 456-459. Also *IEEE Trans. Comp.*, Vol. C-32, pp. 957-959, October 1983.

[7] J. A. Abraham and D. D. Gajski, "Design of Testable Structures Defined by Simple Loops," *IEEE Trans. Computers*, Vol. C-30, pp. 875-884, November 1981.

[8] R. Abramovitz, K. DeVaughn, and R. Patrie, "Testability in a RISC Environment," *Proc. Int. Conf. Comp. Des. (ICCD)*, Port Chester, NY, October 1986, pp. 142-144.

[9] V. K. Agarwal, "Increasing Effectiveness of Built-in-Testing by Output Data Modification," *13th Int. Symp. Fault Tolerant Computing (FTCS-13) Digest of Papers*, pp. 227-234, June 1983.

[10] V. D. Agrawal, K. T. Cheng, D. D. Johnson, and T. Lin, "A Complete Solution to the Partial Scan Problem," *Proc. Int. Test Conf.*, Washington, DC, September 1987, pp. 44-51.

[11] V. D. Agrawal, K. T. Cheng, D. D. Johnson, and T. Lin, "Designing Circuits with Partial Scan," *IEEE Design & Test of Computers*, Vol. 5, pp. 8-15, April 1988.

[12] V. D. Agrawal, S. K. Jain, and D. M. Singer, "A CAD System for Design for Testability," *VLSI Design*, Vol. V, pp. 46-54, Oct. 1984. Also see correction in *VLSI Design*, Vol. V, p. 6, December 1984.

[13] V. D. Agrawal, S. K. Jain, and D. M. Singer, "Automation in Design for Testability," *Proc. Custom Integrated Circuits Conf.*, Rochester, NY, May 1984, pp. 159-163.

[14] M. O. Ahmad and D. V. Poornaiah, "Design of a Logic Circuit for Microprocessor Recovery from a Power Failure and a Transient Fault," *IEEE Trans. Circ. and Syst.*, Vol. CAS-34, pp. 433-436, April 1987.

[15] S. B. Akers, "The Use of Linear Sums in Exhaustive Testing," *Comput. Math. Applic.*, Vol. 13, No. 5/6, pp. 475-483, 1987.

[16] S. B. Akers, "A Parity Bit Signature for Exhaustive Testing," *IEEE Trans. CAD*, Vol. 7, pp. 333-338, March 1988.

[17] S. B. Akers and B. Krishnamurthy, "On Group Graphs and Their Fault Tolerance," *IEEE Trans. Computers*, Vol. C-36, pp. 885-888, July 1987.

[18] A. Albicki and A. Krasniewski, "Speed Versus Testability in NMOS VLSI Systems," *Proc. Int. Conf. CAD (ICCAD-84)*, Santa Clara, CA, November 1984, pp. 105-107.

[19] P. M. Almy and J. L. Rivero, "Using Error Latch Trace to Obtain Diagnostic Information," *Proc. 18th Des. Auto. Conf.*, Nashville, TN, June 1981, pp. 355-359.

[20] A. P. Ambler, M. Paraskeva, D. F. Burrows, W. L. Knight, and I. D. Dear, "Economically Viable Automatic Insertion of Self-Test Features for Custom VLSI," *Proc. Int. Test Conf.*, Washington, D.C., September 1986, pp. 232-243.

[21] L. Anania, et al., "Report on the 1983 Built-In Self Test Workshop," *IEEE Test Technology Newsletter*, pp. 1-5, 1983.

[22] H. Ando, "Testing VLSI with Random Access Scan," *COMPCON Digest of Papers*, pp. 50-52, February 1980.

[23] R. C. Aubusson and I. Catt, "Wafer-Scale Integration -- A Fault-Tolerant Procedure," *IEEE Journal of Solid-State Circuits*, Vol. SC-13, pp. 339-344, June 1978.

[24] L. Avra, "A VHSIC ETM-Bus-Compatible Test and Maintenance Interface," *Proc. Int. Test*

Conf., Washington, DC, September 1987, pp. 964-971.

[25] J. H. Aylor, B. W. Johnson, and B. J. Rector, "Structured Design for Testability in Semicustom VLSI," *IEEE Micro*, Vol. 6, pp. 51-58, February 1986.

[26] P. H. Bardell and W. H. McAnney, "Self-Testing of Multichip Logic Modules," *Int. Test Conf. Digest of Papers*, Philadelphia, PA, November 1982, pp. 200-204.

[27] P. H. Bardell and W. H. McAnney, "Self-Testing of Multichip Logic Modules," *Proc. IEEE Test Conf.*, Philadelphia, PA, 1982, pp. 200-204.

[28] P. H. Bardell and W. H. McAnney, "Parallel Pseudorandom Sequences for Built-In Test," *Proc. Int. Test Conf.*, Philadelphia, PA, October 1984, pp. 302-308.

[29] P. H. Bardell and W. H. McAnney, "Self-Test of Random Access Memories," *Proc. Int. Test Conf.*, Philadelphia, PA, November 1985, pp. 352-355.

[30] P. H. Bardell and W. H. McAnney, "Pseudorandom Arrays for Built-In Tests," *IEEE Trans. Computers*, Vol. C-35, pp. 653-658, July 1986.

[31] P. H. Bardell, W. H. McAnney, and J. Savir, *Built-In Test for VLSI: Pseudorandom Techniques*, Wiley, Somerset, NJ, 1987.

[32] Y. Baron, "Self Diagnostics on System Level by Design," *Proc. Int. Test Conf.*, Washington, D.C., September 1986 %P 921-927.

[33] Z. Barzilai, J. L. Carter, A. K. Chandra, and B. K. Rosen, "Diagnosis Based on Signature Testing," *IBM Research Report*, pp. 1-10, Nov. 1982.

[34] Z. Barzilai, D. Coppersmith, and A. L. Rosenberg, "Exhaustive Generation of Bit Patterns with Applications to VLSI Self-Testing," *IEEE Trans. Computers*, Vol. C-32, pp. 190-194, February 1983.

[35] Z. Barzilai and B. K. Rosen, "Comparison of AC Self-Testing Procedures," *Proc. Int. Test Conf.*, Philadelphia, PA, October 1983, pp. 89-94.

[36] Z. Barzilai, J. Savir, G. Markowski, and M. G. Smith, "VLSI Self-Testing Based on Syndrome Techniques," *Int. Test Conf. Digest of Papers*, Philadelphia, PA, October 1981, pp. 102-109.

[37] Z. Barzilai, J. Savir, G. Markowsky, and M. G. Smith, "The Weighted Syndrome Sums Approach to VLSI Testing," *IEEE Trans. Computers*, Vol. C-30, pp. 996-1000, December 1981.

[38] L. A. Basto and J. R. Kuban, "Test Features of the MC68881 Floating-Point Coprocessor," *Proc. Int. Test Conf.*, Philadelphia, PA, November 1985, pp. 752-757.

[39] J. Beausang and A. Albicki, "Incorporation of the BILBO Technique within an Existing Chip Design," *Proc. Custom Integrated Circ. Conf.*, Portland, OR, May 1985, pp. 328-331.

[40] J. Beausang and A. Albicki, "The Design for Testability Process: Definition and Exploration," *Proc. Int. Conf. Comp. Des. (ICCD-87)*, Rye Brook, NY, October 1987, pp. 362-365.

[41] F. P. M. Beenker, "Systematic and Structured Methods for Digital Board Testing," *VLSI Systems Design*, Vol. VIII, p. 50, January 1987.

[42] F. P. M. Beenker, K. J. E. VanEerdewijk, R. B. W. Gerritsen, F. N. Peacock, and M. VanderStar, "Macro Testing: Unifying IC and Board Test," *IEEE Design & Test of Computers*, Vol. 3, pp. 26-32, December 1986.

[43] R. G. Bennetts, *Design of Testable Logic Circuits*, Addison-Wesley, Reading, MA, 1984.

[44] R. G. Bennetts, "Practical Guidelines for Designing Testable Custom/Semicustom ICs," *VLSI Design*, Vol. V, p. 64, April 1984.

[45] N. Benowitz, D. F. Calhoun, G. E. Anderson, J. E. Bauer, and C. T. Joeckel, "An Advanced Fault Isolation System for Digital Logic," *IEEE Trans. Comp.*, Vol. C-24, pp. 489-497, May 1975.

[46] F. P. Beucler and M. J. Manner, "HILDO: The Highly Integrated Logic Device Observer," *VLSI Design*, Vol. V, p. 88, June 1984.

[47] M. M. Bhat and C. L. McAfee, "Design for Testability in a VLSI Co-Processor," *Proc. Int. Conf. Comp. Des. (ICCD'83)*, Port Chester, NY, October 1983, pp. 113-116.

[48] B. B. Bhattacharya and B. Gupta, "Syndrome Testable Design of Combinational Networks for Detecting Stuck-At and Bridging Faults," *Proc. Int. Test Conf.*, Philadelphia, PA, October 1983, pp. 446-452.

[49] B. B. Bhattacharya and B. Gupta, "Logical

Modeling of Physical Failures and their Inherent Syndrome Testability in MOS LSI/VLSI Networks," *Proc. Int. Test Conf.*, Philadelphia, PA, October 1984, pp. 847-855.

[50] B. B. Bhattacharya and S. C. Seth, "On the Reconvergent Structure of Combinational Circuits with Applications to Compact Testing," *Fault-Tolerant Computing Symp. (FTCS-17) Digest of Papers*, pp. 264-269, July 1987.

[51] D. Bhattacharya and J. P. Hayes, "Fast and Easily Testable Implementation of Arithmetic Functions," *Fault-Tolerant Comp. Symp. (FTCS-16) Digest of Papers*, pp. 324-329, July 1986.

[52] A. Bhattacharyya, "On a Novel Approach of Fault Detection in an Easily Testable Sequential Machine with Extra Inputs and Extra Outputs," *IEEE Trans. Computers*, Vol. C-32, pp. 323-325, March 1983.

[53] D. Bhavsar, "A New Economical Implementation for Scannable Flip-flop in MOS," *IEEE Design & Test of Computers*, Vol. 3, pp. 52-56, June 1986.

[54] D. K. Bhavsar, "Design for Test Calculus: An Algorithm for DFT Rules Checking," *Proc. 20th Des. Auto. Conf.*, Miami Beach, FL, June 1983, pp. 300-307.

[55] D. K. Bhavsar, "Concatenable Polydividers: Bit-sliced LFSR Chips for Board Self-Test," *Proc. Int. Test Conf.*, Philadelphia, PA, November 1985, pp. 86-93.

[56] D. K. Bhavsar and B. Krishnamurthy, "Can We Eliminate Fault Escape in Self Testing by Polynomial Division (Signature Analysis)?," *Proc. Int. Test Conf.*, Philadelphia, PA, October 1984, pp. 134-139.

[57] D. K. Bhavsar and D. G. Miner, "Testability Strategy for a Second Generation VAX Microprocessor Chip," *Proc. Int. Test Conf.*, Washington, DC, September 1987, pp. 818-825.

[58] N. N. Biswas and J. Jacob, "A Testable PLA Design with Minimal Hardware and Test Set," *Proc. Int. Test Conf.*, Philadelphia, PA, November 1985, pp. 583-588.

[59] W. S. Blackley, M. A. Jack, and J. R. Jordan, "A Digital Polarity Correlator Featuring Built-In Self Test and Self Repair Mechanisms," *Proc. Int. Test Conf.*, Philadelphia, PA, October 1983, pp. 289-294.

[60] W. S. Blackley, M. A. Jack, and J. R. Jordan, "A Digital Polarity Correlator with Built-in Self Test and Self Repair," *IEEE Design & Test of Computers*, Vol. 1, pp. 42-49, May 1984.

[61] D. Bondurant and D. Baran, "HC20000: A Fast 20K Gate Array with Built-In Self Test and System Fault Isolation Capabilities," *Proc. Custom Integrated Circ. Conf.*, Rochester, NY, May 1986, pp. 315-318.

[62] P. Bosshart and T. Sridhar, "Test Methodology for a 32-Bit Processor Chip," *Proc. Int. Conf. CAD (ICCAD-86)*, Santa Clara, CA, November 1986, pp. 12-14.

[63] S. Bozorgui-Nesbat, "Design for Testability and Yield at the Transistor Level," *Proc. Int. Test. Conf.*, Washington, DC, September 1987, pp. 172-180.

[64] S. Bozorgui-Nesbat and E. J. McCluskey, "Design for Delay Testing of Programmable Logic Arrays," *Proc. Int. Conf. CAD (ICCAD-84)*, Santa Clara, CA, November 1984, pp. 146-148.

[65] S. Bozorgui-Nesbat and E. J. McCluskey, "Lower Overhead Design for Testability of Programmable Logic Arrays," *IEEE Trans. Computers*, Vol. C-35, pp. 379-383, April 1986. Also *Proc. Int. Test Conf.*, Philadelphia, PA, October 1984, pp. 856-865.

[66] M. A. Breuer and A. A. Ismaeel, "Roving Emulator as a Fault Detection Mechanism," *IEEE Trans. Computers*, Vol. C-35, pp. 933-939, November 1986.

[67] H. H. Butt and Y. M. El-ziq, "Impact of Mixed-Mode Self-Test on Life Cycle Cost of VLSI Based Designs," *Proc. Int. Test Conf.*, Philadelphia, PA, October 1984, pp. 338-347.

[68] P. Camurati and P. Prinetto, "ProTest: A Design for Testability Oriented Prolog Hardware Description Language," *Proc. Int. Conf. Comp. Des. (ICCD-87)*, Rye Brook, NY, October 1987, pp. 297-300.

[69] J. L. Carter, "The Theory of Signature Testing for VLSI," *ACM*, pp. 66-76, 1982.

[70] W. C. Carter, "Signature Testing with Guaranteed Bounds for Fault Coverage," *Int. Test Conf. Digest of Papers*, Philadelphia, PA, November 1982, pp. 75-82.

[71] W. C. Carter, "The Ubiquitous Parity Bit," *Fault Tolerant Computing Symp. (FTCS-12)*

Digest of Papers, pp. 289-296, June 1982.

[72] W. C. Carter, "Improved Parallel Signature Checkers/Analyzers," *Fault-Tolerant Comp. Symp. (FTCS-16) Digest of Papers*, pp. 416-421, July 1986.

[73] E. Cerny, G. Bois, and M. Aboulhamid, "Built-in Self-Test of a CMOS ALU," *Fault-Tolerant Comp. Symp. (FTCS-16) Digest of Papers*, pp. 28-33, July 1986.

[74] A. Chatterjee and J. A. Abraham, "On the C-Testability of Generalized Counters," *IEEE Trans. CAD*, Vol. CAD-6, pp. 713-726, September 1987.

[75] K. K. Chau and C. R. Kime, "Selective I/O Scan: A Diagnosable Design Technique for VLSI Systems," *Comput. Math. Applic.*, Vol. 13, No. 5/6, pp. 485-502, 1987.

[76] J. Chavade, M. Vergniault, P. Rousseau, Y. Crouzet, and C. Landrault, "A Monolithic Self-Checking Error Detection Processor," *Test Conference Digest of Papers*, Philadelphia, PA, November 1980, pp. 279-286.

[77] C. H. Chen, "VLSI Design for Testability," *IEEE Test Conference, Digest of Papers*, Cherry Hill, NJ, 1979, pp. 306-309.

[78] C. L. Chen, "Linear Dependencies in Linear Feedback Shift Registers," *IEEE Trans. Computers*, Vol. C-35, pp. 1086-1088, December 1986.

[79] C. L. Chen, "Exhaustive Test Pattern Generation Using Cyclic Codes," *IEEE Trans. Computers*, Vol. 37, pp. 225-228, February 1988.

[80] C. Y. Chen, W. K. Fuchs, and J. A. Abraham, "Efficient Concurrent Error Detection in PLAs and ROMs," *Proc. Int. Conf. Comp. Des. (ICCD)*, Port Chester, NY, October 1985, pp. 525-529.

[81] T. H. Chen and M. A. Breuer, "Automatic Design for Testability Via Testability Measures," *IEEE Trans. Computer-Aided Design*, Vol. CAD-4, pp. 3-11, January 1985.

[82] Y. H. Choi and M. Malek, "A Fault-Tolerant VLSI Sorter," *Proc. Int. Conf. Comp. Des. (ICCD)*, Port Chester, NY, October 1985, pp. 510-513.

[83] P. G. Corrin, "Application of the DA-X Design System to Paracell VLSI with Self-Test," *Proc. Int. Conf. Comp. Des. (ICCD)*, Port Chester, NY, October 1985, pp. 688-691.

[84] G. L. Craig and C. R. Kime, "Pseudo-Exhaustive Adjacency Testing: A BIST Approach for Stuck-Open Faults," *Proc. Int. Test Conf.*, Philadelphia, PA, November 1985, pp. 126-137.

[85] Y. Crouzet and C. Landrault, "Design of Self-Checking MOS-LSI Circuits: Application to a Four-Bit Microprocessor," *IEEE Trans. Computers*, Vol. C-29, pp. 532-537, June 1980.

[86] W. Daehn and J. Gross, "A Test Generator IC for Testing Large CMOS-RAMs," *Proc. Int. Test Conf.*, Washington, DC, September 1986, pp. 18-24.

[87] W. Daehn and J. Mucha, "A Hardware Approach to Self-Testing of Large Programmable Logic Arrays," *IEEE Trans. Computers*, Vol. C-30, pp. 829-833, November 1981.

[88] R. Dandapani, J. H. Patel, and J. A. Abraham, "Design of Test Pattern Generators for Built-In Test," *Proc. Int. Test Conf.*, Philadelphia, PA, October 1984, pp. 315-319.

[89] R. G. Daniels and W. C. Bruce, "Built-In Self-Test Trends in Motorola Microprocessors," *IEEE Design & Test of Computers*, Vol. 2, pp. 64-71, April 1985.

[90] S. DasGupta, P. Goel, R. G. Walther, and T. W. Williams, "A Variation of LSSD and its Implications on Design and Test Pattern Generation in VLSI," *Int. Test Conf. Digest of Papers*, Philadelphia, PA, November 1982, pp. 63-66.

[91] S. DasGupta, R. G. Walther, and T. W. Williams, "An Enhancement to LSSD and Some Applications of LSSD in Reliability, Availability, and Serviceability," *Fault-Tolerant Comp. Symp. (FTCS-11) Digest of Papers*, pp. 32-34, June 1981.

[92] S. Dasgupta, C. R. P. Hartmann, and L. D. Rudolph, "Dual-Mode Logic for Function-Independent Fault Testing," *IEEE Trans. Computers*, Vol. C-29, pp. 1025-1029, November 1980. Also see correction in *IEEE Trans. Comp.*, Vol. C-30, p. 819, Oct. 1981.

[93] R. David, "Testing by Feedback Shift Register," *IEEE Trans. Computers*, Vol. C-29, pp. 668-673, July 1980.

[94] R. David, "Signature Analysis for Multiple Output Circuits," *IEEE Trans. Computers*, Vol. C-35, pp. 830-837, September 1986. Also *Fault-*

Tolerant Comp. Symp. (FTCS-14) Digest of Papers, Kissimmee, FL, June 1984, pp. 366-371.

[95] J. R. Day, "A Fault-Driven, Comprehensive Redundancy Algorithm for Repair of Dynamic RAMs," Proc. Int. Test Conf., Philadelphia, PA, October 1984, pp. 287-293.

[96] J. R. Day, "A Fault-Driven, Comprehensive Redundancy Algorithm," IEEE Design & Test of Computers, Vol. 2, pp. 35-45, June 1985.

[97] E. P. DeBenedictis and C. L. Seitz, "Testing and Structured Design," Int. Test Conf. Digest of Papers, Philadelphia, PA, November 1982, pp. 58-62.

[98] B. I. Dervisoglu, "VLSI Self-Testing Using Exhaustive Bit Patterns," Proc. Int. Conf. Comp. Des. (ICCD), Port Chester, NY, October 1985, pp. 558-561.

[99] E. B. Eichelberger and E. Lindbloom, "Random-Pattern Coverage Enhancement and Diagnosis for LSSD Logic Self-Test," IBM J. Res. Develop., Vol. 27, pp. 265-272, May 1983.

[100] E. B. Eichelberger and T. W. Williams, "A Logic Design Structure for LSI Testability," J. Des. Aut. and Fault. Tol. Comp., Vol. 2, pp. 165-178, May 1978.

[101] H. Eiki, K. Inagaki, and S. Yajima, "Autonomous Testing and Its Applications to Testable Design of Logic Circuits," Fault-Tolerant Comp. Symp. (FTCS-10) Digest of Papers, pp. 173-178, October 1980.

[102] Y. M. El-ziq, "S³: VLSI Self-Test Using Signature Analysis and Scan Path Techniques," Proc. Int. Conf. CAD (ICCAD-83), Santa Clara, CA, September 1983, pp. 73-76.

[103] Y. M. El-ziq and H. H. Butt, "A Mixed-Mode Built-In Self-Test Technique Using Scan Path and Signature Analysis," Proc. Int. Test Conf., Philadelphia, PA, October 1983, pp. 269-274.

[104] H. Elhuni, A. Vergis, and L. Kinney, "C-Testability of Two-Dimensional Arrays of Combinational Cells," Proc. Int. Conf. on CAD (ICCAD), Santa Clara, CA, November 1985, pp. 74-76.

[105] R. C. Evans, "Testing Repairable RAMs and Mostly Good Memories," Int. Test Conf. Digest of Papers, Philadelphia, PA, October 1981, pp. 49-55.

[106] P. P. Fasang, "BIDCO, Built-In Digital Circuit

Observer," Test Conference Digest of Papers, Philadelphia, PA, November 1980, pp. 261-266.

[107] P. P. Fasang, "A Fault Detection and Isolation Technique for Microcomputers," Int. Test Conf. Digest of Papers, Philadelphia, PA, November 1982, pp. 214-219.

[108] P. P. Fasang, J. P. Shen, M. A. Shuette, and W. A. Gwaltney, "Automated Design for Testability of Semicustom Integrated Circuits," Proc. Int. Test Conf., Philadelphia, PA, November 1985, pp. 558-564.

[109] J. Fox, G. Surace, and P. A. Thomas, "A Self-Testing 2-μm CMOS Chip Set for FFT Applications," IEEE J. Solid State Circ., Vol. SC-22, pp. 15-19, February 1987.

[110] P. Franzon, "Interconnect Strategies for Fault Tolerant 2D VLSI Arrays," Proc. Int. Conf. Comp. Des. (ICCD), Port Chester, NY, October 1986, pp. 230-233.

[111] R. A. Frohwerk, "Signature Analysis: A New Digital Field Service Method," Hewlett-Packard Journal, Vol. 28, pp. 2-8, May 1977.

[112] W. K. Fuchs, C. R. Chen, and J. A. Abraham, "Concurrent Error Detection in Highly Structured Logic Arrays," IEEE J. Sol. St. Circ., Vol. SC-22, pp. 583-594,

[113] R. Fujii and J. A. Abraham, "Self-Test for Microprocessors," Proc. Int. Test Conf., Philadelphia, PA, November 1985, pp. 356-361.

[114] R. Fujii and J. A. Abraham, "Approaches to Circuit Level Design for Testability," Proc. Int. Test Conf., September 1986, pp. 480-483.

[115] E. Fujiwara and K. Matsuoka, "A Self-Checking Generalized Prediction Checker and its use for Built-in Testing," IEEE Trans. Computers, Vol. C-36, pp. 86-93, January 1987.

[116] H. Fujiwara, "A New PLA Design for Universal Testability," IEEE Trans. Computers, Vol. C-33, pp. 745-750, August 1984.

[117] H. Fujiwara, Logic Testing and Design for Testability, MIT Press, Cambridge, MA, 1985.

[118] H. Fujiwara and K. Kinoshita, "A Design of Programmable Logic Arrays with Universal Tests," IEEE Trans. Computers, Vol. C-30, pp. 823-827, November 1981.

[119] H. Fujiwara and S. Toida, "The Complexity of Fault Detection: An Approach to Design for Testability," Fault-Tolerant Comp. Symp.

(*FTCS-12*) *Digest of Papers*, pp. 101-108, June 1982.

[120] H. Fujiwara, R. Truer, and V. K. Agarwal, "A Low Overhead, High Coverage, Built-In, Self-Test PLA," *Report No. 84.13*, p. 21, 1984.

[121] H. S. Fung, "A Testable-by-Construction Strategy for the Silc Silicon Compiler," *Proc. Int. Conf. Comp. Des. (ICCD)*, Port Chester, NY, October 1985, pp. 554-557.

[122] H. S. Fung and S. Hirschhorn, "An Automatic DFT System for the Silc Silicon Compiler," *IEEE Design & Test of Computers*, Vol. 3, pp. 45-57, February 1986.

[123] H. S. Fung, S. Hirschhorn, and R. Kulkarni, "Design For Testability in a Silicon Compilation Environment," *22nd Design Automation Conference*, Las Vegas, Nevada, June 1985, pp. 190-196.

[124] K. Furuya, "A Probabilistic Approach to Locally Exhaustive Testing," *Fault-Tolerant Computing Symp. (FTCS-17) Digest of Papers*, pp. 62-65, July 1987.

[125] N. Gaitanis and C. Halatsis, "A New Design Method for m-out-of-n TSC Checkers," *IEEE Trans. Computers*, Vol. C-32, pp. 273-283, March 1983.

[126] P. P. Gelsinger, "Built In Self Test of the 80386," *Proc. Int. Conf. Comp. Des. (ICCD)*, Port Chester, NY, October 1986, pp. 169-173.

[127] P. P. Gelsinger, "Design and Test of the 80386," *IEEE Design & Test of Computers*, Vol. 4, pp. 42-50, June 1987.

[128] M. Gerner and H. Nertinger, "Scan Path in CMOS Semicustom Chips," *Proc. Int. Test Conf.*, Philadelphia, PA, October 1984, pp. 834-842.

[129] G. Giles and K. Scheuer, "Testability Features of the MC68851 PMMU," *Proc. Int. Test Conf.*, Washington, DC, September 1986, pp. 408-411.

[130] P. Golan, O. Novak, and J. Hlavicka, "Pseudoexhaustive Test Pattern Generator with Enhanced Fault-Coverage," *Fault-Tolerant Comp. Symp. (FTCS-16) Digest of Papers*, pp. 404-409, July 1986.

[131] P. Golan, O. Novak, and J. Hlavicka, "Pseudoexhaustive Test Pattern Generator with Enhanced Fault Coverage," *IEEE Trans. Computers*, Vol. 37, pp. 496-500, April 1988.

[132] A. Goundan and J. P. Hayes, "Design of Totally Fault Locatable Combinational Networks," *IEEE Trans. Computers*, Vol. C-29, pp. 33-44, January 1980.

[133] J. Grason and A. W. Nagle, "Digital Test Generation and Design for Testability," *Proc. 17th Design Auto. Conf.*, Minneapolis, MN, June 1980, pp. 175-189.

[134] K. E. Grosspietsch, H. Huber, and A. Mueller, "The Concepts of a Fault-Tolerant and Easily-Testable Associative Memory," *Fault-Tolerant Comp. Symp. (FTCS-16) Digest of Papers*, pp. 34-39, July 1986.

[135] R. K. Gulati and S. M. Reddy, "Concurrent Error Detection in VLSI Array Structures," *Proc. Int. Conf. Comp. Des. (ICCD)*, Port Chester, NY, October 1986, pp. 488-491.

[136] D. S. Ha and S. M. Reddy, "On Testable Self-Timed Logic Circuits," *Proc. Int. Conf. Comp. Des. (ICCD'84)*, Port Chester, NY, October 1984, pp. 296-301.

[137] D. S. Ha and S. M. Reddy, "On the Design of Testable Domino PLAs," *Proc. Int. Test Conf.*, Philadelphia, PA, November 1985, pp. 567-573.

[138] D. S. Ha and S. M. Reddy, "On the Design of Random Pattern Testable PLAs," *Proc. Int. Test Conf.*, Washington, D.C., September 1986, pp. 688-695.

[139] D. S. Ha and S. M. Reddy, "On BIST PLAs," *Proc. Int. Test Conf.*, Washington, DC, September 1987, pp. 342-351.

[140] D. S. Ha and S. M. Reddy, "On the Design of Pseudoexhaustive Testable PLAs," *IEEE Trans. Computers*, Vol. 37, pp. 468-472, April 1988.

[141] S. H. Han and M. Malek, "Two-Dimensional Multiple-Access Testing Technique for Random-Access Memories," *Proc. Int. Conf. Comp. Des. (ICCD)*, Port Chester, NY, October 1986, pp. 248-251.

[142] S. H. Han and M. Malek, "A New Technique for Error Detection and Correction in Semiconductor Memories," *Proc. Int. Test Conf.*, Washington, DC, September 1987, pp. 864-870.

[143] S. Z. Hassan, "Signature Testing of Sequential Machines," *IEEE Trans. Computers*, Vol. C-33, pp. 762-764, August 1984. Also *Proc. Int. Test Conf.*, Philadelphia, PA, October 1983, pp. 714-718.

[144] S. Z. Hassan, D. J. Lu, and E. J. McCluskey, "Parallel Signature Analyzers -- Detection Capability and Extensions," *Compcon Spring, Digest of Papers*, pp. 440-445, February 1983.

[145] S. Z. Hassan and E. J. McCluskey, "Testing PLA's Using Multiple Parallel Signature Analyzers," *13th Int. Symp. Fault Tolerant Computing (FTCS-13) Digest of Papers*, pp. 422-425, June 1983.

[146] S. Z. Hassan and E. J. McCluskey, "Enhancing the Effectiveness of Parallel Signature Analyzers," *Proc. Int. Conf. CAD (ICCAD-84)*, Santa Clara, CA, November 1984, pp. 102-104.

[147] S. Z. Hassan and E. J. McCluskey, "Increased Fault Coverage through Multiple Signatures," *Fault-Tolerant Computing Symp. (FTCS-14), Digest of Papers*, pp. 354-365, June 1984.

[148] S. Z. Hassan and E. J. McCluskey, "Pseudo-Exhaustive Testing of Sequential Machines Using Signature Analysis," *Proc. Int. Test Conf.*, Philadelphia, PA, October 1984, pp. 320-326.

[149] K. Hatayama, T. Hayashi, K. Moriwaki, S. Suzuki, and M. Takakura, "Automatic Test Generation for Sequential Circuits with Irregular Scan Structure," *Proc. Int. Conf. CAD (ICCAD-86)*, Santa Clara, CA, November 1986, pp. 102-105.

[150] T. Hayashi, K. Hatayama, Y. Kunitomo, and S. Kuboki, "An Approach to Design Automation for Highly Testable Logic Circuits," *Proc. Int. Conf. CAD (ICCAD-86)*, Santa Clara, CA, November 1986, pp. 98-101.

[151] J. P. Hayes, "Minimization of Fanout in Switching Networks," *Proceedings of 15th Annual Symposium on Switching and Automata Theory*, 1974.

[152] J. P. Hayes, "Check Sum Methods for Test Data Compression," *Journal of Design Automation and Fault-Tolerant Computing*, Vol. 1, pp. 3-17, Oct. 1976.

[153] J. P. Hayes, "The Fanout Structure of Switching Functions," *JACM*, Vol. 22, pp. 551-571, Oct. 75.

[154] A. Hlawiczka, "Compression of Three-State Data Serial Streams by Means of a Parallel LFSR Signature Analyzer," *IEEE Trans. Computers*, Vol. C-35, pp. 732-741, August 1986.

[155] A. Hlawiczka, "Parallel Multisignature Analysis of Faults in the Multi-output Digital System," *Fault-Tolerant Comp. Symp. (FTCS-16) Digest of Papers*, pp. 398-403, July 1986.

[156] H. Hofestadt and M. Gerner, "Qualitative Testability Analysis and Hierarchical Test Pattern Generation – A New Approach to Design for Testability," *Proc. Int. Test Conf.*, Washington, DC, September 1987, pp. 538-546.

[157] S. J. Hong and D. L. Ostapko, "FITPLA: A Programmable Logic Array for Function Independent Testing," *Fault-Tolerant Comp. Symp. (FTCS-10) Digest of Papers*, pp. 131-136, October 1980.

[158] S. Horiguchi, H. Yoshimura, M. Nagatani, and K. Fukami, "The Design of Dedicated 32-Bit Processors," *IEEE Design & Test of Computers*, Vol. 4, pp. 52-58, June 1987.

[159] P. W. Horstman, "Design for Testability Using Logic Programming," *Proc. Int. Test Conf.*, Philadelphia, PA, October 1983, pp. 706-713.

[160] M. C. Howells and V. K. Agarwal, "Yield and Reliability Enhancement of Large Area Binary Tree Architectures," *Fault-Tolerant Computing Symp. (FTCS-17) Digest of Papers*, pp. 290-295, July 1987.

[161] T. C. Hsiao and S. C. Seth, "The Use of Rademacher-Walsh Spectrum in Testing and Design of Digital Circuits," *Proc. Int. Conf. Circ. Computers (ICCC'82)*, New York, NY, September 1982, pp. 202-205.

[162] K. A. Hua, J. Y. Jou, and J. A. Abraham, "Built-In Tests for VLSI Finite-State Machines," *Fault-Tolerant Comput. Symp. (FTCS-14), Digest of Papers*, pp. 292-297, June 1984.

[163] C. L. Hudson Jr. and G. D. Peterson, "Parallel Self-Test with Pseudo-Random Test Patterns," *Proc. Int. Test Conf.*, Washington, DC, September 1987, pp. 954-963.

[164] R. J. Illman, "Self-Tested Data Flow Logic: A New Approach," *IEEE Design & Test of Computers*, Vol. 2, pp. 50-58, April 1985.

[165] J. Inoue, T. Matsumura, M. Tanno, and J. Yamada, "Parallel Testing Technology for VLSI Memories," *Proc. Int. Test Conf.*, Washington, DC, September 1987, pp. 1066-1071.

[166] A. Ivanov and V. K. Agarwal, "On a Fast Method to Monitor the Behaviour of Signature Analysis Registers," *Proc. Int. Test Conf.*,

Washington, DC, September 1987, pp. 645-655.

[167] K. Iwasaki, N. Yamaguchi, and T. Nishimukai, "Analysis and Proposal of Signature Circuit for LSI Testing," *Proc. Int. Test Conf.*, Washington, DC, September 1987, pp. 517-522.

[168] S. V. Iyengar and L. L. Kinney, "Concurrent Testing of Flow of Control in Simple Microprogrammed Control Units," *Int. Test Conf. Digest of Papers*, Philadelphia, PA, November 1982, pp. 469-479.

[169] V. S. Iyengar and L. L. Kinney, "Concurrent Fault Detection in Microprogrammed Control Units," *IEEE Trans. Computers*, Vol. C-34, pp. 810-821, September 1985.

[170] S. K. Jain and C. E. Stroud, "Built-in Self Testing of Embedded Memories," *IEEE Design & Test of Computers*, Vol. 3, pp. 27-37, October 1986.

[171] N. Jarwala and D. K. Pradhan, "An Easily Testable Architecture for Multi-Megabit RAMs," *Proc. Int. Test Conf.*, Washington, DC, September 1987, pp. 750-758.

[172] N. Jarwala and D. K. Pradhan, "Cost Analysis of On Chip Error Control Coding for Fault Tolerant Dynamic RAMs," *Fault-Tolerant Computing Symp. (FTCS-17) Digest of Papers*, pp. 278-283, July 1987.

[173] W. K. Jenkins, "The Design of Error-Checkers for Self-Checking Residue Number Arithmetic," *IEEE Trans. Computers*, Vol. C-32, pp. 388-396, April 1983.

[174] N. K. Jha and J. A. Abraham, "Testable CMOS Logic Circuits Under Dynamic Behavior," *Proc. Int. Conf. CAD (ICCAD-84)*, Santa Clara, CA, November 1984, pp. 131-133.

[175] N. K. Jha and J. A. Abraham, "Totally Self-Checking MOS Circuits under Realistic Physical Failures," *Proc. Int. Conf. Comp. Des. (ICCD'84)*, Port Chester, NY, October 1984, pp. 665-670.

[176] N. K. Jha and J. A. Abraham, "Design of Testable CMOS Logic Circuits under Arbitrary Delays," *IEEE Trans. on CAD*, Vol. CAD-4, pp. 264-269, July 1985.

[177] N. K. Jha and M. B. Vora, "A Systematic Code for Detecting t-Unidirectional Errors," *Fault-Tolerant Computing Symp. (FTCS-17) Digest of Papers*, pp. 96-101, July 1987.

[178] R. Joersz and C. R. Kime, "A Distributed Hardware Approach to Built-In Self Test," *Proc. Int. Test Conf.*, Washington, DC, September 1987, pp. 972-980.

[179] N. A. Jones and K. Baker, "An Intelligent Knowledge-Based System Tool for High-Level BIST Design," *Proc. Int. Test Conf.*, Washington, D.C., September 1986, pp. 743-749.

[180] J. Kalinowski, A. Albicki, and J. Beausang, "Test Control Signal Distribution in Self-Testing VLSI Circuits," *Proc. Int. Conf. CAD (ICCAD-86)*, Santa Clara, CA, November 1986, pp. 60-63.

[181] N. Kanopoulos and G. T. Mitchell, "Testing of Bit-Serial Signal Processors," *Proc. Int. Test Conf.*, Philadelphia, PA, October 1983, pp. 719-725.

[182] N. Kanopoulos and G. T. Mitchell, "Design for Testability and Self-Testing Approaches for Bit-Serial Signal Processors," *IEEE Design & Test of Computers*, Vol. 1, pp. 52-59, May 1984.

[183] M. Karpovsky and P. Nagvajara, "Optimal Time and Space Compression of Test Response for VLSI Devices," *Proc. Int. Test Conf.*, Washington, DC, September 1987, pp. 523-529.

[184] M. Kawai, S. Funatsu, and A. Yamada, "Application of Shift Register Approach and Its Effective Implementation," *Test Conference Digest of Papers*, Philadelphia, PA, November 1980, pp. 22-25.

[185] M. Kawashima, M. Takechi, K. Ikuzaki, K. Kishida, K. Itoh, M. Fujita, T. Nakao, and I. Masuda, "An 18K 1 μm CMOS Gate Array with High Testability Structure," *Proc. Custom Integrated Circ. Conf.*, Portland, OR, May 1987, pp. 52-55.

[186] S. Kazmi and K. VanEgmond, "Simulation and Testing of VTI Gate Arrays," *Proc. Custom Integrated Circ. Conf.*, Rochester, NY, May 1986, pp. 409-411.

[187] J. Khakbaz, "A Testable PLA Design with Low Overhead and High Fault Coverage," *IEEE Trans. Computers*, Vol. C-33, pp. 743-745, August 1984. Also *Fault-Tolerant Comp. Symp. (FTCS-13) Digest of Papers*, Milan, Italy, June 1983, pp. 426-429.

[188] J. Khakbaz and S. Bozorgui-Nesbat, "Minimizing Extra Hardware for Fully Testable PLA Design," *Proc. Int. Conf. on CAD (ICCAD)*,

Santa Clara, CA, November 1985, pp. 102-104.

[189] J. Khakbaz and E. J. McCluskey, "Self-Testing Embedded Parity Checkers," *IEEE Trans. Computers*, Vol. C-33, pp. 753-756, August 1984.

[190] M. Khare and A. Albicki, "Cellular Automata used for Test Pattern Generation," *Proc. Int. Conf. Comp. Des. (ICCD-87)*, Rye Brook, NY, October 1987, pp. 56-59.

[191] C. R. Kime, H. H. Kwan, J. K. Lemke, and G. B. Williams, "A Built-In Test Methodology for VLSI Data Paths," *Proc. Int. Test Conf.*, Philadelphia, PA, October 1984, pp. 327-337.

[192] R. M. King and P. Banerjee, "A Novel Circuit Design Providing Concurrent Error Detection in PLAs," *Proc. Int. Conf. Comp. Des. (ICCD)*, Port Chester, NY, October 1986, pp. 588-591.

[193] K. Kinoshita and K. K. Saluja, "Built-In Testing of Memory Using an On-Chip Compact Testing Scheme," *IEEE Trans. Computers*, Vol. C-35, pp. 862-870, October 1986. Also *Proc. Int. Test Conf.*, Philadelphia, PA, October 1984, pp. 271-281.

[194] B. Koehler, "Designing a Microcontroller Supercell for Testability," *VLSI Design*, Vol. IV, p. 44, October 1983.

[195] Y. Koga, Y. Suzuki, and K. Mizukami, "Logic Elements for Fail-Safe Circuit Design," *Fault-Tolerant Comp. Symp. (FTCS-10) Digest of Papers*, pp. 351-353, October 1980.

[196] Z. Kohavi and P. Lavallee, "Design of Diagnosable Sequential Machines," in *Proc. Joint Computer Conf.*, , Spring 1967, pp. 713-718.

[197] D. Komonytsky, "LSI Self-Test Using Level Sensitive Scan Design and Signature Analysis," *Int. Test Conf. Digest of Papers*, Philadelphia, PA, November 1982, pp. 414-424.

[198] B. Konemann, J. Mucha, and G. Zweihoff, "Built-In Test for Complex Digital Integrated Circuits," *IEEE J. Solid-State Circuits*, Vol. SC-15, pp. 315-319, June 1980.

[199] F. D. Koo and G. W. Lee, "Isolating Failures within VLSI Chips that Incorporate Signature Analysis and Set/Scan Techniques," *Proc. Int. Test Conf.*, Philadelphia, PA, November 1985, pp. 372-377.

[200] O. Kowarik, "Self-Repairing Semiconductor Memory Chip with Improved Availability / Reliability," *Proc. Custom Integrated Circ. Conf.*,

Portland, OR, May 1987, pp. 598-601.

[201] A. Krasniewski and A. Albicki, "Automatic Design of Exhaustively Self-testing Chips with BILBO Modules," *Proc. Int. Test Conf.*, Philadelphia, PA, November 1985, pp. 362-371.

[202] A. Krasniewski and A. Albicki, "Self-Testing Pipelines," *Proc. Int. Conf. Comp. Des. (ICCD)*, Port Chester, NY, October 1985, pp. 702-706.

[203] A. Krasniewski and A. Albicki, "Simulation-Free Estimation of Speed Degradation in NMOS Self-Testing Circuits for CAD Applications," *Proc. 22nd Des. Auto. Conf.*, Las Vegas, Nevada, June 1985, pp. 808-811.

[204] A. Krasniewski and S. Pilarski, "Circular Self-Test Path: A Low-Cost BIST Technique," *Proc. 24th Des. Auto. Conf.*, Miami Beach, FL, June 1987, pp. 407-415.

[205] B. Krishnamurthy, "A Dynamic Programming Approach to the Test Point Insertion Problem," *Proc. 24th Des. Auto. Conf.*, Miami Beach, FL, June 1987, pp. 695-705.

[206] R. C. Kroeger, "Testability Emphasis in the General Electric A/VLSI Program," *IEEE Design & Test of Computers*, Vol. 1, pp. 61-65, May 1984.

[207] J. Kuban and J. Salick, "Testability Features of the MC68020," *Proc. Int. Test Conf.*, Philadelphia, PA, October 1984, pp. 821-826.

[208] J. R. Kuban and W. C. Bruce, "Self-Testing the Motorola MC6804P2," *IEEE Design & Test of Computers*, Vol. 1, pp. 33-41, May 1984. Also *Proc. Int. Test Conf.*, Philadelphia, PA, October 1983, pp. 295-300.

[209] S. Kundu and S. M. Reddy, "On the Design of TSC CMOS Combinational Logic Circuits," *Proc. Int. Conf. Comp. Des. (ICCD)*, Port Chester, NY, October 1986, pp. 496-499.

[210] S. Y. Kuo and W. K. Fuchs, "Efficient Spare Allocation in Reconfigurable Arrays," *Proc. 23rd Des. Auto. Conf.*, Las Vegas, Nevada, June 1986, pp. 385-390.

[211] S. Y. Kuo and W. K. Fuchs, "Efficient Spare Allocation in Reconfigurable Arrays," *IEEE Design & Test of Computers*, Vol. 4, pp. 24-31, February 1987.

[212] S. Y. Kuo and W. K. Fuchs, "Fault Diagnosis and Spare Allocation for Yield Enhancement in Large Reconfigurable PLAs," *Proc. Int. Test*

Conf., Washington, DC, September 1987, pp. 944-951.

[213] A. S. LaPaugh and R. J. Lipton, "Total Fault Testing Using the Bipartite Transformation," Proc. Int. Test Conf., Philadelphia, PA, October 1983, pp. 428-434.

[214] A. S. LaPaugh and R. J. Lipton, "Total Stuck-at-Fault Testing by Circuit Transformation," Proc. 20th Des. Auto. Conf., Miami Beach, FL, June 1983, pp. 713-716.

[215] D. O. Lahti and G. C. Chen-Ellis, "PROSPECT: A Production System for Partitioning and Evaluating Chip Testability," Proc. Int. Test Conf., Washington, D.C., September 1986, pp. 360-367.

[216] R. Lake, "A Fast 20K Gate Array with On-Chip Test System," VLSI Systems Design, Vol. VII, pp. 46-55, June 1986.

[217] A. Lam, S. Chau, and H. Luong, "Design of a Class of Self-Exercising Combinational Circuits," Proc. Int. Test Conf., Philadelphia, PA, November 1985, pp. 589-600.

[218] D. L. Landis and W. A. Check, "Essential Maintenance Network Issues for Highly Reliable System-Level Built-In Self-Test," Proc. Int. Conf. Comp. Des. (ICCD-87), Rye Brook, NY, October 1987, pp. 458-461.

[219] D. Laurent, "An Example of Test Strategy for Computer Implemented with VLSI Circuits," Proc. Int. Conf. Comp. Des. (ICCD), Port Chester, NY, October 1985, pp. 679-682.

[220] K. T. Le and K. K. Saluja, "A Novel Approach for Testing Memories Using a Built-In Self Testing Technique," Proc. Int. Test Conf., Washington, D.C., September 1986, pp. 830-839.

[221] J. J. LeBlanc, "LOCST: A Built-In Self-Test Technique," IEEE Design & Test of Computers, Vol. 1, pp. 45-52, November 1984.

[222] F. Lee, V. Coli, and W. Miller, "On-Chip Circuitry Reveals System Logic States," Electronic Design, April 14, 1983.

[223] M. M. Ligthart, E. H. L. Aarts, and F. P. M. Beenker, "Design-For-Testability of PLAs Using Statistical Cooling," Proc. 23rd Des. Auto. Conf., Las Vegas, Nevada, June 1986, pp. 339-345.

[224] M. M. Ligthart, P. Baltus, and M. Freeman, "RPST: A ROM Based Pseudo-Exhaustive Self Test Approach," Proc. Int. Test Conf., Washington, DC, September 1987, pp. 915-922.

[225] R. W. Linderman, C. G. Shephard, K. Taylor, P. W. Coutee, P. C. Rossbach, and J. M. Collins, "A 70MHz 1.2 Micron CMOS 16-Point DFT Processor," Proc. Custom Integrated Circ. Conf., Portland, OR, May 1987, pp. 219-222.

[226] C. Y. Liu, K. K. Saluja, and J. S. Upadhyaya, "BIST-PLA : A Built-In Self-Test Design of Large Programmable Logic Arrays," Proc. 24th Des. Auto. Conf., Miami Beach, FL, June 1987, pp. 385-391.

[227] D. L. Liu and E. J. McCluskey, "Design of CMOS VLSI Circuits for Testability," Proc. Custom Integrated Circ. Conf., Rochester, NY, May 1986, pp. 421-424.

[228] D. L. Liu and E. J. McCluskey, "A CMOS Cell Library Design for Testability," VLSI Systems Design, Vol. VIII, pp. 58-65, May 1987.

[229] D. L. Liu and E. J. McCluskey, "CMOS Scan-Path IC Design for Stuck-Open Fault Testability," IEEE J. Sol. St. Circ., Vol. SC-22, pp. 880-885, October 1987.

[230] D. L. Liu and E. J. McCluskey, "Design of Large Embedded CMOS PLAs for Built-In Self-Test," Proc. Int. Conf. Comp. Des. (ICCD-87), Rye Brook, NY, October 1987, pp. 678-681.

[231] D. L. Liu and E. J. McCluskey, "Designing CMOS Circuits for Switch-Level Testability," IEEE Design & Test of Computers, Vol. 4, pp. 42-49, August 1987.

[232] D. L. Liu and E. J. McCluskey, "High Fault Coverage Self-Test Structures for CMOS ICs," Proc. Custom Integrated Circ. Conf., Portland, OR, May 1987, pp. 68-71.

[233] F. Lombardi, R. Negrini, M. G. Sami, and R. Stefanelli, "Reconfiguration of VLSI Arrays: A Covering Approach," Fault-Tolerant Computing Symp. (FTCS-17) Digest of Papers, pp. 251-256, July 1987.

[234] J. Losq, "Efficiency of Random Compact Testing," IEEE Trans. Comp., Vol. C-27, pp. 516-525, June 1978.

[235] M. B. Lowrie and W. K. Fuchs, "Reconfigurable Tree Architectures Using Subtree Oriented Fault Tolerance," IEEE Trans. Computers, Vol. C-36, pp. 1172-1182, October 1987.

[236] D. J. Lu and E. J. McCluskey, "Recurrent Test Patterns," *Proc. Int. Test Conf.*, Philadelphia, PA, October 1983, pp. 76-82.

[237] H. Maeno, T. Hanibuchi, T. Tada, R. Walters, and T. Eto, "Testing of Embedded RAM Using Exhaustive Random Sequences," *Proc. Int. Test Conf.*, Washington, DC, September 1987, pp. 105-110.

[238] G. P. Mak, J. A. Abraham, and E. S. Davidson, "The Design of PLAs with Concurrent Error Detection," *Fault-Tolerant Comp. Symp. (FTCS-12) Digest of Papers*, pp. 303-310, June 1982.

[239] R. Z. Makki and C. Tiansheng, "Designing Testable Control Paths with Multiple and Feedback Scan-Paths," *Proc. Int. Test Conf.*, Washington, DC, September 1986, pp. 484-492.

[240] T. Mangir, "Design for Testability: An Integrated Approach to VLSI Testing," *Proc. Int. Conf. CAD (ICCAD-83)*, Santa Clara, CA, September 1983, pp. 68-70.

[241] S. R. Manthani and S. M. Reddy, "On CMOS Totally Self-Checking Circuits," *Proc. Int. Test Conf.*, Philadelphia, PA, October 1984, pp. 866-877.

[242] G. Markowsky, "Syndrome Testability can be Achieved by Circuit Modification," *IEEE Trans. Computers*, Vol. C-30, pp. 604-606, August 1981.

[243] T. Masui, F. Niimi, and M. Iwase, "A New Approach to Design for Testability in an LSI Logic Synthesis System," *Proc. Int. Conf. on CAD (ICCAD)*, Santa Clara, CA, November 1985, pp. 105-107.

[244] L. Matterne, J. VanMeerbergen, F. Beenker, V. Mehra, J. Theunissen, and R. Segers, "A C-Testable Booth Multiplier, Designed for a Silicon Compilation Environment," *Proc. Int. Conf. Comp. Des. (ICCD-87)*, Rye Brook, NY, October 1987, pp. 354-357.

[245] C. Maunder, "Paving the way for Testability Standards," *IEEE Design & Test of Computers*, Vol. 3, p. 65, August 1986.

[246] C. Maunder and F. Beenker, "Boundary-Scan − A Framework for Structured Design-for-Test," *Proc. Int. Test Conf.*, Washington, DC, September 1987, pp. 714-723.

[247] P. Mazumder and J. H. Patel, "An Efficient Built-In Self Testing for Random Access Memory," *Proc. Int. Test Conf.*, Washington, DC, September 1987, pp. 1072-1077.

[248] P. Mazumder and J. H. Patel, "Methodologies for Testing Embedded Content Addressable Memories," *Fault-Tolerant Computing Symp. (FTCS-17) Digest of Papers*, pp. 270-275, July 1987.

[249] W. H. McAnney and J. Savir, "There is Information in Faulty Signatures," *Proc. Int. Test Conf.*, Washington, DC, September 1987, pp. 630-636.

[250] E. J. McCluskey, "Built-In Verification Test," *Int. Test Conf. Digest of Papers*, Philadelphia, PA, November 1982, pp. 183-190.

[251] E. J. McCluskey, "Verification Testing," *Proc. 19th Des. Auto. Conf.*, Las Vegas, Nevada, June 1982, pp. 495-500.

[252] E. J. McCluskey, "A Survey of Design for Testability Scan Techniques," *VLSI Design*, Vol. V, p. 38, December 1984.

[253] E. J. McCluskey, "Built-In Self-Test Structures," *IEEE Design & Test of Computers*, Vol. 2, pp. 29-36, April 1985.

[254] E. J. McCluskey, "Built-In Self-Test Techniques," *IEEE Design & Test of Computers*, Vol. 2, pp. 21-28, April 1985.

[255] E. J. McCluskey and S. Bozorgui-Nesbat, "Design for Autonomous Test," *IEEE Trans. Comp.*, Vol. C-30, pp. 860-875, Nov. 1981.

[256] E. J. McCluskey, S. Makar, S. Mourad, and K. D. Wagner, "Probability Models for Pseudorandom Test Sequences," *Proc. Int. Test Conf.*, Washington, DC, September 1987, pp. 471-479.

[257] M. R. Mercer, "Logic Elements for Universally Testable Circuits," *Proc. Int. Test Conf.*, Washington, D.C., September 1986, pp. 493-497.

[258] M. R. Mercer and V. D. Agrawal, "A Novel Clocking Technique for VLSI Circuit Testability," *IEEE Journal of Solid-State Circuits*, Vol. SC-19, p. 207, April 1984.

[259] M. R. Mercer, V. D. Agrawal, and C. M. Roman, "Test Generation for Highly Sequential Scan-Testable Circuits Through Logic Transformation," *Int. Test Conference Digest of Papers*, Philadelphia, PA, Oct. 1981, pp. 561-565.

[260] E. L. Meyer, "Gate Array Testability: A Customer Perspective," *VLSI Systems Design*, Vol. VII, pp. 34-42, June 1986.

[261] W. F. Mikhail, R. W. Bartoldus, and R. A. Rutledge, "The Reliability of Memory with Single-Error Correction," *IEEE Trans. Computers*, Vol. C-31, pp. 560-564, June 1982.

[262] D. M. Miller and J. C. Muzio, "Spectral Fault Signatures for Internally Unate Combinational Networks," *IEEE Trans. Computers*, Vol. C-32, pp. 1058-1062, Nov. 1983.

[263] D. M. Miller and J. C. Muzio, "Spectral Fault Signatures for Single Stuck-at Faults in Combinational Networks," *IEEE Trans. Computers*, Vol. C-33, pp. 765-769, August 1984.

[264] J. D. Milner and J. J. Watters, "A Memory and Testability Cell for 1.25 Micron CMOS Gate Array," *Proc. Custom Integrated Circ. Conf.*, Portland, OR, May 1985, pp. 302-305.

[265] Y. Min, "A PLA Design for Ease of Test Generation," *Fault-Tolerant Comput. Symp. (FTCS-14), Digest of Papers*, pp. 436-442, June 1984.

[266] D. R. Morgan, "Autocorrelation Function of Sequential M-bit Words taken from an N-bit Shift Register (PN) Sequence," *IEEE Trans. Computers*, Vol. C-29, pp. 408-410, May 1980. Also see comments by G. Wustmann in *IEEE Trans. Comp.*, Vol. C-30, p. 241, March 1981.

[267] P. S. Moritz and L. M. Thorsen, "CMOS Circuit Testability," *Proc. Custom Integrated Circ. Conf.*, Portland, OR, May 1985, pp. 311-314.

[268] F. Motika, J. A. Waicukauski, E. Lindbloom, and E. B. Eichelberger, "An LSSD Pseudo Random Pattern Test System," *Proc. Int. Test Conf.*, Philadelphia, PA, October 1983, pp. 283-288.

[269] A. Motohara and H. Fujiwara, "Design for Testability for Complete Test Coverage," *IEEE Design & Test of Computers*, Vol. 1, pp. 25-32, November 1984.

[270] J. P. Mucha, W. Daehn, and J. Gross, "Self-Test in a Standard Cell Environment," *IEEE Design & Test of Computers*, Vol. 3, pp. 35-41, December 1986.

[271] K. Muroi, M. Kitta, T. Ogihara, and S. Murai, "A Hierarchical Logic Design Rule Check Program for Scan Design Circuit," *Proc. Int. Conf. CAD (ICCAD-86)*, Santa Clara, CA, November 1986, pp. 106-109.

[272] A. F. Murray, P. B. Denyer, and D. Renshaw, "Self-Testing in Bit Serial VLSI Parts: High Coverage at Low Cost," *Proc. Int. Test Conf.*, Philadelphia, PA, October 1983, pp. 260-268.

[273] M. Namjoo, "Techniques for Concurrent Testing of VLSI Processor Operation," *Int. Test Conf. Digest of Papers*, Philadelphia, PA, November 1982, pp. 461-468.

[274] S. Nanda and S. M. Reddy, "Design of Easily Testable Microprocessors -- A Case Study," *Int. Test Conf. Digest of Papers*, Philadelphia, PA, November 1982, pp. 480-483.

[275] M. Nicolaidis, "Evaluation of a Self-Checking Version of the MC68000 Microprocessor," *Fault-Tolerant Comp. Symp. (FTCS-15) Digest of Papers*, pp. 350-356, June 1985.

[276] M. Nicolaidis and B. Courtois, "Design of NMOS Strongly Fault Secure Circuits Using Unidirectional Errors Detecting Codes," *Fault-Tolerant Comp. Symp. (FTCS-16) Digest of Papers*, pp. 22-27, July 1986.

[277] M. J. Ohletz, T. W. Williams, and J. P. Mucha, "Overhead in Scan and Self-Testing Designs," *Proc. Int. Test Conf.*, Washington, DC, September 1987, pp. 460-470.

[278] T. Ohsawa, T. Furuyama, Y. Watanabe, H. Tanaka, N. Kushiyama, K. Tsuchida, Y. Nagahama, S. Yamano, T. Tanaka, S. Shinozaki, and K. Natori, "A 60-ns 4-Mbit CMOS DRAM with Built-In Self-Test Function," *IEEE J. Sol. St. Circ.*, Vol. SC-32, pp. 663-668, October 1987.

[279] V. G. Oklobdzija and M. D. Ercegovac, "Testability Enhancement of VLSI Using Circuit Structures," *Proc. Int. Conf. Circ. Computers (ICCC'82)*, New York, NY, September 1982, pp. 198-201.

[280] W. R. Olson and W. C. Chu, "Implementing Built-In Self-Test in a RISC Microprocessor," *Proc. Int. Test Conf.*, Washington, DC, September 1987, pp. 810-817.

[281] R. J. Orsello, "Programmable Logic: Testability by Design," *Proc. Int. Test Conf.*, Philadelphia, PA, November 1985, pp. 565-566.

[282] F. Osman, "Self-Testing as an Extension of Serial Testing," *Proc. Int. Conf. Comp. Des. (ICCD'83)*, Port Chester, NY, October 1983, pp. 117-120.

[283] E. W. Page, "Minimally Testable Reed-Muller Canonical Forms," *IEEE Trans. Computers*, Vol. C-29, pp. 746-750, August 1980.

[284] K. P. Parker, "Compact Testing: Testing with Compressed Data," *Proc. FTCS-6*, June 1976, pp. 93-98.

[285] K. P. Parker, "Testability: Barriers to Acceptance," *IEEE Design & Test of Computers*, Vol. 3, pp. 11-15, October 1986.

[286] R. Parthasarathy and S. M. Reddy, "A Testable Design of Iterative Logic Arrays," *IEEE Trans. Computers*, Vol. C-30, pp. 833-841, November 1981.

[287] R. Parthasarthy, S. M. Reddy, and J. G. Kuhl, "A Testable Design of General Purpose Microprocessors," *Fault-Tolerant Comp. Symp. (FTCS-12) Digest of Papers*, pp. 117-124, June 1982.

[288] J. H. Patel, "Built-In Test for Bit-Sliced ALU," *Proc. Int. Conf. Comp. Des. (ICCD'84)*, Port Chester, NY, October 1984, pp. 308-312.

[289] J. H. Patel and L. Y. Fung, "Multiplier and Divider Arrays with Concurrent Error Detection," *Fault-Tolerant Comp. Symp. (FTCS-12) Digest of Papers*, pp. 325-329, June 1982.

[290] J. H. Patel and L. Y. Fung, "Concurrent Error Detection in Multiply and Divide Arrays," *IEEE Trans. Computers*, Vol. C-32, pp. 417-422, April 1983.

[291] C. C. Perkins, S. Sangani, H. Stopper, and W. Valitski, "Design for In-Situ Chip Testing with a Compact Tester," *Test Conference Digest of Papers*, Philadelphia, PA, November 1980, pp. 29-41.

[292] G. E. Peterson and G. K. Maki, "Binary Tree Structured Logic Circuits: Design and Fault Detection," *Proc. Int. Conf. Comp. Des. (ICCD'84)*, Port Chester, NY, October 1984, pp. 671-676.

[293] S. J. Piestrak, "PLA Implementations of Totally Self-Checking Circuits using m-out-of-n Codes," *Proc. Int. Conf. Comp. Des. (ICCD)*, Port Chester, NY, October 1985, pp. 777-781.

[294] J. S. Pittman and W. C. Bruce, "Test Logic Economic Considerations in a Commercial VLSI Chip Environment," *Proc. Int. Test Conf.*, Philadelphia, PA, October 1984, pp. 31-39.

[295] W. A. Porter, "Error Tolerant Design of Multivalued Logic Functions," *IEEE Trans. Computers*, Vol. C-31, pp. 551-554, June 1982.

[296] D. K. Pradhan, "Sequential Network Design Using Extra Inputs for Fault Detection," *IEEE Trans. Computers*, Vol. C-32, pp. 319-323, March 1983.

[297] D. K. Pradhan, Ed., *Fault-Tolerant Computing Theory and Techniques*, I and II, Prentice-Hall, Englewood Cliffs, NJ, 1986.

[298] D. K. Pradhan and K. Son, "The Effect of Untestable Faults in PLAs and a Design for Testability," *Test Conference Digest of Papers*, Philadelphia, PA, November 1980, pp. 359-367.

[299] M. M. Pradhan, R. E. Tulloss, H. Bleeker, and F. P. M. Beenker, "Developing a Standard for Boundary Scan Implementation," *Proc. Int. Conf. Comp. Des. (ICCD-87)*, Rye Brook, NY, October 1987, pp. 462-466.

[300] D. Radhakrishnan and R. Sharma, "Easily Testable CMOS Cellular Arrays for VLSI," *Proc. Int. Conf. Comp. Des. (ICCD)*, Port Chester, NY, October 1985, pp. 426-429.

[301] J. Rajski and V. K. Agarwal, "Testing Properties and Applications of Inverter-Free PLA's," *Proc. Int. Test Conf.*, Philadelphia, PA, November 1985, pp. 500-507.

[302] K. S. Ramanatha and N. N. Biswas, "A Design for Complete Testability of Programmable Logic Arrays," *Int. Test Conf. Digest of Papers*, Philadelphia, PA, November 1982, pp. 67-74.

[303] K. S. Ramanatha and N. N. Biswas, "A Design for Testability of Undetectable Crosspoint Faults in Programmable Logic Arrays," *IEEE Trans. Computers*, Vol. C-32, pp. 551-557, Jun. 1983.

[304] R. Rasmussen, Y. Chang, and F. White, "Advanced Techniques for Structured ASIC Products," *Proc. Custom Integrated Circ. Conf.*, Rochester, NY, May 1986, pp. 412-415.

[305] S. Rawat and M. J. Irwin, "C-Testability of Unilateral and Bilateral Sequential Arrays," *Proc. Int. Test. Conf.*, Washington, DC, September 1987, pp. 181-188.

[306] M. K. Reddy and S. M. Reddy, "Detecting FET Stuck-Open Faults in CMOS Latches and Flip-flops," *IEEE Design & Test of Computers*, Vol. 3, pp. 17-26, October 1986.

[307] S. M. Reddy and R. Dandapani, "Scan Design Using Standard Flip-Flops," *IEEE Design & Test of Computers*, Vol. 4, pp. 52-54, February 1987.

[308] S. M. Reddy and D. S. Ha, "A New Approach

to the Design of Testable PLA's," *IEEE Trans. Computers*, Vol. C-36, pp. 201-211, February 1987.

[309] S. M. Reddy and D. S. Ha, "On Pseudo-Exhaustive Testable PLAs," *Proc. Int. Conf. Comp. Des. (ICCD-87)*, Rye Brook, NY, October 1987, pp. 454-457.

[310] S. M. Reddy and M. K. Reddy, "Testable Realizations for FET Stuck-Open Faults in CMOS Combinational Logic Circuits," *IEEE Trans. Computers*, Vol. C-35, pp. 742-754, August 1986.

[311] S. M. Reddy, M. K. Reddy, and J. G. Kuhl, "On Testable Design for CMOS Logic Circuits," *Proc. Int. Test Conf.*, Philadelphia, PA, October 1983, pp. 435-445.

[312] H. K. Reghbati, "Tutorial – Fault Detection in PLAs," *IEEE Design & Test of Computers*, Vol. 3, pp. 43-50, December 1986.

[313] D. R. Resnick, "Testability and Maintainability with a New 6K Gate Array," *VLSI Design*, Vol. IV, p. 34, March/April 1983.

[314] H. C. Ritter and B. Muller, "Built-In Test Processor for Self-Testing Repairable Random Access Memories," *Proc. Int. Test Conf.*, Washington, DC, September 1987, pp. 1078-1084.

[315] C. Ronse, *Feedback Shift Registers*, Springer-Verlag, Berlin, 1984.

[316] J. Salick, M. R. Mercer, and B. Underwood, "Built-In Self Test Input Generator for Programmable Logic Arrays," *Proc. Int. Test Conf.*, Philadelphia, PA, November 1985, pp. 115-125.

[317] K. K. Saluja, "Synchronous Sequential Machines: A Modular and Testable Design," *IEEE Trans. Computers*, Vol. C-29, pp. 1020-1025, November 1980.

[318] K. K. Saluja, "An Enhancement of LSSD to Reduce Test Pattern Generation Effort and Increase Fault Coverage," *Proc. 19th Des. Auto. Conf.*, Las Vegas, Nevada, June 1982, pp. 489-494.

[319] K. K. Saluja and R. Dandapani, "A Built-in Self-Testable Design Method for Sequential Circuits," *Fault-Tolerant Comp. Symp. (FTCS-16) Digest of Papers*, pp. 312-317, July 1986.

[320] K. K. Saluja and R. Dandapani, "An Alternative to Scan Design Methods for Sequential Machines," *IEEE Trans. Computers*, Vol. C-35,

pp. 384-388, April 1986.

[321] K. K. Saluja and R. Dandapani, "Testable Design of Single-Output Sequential Machines Using Checking Experiments," *IEEE Trans. Computers*, Vol. C-35, pp. 658-662, July 1986.

[322] K. K. Saluja, H. Fujiwara, and K. Kinoshita, "A Testable Design of Programmable Logic Arrays with Universal Control and Minimal Overhead," *Proc. Int. Test Conf.*, Philadelphia, PA, November 1985, pp. 574-582.

[323] K. K. Saluja, H. Fujiwara, and K. Kinoshita, "A Testable Design of Programmable Logic Arrays with Universal Control and Minimal Overhead," *Comput. Math. Applic.*, Vol. 13, No. 5/6, pp. 503-517, 1987.

[324] K. K. Saluja and M. Karpovsky, "Testing Computer Hardware through Data Compression in Space and Time," *Proc. Int. Test Conf.*, Philadelphia, PA, October 1983, pp. 83-88.

[325] K. K. Saluja, K. Kinoshita, and H. Fujiwara, "An Easily Testable Design of Programmable Logic Arrays for Multiple Faults," *IEEE Trans. Computers*, Vol. C-32, pp. 1038-1046, Nov. 1983.

[326] K. K. Saluja and K. T. Le, "Testable Design of Large Random Access Memories," *Integration, the VLSI Journal*, Vol. 2, pp. 309-330, December 1984.

[327] K. K. Saluja, S. H. Sng, and K. Kinoshita, "Built-in Self-Testing RAM: A Practical Alternative," *IEEE Design & Test of Computers*, Vol. 4, pp. 42-51, February 1987.

[328] K. K. Saluja and S. J. Upadhyaya, "A Built-In Self Testing PLA Design with High Fault Coverage," *Proc. Int. Conf. Comp. Des. (ICCD)*, Port Chester, NY, October 1986, pp. 596-599.

[329] M. A. Samad and J. A. B. Fortes, "Explanation Capabilities in DEFT – A Design-for-Testability Expert System," *Proc. Int. Test Conf.*, Washington, D.C., September 1986, pp. 954-963.

[330] M. G. Sami and R. Stefanelli, "Self-Testing Array Structures," *Proc. Int. Conf. Comp. Des. (ICCD'84)*, Port Chester, NY, October 1984, pp. 677-682.

[331] S. Sato, H. Takahashi, Y. Machida, G. Goto, T. Nakamura, and T. Shirato, "On-Chip Testing for 30K-Gate Masterslice," *Proc. Custom Integrated Circ. Conf.*, Rochester, NY, May 1986, pp. 311-314.

[332] Y. Savaria, V. K. Agarwal, N. Rumin, and J. F. Hayes, "A Design for Machines with Built-In Tolerance to Soft Errors," *Proc. Int. Test Conf.*, Philadelphia, PA, October 1984, pp. 649-659.

[333] Y. Savaria, N. C. Rumin, J. F. Hayes, and V. K. Agarwal, "A Filtering Approach to Soft-Error Tolerance," *Proc. Int. Conf. Comp. Des. (ICCD)*, Port Chester, NY, October 1985, pp. 519-524.

[334] J. Savir, "Syndrome-Testable Design of Combinational Circuits," *IEEE Trans. Comp.*, Vol. C-29, pp. 442-451, June 1980. Correction ibid., 1012-1013 (Nov. 1980).

[335] J. Savir and W. H. McAnney, "Double-Parity Signature Analysis for LSSD Networks," *Proc. Int. Test Conf.*, Washington, DC, September 1987, pp. 510-516.

[336] N. R. Saxena and E. J. McCluskey, "Extended Precision Checksums," *Fault-Tolerant Computing Symp. (FTCS-17) Digest of Papers*, pp. 142-147, July 1987.

[337] N. R. Saxena and J. P. Robinson, "Accumulator Compression Testing," *IEEE Trans. Computers*, Vol. C-35, pp. 317-321, April 1986.

[338] P. Schvan, R. Hadaway, and M. King, "Defectivity and Yield Analysis for VLSI and WSI," *Proc. Int. Conf. Comp. Des. (ICCD)*, Port Chester, NY, October 1986, pp. 89-92.

[339] R. M. Sedmak, "Implementation Techniques for Self-Verification," *Test Conference Digest of Papers*, Philadelphia, PA, November 1980, pp. 267-278.

[340] R. M. Sedmak, "Built-In Self-Test: Pass or Fail?," *IEEE Design & Test of Computers*, Vol. 2, pp. 17-19, April 1985.

[341] M. T. M. Segers, "A Self-Test Method for Digital Circuits," *Int. Test Conf. Digest of Papers*, Philadelphia, PA, October 1981, pp. 79-85.

[342] M. Serra and J. C. Muzio, "Testing Programmable Logic Arrays by Sum of Syndromes," *IEEE Trans. Computers*, Vol. C-36, pp. 1097-1101, September 1987.

[343] J. P. Shen and M. A. Shuette, "On-Line Self-Monitoring Using Signatured Instruction Streams," *Proc. Int. Test Conf.*, Philadelphia, PA, October 1983, pp. 275-282.

[344] S. D. Sherlekar and P. S. Subramanian, "Conditionally Robust Two-Pattern Tests and CMOS Design for Testability," *IEEE Trans. CAD*, Vol. 7, pp. 325-332, March 1988.

[345] F. W. Shih, H. H. Chao, S. Ong, A. L. Diamond, J. F. Y. Tang, and C. A. Trampel, "Testability Design for Micro/370, A System/370 Single Chip Microprocessor," *Proc. Int. Test Conf.*, Washington, DC, September 1986, pp. 412-418.

[346] M. Shimizu, N. Okino, J. Nishiura, and H. Maruyama, "Memory Embedded VLSI Gate Array Testing," *Proc. Int. Test Conf.*, Philadelphia, PA, November 1985, pp. 438-444.

[347] L. A. Shombert and D. P. Siewiorek, "Using Redundancy for Concurrent Testing and Repairing of Systolic Arrays," *Fault-Tolerant Computing Symp. (FTCS-17) Digest of Papers*, pp. 244-249, July 1987.

[348] G. Short, J. Turek, D. Roskell, and R. Simpson, "Testability in the TMS34010 Graphics Systems Processor," *Proc. Custom Integrated Circ. Conf.*, Portland, OR, May 1987, pp. 59-61.

[349] I. Shperling and E. J. McCluskey, "Circuit Segmentation for Pseudo-exhaustive Testing via Simulated Annealing," *Proc. Int. Test Conf.*, Washington, DC, September 1987, pp. 58-66.

[350] M. W. Sievers and A. Avizienis, "Analysis of a Class of Totally Self-Checking Functions Implemented in a MOS LSI General Logic Structure," *Fault-Tolerant Comp. Symp. (FTCS-11) Digest of Papers*, pp. 256-261, June 1981.

[351] A. D. Singh, "An Area Efficient Redundancy Scheme for Wafer Scale Processor Arrays," *Proc. Int. Conf. Comp. Des. (ICCD)*, Port Chester, NY, October 1985, pp. 505-509.

[352] A. D. Singh, "A Reconfigurable Modular Fault Tolerant Binary Tree Architecture," *Fault-Tolerant Computing Symp. (FTCS-17) Digest of Papers*, pp. 298-304, July 1987.

[353] J. E. Smith, "Measures of Effectiveness of Fault Signature Analysis," *IEEE Trans. Comp.*, Vol. C-29, pp. 510-514, June 1980.

[354] R. Sobol, "The Universal Synchronous Machine," *VLSI Design*, Vol. IV, p. 60, November 1983.

[355] A. K. Somani, V. K. Agarwal, and D. Avis, "A Generalized Theory for System Level Diagnosis," *IEEE Trans. Computers*, Vol. C-36, pp. 538-546, May 1987.

[356] F. Somenzi and S. Gai, "Fault Detection in PLAs," *Proc. IEEE*, Vol. 74, May 1986, pp. 655-668.

[357] K. Son and D. K. Pradhan, "Design of Programmable Logic Arrays for Testability," *Test Conference Digest of Papers*, Philadelphia, PA, November 1980, pp. 163-166.

[358] T. Sridhar, "A New Parallel Test Approach for Large Memories," *IEEE Design & Test of Computers*, Vol. 3, pp. 15-22, August 1986. Also *Proc. Int. Test Conf.*, Philadelphia, PA, November 1985, pp. 462-470.

[359] T. Sridhar and J. P. Hayes, "Design of Easily Testable Bit-sliced Systems," *IEEE Trans. Computers*, Vol. C-30, pp. 842-854, November 1981.

[360] T. Sridhar, D. S. Ho, T. J. Powell, and S. M. Thatte, "Analysis and Simulation of Parallel Signature Analyzers," *Int. Test Conference, Digest of Papers*, Philadelphia, PA, Nov. 1982, pp. 656-661.

[361] T. Sridhar and S. M. Thatte, "Concurrent Checking of Program Flow in VLSI Processors," *Int. Test Conf. Digest of Papers*, Philadelphia, PA, November 1982, pp. 191-199.

[362] C. W. Starke, "Built-In Test for CMOS Circuits," *Proc. Int. Test Conf.*, Philadelphia, PA, October 1984, pp. 309-314.

[363] S. Strom, "ROM-resident software self-tests microcomputers," *Electronic Design*, Vol. 28, pp. 131-132, 134, June 1980.

[364] J. S. R. Subrahmanyam and P. P. Chaudhuri, "A Divide and Conquer Testing Strategy for Detection of Multiple Faults by SFDTS," *Proc. Int. Test Conf.*, Washington, D.C., September 1986, pp. 997-1004.

[365] Z. Sun and L. T. Wang, "Self-Testing of Embedded RAMs," *Proc. Int. Test Conf.*, Philadelphia, PA, October 1984, pp. 148-156.

[366] A. K. Susskind, "A Technique for Making Asynchronous Sequential Circuits Readily Testable," *Proc. Int. Test Conf.*, Philadelphia, PA, October 1984, pp. 842-846.

[367] J. C. Sutton III and J. G. Bredeson, "Minimal Redundant Logic for High Reliability and Irredundant Testability," *IEEE Tran. Computers*, Vol. C-29, pp. 648-655, July 1980.

[368] Y. Takefuji, Y. Adachi, and H. Aiso, "A Novel Approach to Fault-Tolerant Sequential Circuits," *Proc. Int. Conf. Circ. Computers (ICCC'82)*, New York, NY, September 1982, pp. 206-209.

[369] Y. Tamir and C. Sequin, "Reducing Common Mode Failures in Duplicate Modules," *Proc. Int. Conf. Comp. Des. (ICCD'84)*, Port Chester, NY, October 1984, pp. 302-307.

[370] E. Tammaru and J. B. Angell, "Redundancy for LSI Yield Enhancement," *IEEE J. of Solid-State Circuits*, Vol. SC-2, pp. 172-182, December 1967.

[371] S. B. Tan, K. Totton, K. Baker, P. Varma, and R. Porter, "A Fast Signature Simulation Tool for Built-In Self-Testing Circuits," *Proc. 24th Des. Auto. Conf.*, Miami Beach, FL, June 1987, pp. 17-25.

[372] D. T. Tang and C. L. Chen, "Logic Test Pattern Generation Using Linear Codes," *13th Int. Symp. Fault Tolerant Computing (FTCS-13) Digest of Papers*, pp. 222-226, June 1983.

[373] D. T. Tang and L. S. Woo, "Exhaustive Test Pattern Generation with Constant Weight Vectors," *IEEE Trans. Computers*, Vol. C-32, pp. 1145-1150, Dec. 1983.

[374] D. L. Tao and P. K. Lala, "A Concurrent Testing Strategy for PLAs," *Proc. Int. Test Conf.*, Washington, D.C., September 1986, pp. 705-709.

[375] D. L. Tao and P. K. Lala, "Three-Level Totally Self-Checking Checker for 1-out-of-N Code," *Fault-Tolerant Computing Symp. (FTCS-17) Digest of Papers*, pp. 108-113, July 1987.

[376] S. M. Thatte, D. S. Ho, H. T. Yuan, T. Sridhar, and T. J. Powell, "An Architecture for Testable VLSI Processors," *Int. Test Conf. Digest of Papers*, Philadelphia, PA, November 1982, pp. 484-492.

[377] P. Thorel, R. David, J. Pulou, and J. L. Rainard, "Design for Random Testability," *Proc. Int. Test Conf.*, Washington, DC, September 1987, pp. 923-930.

[378] C. Timoc, F. Scott, K. Wickman, and L. Hess, "Adaptive Self-Test for a Microprocessor," *Proc. Int. Test Conf.*, Philadelphia, PA, October 1983, pp. 701-703.

[379] C. C. Timoc, *Selected Reprints on Logic Design for Testability*, Computer Society Press, Washington, D.C., 1984.

[380] C. C. Timoc, J. M. Favennec, and C. L.

Blanche, "A Testable Regular Design," *Proc. Int. Conf. Circ. Computers (ICCC'82)*, New York, NY, September 1982, pp. 210-213.

[381] S. P. Tomas and J. P. Shen, "A Roving Monitoring Processor for Detection of Control Flow Errors in Multiple Processor Systems," *Proc. Int. Conf. Comp. Des. (ICCD)*, Port Chester, NY, October 1985, pp. 531-539.

[382] R. Treuer, H. Fujiwara, and V. K. Agarwal, "Implementing a Built-In Self-Test PLA Design," *IEEE Design & Test of Computers*, Vol. 2, pp. 37-48, April 1985.

[383] E. Trischler, "Incomplete Scan Path with an Automatic Test Generation Methodology," *Int. Test Conf. (ITC-80), Digest of Papers*, November 1980, pp. 153-162.

[384] E. Trischler, "Testability Analysis and Incomplete Scan Path," *Proc. Int. Conf. CAD (ICCAD-83)*, Santa Clara, CA, September 1983, pp. 38-39.

[385] E. Trischler, "ATWIG, An Automatic Test Pattern Generator with Inherent Guidance," *Proc. Int. Test Conf.*, Philadelphia, PA, October 1984, pp. 80-87.

[386] D. R. Tryon, "Self-Testing with Correlated Faults," *Proc. 23rd Des. Auto. Conf.*, Las Vegas, Nevada, June 1986, pp. 374-377.

[387] F. F. Tsui, "The Cost and Speed Barriers in LSI/VLSI Testing -- Can They be Overcome by Testability Design?," *Proc. Int. Test Conf.*, Philadelphia, PA, November 1985, pp. 892-906.

[388] F. F. Tsui, *LSI-VLSI Testability Design*, McGraw-Hill, New York, 1986.

[389] C. H. Tung and J. P. Robinson, "Design of Concurrently Testable Microprogrammed Control Units," *Proc. Int. Conf. Comp. Des. (ICCD)*, Port Chester, NY, October 1986, pp. 492-495.

[390] C. H. Tung and J. P. Robinson, "A Fast Algorithm for Optimum Syndrome Space Compression," *IEEE Trans. Computers*, Vol. 37, pp. 228-232, February 1988.

[391] J. Turino, "A Totally Universal Reset, Initialization (and) Nodal Observation Circuit," *Proc. Int. Test Conf.*, Philadelphia, PA, October 1984, pp. 878-883.

[392] K. J. E. VanEerdewijk and F. P. M. Beenker, *A Modular Boundary Scan Implementation*, Philips Research Labs Report, Eindhoven, The Netherlands, 1986.

[393] P. Varma, A. Ambler, and K. Baker, "On-Chip Testing of Embedded PLAs," *Proc. Custom Integrated Circ. Conf.*, Portland, OR, May 1985, pp. 306-310.

[394] P. Varma, A. P. Ambler, and K. Baker, "An Analysis of the Economics of Self-Test," *Proc. Int. Test Conf.*, Philadelphia, PA, October 1984, pp. 20-30.

[395] P. Varma, A. P. Ambler, and K. Baker, "On-Chip Testing of Embedded RAMs," *Proc. Custom Integrated Circ. Conf.*, Rochester, NY, May 1984, pp. 286-290.

[396] N. Vasanthavada and P. N. Marinos, "An Operationally Efficient Scheme for Exhaustive Test-Pattern Generation Using Linear Codes," *Proc. Int. Test Conf.*, Philadelphia, PA, November 1985, pp. 476-482.

[397] D. K. Verbeek and W. C. Bruce, "Testability Features of the MC68HC11," *Proc. Int. Test Conf.*, Philadelphia, PA, November 1985, pp. 744-751.

[398] A. R. Virupakshia and V. C. V. P. Reddy, "A Simple Random Test Procedure for Detection of Single Intermittent Fault in Combinational Circuits," *IEEE Trans. Computers*, Vol. C-32, pp. 594-597, Jun. 1983.

[399] P. T. Wagner, "Interconnect Testing with Boundary Scan," *Proc. Int. Test Conf.*, Washington, DC, September 1987, pp. 52-57.

[400] J. A. Waicukauski, V. P. Gupta, and S. T. Patel, "Diagnosis of BIST Failures by PPSFP Simulation," *Proc. Int. Test Conf.*, Washington, DC, September 1987, pp. 480-484.

[401] S. M. Walters, F. G. Gray, and R. A. Thompson, "Self-Diagnosing Cellular Implementations of Finite-state Machines," *IEEE Trans. Computers*, Vol. C-30, pp. 953-959, December 1981.

[402] F. C. Wang and D. K. Bhavsar, "A Bus Organized Self-Test Processor Architecture," *Proc. Custom Integrated Circuits Conf.*, Rochester, NY, May 1984, pp. 164-167.

[403] F. C. Wang, G. Nurie, and M. Brashler, "An Integrated Design for Testability System," *Proc. Int. Conf. on CAD (ICCAD)*, Santa Clara, CA, November 1985, pp. 108-110.

[404] L. T. Wang and E. J. McCluskey, "A New

Condensed Linear Feedback Shift Register for VLSI/System Testing," *Fault-Tolerant Comput. Symp. (FTCS-14), Digest of Papers*, pp. 360-365, June 1984.

[405] L. T. Wang and E. J. McCluskey, "Complete Feedback Shift Register Design for Built-in Self Test," *Proc. Int. Conf. CAD (ICCAD-86)*, Santa Clara, CA, November 1986, pp. 56-59.

[406] L. T. Wang and E. J. McCluskey, "Condensed Linear Feedback Shift Register (LFSR) Testing − A Pseudoexhaustive Test Technique," *IEEE Trans. Computers*, Vol. C-35, pp. 367-370, April 1986.

[407] L. T. Wang and E. J. McCluskey, "Feedback Shift Registers for Self-Testing Circuits," *VLSI Systems Design*, Vol. VII, pp. 50-58, December 1986.

[408] L. T. Wang and E. J. McCluskey, "Built-In Self-Test for Sequential Machines," *Proc. Int. Test Conf.*, Washington, DC, September 1987, pp. 334-341.

[409] L. T. Wang and E. J. McCluskey, "Circuits for Pdeudo-Exhaustive Test Pattern Generation using Shortened Cyclic Codes," *Proc. Int. Conf. Comp. Des. (ICCD-87)*, Rye Brook, NY, October 1987, pp. 450-453.

[410] L. T. Wang, E. J. McCluskey, and S. Mourad, "Shift Register Testing of Sequential Machines," *Fault-Tolerant Computing Symp. (FTCS-17) Digest of Papers*, pp. 66-71, July 1987.

[411] D. Westcott, "The Self-Assist Test Approach to Embedded Arrays," *Int. Test Conf. Digest of Papers*, Philadelphia, PA, October 1981, pp. 203-207.

[412] C. L. Wey, "On Yield Consideration for the Design of Redundant Programmable Logic Arrays," *IEEE Trans. CAD*, Vol. 7, pp. 528-535, April 1988.

[413] K. D. Wilken and J. P. Shen, "Embedded Signature Monitoring: Analysis and Technique," *Proc. Int. Test Conf.*, Washington, DC, September 1987, pp. 324-333.

[414] M. J. Y. Williams and J. B. Angell, "Enhancing Testability of Large-Scale Integrated Circuits via Test Points and Additional Logic," *IEEE Trans. Computers*, Vol. C-22, pp. 46-60, Jan. 1973.

[415] T. W. Williams, "Design For Testability," in *Computer Design Aids for VLSI Circuits*, P.

Antognetti, D. O. Pederson, and H. deMan, Eds., Sijthoff & Noordhoff, Rockville, MD, 1981, pp. 359-416.

[416] T. W. Williams, "Integrating the Approaches to Structured Design for Testability," *VLSI Design*, Vol. IV, p. 34, October 1983.

[417] T. W. Williams, W. Daehn, M. Gruetzner, and C. W. Starke, "Aliasing Errors with Primitive and Non-Primitive Polynomials," *Proc. Int. Test Conf.*, Washington, DC, September 1987, pp. 637-644.

[418] T. W. Williams and E. B. Eichelberger, "Random Patterns With a Structured Sequential Logic Design," *Semicond. Test Symp.*, pp. 19-27, October 1977.

[419] T. W. Williams and K. P. Parker, "Design for Testability − A Survey," *IEEE Trans. Computers*, Vol. C-31, pp. 2-15, January 1982.

[420] T. W. Williams and K. P. Parker, "Design for Testability − A Survey," *Proc. IEEE*, Vol. 71, Jan. 1983, pp. 98-112.

[421] C. C. Wu and T. S. Wu, "Concurrent Error Correction in Unidirectional Linear Arithmetic Arrays," *Fault-Tolerant Computing Symp. (FTCS-17) Digest of Papers*, pp. 136-141, July 1987.

[422] D. M. Wu, E. S. Haarer, J. M. Monzel, and C. E. Radke, "Design for Testability and Yield at the Transistor Level," *Proc. Int. Test. Conf.*, Washington, DC, September 1987, pp. 158-165.

[423] H. J. Wunderlich, "Self Test Using Unequiprobable Random Patterns," *Fault-Tolerant Computing Symp. (FTCS-17) Digest of Papers*, pp. 258-263, July 1987.

[424] S. Yajima and T. Aramaki, "Autonomously Testable Programmable Logic Arrays," *Fault-Tolerant Comp. Symp. (FTCS-11) Digest of Papers*, pp. 41-46, June 1981.

[425] T. Yamada, "Syndrome-Testable Design of Programmable Logic Arrays," *Proc. Int. Test Conf.*, Philadelphia, PA, October 1983, pp. 453-458.

[426] N. Yamaguchi, T. Funabashi, K. Iwasaki, T. Shimura, Y. Hagiware, and K. Minorikawa, "A Self-Testing Method for Modular Structured Logic VLSIs," *Proc. Int. Conf. CAD (ICCAD-84)*, Santa Clara, CA, November 1984, pp. 99-101.

[427] K. Yamashita, A. Kanasugi, S. Hijiya, G. Goto,

N. Matsumura, and T. Shirato, "A Wafer-Scale 170,000-Gate FFT Processor with Built-In Test Circuits," *Proc. Custom Integrated Circ. Conf.*, Portland, OR, May 1987, pp. 207-210.

[428] T. C. Yang and C. W. Chiou, "Design of Self-Checking PLAs Using Alternating Logic," *Proc. Int. Test. Conf.*, Washington, DC, September 1987, pp. 189-196.

[429] M. M. Yen, W. K. Fuchs, and J. A. Abraham, "Concurrent Error Detection in Highly Structured Logic Arrays," *IEEE J. Sol. St. Circ.*, Vol. SC-22, pp. 595-605,

[430] J. J. Zasio, "Non-Stuck Testing of CMOS VLSI," *Proc. Compcon*, Spring 1985, pp. 388-391.

[431] Y. Zorian and V. K. Agarwal, "A General Scheme to Optimize Error Masking in Built-in Self-Testing," *Fault-Tolerant Comp. Symp. (FTCS-16) Digest of Papers*, pp. 410-415, July 1986.

[432] Y. Zorian and V. K. Agrawal, "Higher Certainty of Error Coverage by Output Data Modification," *Proc. Int. Test Conf.*, Philadelphia, PA, October 1984, pp. 140-147.

4.7: ATE, Test Programming and Other Production Testing Topics

[1] M. Abramovici, "A Maximal Resolution Guided-Probe Testing Algorithm," *Proc. 18th Des. Auto. Conf.*, Nashville, TN, June 1981, pp. 189-195.

[2] D. P. Ahrens, P. J. Bednarczyk, D. L. Denburg, and R. M. Robertson, "TPG2 − An Automatic Test Program Generator for Custom ICs," *Proc. Int. Test Conf.*, Philadelphia, PA, October 1984, pp. 762-767.

[3] R. Albrow, "Test Pattern Compaction in VLSI Testers," *Proc. Int. Test Conf.*, Philadelphia, PA, October 1983, pp. 12-17.

[4] R. Albrow and G. Robinson, "VLSI CAT: Filling the Void Between CAD and Testing," *VLSI Design*, Vol. III, p. 20, September/October 1982.

[5] R. W. Allen, C. D. Chen, M. M. Ervin-willis, K. R. Rahlfs, R. E. Tulloss, and S. L. Wu, "DORA: A System of CAD Post-processors Providing Test Programs and Automatic Diagnostics Data for Digital Device and Board Manufacture," *Int. Test Conf., Digest of Papers*, Philadelphia, PA, October 1981, pp. 555-560.

[6] R. W. Allen, M. M. Ervin-Willis, and R. E. Tulloss, "DORA: CAD Interface to Automatic Diagnostics," *Proc. 19th Des. Auto. Conf.*, Las Vegas, Nevada, June 1982, pp. 559-565.

[7] R. W. Allen, J. A. Malleo-Roach, P. A. Randise, G. D. Roush, and J. D. Yeager, "DORA2 System for the UNIX® Operating System," *Proc. Int. Test Conf.*, Washington, DC, September 1987, pp. 392-398.

[8] L. Apfelbaum, "Improving In-Circuit Diagnosis of Analog Networks with Expert Systems Techniques," *Proc. Int. Test Conf.*, Washington, D.C., September 1986, pp. 947-953.

[9] N. Arai, M. Homma, and Y. Yamanaka, "Parallel Testing of Random Logic LSIs," *Proc. Int. Test Conf.*, Philadelphia, PA, October 1984, pp. 827-831.

[10] M. Arao, T. Tadokoro, H. Maruyama, and S. Kamata, "Tester Correlation Problem in Memory Testers used in Production Lines," *Proc. Int. Test Conf.*, Philadelphia, PA, October 1983, pp. 464-470.

[11] D. H. Armstrong, "Pitfalls in Testing Digital ASIC Devices," *Proc. Custom Integrated Circ. Conf.*, Portland, OR, May 1987, pp. 573-578.

[12] Y. Arzoumanian and J. Waicukauski, "Fault Diagnosis in an LSSD Environment," *Int. Test Conf. Digest of Papers*, Philadelphia, PA, October 1981, pp. 86-88.

[13] R. W. Atherton and D. M. Campbell, "Use of In-Fab Parametric Testing for Process Control of Semiconductor Manufacturing," *Proc. Int. Test Conf.*, Philadelphia, PA, October 1983, pp. 238-247.

[14] R. W. Atherton, L. Ekkelkamp, and C. Schmitz, "Logic Device Characterization Using Computer-Aided Test and Analysis," *Proc. Int. Test Conf.*, Philadelphia, PA, October 1984, pp. 367-381.

[15] R. W. Atherton, A. H. Miller Jr., and J. E. Dayhoff, "Operations Management and Analysis in the Management of Electronic Testing," *Proc. Int. Test Conf.*, Philadelphia, PA, October 1983, pp. 418-426.

[16] R. W. Atherton and J. L. Mudge, "Microprocessor Speed Optimization Using Pattern-Recognition Analysis of Parametric Test Data," *Proc. Int. Test Conf.*, Philadelphia, PA, November 1985, pp. 938-948.

[17] D. J. Azaren, J. B. Cho, K. A. Fucik, A. M. Miscione, and R. P. O'Connell, "A Fault-Isolation Test (FIT) Chip for Process Enhancement and Fault Detection," *Proc. Int. Conf. Comp. Des. (ICCD)*, Port Chester, NY, October 1986, pp. 256-259.

[18] R. Balasubramaniam and P. Feder, "Test Strategy for a 32-Bit Microprocessor Module with Memory Management Unit," *Proc. Int. Test Conf.*, Philadelphia, PA, October 1984, pp. 598-603.

[19] D. Bandes, "Exploratory Data Analysis Makes Testing More Valuable for Semiconductor Manufacturing," *Proc. Int. Test Conf.*, Philadelphia, PA, October 1984, pp. 350-358.

[20] D. Bandes, "Exploratory Data Analysis for Semiconductor Manufacturing," *IEEE Design & Test of Computers*, Vol. 2, pp. 45-55, June 1985.

[21] M. R. Barber, "Fundamental Timing Problems in Testing MOS VLSI on Modern ATE," *IEEE Design & Test of Computers*, Vol. 1, pp. 90-97, August 1984.

[22] P. H. Bardell and W. H. McAnney, "A View From the Trenches: Production Testing of a Family of VLSI Multichip Modules," *Fault-Tolerant Comp. Symp. (FTCS-11) Digest of Papers*, pp. 281-283, June 1981.

[23] J. Bateson, *In-Circuit Testing*, Van Nostrand Reinhold, New York, 1985.

[24] S. D. Bedrosian, "The Role of Pattern Recognition in VLSI Testing," *Proc. Int. Test Conf.*, Washington, D.C., September 1986, pp. 750-754.

[25] C. Bellon and R. Velazco, "Hardware and Software Tools for Microprocessor Functional Test," *Proc. Int. Test Conf.*, Philadelphia, PA, October 1984, pp. 804-810.

[26] L. Bergher, J. Laurent, B. Courtois, and J. P. Collin, "Towards Automatic Failure Analysis of Complex ICs Through E-Beam Testing," *Proc. Int. Test Conf.*, Washington, DC, September 1986, pp. 465-471.

[27] W. E. D. Beste, "Tools for Test Development," *VLSI Systems Design*, Vol. VII, pp. 92-97, July 1986.

[28] W. E. D. Beste, "Intent Capture Concepts for Simplifying Device Simulation and Test," *Proc. Int. Test. Conf.*, Washington, DC, September 1987, pp. 261-266.

[29] G. P. Bosse, "High Speed Redundancy Processor," *Proc. Int. Test Conf.*, Philadelphia, PA, October 1984, pp. 282-286.

[30] G. H. Bowers Jr. and B. G. Pratt, "Low-Cost Testers: Are They Really Low Cost?," *IEEE Design & Test of Computers*, Vol. 2, pp. 20-28, June 1985. Also *Proc. Int. Test Conf.*, Philadelphia, PA, Oct. 1984, pp. 40-49.

[31] T. G. Breitenwischer, "Logic Verification and Production Testing of Non-Structured Embedded VLSI Blocks," *Proc. Custom Integrated Circ. Conf.*, Portland, OR, May 1987, pp. 62-65.

[32] R. S. Broughton and M. G. Brashler, "The Future is Now: Extending CAE into Test of Custom VLSI," *Proc. Int. Test Conf.*, Philadelphia, PA, October 1984, pp. 462-465.

[33] C. Buck, "The Economic Benefits of Test During Burn-In: Real-World Experiences," *Proc. Int. Test Conf.*, Washington, DC, September 1987, pp. 1086-1093.

[34] M. G. Buehler and L. W. Linholm, "Role of Test Chips in Coordinating Logic and Circuit Design and Layout Aids for VLSI," *Solid State Technology*, pp. 67-87, Sept. 1981.

[35] M. Campbell, "Monitored Burn-In (A Case Study for In-situ Testing and Reliability Studies)," *Proc. Int. Test Conf.*, Philadelphia, PA, October 1984, pp. 518-523.

[36] D. C. Chang and A. A. Grillo, "Test Considerations for Components with Redundant Elements," *Int. Test Conf. Digest of Papers*, Philadelphia, PA, November 1982, pp. 111-118.

[37] J. M. Chang, W. T. Krakow, and G. Kedem, "A Generic Test Program Translator (GTPT) for Tester-per-Pin ATE," *Proc. Int. Test Conf.*, Washington, DC, September 1987, pp. 1044-1051.

[38] P. Chang, E. Richards, and D. Richter, "The Pin Module: A High Accuracy Concept in Very High Frequency Pin Electronics," *Int. Test Conf. Digest of Papers*, Philadelphia, PA, October 1981, pp. 154-166.

[39] Y. H. E. Chang, D. E. Hoffman, A. J. Gruodis, and J. E. Dickol, "A 250 MHz Advanced Test System," *Proc. Int. Test Conf.*, Washington, DC, September 1987, pp. 68-75.

[40] I. Chen and A. J. Strojwas, "A Methodology for Optimal Test Structure Design," *Proc. Custom Integrated Circ. Conf.*, Portland, OR, May 1985,

pp. 520-523.

[41] I. Chen and A. J. Strojwas, "RYE: A Realistic Yield Simulator for VLSIC Structural Failures," *Proc. Int. Test Conf.*, Washington, DC, September 1987, pp. 31-42.

[42] V. S. Cherkassky and L. L. Kinney, "A Group Probing Strategy for Testing Large Number of Chips," *Proc. Int. Test Conf.*, Washington, D.C., September 1986, pp. 853-856.

[43] R. S. Chomiczewski, "VIVED – A Visual Vector Editor," *Proc. Int. Test Conf.*, Washington, D.C., September 1986, pp. 621-625.

[44] D. S. Cleverley, "The Role of Testing in Achieving Zero Defects," *Proc. Int. Test Conf.*, Philadelphia, PA, October 1983, pp. 248-253.

[45] S. A. Cohen and J. N. Chen, "Maintaining Timing Accuracy in High Pin-Count VLSI Module Test System," *Proc. Int. Test Conf.*, Washington, DC, September 1987, pp. 779-789.

[46] D. P. Cohoon and J. Sheridan, "Case History of Networking a Wafer-Sort Area," *Proc. Int. Test Conf.*, Washington, DC, September 1986, pp. 84-88.

[47] S. Concina, G. Liu, L. Lattanzi, S. Reyfman, and N. Richardson, "Software Integration in a Workstation-Based E-Beam Tester," *Proc. Int. Test Conf.*, Washington, D.C., September 1986, pp. 644-649.

[48] S. Concina and N. Richardson, "Workstation-Driven E-Beam Prober," *Proc. Int. Test Conf.*, Washington, DC, September 1987, pp. 554-560.

[49] S. E. Concina and G. S. Liu, "Integrating Design Information for IC Diagnosis," *Proc. 24th Des. Auto. Conf.*, Miami Beach, FL, June 1987, pp. 251-257.

[50] W. K. Conroy Jr., "Making Accurate Measurements on ATE," *Test Conference Digest of Papers*, Philadelphia, PA, November 1980, pp. 308-312.

[51] M. Contini, "The AUTOPAL Test Process," *Proc. Int. Test Conf.*, Philadelphia, PA, November 1985, pp. 279-285.

[52] F. Cox, L. Konneker, and D. Moreland, "Visual Programming for Analog/Hybrid ATE," *Proc. Int. Test Conf.*, Washington, D.C., September 1986, pp. 631-636.

[53] G. C. Cox, "Transmission Line Testing of CMOS – A Full Implementation," *Proc. Int.*

Test Conf., Washington, DC, September 1987, pp. 486-495.

[54] S. R. Craig, "ATE for Incoming Inspection: The Total Cost," *Test Conference Digest of Papers*, Philadelphia, PA, November 1980, pp. 210-212.

[55] C. Crapuchettes, "Testing CMOS I_{DD} on Large Devices," *Proc. Int. Test Conf.*, Washington, DC, September 1987, pp. 310-315.

[56] G. Crichton, P. Fazekas, and E. Wolfgang, "Electron Beam Testing of Microprocessors," *Test Conference Digest of Papers*, Philadelphia, PA, November 1980.

[57] M. Dahl, "Closed-Loop Error Correction: A Unique Approach to Test System Calibration," *Proc. Int. Test Conf.*, Washington, DC, September 1987, pp. 772-778.

[58] B. Davis, *The Economics of Automatic Testing*, McGraw-Hill, London, UK, 1982.

[59] D. L. Denburg, "A Testing Environment for Custom IC Development," *Proc. Custom Integrated Circuits Conf.*, Rochester, NY, May 1984, pp. 156-158.

[60] I. Deol, "Automatic Analysis of Circuits for Tester Skew and Clock Distribution for VLSI Circuits," *Proc. Int. Conf. Comp. Des. (ICCD-87)*, Rye Brook, NY, October 1987, pp. 350-353.

[61] P. Deves, J. P. Marx, P. Dague, and O. Raiman, "DEDALE: An Expert System for Troubleshooting Analogue Circuits," *Proc. Int. Test Conf.*, Washington, DC, September 1987, pp. 586-594.

[62] S. W. Director, "Manufacturing-Based Simulation: An Overview," *Proc. Custom Integrated Circ. Conf.*, Portland, OR, May 1987, pp. 107-113.

[63] A. Downey, "A Three Mode Command Language for ATE," *Int. Test Conf. Digest of Papers*, Philadelphia, PA, October 1981, pp. 489-494.

[64] A. E. Downey, "WAVEFORM: A Software Tool for Efficient Test Program Development," *Proc. Int. Test Conf.*, Philadelphia, PA, November 1985, pp. 672-676.

[65] A. L. Downey, "Test Program Optimization Techniques for a High Speed Performance VLSI Tester," *Proc. Int. Test Conf.*, Philadelphia, PA, October 1983, pp. 33-38.

[66] R. Dunn, A. Kwan, D. Rogers, D. Sandstrom, and C. Sie, "System to Optimize Test Quality and Efficiency for Memories and LSI," *Int. Test Conf. Digest of Papers*, Philadelphia, PA, October 1981, pp. 31-37.

[67] D. R. Emberson, "A Tightly Coupled Multiprocessor for VLSI Testing," *Proc. Int. Test Conf.*, Philadelphia, PA, October 1983, pp. 25-28.

[68] K. Y. Enright and B. J. VanAuken Jr., "The Role of Design Automation Systems in IBM GTD Bipolar Product Qualification," *Proc. Custom Integrated Circ. Conf.*, Rochester, NY, May 1984, pp. 300-304.

[69] A. Etherington, "Interfacing Design to Test Using the Electronic Design Interchange Format (EDIF)," *Proc. Int. Test Conf.*, Washington, DC, September 1987, pp. 378-383.

[70] L. J. Falkenstrom, D. Keezer, A. Patterson, R. M. Rolfe, and J. Wolcott, "Tester Independent Support Software System (TISSS)," *Proc. Int. Test Conf.*, Philadelphia, PA, November 1985, pp. 685-690.

[71] J. J. Faran Jr., "Selection of Test Strategy for Best Return on Investment," *Test Conference Digest of Papers*, Philadelphia, PA, November 1980, pp. 213-219.

[72] D. F. Farnholtz, "Operational Life Testing of Electronic Components," *IEEE Design & Test of Computers*, Vol. 2, pp. 50-56, Dec., 1985.

[73] M. Faucher, "Pattern Recognition of Bit Fail Maps," *Proc. Int. Test Conf.*, Philadelphia, PA, October 1983, pp. 460-463.

[74] W. G. Fee, *Tutorial – LSI Testing*, Computer Society Press, Washington, D.C., 1978.

[75] A. D. Flowers, K. Mathur, and J. Isakson, "Statistical Process Control Using the Parametric Tester," *Proc. Int. Test Conf.*, Washington, D.C., September 1986, pp. 422-427.

[76] D. J. Fouts, J. M. Johnson, S. E. Butner, and S. I. Long, "System Architecture of a Gallium Arsenide One-Gigahertz Digital IC Tester," *Computer*, Vol. 20, pp. 58-70, May 1987.

[77] S. Freeman, "Automatic Test Program Generation for Analog Circuits: Initial Success in Demonstrating a new Approach," *Proc. Int. Conf. Circ. Computers (ICCC-80)*, Port Chester, NY, October 1980, pp. 937-940.

[78] J. F. Frenzel and P. N. Marinos, "Power Supply Current Signature (PSCS) Analysis: A New Approach to System Testing," *Proc. Int. Test Conf.*, Washington, DC, September 1987, pp. 125-135.

[79] T. Fujieda and N. Zenke, "Testing Asynchronous Devices," *Proc. Int. Test Conf.*, Washington, DC, September 1987, pp. 871-875.

[80] R. Garcia, "The Fairchild Sentry 50 Tester: Establishing New Performance Limits," *IEEE Design & Test of Computers*, Vol. 1, pp. 101-109, May 1984.

[81] S. J. Gelman, "VEEP – A Vector Editor and Preparer," *Proc. 19th Des. Auto. Conf.*, Las Vegas, Nevada, June 1982, pp. 771-776.

[82] P. B. Ghate, "Reliability of VLSI Interconnections," *Proc. Int. Conf. Comp. Des. (ICCD-87)*, Rye Brook, NY, October 1987, pp. 240-243.

[83] D. Gleis and K. Hoffmann, "Test of DRAMs by Masked Alpha-Radiation," *Proc. Int. Test Conf.*, Washington, DC, September 1987, pp. 858-863.

[84] P. Goel and M. T. McMahon, "Electronic Chip-in-Place Test," *Int. Test Conf. Digest of Papers*, Philadelphia, PA, November 1982, pp. 83-90. Also *Proc. 19th Des. Auto. Conf.*, Las Vegas, Nevada, June 1982, pp. 482-488.

[85] B. Goetz, "Reliability in a Custom Integrated Circuit Environment," *Proc. Custom Integrated Circ. Conf.*, Rochester, NY, May 1984, pp. 305-308.

[86] S. Gorlich, H. Harbeck, P. Keβler, E. Wolfgang, and K. Zibert, "Integration of CAD, CAT and Electron Beam Testing for IC-Internal Logic Verification," *Proc. Int. Test Conf.*, Washington, DC, September 1987, pp. 566-574.

[87] Y. Goto, K. Ozaki, T. Ishizuka, A. Ito, Y. Furukawa, and T. Inagaki, "Electron Beam Prober for LSI Testing with 100 ps Time Resolution," *Proc. Int. Test Conf.*, Philadelphia, PA, October 1984, pp. 543-549.

[88] L. J. Grasso, C. E. Morgan, M. A. Peloquin, and F. Rajan, "A 250 MHz Test System's Timing and Automatic Calibration," *Proc. Int. Test Conf.*, Washington, DC, September 1987, pp. 76-84.

[89] A. J. Gruodis and D. E. Hoffman, "250-MHz Advanced Test System," *IEEE Design & Test of Computers*, Vol. 5, pp. 24-35, April 1988.

[90] R. M. Haas and D. B. Day, "The Integration of

Design and Test, Part 2: Prototype Tester for Hardware Verification," *VLSI Design*, p. 84, VI.

[91] H. K. Haill and J. R. Birchak, "Multilayer PC Board Design Approximations for High Speed Functional Testing," *Proc. Int. Test Conf.*, Washington, DC, September 1987, pp. 354-362.

[92] P. T. Harding and J. C. Howland, "Turning Test Data into Information," *Proc. Int. Test Conf.*, Philadelphia, PA, October 1983, pp. 659-665.

[93] D. E. Harpel and E. R. Hnatek, "Practical Insights into 1 Meg DRAM Evaluation," *Proc. Int. Test Conf.*, Washington, DC, September 1987, pp. 738-749.

[94] S. Z. Hassan, N. Aten, J. Tessier, and F. C. Chong, "Testing and Diagnosing Wafer Scale Integration (WSI) Logic," *Proc. Int. Conf. CAD (ICCAD-84)*, Santa Clara, CA, November 1984, pp. 108-110.

[95] C. D. Havener, "Issues that Arise in Translating VLSI Test Programs between Testers," *Proc. Int. Test Conf.*, Washington, D.C., September 1986, pp. 875-885.

[96] B. L. Havlicsek, "A Knowledge Based Diagnostic System for Automatic Test Equipment," *Proc. Int. Test Conf.*, Washington, D.C., September 1986, pp. 930-938.

[97] Y. Hayasaka, K. Shimotori, and K. Okada, "Testing System for Redundant Memory," *Int. Test Conf. Digest of Papers*, Philadelphia, PA, November 1982, pp. 240-244.

[98] J. T. Healy, *Automatic Testing and Evaluation of Digital Integrated Circuits*, Reston Publishing Company, Inc., Reston, VA, 1981.

[99] J. T. Healy, "An Information Processing Software System for ATE," *Proc. Int. Test Conf.*, Philadelphia, PA, October 1984, pp. 497-512.

[100] J. T. Healy, "The Marriage of CAE Workstations and ATE," *VLSI Systems Design*, Vol. VI, pp. 94-102, September 1985.

[101] H. D. Helms, "Various Architectures of Systems for Measuring Early-Life Failure Rates of Semiconductor Components," *Proc. Int. Test Conf.*, Philadelphia, PA, November 1985, pp. 540-543.

[102] F. J. Henley, "An Automated Laser Prober to Determine VLSI Internal Node Logic States," *Proc. Int. Test Conf.*, Philadelphia, PA, October 1984, pp. 536-542.

[103] F. J. Henley, "Functional Testing and Failure Analysis of VLSI Using Laser Probe," *Proc. Custom Integrated Circuits Conf.*, Rochester, NY, May 1984, pp. 181-186.

[104] F. J. Henley, "Tests of Hermetically Sealed LSI/VLSI Devices by Laser Photoexcitation Logic Analysis," *Proc. Int. Test Conf.*, Washington, D.C., September 1986, pp. 607-610.

[105] B. Henshaw, "An MC68020 Users Test Program," *Proc. Int. Test Conf.*, Washington, DC, September 1986, pp. 386-393.

[106] R. D. Hess, M. E. Ausec, R. F. Biedronski, and R. H. Rector, "Automated Test Program Generation for Semicustom Devices," *VLSI Design*, Vol. IV, p. 51, October 1983.

[107] R. L. Hickling, "Tester Independent Problem Representation and Tester Dependent Program Generation," *Proc. Int. Test Conf., Philadelphia, PA*, October 1983, pp. 476-482.

[108] T. Hidai, T. Matsumoto, and F. Tsuruda, "Test Program Debugging Environment for Linear IC Testers," *Proc. Int. Test Conf.*, Washington, D.C., September 1986, pp. 869-874.

[109] K. Hiwada and T. Tamamura, "Dynamic Test System for High Speed Mixed Signal Devices," *Proc. Int. Test Conf.*, Washington, DC, September 1987, pp. 370-375.

[110] E. R. Hnatek, "Thoughts on VLSI Burn-In," *Proc. Int. Test Conf.*, Philadelphia, PA, October 1984, pp. 531-534.

[111] E. R. Hnatek, "IC Quality − Where Are We?," *Proc. Int. Test Conf.*, Washington, DC, September 1987, pp. 430-445.

[112] E. R. Hnatek and B. R. Wilson, "An Evaluation of the 2816 EEPROM," *Int. Test Conf. Digest of Papers*, Philadelphia, PA, November 1982, pp. 225-235.

[113] E. R. Hnatek and B. R. Wilson, "Practical Considerations in Testing Semicustom and Custom ICs," *VLSI Design*, Vol. VI, p. 20, March 1985.

[114] J. Hom and H. Ranga, "PASCAL-T: A Device Engineer's Programming Language," *Test Conference Digest of Papers*, Philadelphia, PA, November 1980, pp. 331-337.

[115] L. K. Horning, J. M. Soden, R. R. Fritzemeier, and C. F. Hawkins, "Measurements of Quiescent Power Supply Current for CMOS ICs in Production Testing," *Proc. Int. Test Conf.*,

Washington, DC, September 1987, pp. 300-309.

[116] W. J. Horth, F. G. Hall, and R. G. Hillman, "Microelectronics Device Electrical Test Implementation Problems on Automated Test Equipment," *Int. Test Conf. Digest of Papers*, Philadelphia, PA, November 1982, pp. 299-307.

[117] M. C. M. Hoye, "Artificial Intelligence in Semiconductor Manufacturing for Process Development, Functional Diagnostics, and Yield Crash Prevention," *Proc. Int. Test Conf.*, Washington, D.C., September 1986, pp. 939-946.

[118] J. T. G. Hsu, R. B. L. Lee, and G. D. Burroughs, "Efficient Testing of RISC Microprocessors," *Proc. Int. Conf. CAD (ICCAD-86)*, Santa Clara, CA, November 1986, pp. 15-18.

[119] C. Huang, H. Choe, R. Rabe, and K. Golke, "Latch-up Analysis in CMOS Static 4K RAMs Using Laser Scanning," *Proc. Custom Integrated Circuits Conf.*, Rochester, NY, May 1984, pp. 176-180.

[120] R. A. Hughes, "Analysis of Semiconductor Test Data Using Pattern Recognition Techniques," *Test Conference Digest of Papers*, Philadelphia, PA, November 1980, pp. 301-307.

[121] A. Hunger and A. Gaertner, "Functional Characterization of Microprocessors," *Proc. Int. Test Conf.*, Philadelphia, PA, October 1984, pp. 794-803.

[122] R. E. Huston, "An Analysis of ATE Testing Costs," *Proc. Int. Test Conf.*, Philadelphia, PA, October 1983, pp. 396-411.

[123] G. Illes, "ATE Cost Effectivity: How Much Performance Can You Afford?," *Proc. Int. Test Conf.*, Washington, DC, September 1987, pp. 1005-1013.

[124] "International Test Conference Roundtable: What's in Store for High-Performance Testers?," *IEEE Design & Test of Computers*, Vol. 4, pp. 55-59, February 1987.

[125] G. W. Jacob, "ATE Throughput Prediction for Test Planning," *Test Conference Digest of Papers*, Philadelphia, PA, November 1980, pp. 203-209.

[126] G. W. Jacob, "Preparation of Product Test Plan," *Int. Test Conf. Digest of Papers*, Philadelphia, PA, October 1981, pp. 340-347.

[127] H. Jacobs, "Verification of a Second Generation 32-Bit Microprocessor," *Computer*, Vol. 19, pp. 64-70, April 1986.

[128] F. Jensen and N. E. Petersen, *Burn-In*, John Wiley & Sons, Chichester, U.K., 1982.

[129] W. K. Jones, "Managing Your Test Cost for the '80's," *Int. Test Conf. Digest of Papers*, Philadelphia, PA, November 1982, pp. 569-573.

[130] A. Kanadjian, D. Rodgers, and M. Shepherd, "FIFO Test Program Development," *Proc. Int. Test Conf.*, Washington, D.C., September 1986, pp. 819-825.

[131] S. Kannari, Y. Furukawa, S. Sumida, and S. Takeshita, "New High Precision and High Speed AC Level Calibration Method," *Proc. Int. Test. Conf.*, Washington, DC, September 1987, pp. 236-241.

[132] M. Kawai, T. Shimono, and S. Funatsu, "Test Data Quality Assurance," *Proc. Int. Test Conf.*, Washington, D.C., September 1986, pp. 848-852.

[133] T. Kazamaki, "Milestones of New-Generation ATE," *IEEE Design & Test of Computers*, Vol. 2, pp. 83-89, October 1985.

[134] S. Kazmi and K. VanEgmond, "Simulation and Testing of VTI Gate Arrays," *Proc. Custom Integrated Circ. Conf.*, Rochester, NY, May 1986, pp. 409-411.

[135] M. Keating, "Schematic Timing Errors in VLSI Test Systems," *Proc. Int. Test. Conf.*, Washington, DC, September 1987, pp. 198-205.

[136] M. Keating and D. Meyer, "A New Approach to Dynamic IDD Testing," *Proc. Int. Test Conf.*, Washington, DC, September 1987, pp. 316-321.

[137] R. Kinch and C. Pottle, "Automatic Test Generation for Electron-Beam Testing of VLSI Circuits," *Proc. Int. Conf. Circ. Computers (ICCC'82)*, New York, NY, September 1982, pp. 548-551.

[138] T. King, "Advanced Test System Software Architecture Blends High Speed with User Friendliness," *Proc. Int. Test Conf.*, Philadelphia, PA, October 1984, pp. 606-613.

[139] N. Kirschner, "An Interactive Descrambler Program for RAMs with Redundancy," *Int. Test Conf. Digest of Papers*, Philadelphia, PA, November 1982, pp. 252-257.

[140] R. E. Kizis and R. T. Herberg, "PLT Language and Language Processing System," *Test Conference Digest of Papers*, Philadelphia, PA,

November 1980, pp. 338-345.

[141] U. Ko, D. G. Patel, and F. J. Henley, "Contactless VLSI Laser Probing," *Proc. Int. Test Conf.*, Philadelphia, PA, November 1985, pp. 930-935.

[142] H. Koike, K. Doi, J. Iwamura, K. Maeguchi, T. Sato, and H. Tango, "Internal Testing of an 8-Bit Single Chip CMOS/SOS Microcomputer Using an Electron Beam Tester," *Proc. Int. Conf. Circ. Computers (ICCC'82)*, New York, NY, September 1982, pp. 552-555.

[143] P. Kollensperger, A. Krupp, M. Strum, R. Weyl, F. Widulla, and E. Wolfgang, "Automated Electron Beam Testing of VLSI Circuits," *Proc. Int. Test Conf.*, Philadelphia, PA, October 1984, pp. 550-556.

[144] A. J. Kombol, "Processing of Test Data Between Design and Testing," *Proc. Int. Test Conf.*, Philadelphia, PA, October 1984, pp. 789-791.

[145] R. Kramer, "Testing Mixed-Signal Devices," *IEEE Design & Test of Computers*, Vol. 4, pp. 12-20, April 1987.

[146] N. Kuji and T. Tamama, "An Automated E-Beam Tester with CAD Interface, FINDER: A Powerful Tool for Fault Diagnosis of ASICs," *Proc. Int. Test Conf.*, Washington, D.C., September 1986, pp. 857-863.

[147] N. Kuji, T. Tamama, and M. Nagatani, "FINDER: A CAD System-Based Electron Beam Tester for Fault Diagnosis of VLSI Circuits," *IEEE Trans. on CAD*, Vol. CAD-5, pp. 313-319, April 1986.

[148] N. Kuji, T. Tamama, and T. Yano, "A Fully Automated Electron-Beam Test System for VLSI Circuits," *IEEE Design & Test of Computers*, Vol. 2, pp. 74-82, October 1985.

[149] Y. Kuramitsu and Y. Gamo, "A Suitable Test System for Gate Array," *Proc. Int. Test Conf.*, Philadelphia, PA, October 1983, pp. 21-24.

[150] E. Kurtzweil and L. Jambut, "Importance of Asynchronous Refreshing in Memory Testing," *Int. Test Conf. Digest of Papers*, Philadelphia, PA, October 1981, pp. 38-43.

[151] E. Kurzweil and L. Jambut, "Access Time Evaluation of Fast Static MOS Memories," *Proc. Int. Test Conf.*, Philadelphia, PA, October 1984, pp. 263-270.

[152] S. Ladd, "Implementing a Self-Managed Test Vector Memory with One Million Elements," *Proc. Int. Test Conf.*, Philadelphia, PA, October 1983, pp. 18-20.

[153] G. E. Lahti, "Flexibility – Enhancing the Menu Based VLSI Test System," *Proc. Int. Test Conf.*, Washington, DC, September 1987, pp. 1052-1057.

[154] M. Landry, "Production Testing of PCM (Digital) Audio Circuits," *Proc. Int. Test Conf.*, Philadelphia, PA, October 1983, pp. 767-770.

[155] J. P. LeBlanc Jr., "An STL Gate Array Reliability Test Bar," *Int. Test Conf. Digest of Papers*, Philadelphia, PA, November 1982, pp. 263-268.

[156] R. Leckie, "A Model for Analyzing Test Capacity, Cost, and Productivity," *Proc. Int. Test Conf.*, Washington, DC, September 1986, pp. 213-218.

[157] S. D. Lee and L. D. Li, "A Comprehensive Approach to Test Program Debugging for High Performance VLSI Test Systems," *Proc. Int. Test Conf.*, Philadelphia, PA, November 1985, pp. 652-665.

[158] S. D. Lee and T. Middleton, "Behavioral Simulation of VLSI Test System Aids Debugging and Analysis of Test Programs," *Proc. Int. Test Conf.*, Philadelphia, PA, October 1984, pp. 614-620.

[159] H. S. Lehman and H. J. Jones, "Semiconductor Component Quality," *Proc. Custom Integrated Circ. Conf.*, Rochester, NY, May 1984, pp. 281-285.

[160] R. Y. Li, S. C. Diehl, and S. Harrison, "Power Supply Noise Testing of VLSI Chips," *Proc. Int. Test Conf.*, Philadelphia, PA, October 1983, pp. 366-370.

[161] H. Lin, R. Rajapakse, M. Dhodhi, H. S. Jin, and J. F. McDonald, "Use of the Focused Ion Beam for Unified Lithography, Testing and Repair in Wafer Scale Packaging," *Proc. Int. Conf. Comp. Des. (ICCD)*, Port Chester, NY, October 1986, pp. 225-229.

[162] M. G. Lin, M. Weitz, A. K. Yuen, and K. Rose, "Testing the 8086," *Test Conference Digest of Papers*, Philadelphia, PA, November 1980, pp. 426-432.

[163] E. Lindbloom, S. Matheson, and J. Catanzaro, "VLSI Testing, Diagnostics and Qualification," *Proc. Int. Conf. Circ. Computers (ICCC'82)*, New York, NY, September 1982, pp. 341-345.

[164] D. D. Litten, "A Tester Architecture for Low-Level Semiconductor Capacitance Measurements in a Production Environment," *Proc. Int. Test Conf.*, Washington, DC, September 1987, pp. 502-507.

[165] B. C. S. Liu, "Automated Characterization Program for Microprocessors," *Semiconductor Test Conf., Digest of Papers*, Cherry Hill, NJ, October 1978, pp. 209-217.

[166] C. M. Liu, A. V. Kordesh, P. Y. Chee, I. S. Liu, and M. Khambaty, "A Comprehensive Testchip and Data Analysis Software for Technology Development and Process Control in a Custom VLSI Manufacturing Environment," *Proc. Custom Integrated Circ. Conf.*, Rochester, NY, May 1986, pp. 302-306.

[167] A. Lowenstein and G. Winter, "VHDL's Impact on Test," *IEEE Design & Test of Computers*, Vol. 3, pp. 48-53, April 1986.

[168] W. Lukaszek, W. Yarbrough, and K. Grambow, "CMOS Process Problem Debugging Using Complementary Defect Monitors," *Proc. Int. Test Conf.*, Washington, DC, September 1987, pp. 21-30.

[169] G. V. Lukianoff, J. S. Wolcott, and J. M. Morrissey, "Electron-Beam Testing of VLSI Dynamic RAMs," *Int. Test Conf. Digest of Papers*, Philadelphia, PA, October 1981, pp. 68-76.

[170] K. Lunneborg, "A Unified Test Plan for LSI or VLSI Components," *Int. Test Conf. Digest of Papers*, Philadelphia, PA, October 1981, pp. 9-14.

[171] Lutoff and C. Robach, "Expert System for Test Strategy Generation," *Proc. Int. Test Conf.*, Washington, DC, September 1987, pp. 576-585.

[172] B. G. MacAloney and P. Littlejohn, "Manufacturing Productivity: Automated vs Manual Test-Data-Management Systems," *Int. Test Conf. Digest of Papers*, Philadelphia, PA, November 1982, pp. 339-345.

[173] N. H. MacDonald and G. B. Neish, "AN Algorithmic Approach to the Testing of a Wafer Scale Integrated (WSI) Circuit," *Int. Test Conf. Digest of Papers*, Philadelphia, PA, November 1982, pp. 590-600.

[174] M. Mahoney, *DSP-Based Testing of Analog and Mixed-Signal Circuits (tutorial)*, Computer Society Press, Washington, DC, 1987.

[175] M. V. Mahoney, "New Techniques for High Speed Analog Testing," *Proc. Int. Test Conf.*, Philadelphia, PA, October 1983, pp. 589-597.

[176] S. K. Malik and E. F. Chace, "MOS Gate Oxide Quality Control and Reliability Assessment by Voltage Ramping," *Proc. Int. Test Conf.*, Philadelphia, PA, October 1984, pp. 384-389.

[177] S. K. Malik, J. E. Gunn, and R. E. Camenga, "Future of Temperature and Humidity Testing: Highly Accelerated Temperature and Humidity Stress Test (HAST)," *Proc. Int. Test Conf.*, Philadelphia, PA, October 1983, pp. 790-795.

[178] W. Maly, "Optimal Order of the VLSI IC Testing Sequence," *Proc. 23rd Des. Auto. Conf.*, Las Vegas, Nevada, June 1986, pp. 560-566.

[179] W. Maly, B. Trifilo, R. A. Hughes, and A. Miller, "Yield Diagnosis through Interpretation of Tester Data," *Proc. Int. Test Conf.*, Washington, DC, September 1987, pp. 10-20.

[180] T. E. Mangir and A. Avizienis, "Fault-Tolerant Design for VLSI: Effect of Interconnect Requirements on Yield Improvement of VLSI Designs," *IEEE Trans. Computers*, Vol. C-31, pp. 609-615, July 1982.

[181] P. N. Manikas and S. G. Eichenlaub, "Reducing the Cost of Quality through Test Data Management," *Proc. Int. Test Conf.*, Philadelphia, PA, October 1983, pp. 412-417.

[182] M. Mannan, P. Retlewski, and A. Hasan, "Failure Analyzer for Gate Arrays," *Proc. Int. Test Conf.*, Washington, DC, September 1987, pp. 228-233.

[183] G. Marks, "Parallel Testing of Non-Volatile Memories," *Proc. Int. Test Conf.*, Philadelphia, PA, October 1983, pp. 738-743.

[184] L. Masters, "The Path to Smart Power ATE," *Proc. Int. Test. Conf.*, Washington, DC, September 1987, pp. 242-247.

[185] J. M. McArdle, "A 250MHz Advanced Test System – System Software," *Proc. Int. Test Conf.*, Washington, DC, September 1987, pp. 85-93.

[186] R. M. McDermott and D. Stern, "Switch Directed Dynamic Causal Networks -- A Paradigm for Electronic System Diagnosis," *Proc. 24th Des. Auto. Conf.*, Miami Beach, FL, June 1987, pp. 258-264.

[187] C. McMinn, "The Impact of a VLSI Test

System on the Test Throughput Equation," *Proc. Int. Test Conf.*, Philadelphia, PA, October 1983, pp. 354-361.

[188] G. F. Meravi, J. J. Bell, and J. C. Bernier, "Analysis of Gate Array Failures Using Functional ATE," *Proc. Int. Test Conf.*, Philadelphia, PA, October 1983, pp. 676-681.

[189] T. Middleton, "Functional Test Vector Generation for Digital LSI/VLSI Devices," *Proc. Int. Test Conf.*, Philadelphia, PA, October 1983, pp. 682-691.

[190] T. Middleton, "Recycling Functional Test Vectors: Techniques and Tools for Pattern Conversion," *Proc. Int. Test Conf.*, Philadelphia, PA, November 1985, pp. 291-301.

[191] G. R. R. Milde, "Design and Electrical Characterization of Test Fixtures for High-Speed Digital ICs," *Proc. Int. Test Conf.*, Washington, DC, September 1987, pp. 363-369.

[192] A. H. Miller Jr., "Sizing a Test Data Management System for an ASIC Manufacturing Environment," *Proc. Int. Test Conf.*, Washington, DC, September 1987, pp. 680-686.

[193] J. Miyamoto and M. A. Horowitz, "A Single-Chip LSI High-Speed Functional Tester," *IEEE J. Sol. St. Circ.*, Vol. SC-22, pp. 820-828, October 1987.

[194] T. Moore and S. Garner, "Autoprobing on the L200 Functional Tester," *IEEE Design & Test of Computers*, Vol. 2, pp. 44-49, December 1985.

[195] N. Morgan, "An Automated, Menu Screen Generation Software Tool for VLSI ATE Programming and Operation," *Proc. Int. Test Conf.*, Washington, D.C., September 1986, pp. 612-620.

[196] S. Morris and B. Baril, "Bridging the Gap between CAE and Testing," *VLSI Design*, Vol. VI, p. 92, April 1985.

[197] J. M. Morrissey, H. C. Chow, R. Devries, and C. Megivern, "An Approach to Memory Testing, Diagnostics and Analysis," *Int. Test Conf. Digest of Papers*, Philadelphia, PA, October 1981, pp. 56-67.

[198] A. Mostacciuolo, "Transmission Problems Encountered when Testing Memory Devices in Parallel on Memory ATE," *Proc. Int. Test Conf.*, Washington, D.C., September 1986, pp. 808-818.

[199] T. J. Mulrooney, "Inexpensive Microprocessor Testing of Custom Integrated Circuits on Wafers, Packages, and Boards," *Proc. Int. Test Conf.*, Washington, D.C., September 1986, pp. 561-567.

[200] W. Murakami, "Parametric Testing for MOS Process Control and Diagnostics," *Semiconductor Test Conf., Digest of Papers*, Cherry Hill, NJ, October 1978, pp. 29-40.

[201] K. Muranaga, "Statistical and Practical Aspects of Testing LSI and VLSI Devices," *Test Conference Digest of Papers*, Philadelphia, PA, November 1980, pp. 289-294.

[202] K. Muranaga, K. Sakurada, and Y. Oikawa, "Language Independent Test Generation (LITG)," *Proc. Int. Test Conf.*, Philadelphia, PA, November 1985, pp. 263-270.

[203] L. S. Musolino and T. R. Conrad, "Early Life Reliability Monitoring of AT&T-C&ES Manufactured Electronic Components," *Proc. Int. Test Conf.*, Washington, DC, September 1987, pp. 446-450.

[204] M. Mydill, "A Generic Procedure for Evaluating VLSI Test System Timing Accuracy," *Proc. Int. Test. Conf.*, Washington, DC, September 1987, pp. 214-225.

[205] V. V. Nickel and P. A. Rosenberg, "An Innovative Interactive System to Generate Testware," *Test Conference Digest of Papers*, Philadelphia, PA, November 1980, pp. 321-325.

[206] Y. Nishimura, M. Hamada, H. Hidaka, H. Ozaki, K. Fujishima, and Y. Hayasaka, "Redundancy Test for 1 Mbit DRAM Using Multi-Bit-Test Mode," *Proc. Int. Test Conf.*, Washington, D.C., September 1986, pp. 826-829.

[207] J. Nishiura, T. Maruyama, H. Maruyama, and S. Kamata, "Testing VLSI Microprocessor with New Functional Capability," *Int. Test Conf. Digest of Papers*, Philadelphia, PA, November 1982, pp. 628-633.

[208] J. G. Noguera and D. T. Amm, "An Efficient Statistical Procedure to Determine Guardbands for Parametric Testing of Integrated Circuits," *Proc. Custom Integrated Circ. Conf.*, Rochester, NY, May 1986, pp. 404-408.

[209] S. Ohteru, T. Kato, S. Hashimoto, K. Watabe, and K. Minegishi, "Digital Circuit Test System Using Statistical Method," *Fault-Tolerant Comp. Symp. (FTCS-10) Digest of Papers*, pp.

179-181, October 1980.

[210] T. Okamoto, H. Shibata, and K. Kinoshita, "Design of High-Level Test Language for Digital LSI," *Proc. Int. Test Conf.*, Philadelphia, PA, October 1983, pp. 508-513.

[211] J. S. Pabst, "Timing Accuracy and Yield Estimation," *Proc. Int. Test Conf.*, Washington, D.C., September 1986, pp. 778-787.

[212] J. S. Pabst, "Elements of VLSI Production Test Economics," *Proc. Int. Test Conf.*, Washington, DC, September 1987, pp. 982-986.

[213] C. J. Pany, "Simplifying Analog Device Test Program Generator," *Proc. Int. Test Conf.*, Philadelphia, PA, November 1985, pp. 286-290.

[214] K. P. Parker, *Integrating Design and Test: Using CAE Tools for ATE Programming*, Computer Society Press, Washington, DC, 1987.

[215] M. Pasturel, "What Makes PASCAL a Modern Test Language?," *Test Conference Digest of Papers*, Philadelphia, PA, November 1980, pp. 326-330.

[216] G. A. Perone, R. S. Malfatt, J. P. Kain, and W. I. Goodheim, "A Closer Look at Testing Costs," *Int. Test Conf. Digest of Papers*, Philadelphia, PA, November 1982, pp. 574-578.

[217] G. D. Peterson, R. D. Peterson, and L. Blake, "MITEG: An Integrated Test Program Generation System," *Proc. Int. Test. Conf.*, Washington, DC, September 1987, pp. 267-275.

[218] D. Petrich, "Achieving Accurate Timing Measurement on TTL/CMOS Devices," *IEEE Design & Test of Computers*, Vol. 3, pp. 33-42, August 1986.

[219] C. Pieper, "Stimulus Data Interchange Format, Part 1: Test Issues," *VLSI Systems Design*, Vol. VII, pp. 76-81, July 1986.

[220] C. Pieper, "Stimulus Data Interchange Format, Part 2: Test Specifications," *VLSI Systems Design*, Vol. VII, pp. 56-60, August 1986.

[221] J. S. Pittman and W. C. Bruce, "Test Logic Economic Considerations in a Commercial VLSI Chip Environment," *Proc. Int. Test Conf.*, Philadelphia, PA, October 1984, pp. 31-39.

[222] W. Ponik, "Teradyne's J967 VLSI Test System: Getting VLSI to Market on Time," *IEEE Design & Test of Computers*, Vol. 2, pp. 57-62, December 1985.

[223] F. Pool, J. Hop, J. P. L. Lagerberg, and C. DaCostat, "Testing a 317K Bit High Speed Video Memory with a VLSI Test System," *Proc. Int. Test Conf.*, Philadelphia, PA, October 1984, pp. 294-299.

[224] R. N. Powell, "IBM's VLSI Logic Test System," *Int. Test Conf. Digest of Papers*, Philadelphia, PA, October 1981, pp. 388-392.

[225] G. Prokter, "The Logic Simulator-Tester Link: It's a Two-way Street," *Proc. Int. Test. Conf.*, Washington, DC, September 1987, pp. 254-260.

[226] P. Puri and H. Beckham, "How to use a General Purpose Tester as a Custom VLSI Design Tool," *Test Conference Digest of Papers*, Philadelphia, PA, November 1980, pp. 421-425.

[227] C. Pynn, *Strategies for Electronics Test*, McGraw-Hill, New York, 1986.

[228] M. Ravn, "A Mixed-Signal Test Program Development Environment," *VLSI Systems Design*, Vol. VIII, pp. 32-37, August 1987.

[229] M. A. Rich and D. E. Gentry, "The Economics of Parallel Testing," *Proc. Int. Test Conf.*, Philadelphia, PA, October 1983, pp. 728-737.

[230] N. Richardson, "E-Beam Probing for VLSI Circuit Debug," *VLSI Systems Design*, Vol. VIII, pp. 24-29,58, August 1987.

[231] W. S. Richardson, "Test Pattern Portability for Microprocessors," *Int. Test Conf. Digest of Papers*, Philadelphia, PA, November 1982, pp. 587-589.

[232] R. M. Robertson, P. J. Bednarczyk, and D. L. Denburg, "TPG2 – An Automatic Test Program Generation System for Design and Manufacture of ASICs," *Proc. Int. Test Conf.*, Washington, DC, September 1987, pp. 96-104.

[233] R. M. Rolfe, "High-Volume Production Testing and its Impact on the Development of Microprocessor Prototyping Tools," *Int. Test Conf. Digest of Papers*, Philadelphia, PA, October 1981, pp. 402-403.

[234] E. Rosenfeld, "Accuracy and Repeatability with DSP Test Methods," *Proc. Int. Test Conf.*, Washington, D.C., September 1986, pp. 788-795.

[235] E. Rosenfeld, "Test Fixture Design for High Speed Converter Testing," *Proc. Int. Test Conf.*, Washington, DC, September 1987, pp. 496-501.

[236] E. Rosenfeld and J. Janec, "Automatic Test of

High Data Rate Modems,'' *Proc. Int. Test Conf.*, Washington, DC, September 1987, pp. 120-124.

[237] C. R. Saikley and R. Muething, ''A Rapid, Low-Cost Technique for Precise AC Calibration in a Focused ASIC Tester,'' *Proc. Int. Test Conf.*, Washington, DC, September 1987, pp. 766-771.

[238] E. Sarkany, J. Feeney, and J. Muhr, ''A Functional Test Program Generator,'' *Proc. Int. Test Conf.*, Washington, D.C., September 1986, pp. 864-868.

[239] M. Schell and M. Sigler, ''Automated Analysis of Static RAM Failures,'' *Int. Test Conf. Digest of Papers*, Philadelphia, PA, November 1982, pp. 522-525.

[240] A. Schlafly, ''Compact Test Vectors for Gate Arrays,'' *VLSI Design*, Vol. V, p. 89, October 1984.

[241] E. O. Schlotzhauer, ''Real-World Board Test Effectiveness,'' *IEEE Design & Test of Computers*, Vol. 5, pp. 16-23, April 1988.

[242] H. D. Schnurman, L. J. Vidunas, and R. M. Peters, ''A System for Automatically Testing VLSI High Speed RAM's,'' *Proc. Int. Conf. Comp. Des. (ICCD'84)*, Port Chester, NY, October 1984, pp. 439-444.

[243] H. D. Schnurmann and R. M. Peters, ''An Interactive Test Data System for LSI Production Testing,'' *Proc. 17th Des. Auto. Conf.*, Minneapolis, MN, June 1980, pp. 362-366.

[244] H. D. Schnurmann, R. M. Peters, and L. J. Vidunas, ''A System for Testing LSI Multi-chip Modules Using Through-the-pin Testing,'' *Proc. Int. Conf. Circ. Computers (ICCC'82)*, New York, NY, September 1982, pp. 334-340.

[245] B. Schusheim, ''Automatic Test of LAN Transceivers,'' *Proc. Int. Test. Conf.*, Washington, DC, September 1987, pp. 136-146.

[246] T. A. Senna, ''Calculating VOH for LSI 10K ECL,'' *Int. Test Conf. Digest of Papers*, Philadelphia, PA, November 1982, pp. 615-619.

[247] S. C. Seth and V. D. Agrawal, ''Forecasting Reject Rate of Tested LSI Chips,'' *IEEE Electron Device Letters*, Vol. EDL-2, p. 286, Nov. 1981.

[248] S. C. Seth and V. D. Agrawal, ''Characterizing the LSI Yield from Wafer Test Data,'' *IEEE Trans. on CAD*, Vol. CAD-3, pp. 123-126, April

1984. Also in *Proc. Int. Conf. Circ. Comp. (ICCC'82)*, New York, September 1982, pp. 556-559.

[249] N. Shah and H. Ranga, ''A test Analysis Program for Memory Testing,'' *Int. Test Conf. Digest of Papers*, Philadelphia, PA, October 1981, pp. 476-483.

[250] S. Shalem, ''DIP – A Diagnostic Processor,'' *Proc. Int. Test Conf.*, Philadelphia, PA, November 1985, pp. 271-278.

[251] S. Shalem and I. Carmon, ''Testing the Design of the MS32532 Microprocessor,'' *Proc. Int. Conf. Comp. Des. (ICCD-87)*, Rye Brook, NY, October 1987, pp. 181-184.

[252] C. E. Shalvoy, ''Testing During Burn-In: Economical Alternative for Testing Memories,'' *Int. Test Conf. Digest of Papers*, Philadelphia, PA, November 1982, pp. 258-260.

[253] B. Sharma, C. McIntyre, G. Lebonville, and J. Avila, ''Integrated Test Program Development Package,'' *Proc. Int. Test Conf.*, Philadelphia, PA, November 1985, pp. 666-671.

[254] T. Shigematsu, T. Sakamoto, and Y. Yamanaka, ''A New Approach to DC Parameter Measurement in the Day of VLSI,'' *Proc. Int. Test Conf.*, Philadelphia, PA, October 1983, pp. 362-365.

[255] F. W. Shih, ''Real Time Product Characterization by Fault Modeling and Pattern Recognitions,'' *Proc. Int. Test Conf.*, Philadelphia, PA, October 1983, pp. 692-700.

[256] D. K. Shirachi, ''Codec Testing Using Synchronized Analog and Digital Signals,'' *IEEE Design & Test of Computers*, Vol. 2, pp. 56-63, June 1985.

[257] T. Shiragasawa, M. Sugano, Y. Mano, and M. Noyori, ''An On-Line Laser Probing System for Diagnosing Scaled VLSI,'' *Proc. Int. Test Conf.*, Philadelphia, PA, November 1985, pp. 634-642.

[258] B. Simon, J. Prado, and L. Day, ''Software Tools for Analysis of Wafer Sort Yield Data,'' *Proc. Int. Test Conf.*, Washington, DC, September 1987, pp. 670-679.

[259] D. R. Simpkins, ''Testing Fmax in a Production Environment,'' *Proc. Int. Test Conf.*, Washington, D.C., September 1986, pp. 771-777.

[260] B. B. Sindahl, ''Interactive Graphical Analysis of Bit-Fail Map Data Using Interactive Pattern

Recognition," *Proc. Int. Test Conf.*, Washington, DC, September 1987, pp. 687-692.

[261] R. F. Smoody, "ARNOLD: Applying an AI Workstation to Production Test Code Generation," *Proc. Int. Test Conf.*, Washington, D.C., September 1986, pp. 740-742.

[262] B. Snoulten and J. Peacock, "ANGEL – Algorithmic Pattern Generation System," *Int. Test Conf. Digest of Papers*, Philadelphia, PA, October 1981, pp. 484-488.

[263] D. C. Snyder, E. S. Stokes, and R. C. Mahoney, "Inside a Modern Test Language Compiler," *Proc. Int. Test Conf.*, Philadelphia, PA, October 1983, pp. 514-525.

[264] P. Solecky and R. L. Panko, "Test Data Verification – Not Just the Final Step for Test Data before Release for Production Testing," *Proc. 18th Des. Auto. Conf.*, Nashville, TN, June 1981, pp. 881-890.

[265] R. W. Spearman Jr. and F. D. Patch, "Quality and Control Self-Test," *Test Conference Digest of Papers*, Philadelphia, PA, November 1980, pp. 257-260.

[266] G. F. Sprott, "An Adaptable Emulation Support Environment for Microprocessor Systems," *Proc. Int. Test Conf.*, Philadelphia, PA, October 1983, pp. 483-488.

[267] C. H. Stapper, "Modeling of Defects in Integrated Circuit Photolithographic Patterns," *IBM J. Res. Develop.*, Vol. 28, pp. 461-475, July 1984.

[268] C. H. Stapper, "On yield, fault distributions, and clustering of particles," *IBM Jour. R. & D.*, Vol. 30, pp. 326-338, May 1986.

[269] C. H. Stapper, F. M. Armstrong, and K. Saji, "Integrated Circuit Yield Statistics," *Proceedings of The IEEE*, Vol. 71, April 1983, pp. 453-470.

[270] A. K. Stevens, *Introduction to Component Testing*, Addison-Wesley, Reading, MA, 1986.

[271] D. M. Stewart, "Production Test and Repair of 256k Dynamic RAMs with Redundancy," *Proc. Int. Test Conf.*, Philadelphia, PA, October 1983, pp. 471-474.

[272] A. C. Stover, *ATE: Automatic Test Equipment*, McGraw-Hill, New York, 1984.

[273] A. J. Strojwas and S. W. Director, "A Pattern Recognition Based Method for IC Failure Analysis," *IEEE Trans. on CAD*, Vol. CAD-4, pp. 76-92, January 1985. Also *Proc. Int. Conf. Circ. Comp. (ICCC'82)*, New York, NY, Sept. 1982, pp. 560-563.

[274] T. Sudo, A. Yoshii, T. Tamama, N. Narumi, and Y. Sakagawa, ""ULTIMATE": A 500-MHz VLSI Test System with High Timing Accuracy," *Proc. Int. Test. Conf.*, Washington, DC, September 1987, pp. 206-213.

[275] S. Sugamori, K. Takeuchi, H. Maruyama, and S. Kamata, "High-Fidelity Device Tester Interface," *Proc. Int. Test Conf.*, Philadelphia, PA, October 1983, pp. 371-378.

[276] T. Tada, T. Kobayashi, K. Okada, and Y. Kuramitsu, "Testing of Sence Amplifier in Dynamic Memory," *Int. Test Conf. Digest of Papers*, Philadelphia, PA, November 1982, pp. 245-251.

[277] R. Takagi and R. Yoshino, "Custom VLSI Test System," *Proc. Int. Test Conf.*, Philadelphia, PA, November 1985, pp. 431-436.

[278] T. Tamama and N. Kuji, "Automated Fault Diagnostic EB Tester and its Application to a 40K-Gate VLSI Circuit," *Proc. Int. Test Conf.*, Philadelphia, PA, November 1985, pp. 643-649.

[279] T. Tamama and N. Kuji, "Integrating an Electron-Beam System into VLSI Fault Diagnosis," *IEEE Design & Test of Computers*, Vol. 3, pp. 23-29, August 1986.

[280] K. P. Taschioglou, "Applying Quality Curves for Economic Comparisons of Alternative Test Strategies," *Int. Test Conf. Digest of Papers*, Philadelphia, PA, October 1981, pp. 331-339.

[281] K. P. Taschioglou, "A Convenient Algebra of Quality for Interpreting ATE Test Data," *Proc. Int. Test Conf.*, Philadelphia, PA, October 1983, pp. 796-803.

[282] J. Teisher, "Improved Workstation/Tester Interface is the Key to the Quality of Test-Program Generation," *Proc. Int. Test Conf.*, Washington, D.C., September 1986, pp. 626-630.

[283] A. Tejeda and G. Conner, "Innovative Video RAM Testing," *Proc. Int. Test Conf.*, Washington, D.C., September 1986, pp. 798-807.

[284] N. N. Tendolkar, "Diagnosis of TCM Failures in the IBM 3081 Processor Complex," *Proc. 20th Des. Auto. Conf.*, Miami Beach, FL, June 1983, pp. 196-200.

[285] "Test Fixtures – How Effective are They?," *IEEE Design & Test of Computers*, Vol. 5, pp. 48-57, April 1988.

[286] K. Thangamuthu, M. Macari, and S. Cohen, "Automated Contactless Digital Test System for VLSI," *Int. Test Conf. Digest of Papers*, Philadelphia, PA, November 1982, pp. 634-638.

[287] C. Tinaztepe, "CADDIF Data Interchange Format and a Methodology to Link Simulation and Test," *Proc. Int. Test Conf.*, Washington, DC, September 1987, pp. 384-391.

[288] C. Tinaztepe and N. Prywes, "Use of NOPAL in Generating Programs for Testing Analog Systems and Circuit Boards," *Proc. Int. Conf. Circ. Computers (ICCC-80)*, Port Chester, NY, October 1980, pp. 924-927.

[289] J. D. Tobey, "Reducing Test Program Development Time for Memory Devices," *Proc. Int. Test Conf.*, Philadelphia, PA, November 1985, pp. 949-953.

[290] K. E. Torku and D. A. Kiesling, "Noise Problems in Testing VLSI Hardware," *IEEE Design & Test of Computers*, Vol. 2, pp. 36-43, December 1985.

[291] K. E. Torku, J. A. Monzel, and C. E. Radke, "Performance Assurance of Memories Embedded in VLSI Chips," *Proc. Int. Test Conf.*, Washington, DC, September 1986, pp. 154-160.

[292] H. W. Trombley, A. L. Robinson, and J. P. Hayes, "Multiplexed Test Structures for IC Process Evaluation," *Proc. Int. Test Conf.*, Washington, DC, September 1987, pp. 451-457.

[293] A. Tuszynski, "Memory Chip Test Economics," *Proc. Int. Test Conf.*, Washington, DC, September 1986, pp. 190-194.

[294] J. VanHorn, "Accurate, Cost-Effective Performance Screening of VLSI Circuit Designs," *Proc. Int. Test Conf.*, Washington, DC, September 1986, pp. 169-175.

[295] A. P. VandenHeuvel and N. F. Khory, "A Basis for Setting Burn-in Yield Criteria," *IEEE Design & Test of Computers*, Vol. 2, pp. 29-34, June 1985. Also *Proc. Int. Test Conf.*, Philadelphia, PA, October 1984, pp. 524-530.

[296] R. H. VanderKloot, "Analog VLSI Devices Demand a new Tester Architecture," *Proc. Int. Test. Conf.*, Washington, DC, September 1987, pp. 248-251.

[297] P. Varma, A. P. Ambler, and K. Baker, "An Analysis of the Economics of Self-Test," *Proc. Int. Test Conf.*, Philadelphia, PA, October 1984, pp. 20-30.

[298] J. D. Vollmar, "A High-Speed Window-Based Pattern Debugger," *Proc. Int. Test Conf.*, Washington, DC, September 1987, pp. 1058-1064.

[299] K. Wada, S. Tazawa, and K. Kubota, "A Flexible Database System and its Application in VLSI Process Development," *Proc. Int. Test Conf.*, Philadelphia, PA, October 1984, pp. 359-366.

[300] J. H. Walker, "The ASIC Designer's Test Engineering Responsibilities," *VLSI Systems Design*, Vol. VII, pp. 56-61, February 1986.

[301] S. Watkins and K. Liu, "C: An Important Tool for Test Software Development," *Proc. Int. Test Conf.*, Philadelphia, PA, October 1984, pp. 636-640.

[302] I. M. Watson, J. A. Newkirk, R. Mathews, and D. B. Boyle, "ICTEST: A Unified System for Functional Testing and Simulation of Digital ICs," *Int. Test Conf. Digest of Papers*, Philadelphia, PA, November 1982, pp. 499-502.

[303] T. Westerhoff, "The Role of the Engineering Workstation in Test Program Development," *Proc. Int. Test Conf.*, Philadelphia, PA, October 1984, pp. 493-496.

[304] R. L. White, "TRS and DTS: IC Test Result Standards," *Proc. Int. Test Conf.*, Philadelphia, PA, November 1985, pp. 678-684.

[305] J. G. Wilber, "Enhancing Device Test Programming Productivity: The CATalyst Automated Test Program Generator," *Proc. Int. Test Conf.*, Philadelphia, PA, November 1985, pp. 252-262.

[306] A. J. Wilkinson, "MIND: An Inside Look at an Expert System for Electronic Diagnosis," *IEEE Design & Test of Computers*, Vol. 2, pp. 69-77, August 1985.

[307] A. J. Wilkinson, "Benchmarking an Expert System for Electronic Diagnosis," *Proc. Int. Test Conf.*, Washington, D.C., September 1986, pp. 964-971.

[308] L. Williams, J. Errico, T. Davis, and P. Janson, "The 90 Percent Solution, Automatic Generation of Parametric Test Programs," *Semiconductor Test Conf., Digest of Papers*, Cherry Hill, NJ, October 1978, pp. 23-28.

[309] B. R. Wilson and E. R. Hnatek, "Problems Encountered in Developing VLSI Test Programs for COT (A Practical Outlook)," *Proc. Int. Test Conf.*, Philadelphia, PA, October 1984, pp. 778-788.

[310] E. Wolfgang, "Elecectron Beam Testing," in *Handbook of Advanced Semiconductor Technology and Computer Technology*, G. Rabbat, Ed., Van Norstrand Reinhold, New York, 1988.

[311] D. M. Wu, C. C. Beh, and C. E. Radke, "Improve Yield and Quality through Testability Analysis of VLSI Circuits," *Proc. Int. Test Conf.*, Philadelphia, PA, October 1984, pp. 713-717.

[312] D. M. Wu and C. E. Radke, "The Effect of Random Defects and Tester Accuracy on the Quality and Yield of VLSI Circuits," *Fault-Tolerant Comput. Symp. (FTCS-14), Digest of Papers*, pp. 56-63, June 1984.

[313] T. Yano and H. Okamoto, "Fast Fault Diagnostic Method Using Fault Dictionary for Electron Beamm Tester," *Proc. Int. Test Conf.*, Washington, DC, September 1987, pp. 561-565.

[314] P. S. Yu, C. M. Krishna, and Y. H. Lee, "Optimal Design and Sequential Analysis of VLSI Testing Strategy," *IEEE Trans. Computers*, Vol. 37, pp. 339-347, March 1988.

[315] L. M. Zobniw, "Designing the VLSI Device-to-Board Test Ukraine Translator," *Proc. Int. Test Conf.*, Philadelphia, PA, October 1983, pp. 489-496.

Subject Index

Author Biographies

Vishwani D. Agrawal received the B.Sc. degree from the University of Allahabad, Allahabad, India, the B.E. degree from the University of Roorkee, Roorkee, India, the M.E. degree from the Indian Institute of Science, Bangalore, India, and the Ph.D. degree from the University of Illinois at Urbana-Champaign, in 1960, 1964, 1966, and 1971, respectively.

During 1970-71, he worked on the Illiac IV project at the Automation Technology, Inc., Champaign, Illinois. During 1971-72, as a senior scientist at the E.G.&G, Inc., Albuquerque, New Mexico, he worked on electromagnetic pulse. From 1972 to 1975, he was an Assistant Professor at the Indian Institute of Technology, New Delhi, India. From 1975 to 1978, he worked on spacecraft antenna design at the TRW Space & Defense Systems Group in Redondo Beach, California. Since 1978, he has worked in several positions, including supervising the CAD group on VLSI testing and verification, at the AT&T Bell Laboratories in Murray Hill, New Jersey. He has made significant contributions to the development of CAD tools and techniques for test generation, fault simulation, testability analysis, scan and built-in self-test, and timing analysis of digital VLSI circuits.

Dr. Agrawal is a fellow of the IEEE, a fellow of the IETE (India), and a member of the ACM. From 1985 to 1987, he was the Editor-in-Chief of the *IEEE Design & Test of Computers* magazine. He has served on the program committees of several IEEE conferences and workshops: FTCS, ITC, BIST Workshop, and DFT Workshop. He is currently a member of the program committees of the 25th ACM/IEEE Design Automation Conference and the 1988 International Test Conference. He was a co-organizer of the First International Workshop on VLSI Design in Madras, India in 1985.

He has published over *eighty* papers and has received *four* best paper awards. He holds a patent on a scan testable circuit.

Sharad C. Seth received the B. Eng. degree in 1964 from University of Jabalpur, India, the M. Tech. degree in 1966 from the Indian Institute of Technology, Kanpur, India, and the Ph.D. (EE) degree in 1970 from the University of Illinois, Urbana-Champaign. Since then he has been with the Department of Computer Science at the University of Nebraska, Lincoln, where he is currently a professor, teaching courses in the areas of VLSI design/testing and computer architecture.

Prof. Seth spent the academic years 1974-75 and 1982-83 on sabbatical leave at the Indian Institute of Technology, Kanpur, India. He has worked at the Bell Laboratories, Murray Hill, New Jersey, as a member of the technical staff and a consultant since 1980, most recently delivering a course on VLSI testing in March 1988. He has been a consultant to the industry, the Rensselaer Polytechnic Institute, and the National Institute of Health in the areas of testing, document analysis, and computer graphics. The CAD tools developed by him and his students are being used by leading industrial laboratories, universities, and government agencies.

He was a member of the program committees of the IEEE International Test Conference (ITC) during the years 1982-86. Currently he is on the program-committee of the IEEE International Symposium on Fault Tolerant Computing. At ITC, Prof. Seth has been a session chairman and the coordinator of a tutorial course on test generation for VLSI chips. He is the Editor of Short Papers for the IEEE *Design & Test of Computers* magazine. He has published over 40 papers in journals and conference proceedings and has lectured extensively at universities and research laboratories in the United States, India, and Italy.

Dr. Seth is a senior member of IEEE, and a member of ACM. He is married and enjoys the musical talents of his wife and two children.

Other Computer Society Press Texts

Ada Programming Language
Edited by S.H. Saib and R.E. Fritz
(ISBN 0-8186-0456-5); 548 pages

Advanced Computer Architecture
Edited by D.P. Agrawal
(ISBN 0-8186-0667-3); 400 pages

**Advanced Microprocessors and High-Level Language
Computer Architectures**
Edited by V. Milutinovic
(ISBN 0-8186-0623-1); 608 pages

Communication and Networking Protocols
Edited by S.S. Lam
(ISBN 0-8186-0582-0); 500 pages

Computer Architecture
Edited by D.D. Gajski, V.M. Milutinovic,
H.J. Siegel, and B.P. Furht
(ISBN 0-8186-0704-1); 602 pages

**Computer Communications: Architectures, Protocols, and
Standards (Second Edition)**
Edited by William Stallings
(ISBN 0-8186-0790-4); 448 pages

Computer Graphics (2nd Edition)
Edited by J.C. Beatty and K.S. Booth
(ISBN 0-8186-0425-5); 576 pages

Computer Graphics Hardware: Image Generation and Display
Edited by H.K. Reghbati and A.Y.C. Lee
(ISBN 0-8186-0753-X); 384 pages

Computer Graphics: Image Synthesis
Edited by Kenneth Joy, Max Nelson, Charles Grant, and Lansing
Hatfield
(ISBN 0-8186-8854-8); 384 pages

Computer and Network Security
Edited by M.D. Abrams and H.J. Podell
(ISBN 0-8186-0756-4); 448 pages

Computer Networks (4th Edition)
Edited by M.D. Abrams and I.W. Cotton
(ISBN 0-8186-0568-5); 512 pages

Computer Text Recognition and Error Correction
Edited by S.N. Srihari
(ISBN 0-8186-0579-0); 364 pages

Computers for Artificial Intelligence Applications
Edited by B. Wah and G.-J. Li
(ISBN 0-8186-0706-8); 656 pages

Database Management
Edited by J.A. Larson
(ISBN 0-8186-0714-9); 448 pages

**Digital Image Processing and Analysis: Volume 1: Digital
Image Processing**
Edited by R. Chellappa and A.A. Sawchuk
(ISBN 0-8186-0665-7); 736 pages

**Digital Image Processing and Analysis: Volume 2: Digital
Image Analysis**
Edited by R. Chellappa and A.A. Sawchuk
(ISBN 0-8186-0666-5); 670 pages

Distributed Control (2nd Edition)
Edited by R.E. Larson, P.L. McEntire, and J.G. O'Reilly
(ISBN 0-8186-0451-4); 382 pages

Distributed Database Management
Edited by J.A. Larson and S. Rahimi
(ISBN 0-8186-0575-8); 580 pages

DSP-Based Testing of Analog and Mixed-Signal Circuits
Edited by M. Mahoney
(ISBN 0-8186-0785-8); 272 pages

End User Facilities in the 1980's
Edited by J.A. Larson
(ISBN 0-8186-0449-2); 526 pages

Fault-Tolerant Computing
Edited by V.P. Nelson and B.D. Carroll
(ISBN 0-8186-0677-0 (paper) 0-8186-8667-4 (case)); 432 pages

Gallium Arsenide Computer Design
Edited by V.M. Milutinovic and D.A. Fura
(ISBN 0-8184-0795-5); 368 pages

Human Factors in Software Development (2nd Edition)
Edited by B. Curtis
(ISBN 0-8186-0577-4); 736 pages

Integrated Services Digital Networks (ISDN) (Second Edition)
Edited by W. Stallings
(ISBN 0-8186-0823-4); 404 pages

**Integrating Design and Test: Using CAE Tools for ATE
Programming: Monograph**
Written by K.P. Parker
(ISBN 0-8186-8788-6 (case)); 160 pages

**Interconnection Networks for Parallel and Distributed
Processing**
Edited by C.-l. Wu and T.-y. Feng
(ISBN 0-8186-0574-X); 500 pages

**JSP and JSD: The Jackson Approach to Software
Development**
Edited by J.R. Cameron
(ISBN 0-8186-8516-6); 264 pages

Local Network Equipment
Edited by H.A. Freeman and K.J. Thurber
(ISBN 0-8186-0605-3); 384 pages

Local Network Technology (3rd Edition)
Edited by W. Stallings
(ISBN-0-8186-0825-0); 512 pages

For Further Information:

The Computer Society, 10662 Los Vaqueros Circle, Los Alamitos, CA 90720

The Computer Society, 13 , Avenue de l'Aquilon, 2, B-1200 Brussels, BELGIUM

Modern Design and Analysis of Discrete-Event Computer Simulations
Edited by E.J. Dudewicz and Z. Karian
(ISBN 0-8186-0597-9); 486 pages

National Computer Policies: Monograph
Written by Ben G. Matley and Thomas A. McDannold
(ISBN 0-8186-8784-3); 192 pages

New Paradigms for Software Development
Edited by William Agresti
(ISBN 0-8186-0707-6); 304 pages

Object-Oriented Computing—Volume 1: Concepts
Edited by Gerald E. Peterson
(ISBN 0-8186-0821-8); 214 pages

Object-Oriented Computing—Volume 2: Implementations
Edited by Gerald E. Peterson
(ISBN 0-8186-0822-6); 324 pages

Office Automation Systems (Second Edition)
Edited by H.A. Freeman and K.J. Thurber
(ISBN 0-8186-0711-4); 320 pages

Physical Level Interfaces and Protocols: Monograph
Written by Uyless Black
(ISBN 0-8186-8824-6); approx 272 pages

Programming Productivity: Issues for the Eighties (Second Edition)
Edited by C. Jones
(ISBN 0-8186-0681-9); 472 pages

Protecting Your Proprietary Rights in the Computer and High Technology Industries: Monograph
Written by Tobey B. Marzouk, Esq.
(ISBN 0-8186-8754-1); 224 pages

Recent Advances in Distributed Data Base Management
Edited by C. Mohan
(ISBN 0-8186-0571-5); 500 pages

Reduced Instruction Set Computers
Edited by W. Stallings
(ISBN 0-8186-0713-0); 384 pages

Reliable Distributed System Software
Edited by J.A. Stankovic
(ISBN 0-8186-0570-7); 400 pages

Robotics Tutorial (2nd Edition)
Edited by C.S.G. Lee, R.C. Gonzalez, and K.S. Fu
(ISBN 0-8186-0658-4); 630 pages

Software Design Techniques (4th Edition)
Edited by P. Freeman and A.I. Wasserman
(ISBN 0-8186-0514-0); 736 pages

Software Engineering Project Management
Edited by R. Thayer
(ISBN 0-8186-0751-3); 512 pages

Software Maintenance
Edited by G. Parikh and N. Zvegintzov
(ISBN 0-8186-0002-0); 360 pages

Software Management (3rd Edition)
Edited by D.J. Reifer
(ISBN 0-8186-0678-9); 526 pages

Software-Oriented Computer Architecture
Edited by E. Fernandez and T. Lang
(ISBN 0-8186-0708-4); 376 pages

Software Quality Assurance: A Practical Approach
Edited by T.S. Chow
(ISBN 0-8186-0569-3); 506 pages

Software Restructuring
Edited by R.S. Arnold
(ISBN 0-8186-0680-0); 376 pages

Software Reusability
Edited by Peter Freeman
(ISBN 0-8186-0750-5); 304 pages

Structured Testing
Edited by T.J. McCabe
(ISBN 0-8186-0452-2); 160 pages

Supercomputers: Design and Applications
Edited by K. Hwang
(ISBN 0-8186-0581-2); 600 pages

Test Generation for VLSI Chips
Edited by V.D. Agrawal and S.C. Seth
(ISBN 0-8186-8786-X); 416 pages

VLSI Technologies: Through the 80s and Beyond
Edited by D.J. McGreivy and K.A. Pickar
(ISBN 0-8186-0424-7); 346 pages

VLSI Testing and Validation Techniques
Edited by H. Reghbati
(ISBN 0-8186-0668-1); 616 pages

Selected Reprints: Dataflow and Reduction Architectures
Edited by S.S. Thakkar
(ISBN 0-8186-0759-9); 460 pages

Selected Reprints on Logic Design for Testability
Edited by C.C. Timoc
(ISBN 0-8186-0573-1); 324 pages

Selected Reprints: Microprocessors and Microcomputers (3rd Edition)
Edited by J.T. Cain
(ISBN 0-8186-0585-5); 386 pages

Selected Reprints in Software (3nd Edition)
Edited by M.V. Zelkowitz
(ISBN 0-8186-0789-0); 400 pages

Selected Reprints on VLSI Technologies and Computer Graphics
Edited by H. Fuchs
(ISBN 0-8186-0491-3); 490 pages